Anglo-America

A REGIONAL GEOGRAPHY OF THE
UNITED STATES AND CANADA

Anglo-

America

A REGIONAL GEOGRAPHY

OF THE UNITED STATES AND CANADA

PAUL F. GRIFFIN, Ph.D.
Professor of Geography
Oregon College of Education
Monmouth, Oregon

ROBERT N. YOUNG, Ph.D.
Executive Director
Tri-County Regional Planning Commission
Lansing, Michigan

RONALD L. CHATHAM, Ph.D.
Assistant Professor of Geography
Oregon College of Education
Monmouth, Oregon

PUBLISHERS • SAN FRANCISCO

Preface

All civilized people want to know if they are making the best possible use of the natural potentialities of the regions they inhabit. Such knowledge has obvious immediate economic importance to farmers, businessmen, and others. Often overlooked, however, is its fundamental importance to *all* the inhabitants—for the wiser the use of natural resources, the greater the standard of living that is attainable. Moreover, knowledge of the natural resources and economic possibilities of the various regions of the earth is of paramount importance to understanding the economic, social, and political problems of the people of these regions. It is the purpose of this book to inform the student of the physical, economic, and cultural nature of one great region of the world—his own Anglo-America.

Anglo-America is an area of great contrasts in climate, landforms, soils, natural vegetation, population distribution, culture, and economic opportunities. A special approach is required in the face of such diversity. Since the physical world is less subject to change, the authors believe that a regional division based upon differences in land elevation or slope is the best approach to teaching geography. Anglo-America has been divided into 22 regions on this basis; to each of these regions a chapter has been devoted.

The 345 maps, charts, tables, and illustrations in the book have been selected with great care to give the student a more accurate knowledge of the natural features of the regions and of the various economic activities. The location and landform maps—the latter aero survey relief maps never before used in a geography of Anglo-America—should prove especially helpful to the student. Every effort has been made to use only the most recent data available; census statistics are those of 1960.

The authors express their indebtedness and gratitude to Dr. Roy E. Lieuallen, President of Oregon College of Education, for his warm support; to Earle Meyer Chiles for his generous effort in selecting and procuring many of the charts, maps, and photographs used in the book; to Margaret Hanna and Ronna Mathews, our typists; to Ernest Andersen and Peter Smith for cartographic and photographic help; and to Florence Griffin and Joan Chatham for their editorial assistance.

January, 1962

PAUL F. GRIFFIN
ROBERT N. YOUNG
RONALD L. CHATHAM

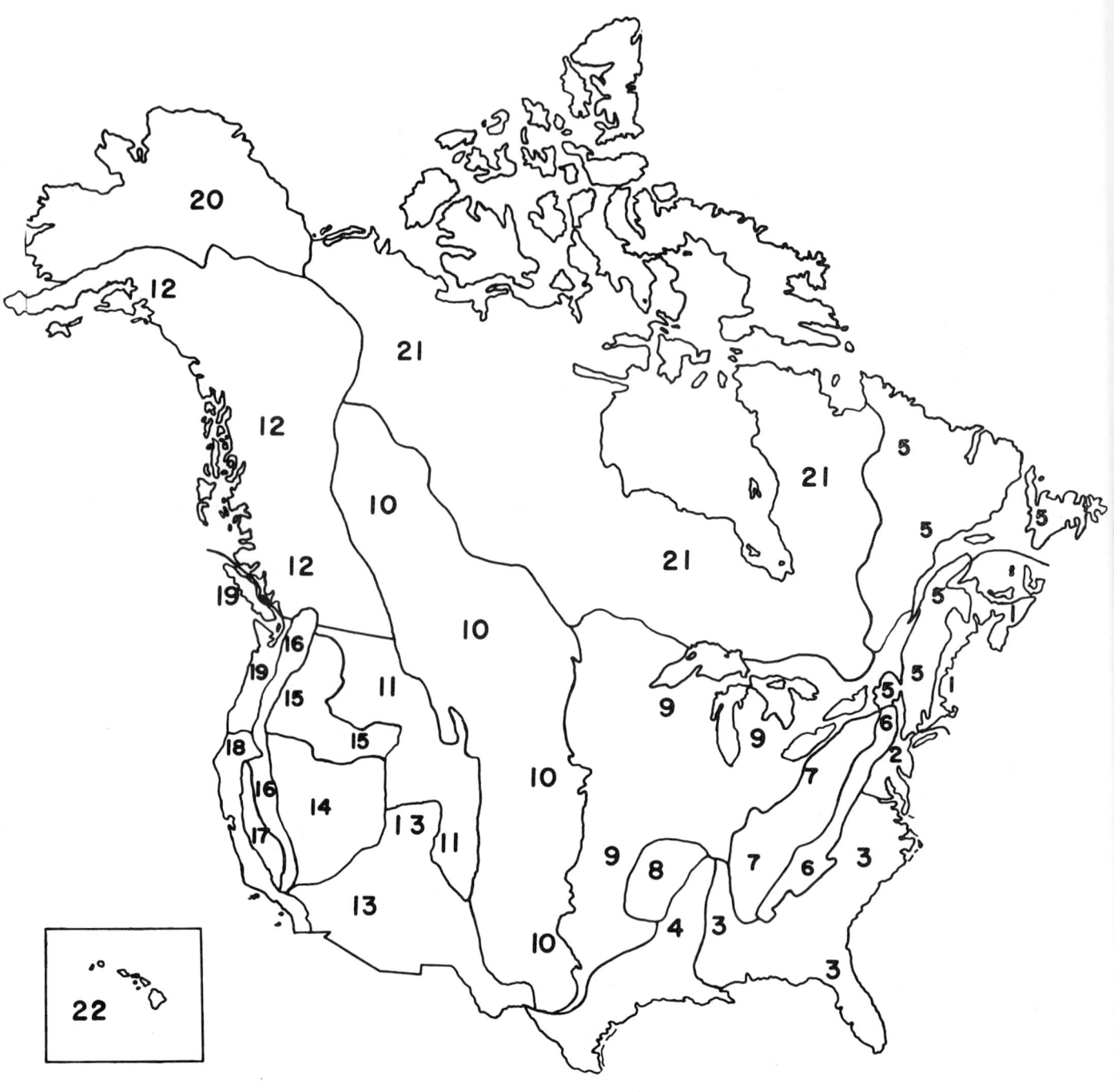

REGIONS OF ANGLO-AMERICA—KEY TO LOCATION MAPS AND CHAPTERS

Regions indicated on this map are treated in chapters bearing the same numbers.

Contents

Maps, Charts, Illustrations, and Tables

MAPS, CHARTS, AND ILLUSTRATIONS

TABLES

Introduction

(Relief map copyright Aero Service Corp.)

ANGLO-AMERICA (the United States and Canada) occupies a highly strategic position in the world's land mass because of its location in the Western and Northern Hemispheres, its vast natural resources, the unsurpassed intensity of its postwar industrial growth, its role in regional and world organizations, and the distinctive national characteristics and traditions that its people have developed.

CANADA

The second largest country in the world (in home territory),[1] with an area of 3,851,755 square miles, Canada comprises the northern half of Anglo-America (with the exception of Alaska). Canada is shaped like a distorted parallelogram, the corner salients of which emphasize the country's strategic position as the nearest neighbor of the paramount powers of the modern world. On the east lies the province of Newfoundland, the sentinel of the St. Lawrence gateway, which commands the shortest ocean route to the continent of Europe. On the south, peninsular Ontario thrusts deep into the heart of the United States, the nation with which Canada shares close and extensive contacts across 4,000 miles of common and unfortified frontier. On the west, British Columbia, flanked by Alaska, faces populous China and Japan across the North Pacific. On the north, the Canadian Arctic Archipelago guards the approaches to Anglo-America from the Eurasian land mass to make Canada a neighbor of the Soviet Union and the dead center of the new heartland of air-age geography.

Economically, Canada is going through a period of tremendous growth and development. Exploitation of her vast mineral deposits—more than 60 metals and nonmetals—adds more than $2 billion a year to the economy. Major developments have taken place in uranium, iron ore, nickel, copper, asbestos, crude petroleum, and natural gas. Canada ranks first among the nations in production of newsprint, nickel, asbestos, and platinum; second in wood pulp, gold, aluminum, zinc, uranium, and hydroelectric power; third in silver and sawn lumber; and fourth in wheat, copper, and lead.

[1] The U.S.S.R. is the largest, with an area of 8,599,776 square miles.

Because of recent discoveries of vast new energy resources—oil, natural gas, and uranium—and the continued expansion of low-cost hydroelectric power basic to the aluminum, pulp and paper, electrometallurgical, and electrochemical industries, Canada's industrial base has been broadened considerably since World War II. The development of widely distributed nonferrous metals, the revolutionary growth of iron ore mining, and the opening of the previously inaccessible resources of the Canadian Shield through the application of new scientific and technological methods in transportation, surveying, and exploitation have been other major factors.

Two decades of war and postwar expansion have placed Canada firmly among the half-dozen leading industrial nations of the world. A stable government, a fresh consciousness of national unity, a confidence in its tremendous industrial potential for creating business stability and a climate for vast capital investment, new discoveries of immense mineral resources, the development of varied sources of energy for industry, and the application of the latest technological processes in the exploitation of a wealth of resources—all have been contributing factors. The greatest influence, however, has been the increasing world dependence on Canada as a source of industrial materials.

Manufacturing industries now account for more than a third of the value of all goods and services produced in Canada. Before World War II only a few industries (such as pulp and paper, transportation equipment, and farm implements) were prominent. During and since the war, expansion has been particularly striking in the fields of toolmaking, electrical apparatus, chemicals, petrochemicals, aircraft and electronics equipment, and aluminum.

Thus Canada, with only two-thirds of one per cent of the world's population, has emerged as a highly industrial and urban society producing high-quality consumer and capital goods to meet the demands of its own people and to distribute to world markets.

Agriculture is still Canada's leading primary industry. The many variations in climate and soil of the country generally, contribute to the production of a great assortment of farm products. Only in Newfoundland is agriculture of minor importance. Of the nation's 18 million

Table A

Population and Area of Canada by Provinces and Territories*

PROVINCE, TERRITORY	CAPITAL	AREA (SQUARE MILES)	POPULATION (1960)
NEWFOUNDLAND	ST. JOHN'S	156,185	459,000
PRINCE EDWARD ISLAND	CHARLOTTETOWN	2,184	103,000
NOVA SCOTIA	HALIFAX	21,425	723,000
NEW BRUNSWICK	FREDERICTON	28,354	600,000
QUEBEC	QUEBEC	594,860	5,106,000
ONTARIO	TORONTO	412,528	6,089,000
MANITOBA	WINNIPEG	251,000	899,000
SASKATCHEWAN	REGINA	251,700	910,000
ALBERTA	EDMONTON	255,285	1,283,000
BRITISH COLUMBIA	VICTORIA	366,255	1,606,000
YUKON TERRITORY	WHITEHORSE	207,076	14,000
NORTHWEST TERRITORIES	....	1,304,903	22,000
TOTAL		3,851,755	17,814,000

* Source: Canada, The Official Handbook, Ottawa: Edmond Cloutier, 1961.

people, nearly three million live on the 623,000 farms that occupy 174 million acres of agricultural land.

Mixed farming predominates in most of the provinces. The average farmer produces one or more kinds of grain as feed for small herds of dairy or meat animals and small flocks of poultry. Livestock are grazed on pasture in summer; in winter, in addition to grain, they are fed hay and other home-grown forage crops stored on the farm.

Specialized agriculture has developed in the drier areas of the Prairies, where wheat is the major crop, and along the rivers in southern Alberta and southwestern Saskatchewan, where irrigated crops such as sugar beets, peas, and sweet corn are cultivated. Large areas in the foothills and plateaus of the Rocky Mountains are devoted to cattle or sheep ranching; sheep also are grazed on the open plains.

The bulk of the Canadian population is of British and French descent. The former group comprises a little less than half the population; the latter makes up nearly a third; the remainder consists of many nationality groups. Of these, people of German ancestry dominate, to account for about 4.5 per cent of the nation's population. Native Indians and Eskimos make up only 1.2 per cent.

Most of Canada's population is concentrated in a belt 200 miles wide just north of the Great Lakes and extending eastward along the St. Lawrence River. About one million square miles, or a third of Canada, lie north of this belt and there are only about 10,000 Canadians living there—one person to each 100 square miles.

Canada's population is increasing at the rate of 2.8 per cent per year—more rapidly than the world rate of 1.7 per cent—and this rate is outdistancing such populous areas as India, southeast Asia, and Japan.

THE UNITED STATES

The United States encompasses an area of 3,614,257 square miles and has a population exceeding 180 million. Forty-eight of the states lie in the middle latitudes of the North American continent, stretching 3,000 miles from the Atlantic Ocean on the east to the Pacific Ocean on the west. On the north they are bordered by Canada, on the south by Mexico. The admission of Alaska and Hawaii to the Union projected the United States far into the Pacific, with the Aleutian Islands stretching some 1,200 miles toward Japan, and with Hawaii lying approximately 2,100 miles west of San Francisco.

Few if any nations of the world were as generously endowed as the United States in its original abundance of natural resources—soils, minerals, forests, and water—and favorable climates for agricultural production. The utilization of these resources has given the American people the highest material standard of living in the world. So recklessly have Americans made inroads on their natural endowment, however, that many of these vital resources have been depleted. An adequate, dependable, and continuing supply of raw materials is indispensable to the United States and its industries in meeting the needs of an expanding population, a rising standard of living, and the demands of national security.

MINERALS

The United States has a great wealth of mineral resources. Its seven large coal fields—Appalachian, Northern Interior, Eastern Interior, Western Interior, Southwest Texas, Rocky Mountain, and Eastern Pennsylvania Anthracite—contain nearly one-third of the world's coal reserves. Much of this coal is of good coking quality and can be mined easily by machine methods. Coal is mined in more than half of the 50 states.

The United States has seven major petroleum fields: Appalachian; Lima, Ohio; Indiana-Illinois; Midcontinent; Gulf Coast; Rocky Mountain; and California. These fields account for nearly one-half of the world's petroleum and natural gas production. Thirty-three of the 50 states are oil or oil and gas producers, with Texas, California, Louisiana, Oklahoma, Kansas, and Wyoming leading in the order named.

There are about 450,000 oil and gas wells in the United States. The production, refining, and marketing of such petroleum products as gasoline, lubricating oil, fuel oil, and kerosene make up one of the largest American industries, employing more than one million people.

The United States is the world's largest producer of iron ore, copper, lead, zinc, cadmium, cement, and boron. Domestic production of iron ore has averaged over 100 million gross tons annually since 1950. More than 30,000 men are directly engaged in producing iron ore, and many times that number are employed in transporting it and in processing it to fin-

ished products. The progressive expansion of copper production in the United States began with the discovery of large deposits of native copper near Lake Superior in Michigan about 1845. Extensive ore bodies were found in Arizona, Montana, New Mexico, and Utah in the last half of the 19th century, and today the mining districts in these states account for approximately 85 per cent of the nation's copper production, which has grown from 730 tons of recoverable copper in 1850 to about one million tons annually since 1955.

Bauxite, sulphur, lime, salt, clays, slate, and many other essential minerals are also produced in quantity. The same can be said about mineral fertilizers from tremendous phosphate deposits in Florida, Idaho, and Tennessee, and from nitrogen fixing plants throughout the Tennessee Valley.

FORESTS

Forest land occupies about one-third of the United States. Forests are used for their timber; for livestock grazing; for the management of water sheds to prevent soil erosion and to conserve water for power, irrigation, and navigation; and for public recreation.

There are more than 1,100 different kinds of trees in the American forests. Of these, about 100 have commercial value, and 29 are widely used in the production of lumber, plywood, and wood pulp. In order of importance, these include: Southern pine, Douglas fir, oak, hemlock, gum, maple, spruce, cypress, and redwood.

The two leading lumbering regions are in the Southern States and the three Pacific Coast States. Oregon leads all other states in lumbering. However, 31 of the 50 states produce important commercial tree crops.

AGRICULTURE

The United States is the world's largest single producer of agricultural products. It is the world's largest producer of wheat, corn, cotton, citrus fruits, meat, milk, butter, and cheese. It ranks high in cattle, beet sugar, and tobacco. Its farms usually grow about one-half the world's corn, one-fifth the world's wheat, and one-half the world's cotton. Agriculture represents 22 per cent of domestic exports.

The United States has 3,710,000 farms, containing a total of 1,123,690,000 acres. Farms average about 302 acres in size. More than one-fourth have less than 50 acres. More than one-fifth have from 100 to 180 acres. About one-fifth have more than 180 acres.

Of the total farm area, about 391 million acres, or 33 per cent of the total, are used for growing crops. The crop area is equal to 4.85 acres for each person in the United States. About 20 million people live on American farms. Actual farm workers, however, number slightly more than seven million.

The amount of machinery in use on American farms has more than doubled since 1940. American farmers use twice as many mechanical corn pickers and three times as many milking machines as they did in 1940. Farm power equipment in 1960 was valued at nearly $16 billion.

Output per farm worker more than doubled between 1920 and 1960. In 1800, three out of every four American workers were required to produce the food needed in the country. In 1960, only one worker out of every seven was required.

Farming throughout the United States generally has assumed its present form in response to well-defined physical, biological, and economic forces and conditions.

The physical factors that influence types of farming are mainly climate, topography, and soils. Agriculture in the humid East varies primarily with temperature and soils, but in most of the West the principal influences are altitude, precipitation, and availability of water for irrigation. In the East the agricultural regions tend to extend east and west, following the temperature zones; in the West the regions are determined by rainfall belts or mountain ranges and valleys, which extend north and south.

A high degree of correlation between soils and types of farming in the United States is evident, especially where rainfall is not a controlling factor. For example, the Corn Sub-region coincides closely with the important regions of prairie soils. Wheat regions are associated chiefly with the chernozem soils. The principal dairy regions are found in the stony loam soil regions of podzolic soils. The red and yellow soils of the Southern Piedmont and the alluvial soils in the Mississippi River Delta are important cotton soils. The chief fruit and truck farm areas are found in the regions of red soils in the Pacific valleys and in the sandy soils of Florida and the Atlantic Coast.

Among the biological factors, weeds, insect pests, plant and animal diseases, and development of new varieties and strains of crops affect the type of farming. Land that is badly infested with weeds is unsuitable for flaxseed, for example, and the crop cannot be grown profitably on such land. The boll weevil, which spread from Texas to North Carolina between 1892 and 1920, has encouraged diversification of crops in the Cotton Belt more than any other single factor. Likewise, the corn borer may cause Corn Belt farmers to make radical changes in their cropping systems unless practicable methods of control are discovered and put into effect. On the other hand, further developments in hybrid corn may extend the crop to new areas. Texas fever was one of the chief factors restricting cattle raising in the southern parts of the United States.

Some of the economic forces that influence types of farming are costs of production, distances from market, transportation costs, tariffs, freight rate zoning, mechanization, perishability of product, and consumer demand.

MANUFACTURING

If you can imagine one region comprising the English coal fields, the industrial Ruhr and Saar, the Ukraine Breadbasket, and the Middle East oil fields, you will have some conception of the great industrial potential of the United States.

The Northeast is an area of specialized industry, producing shoes, cotton textiles, woolens, brass and hardware, small arms and ammunition, jewelry, and electronic equipment. The Middle West is the crossroads of industries based on local deposits of iron ore, coal, lead, copper, and oil. Its cities serve as the focal points for both rail and Great Lakes traffic to, from, and through the Midwest. The Great Lakes part of this region also is located in the heart of the American manufacturing belt. Iron and steel form the basic industries, with great concentrations of mills at Chicago, Illinois; Detroit, Michigan; Cleveland, Ohio; Youngstown, Ohio; Pittsburgh, Pennsylvania; and Buffalo, New York. There also are located

Table B
Population and Area of the United States by States*

STATE	CAPITAL	AREA (SQUARE MILES)	POPULATION (1960)
ALABAMA	MONTGOMERY	51,609	3,266,000
ALASKA	JUNEAU	586,400	226,000
ARIZONA	PHOENIX	113,909	1,302,000
ARKANSAS	LITTLE ROCK	53,104	1,786,000
CALIFORNIA	SACRAMENTO	158,693	15,717,000
COLORADO	DENVER	104,247	1,754,000
CONNECTICUT	HARTFORD	5,009	2,535,000
DELAWARE	DOVER	2,057	446,000
FLORIDA	TALLAHASSEE	58,560	4,952,000
GEORGIA	ATLANTA	58,876	3,943,000
HAWAII	HONOLULU	6,439	633,000
IDAHO	BOISE	83,557	667,000
ILLINOIS	SPRINGFIELD	56,400	10,081,000
INDIANA	INDIANAPOLIS	36,291	4,662,000
IOWA	DES MOINES	56,290	2,758,000
KANSAS	TOPEKA	82,276	2,179,000
KENTUCKY	FRANKFORT	40,395	3,038,000
LOUISIANA	BATON ROUGE	48,523	3,257,000
MAINE	AUGUSTA	33,215	969,000
MARYLAND	ANNAPOLIS	10,577	3,101,000
MASSACHUSETTS	BOSTON	8,257	5,149,000
MICHIGAN	LANSING	58,216	7,823,000
MINNESOTA	ST. PAUL	84,068	3,414,000
MISSISSIPPI	JACKSON	47,716	2,178,000
MISSOURI	JEFFERSON CITY	69,674	4,320,000
MONTANA	HELENA	147,138	675,000
NEBRASKA	LINCOLN	77,227	1,411,000
NEVADA	CARSON CITY	110,540	285,000
NEW HAMPSHIRE	CONCORD	9,304	607,000
NEW JERSEY	TRENTON	7,836	6,067,000
NEW MEXICO	SANTA FE	121,666	951,000
NEW YORK	ALBANY	49,576	16,782,000
NORTH CAROLINA	RALEIGH	52,712	4,556,000
NORTH DAKOTA	BISMARCK	70,665	632,000
OHIO	COLUMBUS	41,222	9,706,000
OKLAHOMA	OKLAHOMA CITY	69,919	2,328,000
OREGON	SALEM	96,981	1,769,000
PENNSYLVANIA	HARRISBURG	45,333	11,319,000
RHODE ISLAND	PROVIDENCE	1,214	859,000
SOUTH CAROLINA	COLUMBIA	31,055	2,382,000
SOUTH DAKOTA	PIERRE	77,047	681,000
TENNESSEE	NASHVILLE	42,244	3,567,000
TEXAS	AUSTIN	267,339	9,580,000
UTAH	SALT LAKE CITY	84,916	891,000
VERMONT	MONTPELIER	9,609	390,000
VIRGINIA	RICHMOND	40,815	3,967,000
WASHINGTON	OLYMPIA	68,192	2,853,000
WEST VIRGINIA	CHARLESTON	24,181	1,860,000
WISCONSIN	MADISON	56,154	3,952,000
WYOMING	CHEYENNE	97,014	330,000
TOTAL		3,614,257	178,556,000

* Source: U. S. Bureau of the Census.

tool and die industries, heavy marine engine manufacturing, and the manufacturing of agricultural implements. Meat packing and food processing plants, too, are well represented in these areas.

The Southern Piedmont is the center of the nation's textile industry. It is also a leader in the manufacture of synthetic fabrics. Appalachian coal, cheap hydroelectric power, and low-cost labor are attracting many new industries to the area. The oil, sulphur, and natural gas deposits along the Gulf Coast of Texas and Louisiana also have helped to enrich the region. Petroleum refining, petrochemicals, aluminum refining, and chemical industries add millions of dollars to the economy.

Many light industries have been attracted to the Pacific Northwest by low-cost hydroelectric power from Grand Coulee and Bonneville Dams and by a favorable climate for manufacturing and working. Chief of these enterprises are the aluminum industry, the airplane industry, and shipbuilding.

Southern and central California are new industrial meccas. Furniture, cinema, television, sportswear, photographic supply, electronics, metal fabricating, automotive assembly, food processing, and airplane industries are concentrated in southern California around Los Angeles. Inland from Los Angeles some 60 miles is Fontana, a gigantic iron and steel center based on local iron ore and Utah coal. Around San Francisco, canning industries, shipbuilding, sugar refining, and electronics dominate.

TRANSPORTATION

United States cities and towns are connected by more than three million miles of roads and highways, half of which are surfaced with concrete, macadam, or stone. The most widely used means of transportation in the United States is the private automobile. There are more than 59 million automobiles, or one for every three persons. Motor trucks are used extensively to transport freight. It is estimated that trucks of all kinds carry about the same amount of freight as railroads—more than two billion tons a year, but the trucks are used mostly for short hauls. The United States has about 29 per cent of the world's railroad mileage. The trackage operated by the 705 American railroads grew from 9,000 miles in 1850 to 226,000 miles in 1960. Additional tracks in railroad yards and sidings make the total trackage 400,000 miles.

The country has 35 scheduled air lines operating more than 1,000 planes on domestic and overseas routes. In addition to scheduled air lines, 2,601 smaller companies operate passenger and freight services on a nonscheduled basis.

POPULATION

The United States is the fourth most populous nation in the world. Its population of 180 million people is exceeded only by China (669 million), India (403 million), and the Soviet Union (209 million). Rate of increase in the population is about 1.7 per cent annually, an increase in keeping with the world average.

The West leads all other sections of the country in both the amount and rate of growth. California surpassed all the states in population growth since 1950. Its 5,100,000 gain over 1950 represents nearly one-fifth of the increase for the United States as a whole.

The United States is a nation of city dwellers. Fifty million Americans live in 128 cities of 100,000 inhabitants or more.

ORGANIZATION OF THE BOOK

A major goal of this book is to record and analyze the impact of the past on modern Anglo-America. Although changes in our environment seem to increase almost geometrically, the over-all view of Anglo-America given here will not be outdated for many years. This is because of the method used to describe and analyze the area.

The subject area is divided into workable regional units. Facts, figures, and analyses about Anglo-America in its entirety do not necessarily give the student a grasp of what makes each area function, nor do they describe what it looks like or tell how it got that way.

The regions used are landform regions, and boundaries between regions are drawn where transitions in landform characteristics are relatively rapid. Such differences in surface configuration from region to region are often sufficiently conspicuous to make even a casual observer aware of them. These differences do not vary from season to season or from year to year. This does not imply, however, that land-form features dominate the character of regions. Within any region it is the combination of physical, cultural, and human elements that provide the total regional character.

The boundaries of mountain and hill regions are generally easy to draw, they tend to be easily identified on the earth's surface. In some places, though, the transition from rolling plain to low hills is gradual; therefore indefinite boundaries must be chosen. Even so, there usually is a zone of relatively rapid change, and on a small scale map that zone of change may take place within the width of the boundary line.

The transition from region to region may be sharp, even spectacular, as it is around the edges of California's Central Valley or along the western boundary of the Western Interior High Plains. But there are places where changes occur so gradually that no two people could agree on the location of a boundary. Such is the case at many spots between the Eastern Interior Low Plains and the Western Interior High Plains. Here the difference is primarily one of elevation, and the definitions of "low" and "high" are arbitrary. The southern boundary of the Bering-Arctic Borderlands, particularly the Canadian section, is also quite difficult to define, partly because accurate information is not available and partly because the region's surface configuration is so diverse.

In this book a major effort is made to establish boundaries that will separate areas having topographical or geological differences. An examination of many publications in the field of geography reveals surprising flexibility in the concept of a region. There are climatic regions, soil regions, natural vegetation regions, economic regions, sociological regions, and the like. To the authors' way of thinking, many of these types of regional definitions involve criteria too subject to variation and change. Consider, for example, the so-called "climatic region." Variations from year to year in precipitation, temperature, and other elements often greatly enlarge or reduce the area in question. Likewise, socio-economic changes are constantly modifying regions based on social and economic factors. Landform regions do not change perceptibly with the passage of time; thus they offer the best divisions for studying

geography. The existence of mountains, plains, plateaus, and uplands cannot be questioned. Their influence upon climate, soils, and the distribution of vegetation is significant. Likewise, the influence of these landforms upon living conditions and upon occupations of people has been persistent.

On the basis of landforms, then, Anglo-America has been divided into 22 regions, with a chapter devoted to each. Before discussing Anglo-America region by region, however, it is necessary to have a general physical overview of the area. It must always be kept in mind that each region is only a small part of a larger whole, and that important relationships exist between regions.

OVERVIEW OF ANGLO-AMERICA

PHYSICAL FEATURES

Physically, Anglo-America is an area of great diversity. Elevations range from 20,300 feet in Alaska (Mt. McKinley) to 282 feet below sea level in California (Death Valley); rainfall varies from less than two inches annually (southeastern California) to more than 450 inches (Mt. Waialeale, Hawaiian Islands); and similar contrasts are found in soil and vegetation types.

Proceeding westward from the shores of the Atlantic Ocean, the fairly narrow Coastal Plain is first sighted. This widens to the south, and finally merges into the Gulf Coastal Plain in Georgia. Breaking the Coastal Plain are the valleys of many rivers, such as the Connecticut, the Hudson, the Delaware, the Susquehanna, and the James. Only one of these, the Hudson, shows its sea level connection to the Great Lakes along the Mohawk depression. The New England Lowlands continue northeastward into the Canadian Maritime Provinces.

At the inland edge of the Coastal Plain, the fall line and the piedmont mark the end of navigation on all rivers except the Hudson. Rising from the piedmont the old, worn Appalachian Highlands stretch northeasterly from central Alabama to the Gaspé Peninsula at the mouth of the St. Lawrence River. Beyond the St. Lawrence, eastern Quebec and Newfoundland continue this upland pattern.

West of the Appalachian barrier the Interior Low Plains dip to the Great Lakes on the north and to the Mississippi River on the south, and encompass the lowlands surrounding Hudson Bay. The South Atlantic-East Gulf Plain takes in all of Florida, goes around the Gulf of Mexico in southern Georgia and Alabama, and then extends up the Mississippi River for 500 miles. West of the Mississippi River this Gulf Plain continues in Louisiana, Arkansas, and Texas.

Beyond the Mississippi River the flat plains begin to rise gradually with an average increase in elevation of ten feet per mile. This almost imperceptible land rise continues across the Great Plains to the base of the Rocky Mountain system. The latter, trending slightly west of north, thrusts its ramparts high above the surface, with many peaks exceeding 14,000 feet.

Between the Rocky Mountains on the east and the Sierra Nevada and Cascade Ranges on the west within the continental United States are the Colorado and Columbia Plateaus and the Basin and Range Province, characterized by interior drainage, playas, and salt-encrusted flats. The Columbia Plateau in the north abuts the Canadian Rockies, a complex of north-south trending ranges.

Finally, the bold scarp of the Sierra Nevada Mountains in eastern California forms the western boundary of the Basin and Range Province. The Cascade Range, beginning in northern California and extending through Oregon and Washington into Canada, marks the western edge of the Columbia Intermontane Province. Many peaks within these ranges exceed 10,000 feet, with Mt. Whitney, the highest point in the United States outside of Alaska, rising 14,496 feet above sea level. Outstanding among the peaks of the high Cascades are Mt. Shasta, Mt. Hood, and Mt. Rainier.

In the south, the land drops from the Sierra Nevada Mountains to the Central Valley of California, and in the north, from the Cascades to the Willamette Valley. Both valleys run to the coastal shelf of the Pacific, which is fringed by coast ranges and notched at San Francisco Bay, the Columbia River, and the Strait of Juan de Fuca. North of British Columbia, the Alaska Range marks the southern boundary of the Yukon-Kuskokwin Basin, a lowland area bounded by the Brooks Range on the north. A narrow coastal plain adjoins the Arc-

tic Ocean north of the Brooks Range. The Aleutian Islands extend west-southwest for 1,200 miles. They are extremely mountainous and consist largely of volcanic rock. Far to the north, the islands of the Arctic Archipelago stand in a partially frozen sea.

Hawaii consists of eight main islands and 15 small, uninhabited islands. The Hawaiian chain lies near the northern limit of the tropics, directly south of the Alaska Peninsula and west of Yucatan, about 2,100 miles from San Francisco. These islands are the summits of a 2,000-mile submarine range of volcanic mountains.

CLIMATE

Because of its large size and latitudinal extent, Anglo-America has a wide range of climates. In general, the following climatic controls are instrumental in developing the varied climates of the region: (1) latitude, (2) mountain barriers, (3) water bodies, (4) ocean currents, (5) prevailing winds, and (6) air masses.

Latitude. In general, the farther the distance from the equator, the cooler the climate. Anglo-America, extending from 25° north latitude in southern Florida to 83° north latitude in Ellesmere Island, Canada, follows this general rule. Canadian winters, for example, are more severe than those of the United States. Snag, in the Yukon, has recorded a low of —86° F., while Montana's coldest recorded temperature is —69.7°.

Water bodies. In winter, water bodies are warmer than the land. Water bodies absorb heat during the period of high sun and retain it over a longer period of time than land bodies, which heat up or cool off rapidly with the ascent or descent of the sun. In summer the reverse is true—the land warms up more rapidly, and the cooler, denser air over the ocean moves inland to replace the warmer, lighter, land air. Thus water bodies are great modifiers of the climate of their surrounding regions. The shores of the Great Lakes, for example, have a much milder winter temperature than inland areas far removed from their ameliorating influence.

Ocean currents. The shores of Anglo-America are bathed by several ocean currents whose temperatures modify that of the adjoining land masses. The Japanese Current imparts a warm-

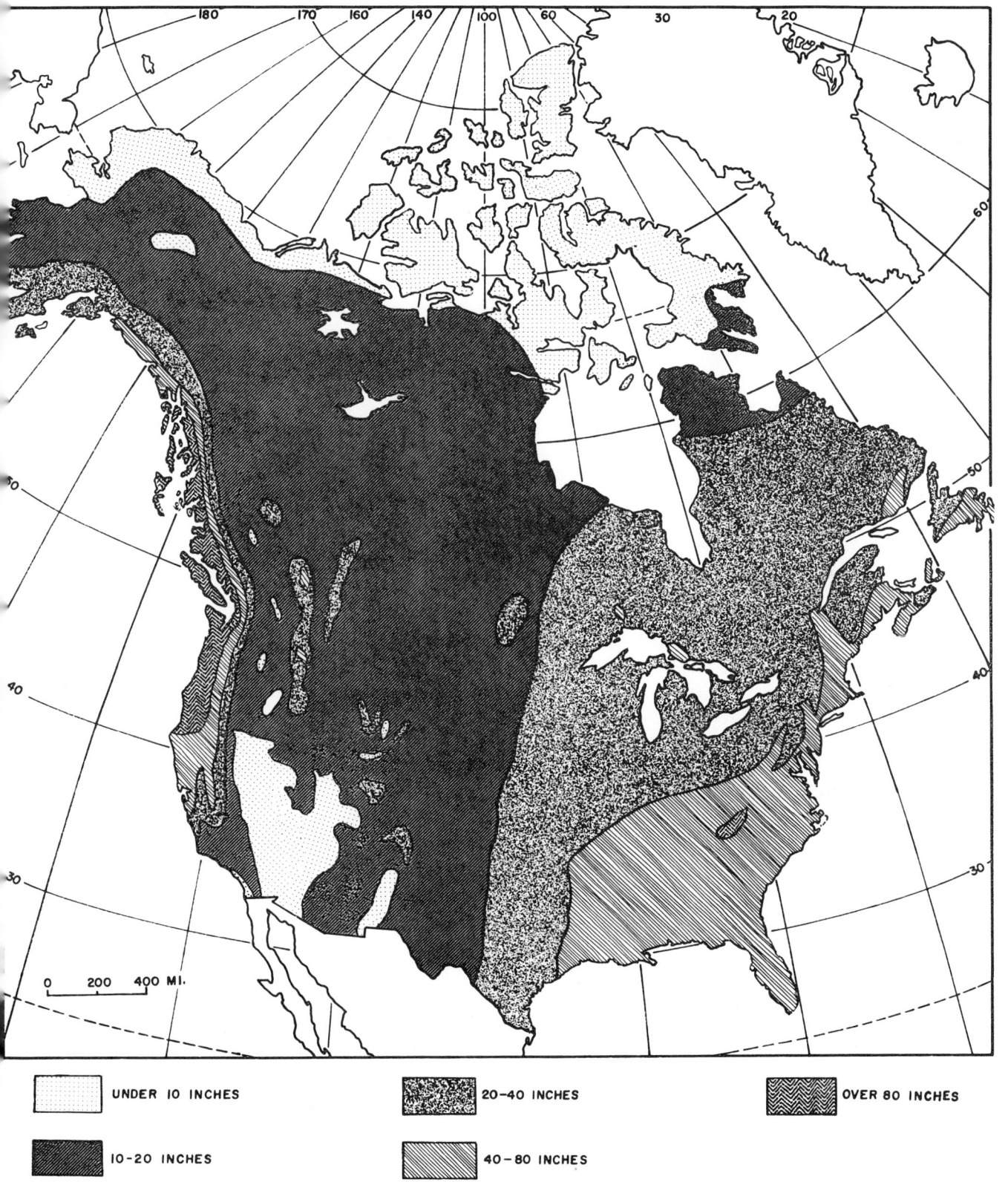

UNDER 10 INCHES

10-20 INCHES

20-40 INCHES

40-80 INCHES

OVER 80 INCHES

Figure A. Rainfall of Anglo-America.

ing effect upon the Alaska Peninsula, British Columbia, and the Pacific Northwest. The Gulf Stream serves a similar function along the Atlantic Seaboard. The cold Labrador Current, coursing the eastern coast of Canada, produces an even colder climate than the latitude might suggest.

Prevailing winds. Although the great latitudinal extent of Anglo-America puts it within the influence of several wind systems, one system in particular is important because of its location. Between 30° and 60° north latitude, where most of the population of Anglo-America is concentrated, lies the zone of the prevailing Westerlies. This current of air pushes air masses from west to east across the country, bringing stormy, changeable weather to the continent, especially during the winter season.

Air masses. Anglo-America is the meeting ground for the various air masses of the North American continent and adjacent ocean bodies. These masses include both cold and warm air. Cold masses of air that influence climate are the Polar Pacific in the North Pacific, the Polar Continental in north-central Canada, and the Polar Atlantic, which affects eastern Canada and the northeastern United States. Warm air masses include the Tropical Continental from northern interior Mexico; the Tropical Gulf, a major source of tropical air in the southeastern United States; and the Tropical Atlantic, which has only a small effect on Anglo-America.

Climatic regions. The interaction between the various modifiers of climate introduces a variety of climatic types in Anglo-America. In the far northern islands of Canada and on the shoreline of the Arctic in both Canada and Alaska, a polar continental climate is present. To the south, stretching in a band 500 to 1,000 miles wide from south-central Alaska to Newfoundland, is found a subarctic regime. The northeastern section of the United States and the southeastern part of Canada have a humid continental climate with cool, short summers in the north and hot, long summers in the south.

The southeastern United States has a humid subtropical climate characterized by hot, humid summers and mild, cool winters. The western interior of the United States and Canada experiences a variety of dry climates—either steppe or desert.

Central and south coastal California possesses a Mediterranean subtropical climate, with warm, dry summers and cool, rainy winters. The coastal portions of northern California, Oregon, Washington, British Columbia, and the panhandle of Alaska have a temperate marine climate, characterized by prolonged cloudy, rainy, but mild winters and short, dry, cool summers.

Precipitation. There is a great variance in precipitation from one part of the Anglo-American land mass to the other. From the Aleutians to northern California west of the crests of the mountains, there is a narrow strip where annual precipitation is over 40 inches; it exceeds 100 inches locally on the coast of British Columbia. East of this belt there is an abrupt drop in precipitation to less than 20 inches annually from southern California northward, and to even less than five inches in parts of what used to be called the "Great American Desert" in the southwestern part of the United States.

From the southeastern part of the United States northeastward to Newfoundland, the average annual precipitation is more than 40 inches.

Soils. The soil of any place is the product of all the local physical forces, and since there are a great number of combinations of biological, geological, and climatic conditions in Anglo-America, there are a great many types of soil.

Northern Canada and northern Alaska possess poor tundra soils of little value for agricultural use. Central and southeastern Canada and central Alaska are made up predominantly of podzol soil that has developed under coniferous forests. It is acid, thin in cover, and generally regarded as poor soil. The northeastern United States is principally an area of gray-brown podzolic soils that rate as fair in terms of crop production. The southeastern United States is a land of red and yellow podzolic-latosolic soils, soils that have been leached of much of their nutrients by rainfall. These soils need heavy applications of fertilizers. In the central part of the United States and in south-central Canada are found the fertile prairie soils. This group, with a north-south extent centering on approximately 95° west longitude, makes up one of the great agricultural soils of the world. To the west of the prairie

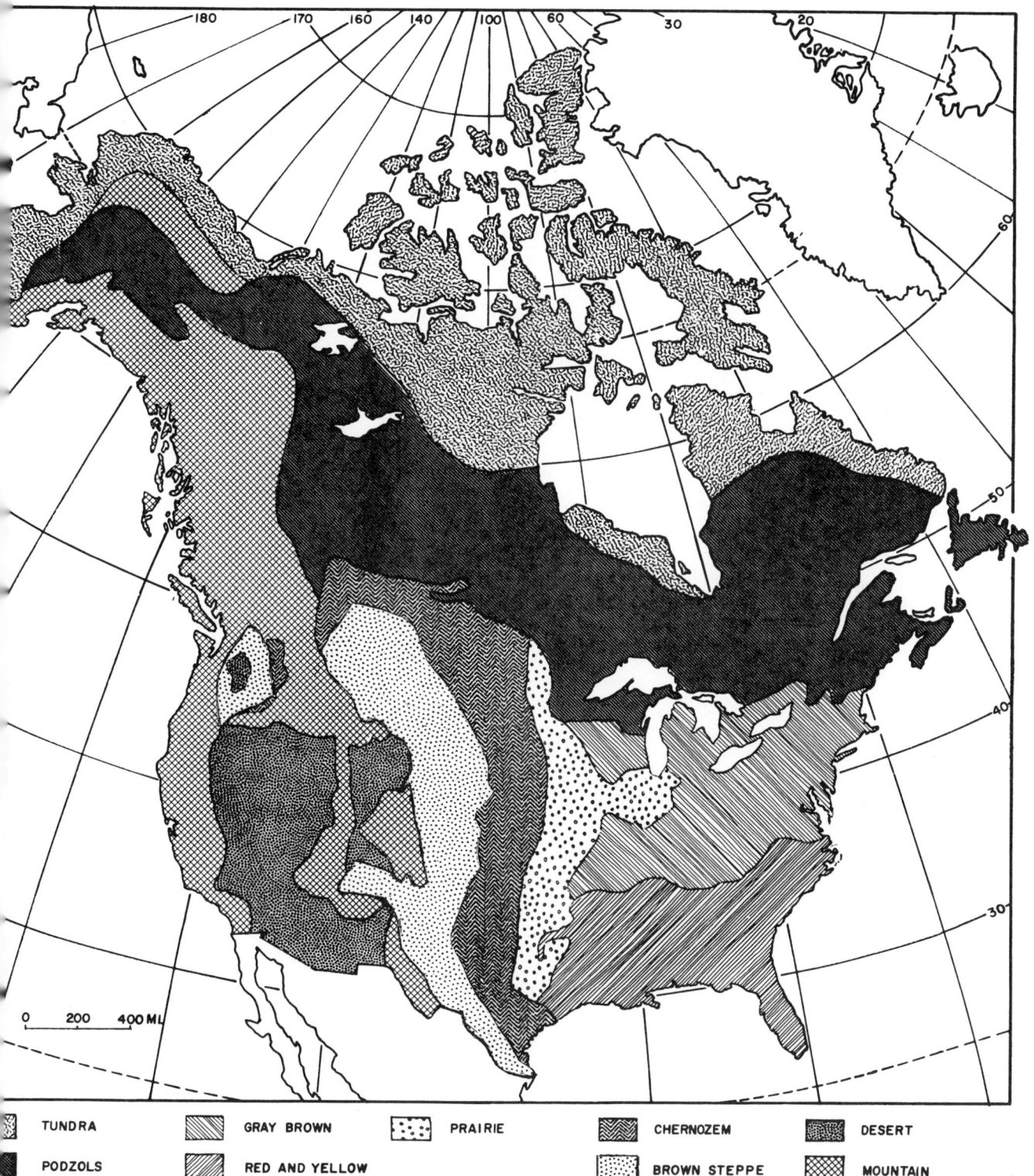

| TUNDRA | GRAY BROWN | PRAIRIE | CHERNOZEM | DESERT |
| PODZOLS | RED AND YELLOW | | BROWN STEPPE | MOUNTAIN |

Figure B. Soil regions of Anglo-America.

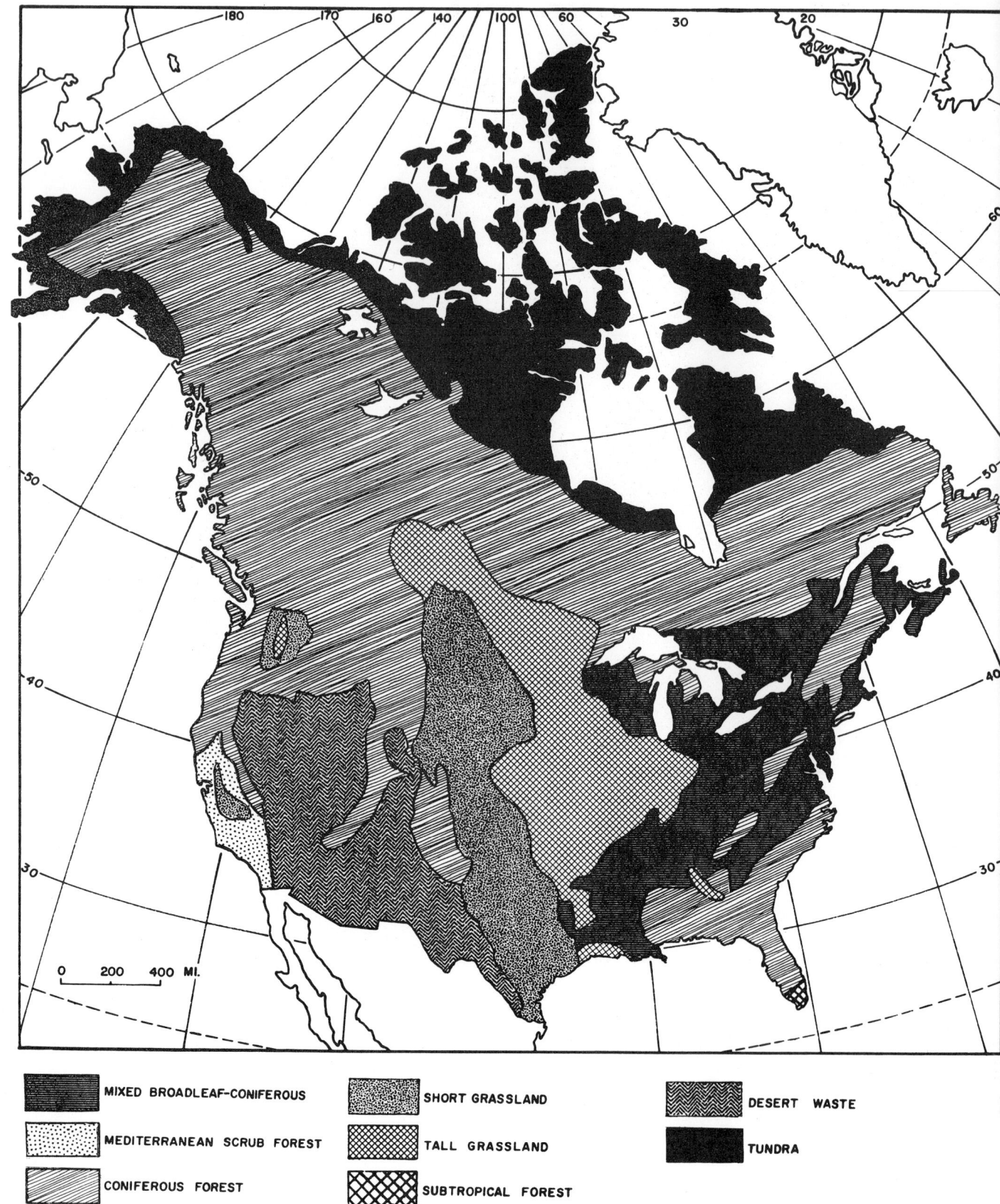

MIXED BROADLEAF-CONIFEROUS	SHORT GRASSLAND	DESERT WASTE
MEDITERRANEAN SCRUB FOREST	TALL GRASSLAND	TUNDRA
CONIFEROUS FOREST	SUBTROPICAL FOREST	

Figure C. Natural vegetation of Anglo-America.

soils, also stretching along a north-south axis, is a narrow band of chernozem or black earth soils. Like the prairie soils, these are extremely fertile and are generally rated among the finest soil groups in the world for crop production, although the area is marginal in terms of adequate precipitation. The western interior section of the United States is composed of various soil groups, ranging from chestnut and brown steppe soils that are considered fair, to desert soils and soils of the mountainous region that vary in fertility and chemical composition. The soils of the Pacific Coast of Anglo-America are mostly mountain soils, although the valleys of the Sacramento, San Joaquin, Willamette, Puget Sound, and smaller valleys contain alluvial soils. The soils of Hawaii are derived mainly from volcanics, although some parent material was alluvium or marine sediment.

NATURAL VEGETATION

The natural vegetation of Anglo-America displays a pattern similar to that of the major soil distribution. Northern Canada and most of Alaska, with the exception of the Panhandle and the central portions, possess a tundra vegetation of mosses, lichens, and flowering plants. Central Alaska, the Panhandle area, and nearly all of central and southern Canada with the exception of the Prairie Provinces is composed of coniferous forests, with the thickness of the forest area varying from place to place. The northeastern part of the United States has both broadleaf deciduous trees and coniferous forests. The White, the Taconic, the northern Appalachian, and other mountain ranges in this section show a predominance of coniferous trees, however. The southeastern United States follows a similar pattern of mixed broadleaf trees and coniferous forests that gradually give way to purely coniferous forests in southern Georgia, Alabama, Mississippi, and Florida. The interior plains of the United States and Canada are the home of grasslands, with tall grass in the east and short grass in the west as a response to variance in precipitation. The Rocky Mountains of Canada and Alaska, and the Sierra Nevada, Cascade, and Coastal Ranges of northern California, Oregon, Washington, and British Columbia have coniferous vegetation. The Basin and Range country of the western and southwestern United States shows a desert shrub complex. The Central Valley of California possesses short grass vegetation, and the Coastal Ranges of central and southern California are primarily the home of Mediterranean scrub forests — with chamise, chapparal, and other characteristic species. The Hawaiian Islands display a mixed assemblage of tropical rain forest vegetation in part, with shrubs, grasses, and brush in other areas.

DRAINAGE

Anglo-America has five great drainage basins: (1) the rivers draining the eastern coast, for most part short, rapid rivers coursing down from the Appalachian Highlands and the upland of eastern Canada, but also including such large systems as the St. Lawrence; (2) the rivers flowing toward the Gulf of Mexico, including such master streams as the Mississippi, the Missouri, the Ohio, the Arkansas, and the Tennessee Rivers; (3) the Pacific slope, with such major streams as the Colorado, the Sacramento-San Joaquin, and the Columbia; (4) the Yukon River, which enters the Bering Sea; and (5) Arctic drainage, including the MacKenzie-Peace system and other streams.

Part I | FLAT TO ROLLING PLAINS OF ATLANTIC AND GULF ANGLO-AMERICA

Plains are man's most important landforms. The world's largest cities are situated at the most accessible points in wide open plains—at points where railways, highways, waterways, airways, and means of communication come to focus, or where ocean trade lanes meet land routes.

The Plains of Atlantic and Gulf Anglo-America are grouped together in Part I because of their similarity in landforms and industrial and commercial development. They are areas of low relief with a very high percentage of almost level land. There are no high steep slopes. Only a few hundred feet may separate the lowest from the highest point throughout a great part of the section.

It is here that man in the greatest numbers has chosen to dwell. More than 31 million people now live in the East Coast belt of cities and suburbs that stretches without interruption from New Hampshire to Virginia. These cities and their suburbs hold 17.5 per cent of the nation's population, do more than 19 per cent of the nation's retail store business, and account for almost 23 per cent of total manufacturing. Similar belts are developing along the Gulf Coast. These population clusters and their problems are treated in the first four chapters.

1 | *New England-Canadian Lowlands*

THE New England-Canadian Lowlands include the southern and eastern two-thirds of Connecticut, all of Rhode Island, the eastern half of Massachusetts, the southeastern corner of New Hampshire, the eastern three-eighths of Maine, the eastern half of New Brunswick, and all of Novia Scotia and Prince Edward Island.

SURFACE FEATURES

From New York City northeast along the Atlantic shore stretches a land whose history is long. Splendid forests once stood by the sea almost everywhere. Today, except for occasional stands those forests have disappeared, leaving rolling hills mantled with smaller trees, shrubs, summer houses, villages, towns, and huge urban centers. The farms of note tend to be concentrated within a few fertile valleys.

From New York's Westchester County to Quebec's Gaspé Peninsula this land looks to the sea. Away from the sea there is still ample water—the fresh water of a multitude of lakes and swamps, remnants of an age when glaciers sculptured the interior highlands and parts of the coastal area, scouring basins and blocking the courses of streams with debris. By and large, this is not a rugged land, but in places it seems rugged. In the north, especially, winters are long and cold, and the soil, if any, is thin.

NEW ENGLAND

Elevation differences are not great along the New England coast and the Maritime Provinces. The local variation in relief—the extreme difference in elevation—is less than 1,000 feet. Connecticut, except for the northeast corner and a small section northeast of Hartford, is in a region of rolling hills and valleys. Near New Haven the rougher interior Berkshire hills approach Long Island Sound to offer southern New England its greatest variation in topography.

Lakes and swamps dot the rolling country of coastal Connecticut, and continue northeastward through Rhode Island, Massachusetts, New Hampshire, and Maine, into the three Maritime Provinces of Canada—New Brunswick, Prince Edward Island, and Nova Scotia. Rhode Island's southern mainland is particularly swampy. This smallest state contains no hills of note. Nearly everywhere there are readily visible evidences of glaciation in addition to the numerous lakes and poorly drained flat areas. Near Kingston, for instance, there are irregular deposits which were laid down at an edge of the ancient ice sheet. Off the coast, Block Island is pitted with depressions left when solid chunks of ice melted and caused the sand and soil covering them to slip into what otherwise would have been a cavity.

Southern Massachusetts is much like Rhode Island, but more gently rolling. Lakes and swamps occupy numerous swales. Much of the topography is hummocky, particularly Barnstable County (Cape Cod) and the islands—Nantucket and Martha's Vineyard. Similar landscape is also found to a lesser extent farther north. In and around Boston Bay are a multitude of small hills resembling half eggshells—possibly formed under a relatively thin waning glacier. Along parts of Cape Cod's east coastline a bluff 100 feet high overlooks the Atlantic. Offshore bars exist in various places, Newburyport, for example; sometimes the bars are backed by coastal marshes.

Relief is slight, ranging from 200 to 300 feet throughout most of this portion of Massachusetts. Inland local elevation differences increase to 500 or even 700 feet, but steep slopes are rare. In New Hampshire relief near the coast is greater than that to the south, but the general aspect remains the same. The only large areas of nearly flat land are scattered along the Merrimack River and near the short Atlantic shoreline.

Northward the region is more rugged. Along Maine's island-studded coast are many bold headlands, some of them at the ocean end of long peninsulas that are nearly surrounded by bays, inlets, and tidal river mouths. The Androscoggin, Kennebec, and Penobscot Rivers, each a major stream, drain most of Maine. Spacious, gently rolling lands suitable for farming are not uncommon. Only in the southwest near Portland and in the Aroostook country in the northeast are there large blocks of agriculturally productive soils.

The very irregular North Atlantic coastline extends northeastward from Portland, mixing land and sea to such an extent that land travel parallel to the shore and near the ocean is virtually impossible. A 25-mile auto trip is likely

Figure 1-1. The Portland Lighthouse stands as a sentinel to ships passing along Maine's rocky coast. (The New England Council, Inc.)

to be the only land means of reaching a neighbor who lives only a mile away by boat.

The summits of such prominent peaks as Mt. Desert and Mt. Megunticook attain elevations of over 1,000 feet within two or three miles of salt water. Much of the shoreline is rocky, with many small sandy beaches in small coves. Inland the topography is more subdued and less spectacular, but there are steep hills scattered in many places in the rolling terrain and among the lakes and swamps. Even in the well-known Aroostook Valley gently sloping land is at a premium. Near Presque Isle, Hedgehog Mountain and several other steep hills serve notice that this is not the rolling plain of southern New England

MARITIME PROVINCES

In general, the northwestern portion of the Maritime Provinces is more rugged than the remainder, where local relief variations rarely exceed 1,000 feet. A prominent exception is found in the vicinity of Fundy National Park, where steep bluffs up to 500 feet high overlook the Bay of Fundy and hills rise to 1,350 feet close by.

New Brunswick is sparsely settled. Homesteads are scattered, a response to the long winters and the rocky soils that make farming difficult. Only along the St. John River is there a nearly continuous string of settlements and they occupy the flatter lands near the stream. In many places, however, the steepest slopes are to be found near rivers, with the upland surfaces more gently rolling. By and large, this area is very similar to its counterpart across the border in Maine.

Prince Edward Island, on the other hand, exhibits very little local relief. In fact, all places on the island are less than 500 feet above sea level. Mudflats prevail along some of the coast, which is indented by many bays and inlets. Charlottetown Harbor, where three rivers, the Hillsborough, Yorke, and Eliot, join, is perhaps the best-known bay.

Nova Scotia is more varied. Separated from New Brunswick by a low isthmus, so flat that ships used to be hauled across it by rail, most of mainland Nova Scotia is rolling country, with some very high concentrations of lakes. Many of the landforms trend northeast-southwest, especially near the Bay of Fundy. Here a single ridge slopes gently toward the bay, with a steep bluff (in some places over 500 feet high) overlooking the Annapolis-Cornwallis Valley, which also trends northeast-southwest.

Southern Novia Scotia is unusually rich in lakes, and the coastline is highly indented along the Bay of Fundy. This is a fascinating peninsula, culturally as well as geographically, where such place names as New Glasgow, Denmark, Lunenburg, and Yarmouth indicate a cultural diversity.

Cape Breton Island, with its Inverness, Margeree, Ingonish, Judique, and Sydney, is equally rich in place names. The magnificent Cape Breton Highlands National Park, with its highest point 1,750 feet above sea level, offers a striking example of scenic grandeur. The Cabot Trail, now an improved road, skirts the base of this wilderness area, but one must leave wheeled vehicles to appreciate fully the rolling, tundra-like upland, which is almost entirely surrounded by steep, seaward-facing slopes unpierced by highway. Where streams leave the upland, which is nearly everywhere over 1,200 feet in elevation, narrow canyons cut into its edges. In the west these streams have removed parts of the upland, leaving "islands" of steep-sided rolling highlands separated from the main mass.

CLIMATE

The varied topography of this region at first leads one to believe that its climates are equally diverse. Such is not the case. Throughout the region summers are cool and winters cold. The length of summer decreases to the north. Winter, the longest season, dominates the northern Maritime Provinces.

The only weather stations in the entire region having average January temperatures above freezing are on the small islands east of Long Island. Even Provincetown at the tip of the Cape Cod Peninsula has a January average below 32° F. Sometimes during winters the thermometer drops to −15° along Rhode Island or Connecticut coasts and to −50° in the Aroostook Valley and the Maritimes.

With these winter temperatures and the sea's proximity, heavy snow might be expected. The southern portion of the region receives an average of 25 to 30 inches, but northern New Brunswick and Cape Breton Island have over 100 inches. The total annual precipitation varies from about 35 to 55 inches (100 inches of snow equals 10 inches of rain), and is well distributed throughout the year, although less falls in the winter.

Winter, with its "nor'easters" and fishermen far from home in small boats, is the season which never seems to end for many of those who live in the region. Such winters may be a factor in producing the hardy souls of conservative stock for which the area is noted.

NATURAL VEGETATION

The New England-Canadian Lowland is a region of forests, cleared in places, cut over at least once almost everywhere, so that very little virgin timber remains. In southern New England, most of the forest cover is gone and the land occupied by man. Deciduous varieties predominate, dropping their broad leaves during the long winters. In Maine, the "Pine Tree State," needleleaf evergreens prevail, although deciduous trees are still common in areas of suitable soils.

White pines are among the best known of Maine's trees. During the days of the sailing ship, these tall, straight trees were much in demand for spars and masts, for they sometimes attain a height of 200 feet.

The Maritimes, too, are dominated by needleleafs, especially red spruce, balsam fir, white pine, hemlock, and white spruce. In swampy areas cedars, tamarack, and black spruce are found. In the valleys and richer areas there are several varieties of ash, birch, maple, elm, and beech. The upland of northern Cape Breton Island is covered by a barren of bog and heath. An unusual vegetative type consisting of salt-

Figure 1-2. In southern New England, forests are everywhere. Nearly every farm has its woodland and there are few places where trees are not found. (Connecticut Development Commission)

tolerant grasses and plants grows on the tidal flats along the shores of Nova Scotia and Prince Edward Island, and especially along the Bay of Fundy, with its 50-foot tidal range.

SETTLEMENT

SOUTHERN NEW ENGLAND

Successive occupancy by Indians, European agriculturists, and manufacturers has left distinctive landscape impressions in southern New England, a land with a long history of settlement. New land in the colonies beckoned to people of all classes in Britain. To the poor it was an escape from unemployment; to the artisan it was independence; to the small landowner it meant cheap, large estates without the crushing burdens of taxation; to the merchant, a chance to sell English surpluses; to the aris-

tocracy, the opportunity for investment of profits.

The new homeland offered advantages the colonists soon learned to use. Here were great tracts of virgin forest to furnish wood for shelter, for protective stockades, and for fuel. The forests offered an abundant supply of game—deer, bear, squirrel, rabbit, quail, and pigeon—as a meat supply for the colonists. Fur-bearing animals were plentiful, and the skins of beaver, mink, otter, fox, and muskrat gave the settlers desirable articles for trade. The forest also yielded edible nuts and berries. Numerous streams flowing to the sea furnished fresh drinking water, a means of transportation and communication, and fish—chiefly salmon, shad, and trout. Along the seaward margins were oysters, scallops, clams, crabs, and an endless variety of fish.

Friendly Indians taught the colonists how to raise native corn and how to fertilize their fields. With the enormous task of clearing off the virgin forest before them, and with an excess of wood on every side, the colonists frequently resorted to fire as the cheapest and quickest method of preparing the area for the raising of crops or the pasturing of animals.

Corn, pumpkins, squash, and beans were planted in small earth mounds and fertilized by dropping fish and seaweed in among the seeds.

With remarkable rapidity, the landscape was radically transformed. No longer was it forbidding. Man in his infinite ingenuity had made the change. From a virgin forest with scattered natural and Indian-made clearings appeared open fields of corn and grain and pastures supporting cattle and sheep. Even the areas of poorer soils were transformed; only the rougher slopes remained unaltered.

During the colonizing period the amount of agricultural labor expended was enormous. Forests had to be cut down and the stumps of trees removed. The boulders and stones that seemed to be everywhere were piled laboriously into the long stone walls characteristic of New England. Today these stone walls — as much a part of the Yankee heritage as Lexington and Concord—are going the way of many things from our rural past. With current farming methods demanding unimpeded acreage for strip cropping, diversion terraces, and other conservation practices, as well as the efficient use of mechanized equipment to boost production, the barricades that for so long have been a part of the New England landscape are being torn down at an accelerated rate.

The great era of stone building was between 1700 and 1875. Innumerable farmers worked themselves into early graves in their endless bout with boulders. And even after the surface rocks were subdued, others had a way of rearing up out of the ground with the spring thaws, encouraging folk tales about rocks that "grew."

New England's thin, stony, and infertile soils and its short growing season (120-150 days) have limited its agriculture severely. Even the favored coastal lowlands and stream valleys could not compete with the more productive plains west of the Appalachians, and the old New England rural economy gradually crumbled. Emigration, first to the new areas of the west, and later to nearby cities, took from each New England generation its most ambitious sons. Gradually the fields reclaimed from the wilderness at so great a cost in human labor and in so short a time reverted to brush. Old farms, the ancestral homes of the present generations of city dwellers, were abandoned and slowly fell into picturesque ruin.

NORTHERN NEW ENGLAND

Although the lowland of northern New England today is sparsely inhabited compared to the industrial sections of Massachusetts, Connecticut, and Rhode Island, its history predates that of perhaps any other portion of the continental United States. Historians dispute the date Maine's history began. If the accounts of explorations by Norsemen are considered, it is possible that Maine was first sighted by these hardy seamen and explorers about A.D. 1000, when Leif Ericson supposedly discovered Vinland. The lack of any definite evidence of Norse explorations passes the credit of discovering Maine to others.

John Cabot, while on his second voyage to the New World in 1498, probably saw the rugged coast of Maine. During the 16th century and the early part of the 17th, the Maine coast attracted many explorers, among them Giovanni da Verrazano (1524), Esteban Gomez (1525), Bartholomew Gilbert (1602), George

Weymouth (1605), and John Smith (1614), who explored and mapped the coast and gave the name New England to the country. The French settled at St. Croix Island in 1604; Popham colonists settled at the mouth of the Kennebec River in 1607—13 years before the Pilgrims landed at Plymouth Rock. The settlement was abandoned the following year. In 1620 the Council of New England, the successor of the Plymouth Company, obtained a grant of the country between 40° and 48° N., extending from sea to sea, and a grant of the territory between the Merrimack and Kennebec Rivers for 60 miles inland under the name of the "Province of Maine." Many grants in this vicinity followed within a few years.

Puritan Massachusetts interpreted its charter to make its northern boundary run east and west from a point three miles north of the source of the Merrimack River. On this basis it claimed almost all the settled portion of Maine. This area remained a part of Massachusetts until 1820, whereupon it was admitted to the Union as a separate state.

MARITIME PROVINCES

The Maritime Provinces are historic parts of Canada. It was in this area, known as Acadia to the early French settlers (later as Nova Scotia to the English), that the first attempt at colonization was made in 1604 when Samuel de Champlain founded Port Royal (Annapolis, Nova Scotia). The first commerce of sparsely populated Acadia was a royal monopoly based on furs and fish.

During the long struggle between France and England for control of North America, Acadia changed hands several times. In 1713, the treaty of Utrecht ceded the peninsular portion (the mainland of Nova Scotia) to the English. During the next half century, English settlements centered on Halifax (founded by the English as a naval base in 1749) and gradually supplanted most of the French Atlantic settlements.

By 1758, the entire territory was in English hands. After 1776, the population was increased by 30,000 Loyalist refugees from the United States. Prince Edward Island became a separate province in 1769, and New Brunswick in 1784.

Figure 1-3. A typical farm scene in the Maritime Provinces. Farming is a family enterprise. Small patches of land are cultivated, mostly with hand tools. Here a hay crop is being harvested. Note the rock outcrop and the more rugged terrain in the background and the sea in the distance. (National Film Board)

The Maritimes have a largely rural population of approximately 1,408,000 (1960), or about 12 per cent of Canada's total of 18 million. The great majority of the people are of British stock; in New Brunswick 38.3 per cent of the people are of French origin. The proportion of Canadian-born is high — 95.9 per cent. The largest city is Halifax, capital of Nova Scotia, with 93,301 people (133,931, including its suburbs). Next is St. John, New Brunswick, with 57,078 (greater St. John: 78,-337). Fredericton, capital of New Brunswick, has a population of 16,108, and Charlottetown, capital of Prince Edward Island, 15,887.

MANUFACTURING

HISTORICAL DEVELOPMENT

Lower New England[1] lives by its wits. The

[1] Massachusetts, Rhode Island, and Connecticut.

Yankee's ways of earning a living are as varied as the region's landscapes. He fishes the blue Atlantic, raises everything from potatoes to wrapper tobacco, teaches the young in internationally famous institutions, sells insurance around the globe, researches things and ideas from atoms to public opinion, finances businesses throughout the world, and collects a handsome sum annually from vacation visitors to his region. These varied ways of life lend color and liveliness to the New England economic scene.

For generations, the prime source of New England's revenue has been the processing of imported raw materials into an incredible array of products sold to the nation and the world.

What keeps New England vigorously going are its 24,000 manufacturing plants—up 50 per cent in number since 1939, its million and a half industrial workers, and its $6 billion manufacturing payroll. Manufacturing is the basic and largest source of income in every New England state.

The industrial period began with handicraft on the farm. Whole families participated during the long, inactive winters. Surpluses accumulated. Wool cloth was exported to England as early as 1609. English merchants, sensing competition, stifled such trade by law. Therefore the New Englander, in order to get rid of his surplus, became a peddler during the winter months. Soon professional peddlers emerged. Traveling on foot with packs, and later on horseback or by sleigh or wagon, the peddlers ranged over a wide area and sold the common necessities of life. Metals imported from England gave great impetus to smithing. As New England grew, the smith became a manufacturer. This led to the growth of artisanship that served an established market in many parts of the Atlantic seaboard. Shortly thereafter, sea peddlers began to transport in the holds of American ships these "Yankee" goods to be sold in foreign markets.

Ships brought hides back to Boston. Skilled labor turned hides into shoes. All these activities provided capital for the factory system and brought the industrial revolution in America to New England first, but not without considerable difficulty. English legislation, designed to prevent export of trade secrets, forbade emigration of trained artisans, skilled operators, or mill workers. Later, the emigration of trained miners was forbidden, and the export of tools, machinery, or even blueprints was banned. But they had no control over the export of ideas in men's minds. It was Samuel Slater, an apprentice of Richard Arkwright (the English inventor of a cotton spinning machine), who brought with him the plans for a textile mill[2] that was set up at Pawtucket, Rhode Island, in 1790. By 1800 there were 30 such mills in New England.

Several factors favored early New England manufacturing. Hundreds of lakes and swamps in the glaciated uplands provided storage for water. These waters, tumbling over numerous rapids and small falls, furnished the power to drive many water wheels. Moreover, the damp

[2] Since England had placed a ban on the export of both blueprints and machinery, Slater created the first textile mill from memory.

climate, so necessary before air conditioning could supply humid conditions artificially, was ideal for spinning and weaving.

Mills were built on waterfalls along streams. There are no single large falls in New England; neither are there sites for huge dams as in the western United States. But the many small falls and rapids were factors in causing manufacturing to be scattered widely in many little towns. Even today New England has only one large industrial center—metropolitan Boston, the trade hub, where the population within city limits is less than one million.

As manufacturing grew, plants were expanded. The small, narrow valleys soon limited plant expansion. Even water power was often outgrown, but because mills were too valuable to be destroyed and too big to move, manufacturing industry tended to stay in New England, expanding all it could. It was cheaper to enlarge the plants and use steam power than to relocate.

By 1850 the combination of a rapidly growing nation, expressed needs, imagination and inventiveness, and the availability of water power and skilled workers had built New England into the most highly industrialized area in the country. Operating in a land with few natural resources, Yankee managers counterbalanced their costs of importing raw materials and exporting finished products by their innovations in manufacturing methods, the dexterity of their employees, and the drive and shrewdness of their salesmen.

Figure 1-4. The Slater Mill, Pawtucket, Rhode Island, birthplace of the American textile industry. (Rhode Island Development Council)

The success of early firms promptly bred competition and New England progressed geometrically: machine begot machine, firm begot firm, and industry begot industry. Manufacturing growth forced the development of faster transportation facilities. These two working in harness steadily swelled the volume and accelerated the rate of exchange of goods and services.

This growth could not last forever. The factors that first slowed and then temporarily halted New England's over-all industrial growth were numerous and complex. Many of them were born outside the region; some evolved from within. They came at different periods, exerted different pressures; hampered or crippled some industries and left others untouched. Even now it is almost impossible to disentangle them and measure their individual effects. But taken together they checked New England sharply and brought about a fundamental change in the character of the region's manufacturing activity.

The power advantages derived by New England from its rivers vanished with the development of steam and electricity. The center of population moved westward and the industries created in its wake served new markets increasingly remote from New England manufacturers. Initially, at least, labor was cheaper in some new industrial areas than in already mature New England. The enormous demands of World War I pressured development of manufacturing communities in or near abundant sources of raw material.

In addition to wrestling with the problems posed by industrial growth elsewhere, New England manufacturing was beset by others arising within its own borders. Civic maturity and a high and steadily rising standard of living boosted local and state tax burdens. To some firms age seemed to bring not wisdom but a hardening of the intellectual arteries and a greater concern with liquidity than with changing consumer demands. Nepotism tended to supplant energetic and venturesome fathers by conservative elder sons, and too many bright younger brothers got their basic training in family plants, then went West and South in search of greener pastures.

THE MODERN PERIOD

Since World War I there have been major economic changes in New England that have improved the well-being of its population conspicuously.

Today there are nearly ten million persons in the area, two million of whom were added during the last 34 years. The decade ahead is likely to add still another million. Probably no other single economic fact will be of more importance to the region. This growing population will provide new markets. In this fact lie both the need and the opportunity for a continuing expansion of economic activity.

In 1920, New England had only seven per cent of its workers in farming, forestry, and fishing, in contrast to the national proportion of 28 per cent. Service industries[3] resulting from higher personal incomes have grown rapidly at the expense of manufacturing growth. Indeed, between 1920 and 1960, the proportion of New England's work force employed in manufacturing dropped from 53 to 42 per cent. But the latter figure is still one-third greater than the national average.

The area is able to pay for the foodstuffs and raw materials it must import by selling manufactured articles to the rest of the nation and the world. Incomes earned in manufacturing operations provide the basic market for a large portion of New England's service industries.

The most striking development in the region's manufacturing history has been the shift in labor force to higher paying, more productive industries in which New England's manufacturers hold a better position in relation to their competitors in other areas.

The slow, steady contraction of the textile industry has been the most publicized, and certainly the dominant, factor in the diminishing importance of nondurable goods industries. The loss in 34 years of 275,000 textile manufacturing jobs was especially difficult for the region because of the degree of dependence on textiles by many communities.

Despite this long record of contraction, the textile industry is still the largest single employer. Remaining firms have demonstrated their ability to produce effectively in New England.

The impact of the nation's defense program during World War II helped speed the transition in manufacturing activity. Military

---

[3] Transportation, communication, utilities, finance, insurance, government, and personal services.

needs are predominantly of the hard goods variety. Procurement, together with the construction of productive capacity for defense, further stimulated the expansion of durable goods manufacturing.

Since 1947, 63 per cent of all new manufacturing jobs added to the economy have been in the electrical machinery and transportation equipment fields. The demand for electronic parts, radar, aircraft instruments, fire control devices, aircraft, and certain naval ships has energized expansion of the metalworking branch of New England manufacturing.

The region has been able to expand its income over the last generation by shifting its manufacturing operations to more productive industries. At the same time, many of the area's traditional industries have survived the transition by means of improved management techniques, by the installment of new equipment in new or modernized plants, and by the development of new methods and new products.

One may expect the New Englander to continue indefinitely the adaptability he has demonstrated for three centuries. As new economic problems arise—and problems are inherent in change—he is certain to find new devices and processes for solving them.

New England is recognized as an outstanding center of advanced research. Research-based industries offer expanding employment and investment opportunities as well as important new market developments. The area has more than 11 per cent of the nation's industrial research laboratories in the instruments, electrical equipment, and machinery industries.

THE TEXTILE INDUSTRY

The American industrial era had its beginning in New England's early cotton mills, with the factory system attaining prominence by the end of the Civil War. Despite the tremendous diversity of products made in New England, a high concentration of manufacturing employment in the textile industries developed. As late as 1919, nearly 30 per cent of all the region's manufacturing jobs were in textiles; in more than 100 New England cities and towns the textile industry was either the sole or the leading employer. Today the composition of the textile industry may be divided into three main categories: (1) heavy—woolens, worsteds, and wool carpets, rugs, and yarn; (2) light—

cotton, rayon, and silk manufacture; (3) miscellaneous—dyeing, finishing, knit goods, hats, and lace goods. Of these, cotton textiles and woolens have been especially significant in New England manufacturing.

New England possessed early advantages for cotton textile manufacture. The abundance of water power facilitated the early use of power-driven machinery. Climate played a role: humid air kept the thread from getting dry and brittle and reduced the amount of electricity in the thread, thus eliminating snarling and tangling. These factors, combined with the proximity of a large market and an abundance of highly skilled labor, enabled New England to become the center of the nation's cotton textile industry. All the early advantages, however, with the possible exception of skilled labor, have been offset by the South. Simple statistics tell the tale. Between 1919 and 1939, New England lost 12.3 million cotton spindles, two-thirds of its total. Industrial misfortune on such a scale is almost without precedent in American life. The drama of New England mill closings, of community after community racked with unemployment, fascinated editors and writers for nearly a generation.

This decline is essentially the result of two factors: (1) failure to keep the plants modern and efficient, and (2) costlier labor and shorter working hours than in the South. The losses at first were in coarse goods, but gradually the South has also encroached on finer cotton goods. Fall River, New Bedford, Lowell, and Lawrence, cities whose names were synonymous with textiles, are now unemployment areas.

New England is the heart of the woolen industry, employing more than half the nation's workers engaged in this enterprise. Boston is the great wool importing port of the nation. Nearly half the region's mills are located in Massachusetts, with the balance shared by Maine and Rhode Island.

APPAREL INDUSTRY

Although the making of apparel is an ancient practice, it was not until the middle of the last century that factory-made clothing developed from the invention of the sewing machine by a native New Englander, Elias Howe. Prior to the Civil War, clothing was made principally in the home or by local seamstresses and tailors.

The principal types of ready-made clothing were cheap garments for slaves and for sailors made during slack periods by the small tailoring establishments of central cities. Modern apparel plants had their roots in shops set up to meet the clothing demands of the forty-niners during the Gold Rush and the need for uniforms during the Civil War.

Although New York City has maintained its early pre-eminence as the center of the nation's garment industry, New England has long been an important apparel manufacturing region. Boston ranked second to New York in cloak manufacturing as early as 1860.

New England is the fourth largest regional employer of workers in the apparel and related trades, being surpassed only by the Middle Atlantic, East North-central, and South Atlantic States. Although apparel plants are scattered, the major concentrations are in or near certain large urban centers. Over half are in Massachusetts, especially Boston, Fall River, New Bedford, Lowell, Lawrence, Worcester, and Springfield. Boston accounts for 33 per cent of the apparel plants in New England and the Fall River-New Bedford area adds 15 per cent more. Providence, New Haven, and Bridgeport have lesser concentrations. There has been some movement of apparel plants into northern New England, but most garment makers prefer city locations.

New England apparel firms stress quality products and conservative styles. Women's and girls' outerwear and men's coats, suits, shirts, and pajamas make up the bulk of the items in the region's clothing industry.

The average size of New England garment shops (47 employees) is about a fourth larger than that for the nation. Although most of the highly skilled jobs are still held by men, women make up a very high proportion of the labor force.

THE SHOE INDUSTRY

The New England shoe industry dates from 1629, when Thomas Beard and Isaac Rickerman, of London, sailed for the colonies with their shoemakers' tools and a supply of leather. At first the shoemaker's handiwork was limited to his own locality because he had to depend upon the neighboring farmers for his supply of raw materials; this was a most uncertain source.

He was equally restricted in a market for his finished wares, since there was no way to ship large numbers of shoes, except by horseback or by wagon at prohibitive cost.

The rise of the textile industry and its resultant effect on urbanization stimulated the shoe industry so, that for decades it ranked second only to textiles in the economy. Today it is usually regarded as second to textiles only as a regional problem industry. The lures of lower wages, tax-free land, free or low-cost plant space, and the shift of population, income, and markets to the West and South have caused a decline in employment in New England's shoe industry. Despite this, New England still leads the nation in shoe production, accounting for about 30 per cent of the national output compared to a peak of 75 per cent in the post-Civil War era.

The industry is highly concentrated in eastern Massachusetts. Whole communities are engaged in the manufacture of shoes. So great is this specialization that Brockton produces men's shoes; Haverhill and Lynn, women's shoes. New England's position has been strengthened further by expansions in Maine and New Hampshire.

If New England wishes to maintain its position in the shoe industry as satisfactorily over the next 25 years as it has over the past 25 it must improve its marketing practices, increase its average plant size, diversify its production (particularly of juvenile shoes), consider community inducements of an economic nature, and scrutinize labor costs.

METALWORKING INDUSTRIES

The metalworking industry, which includes the manufacture of everything from milling machines to safety pins and electric fans, is New England's biggest employer.

An estimated 650,000 men and women, a large percentage of them toolmakers, machinists, and skilled mechanics, work in hundreds of New England metalworking shops. Jet engines, postage meters, parts for auto engines, automatic lathes, builders' hardware, refrigerators, typewriters, machine guns, printing presses, and textile machinery are only a few of the many items in this industry.

Precision machine work is a New England specialty. In hundreds of large and small shops machinists and tool and mold makers turn out precision gauges, testing instruments, taps, dies, aircraft engine parts, gyroscopes, watches, firearms, and Geiger counters.

Basic metals industry. The first ironworks in what is now the United States was established in Saugus, Massachusetts, in 1643. That plant produced the first dies for coining colonial money, the first fire-fighting pumping engine, iron kettles for home cooking, and metal anchors, cranes, and other products to fill the colonists' needs. By 1650, the enterprising settlers, who had brought skilled ironworkers from England, had increased the original output to the point where the Saugus company was able to enter foreign export markets.

Today the basic metals group includes establishments engaged in smelting ore and refining both primary and scrap metals; in rolling, drawing, and alloying those metals; and in manufacturing castings, forgings, and other products.

New England's most important metals industries are those that roll, draw, and alloy nonferrous metals. Establishments of this kind account for slightly more than one-third of the industry's total employment, and wire drawing and iron and steel foundries each account for one-sixth. The region has few blast furnaces, steel works, or rolling mills.

Most of the market requirements must be filled by purchasing steel from distant mills and shipping it to New England fabricators. Past attempts to secure a large integrated steel mill for New England have been based upon a recognition of the serious gap in the region's industrial plant. The discovery and development of extensive foreign iron ore bodies lent encouragement to the possibility. Such a mill, however, would come into direct competition with newly expanded East Coast steel facilities, which have at least two million tons of additional capacity a year. These expansions have taken place principally at Sparrows Point, Maryland, and Morrisville, Pennsylvania.

A small mill, designed to serve part of the New England market for specialty steel, may well be economically feasible. Such a mill could be profitable if sensibly based on new analyses of market demand, competing sources of supply, and well-controlled production costs.

Machinery. The manufacture of nonelec-

Figure 1-5. The Norton Company's modern plant at Worcester, Massachusetts. Norton is the world's largest manufacturer of abrasives, grinding wheels, refractories, and grinding and lapping machines. (Norton Co.)

trical machinery is the second-ranking industry in New England in number of persons employed, income payments to individuals, and in value added in manufacture. Market orientation was one of the dominant factors in the industrial growth of New England, and textile machinery, shoe machinery, and other companies were in a particularly advantageous position during the last century. With a shift to newer industries, such as electronics, the machinery industry must adapt itself to this new market if it is to continue to grow.

The brass and hardware industries. New England has long had an enviable reputation in the brass and hardware industries because of the recognized quality of its output. It supplies one-quarter of the nation's needs for these products by combining highly skilled labor and management. The bulk of the brass industry is centered in the Naugatuck Valley of Connecticut from Ansonia to Torrington. It began in 1802, with the making of brass buttons. Today the items may total half a million, including such diversified products as brass rods, tubes, bearings, brushes, wire, shells, lamp sockets, flashlight parts, garden sprinklers, cosmetic

Figure 1-6. Pratt and Whitney Aircraft plant, East Hartford, Connecticut. Few people think of New England as an aircraft producer, yet there are now 2,600 companies producing aircraft parts or products, approximately one-eighth of the national total. (Pratt and Whitney Aircraft)

containers, snap fasteners, valves, nozzles, diving helmets, and buttons.

Clockmakers started an industry in Bristol about 1850, originating the cheap clock. Connecticut brass clocks, shipped to foreign countries, helped to lay the foundation for America's export trade in the early years of the last century. Today more than 50 per cent of America's clocks are made in Connecticut alone.

Nearly two-thirds of the nation's production of sporting firearms and ammunition is made in Connecticut and those parts of Massachusetts adjacent to Connecticut, with Bridgeport, New Haven, and Hartford, Connecticut, and Springfield, Massachusetts, the leading centers. Local brand names—Winchester, Remington, Colt—are famous. The Winchester rifle, for example, has been called "the gun that won the West." Inevitably these arms and ammunition plants have played an important role in the national defense. The record of war production is staggering. Remington alone expanded its personnel to a peak of 82,500 employees during World War II, turning out war materials valued at $1¼ billion, and operating five huge government-owned ammunition plants in addition to three of its own.

Winchester, Colt, and other arms companies had equally outstanding records. Winchester, for example, was the only commercial producer of the famous Garand rifle. Winchester engineers designed the U.S. Carbine, Caliber 30 M1, and created its new caliber 30 cartridge.

JEWELRY

New England is the nation's leading center for the manufacture of low- and medium-priced jewelry. About 90 per cent of the production is concentrated in the Providence metropolitan area. More jewelry and related items are turned out here than in any other city of the nation, if not of the world. Continued high demand for jewelry coupled with aggressive sales action strengthens the industry's position for the future.

TRANSPORTATION EQUIPMENT

Although the transportation equipment industry ranks eleventh in the number of manufacturing workers employed and accounts for only 3.1 per cent of total manufacturing employment in the region, it is one of the few industries with a growth rate equal to that of the United States as a whole. The industry is well adapted to New England because of its requirements for a comparatively high level of manufacturing skill and the moderate or below-average requirements of industrial power.

Aircraft industry. Most of the growth in transportation equipment is accounted for by the airplane industry. United Aircraft Corporation and its divisions (Pratt and Whitney Aircraft and Hamilton Standard Propellors at East Hartford, Chance Vought Aircraft at Stratford, and Sikorsky Aircraft at Bridgeport) dominate the industry.

Shipbuilding. Other types of transportation equipment offer less spectacular growth potentials. New methods of building small boats through the use of one-piece phenolic moldings combined with plywood or plastics reinforced with glass may open the way for an expansion of boat building.

With the advent of iron and steel ships, New England lost some of its former advantages for shipbuilding. Since the modern ship is built out-of-doors or under huge sheds, the region's frequent rains, heavy snows, and cold weather cause layoffs, interfere with efficiency, and generally handicap shipbuilding.

Most yards, such as those at Bath (Maine) and Portsmouth (New Hampshire) and in Rhode Island and Connecticut, are engaged chiefly in the manufacture of small ships—yachts, torpedo boats, schooners, and motorboats—in which speed is significant. The chief shipbuilding yard is at Quincy, Massachusetts, which builds the largest part of the tonnage.

The Quincy yards are now engaged in producing the new super-class tanker. New England yards produce over ten per cent of the nation's total tonnage.

Automotive assembly. In the motor vehicle field, decentralization of assembly operations from Detroit to regional sites has increased employment. Although procurement policies of the major auto companies now prevent a corresponding decentralization of parts manufacture, the New England parts industry is enjoying a promising growth.

THE CHEMICAL INDUSTRY

The chemical industry represents less than two per cent of New England's manufacturing employment. Nevertheless, its growth rate places it among the most rapidly expanding industries of the region. New England provides a substantial diversified regional market for chemical products, but the industry faces a serious problem in the decline of the textile and leather industries, which have been major consumers of chemicals. There is a lack of most of the basic materials for the chemical industry in New England, and relatively high power rates prevent the manufacture of such products as chlorine, caustic soda, and calcium carbide.

The present strength of the region's chemical industry lies in two fields: (1) bulk products,

Figure 1-7. The U.S.S. Nautilus, the United States' first atomic submarine, at Groton, Connecticut. Although shipbuilding has generally declined, the construction of an atomic-powered submarine by the Electric Boat Division of General Dynamics Corporation may have a tremendous impact on the future of the industry. (Official U.S. Navy photograph)

such as sulfuric acid, fertilizers, and paints, for local consumption; and (2) specialty chemicals characterized by a high value added in processing, the rise of skilled labor, management experience in small plant operation, and use of technological support. Examples of specialty chemicals are household products—special soaps, cleaners and polishes—and such industrial materials as emulsifiers, accelerators, and anti-oxidants.

PULP AND PAPER

During the early years of the 20th century, New England maintained a dominant position in the pulp and paper industry. Since 1930, however, its economic position in this important industry has slowly declined until it now supplies only about 15 per cent of the nation's paper output. Other regions, especially the Far West, have a much greater supply of excellent quality pulpwood. Pulp and paper mills in the West and South are run on a much larger scale and have more up-to-date equipment; the result is more efficient production at lower costs.

The expansion of pulp manufacture in New England is limited by a lack of available sites on rivers in proximity to wood supplies. New England enjoys a definite advantage in paper manufacture, however, in being close to markets. The region's consumption of paper products is very substantial, and nearby New York and Middle Atlantic markets are within easy shipping distance.

PLASTICS

New England is today the foremost section of the country for plastics fabrication, accounting for one-third of the nation's output. The region offers the following advantages to the plastics fabricator: (1) its reputation as a center of well-established firms, (2) availability of skilled die workers who can manufacture the molds necessary for plastics molding, and (3) access to a large market. It has many plastic-consuming industries, such as artificial leather and coated fabrics, electrical appliances, floor coverings, electrical wiring devices, and luggage.

ELECTRONICS

After the extraordinarily rapid rise in the importance of the electronics industry during and following World War II, and because a large share of the original development work has come from New England, this industry merits attention.

New England accounts for 15 per cent of the nation's electronics industry. The strength of its position is traceable to the factors of research, development, and engineering personnel engaged in electronics. Massachusetts Institute of Technology and research laboratories in the Boston area are the hub of electronics developments.

New England electronics manufacturers make tubes and semiconductors, resistors, capacitors, subassemblies, coils, hardware, transformers, insulated wire, and relays. There are no large manufacturers of mass-produced domestic equipment such as radio and television receivers. A number of manufacturers make measuring and control devices, computing and clerical apparatus, and large units such as the Van de Graaff generator for X-ray therapy. There is also considerable manufacture of specialized military supplies.

Two major trends in the electronics industry are toward miniaturization and the use of printed circuits instead of wiring. Using smaller parts favors the more skillful workers, particularly watchmakers, who are largely concentrated in New England. The use of printed circuits as a substitute for wiring involves a number of techniques not formerly associated with the electronics industry, but some of which have much in common with processes like etching and silk-screen printing used in the graphic arts and textile fields. Such skills are available in New England.

Other developments in the components field that hold promise for the area are semiconductors, including rectifiers, transistors, and phototransistors. The mass production of these components shows signs of becoming an important business, although methods are still in an early stage of development.

ATOMIC ENERGY

New England research, education, and industrial facilities are employed extensively in the national atomic energy program despite the fact that no major Atomic Energy Commission installation is located in the area. In the next few years the region should be able to increase its atomic energy activity by seeking additional direct government contracts, by establishing itself more firmly as a center for atomic research and education, and by supplying more of the services, instruments, medicine, and industry required.

MANUFACTURING IN MARITIME CANADA

The sparsely populated Canadian Lowland adjoins the New England Plain and is a part of the same region. Industrial development has scarcely begun, even though the region is richly endowed with raw materials for manufacturing.

Geography and politics have militated against the development of large-scale manufacturing in this area because: (1) it is far removed from Canada's center of population and markets, and (2) high American tariffs bar entry of manufactured goods into densely populated New England and the Middle Atlantic region.

Manufacturing activities are based mainly on the forests and the sea. Pulp and paper, fish processing, sawmilling, and primary iron and steel predominate, accounting for 43 per cent of the region's total production.

NOVA SCOTIA

This province has long been famous for its extensive coal deposits. There are four fields with thick seams of bituminous coal, the most important of which is the Sydney field in Cape Breton, which produces three-quarters or more of the annual output of the region.

Closely associated with coal mining in Cape Breton is the iron and steel industry centered in Sydney. Local coal, iron ore from the Wabana mines in Newfoundland, and limestone for open-hearth flux from Newfoundland insure low-cost steel production. Among the products are steel plate, wire, nails, rails, gun mountings, marine shafting, forgings for warships and cargo ships, locomotive and passenger car axles, and steel railway cars.

Other manufacturing enterprises are varied and small. Amherst is a manufacturing center, specializing in heavy and light engineering works, enamelware, textiles, and boot and shoe manufacturing. Truro, the hub of Nova Scotia, is the chief center of the woolen textile industry, the main products being underwear, woven

Figure 1-8. Yankee Atomic Electric, N. E. Electric Service Company, Rowe, Massachusetts. Production of atomic energy for industry is now under way in New England. Of the nation's 1,338 firms supplying components and related materials in the atomic energy field, 194 (one out of seven) are located in New England. (The New England Council, Inc.)

yardage, and hosiery. Noteworthy also are firms producing electronics equipment, aircraft assemblies, repair and maintenance apparatus, and finished fish products.

NEW BRUNSWICK

One of Canada's eastern provinces, New Brunswick, has a fully equipped harbor (St. John's) on the Atlantic Coast open to shipping all year. Direct rail connections from the seaboard to the rest of Canada and the United States markets are shorter than from any other such port.

New Brunswick reflects an increased industrial production evident across the country. About one-half of the province's manufactured goods are derived from the forest, and of this amount at least two-thirds are manufactured as pulp and paper products.

Diversified manufacturing makes up the other half of total production and includes such articles as foods, ships, fish products, textiles, heating equipment, and boots and shoes.

PRINCE EDWARD ISLAND

Prince Edward Island depends almost entirely for its livelihood on farming and fishing. Several secondary industries, notably canning of fish and farm foods, flourish in urban centers and smaller villages throughout the province. The island offers further opportunities for the development of light industries, particularly for food processing, such as the cucumber pickling plant in Charlottetown.

The island is limited in terms of heavy industry. It is too far from the source of raw materials and the question of transportation is such that it might discourage any move in that direction. There are machine shops, foundries, and woodworking plants in the province, all of which operate on a small scale.

MODERN AGRICULTURE

Although industry dominates the economy of lower New England, Yankee agriculture is still big business and much land is devoted to farming. An agricultural revival has taken place through specialization, designed to meet the city dweller's needs.

THE CONNECTICUT VALLEY

From its origin in northern New Hampshire, the Connecticut River flows 400 miles south-

Figure 1-9. A New Hampshire dairy farm. Much of New England is strewn with glacial debris, which rules out the cultivation of crops but encourages dairying. (The New England Council, Inc.)

ward to Long Island Sound through fertile farmland, wooded hillsides, and thriving industrial cities. It is a land rich in agriculture, industry, and tradition.

The first settlers moved into the valley in 1635, and for the first 50 years self-sufficient farming was the general rule. By 1700, however, farmers were taking advantage of the inexpensive, easy transportation offered by the river and had begun to export some agricultural commodities, including tobacco.

Thus started the first transition in the region's agriculture. In the last half of the 1800's, a second transition in the valley's agriculture began, a shift from diversified general farming to specialization. For more than a century, crop specialization and a shift to urban markets have been the main trends. Of some seven million acres in the Connecticut River country, nearly three million are in farms, most of them in the New England Plain. This is approximately 23 per cent of all of New England's farmland.

The valley's principal sources of farm income are dairy products, tobacco, potatoes, truck crops, and poultry. In general, the more fertile and higher-priced land is located near the river. Crops having a high dollar value per acre are raised in the valley while those of lower value are grown in the foothills. Tobacco is the predominant crop. Farther from the river, potatoes, dairy products, and poultry are emphasized.

Tobacco. Tobacco is the most important agricultural product of the Connecticut River Valley. The area on both sides of the river from the southern borders of Vermont and New Hampshire to Portland, Connecticut, is frequently called "Tobacco Valley." Here, weathered reddish soils derived from weak red sandstones and shales are combined with large additions of commercial fertilizer to produce high yields.

For the most part, Havana seed tobacco is raised in Massachusetts, broadleaf tobacco on the east side of the river in Connecticut, and both varieties on the west side of the river in Connecticut. A large proportion of the nation's shade tobacco is produced in Hartford County. Outdoor tobacco is used primarily as binders, while shade is used almost exclusively for wrappers.

In the late 1890's, cigar manufacturers were turning to Sumatra for their wrappers; the Sumatra leaf was thinner, more finely textured, and the flavor was more neutral. Experiments revealed that Connecticut Valley farmers could raise wrapper tobacco with the same qualities as the Sumatra leaf by simulating the climatic conditions of Sumatra.

Ten large tobacco corporations produce about 75 per cent of the shade tobacco. A large share of the fields are owned by these interests, but they lease land and contract with farmers as well. Conversely, outdoor tobacco is raised almost entirely by individual growers.

In the entire field of agriculture, there are few undertakings that require as much hand labor as raising tobacco. The demand for hand labor creates a real problem in this highly industrialized area where competition makes labor scarce and expensive.

Tobacco growers are keenly conscious of this problem. By recruiting Puerto Ricans, as well as local and Southern school children 14 years and older, the Shade Growers Association helps its members obtain approximately 15,000 seasonal workers to supplement the 5,000 permanent employees.

The current tobacco production of the Connecticut Valley is greater than domestic consumption. Since the end of World War II, a substantial portion of the crop has been exported or purchased by the Federal government through nonrecourse loans under the Price Support Law.

Onions. Though not as important as tobacco, onion production is significant. Centralized in a relatively small area in Hampshire and Franklin Counties, Massachusetts, the industry today is not as large or prosperous as it was 15 years ago. In 1940 there were over 5,000 acres in onions; by 1952, plantings had plunged to about 700 acres. The downward trend continues; in 1960, about 500 acres were under cultivation.

There have been two prime reasons for this decline. Onions require much hand labor, which is increasingly difficult and expensive to obtain. A second reason has been the inability of producers to control thrips, a species of insect that thrives on onions. Mechanization is reducing labor needs, and a recently developed insecticide holds promise of controlling thrips.

Figure 1-10. Tents of cheesecloth are spread over tobacco in the Connecticut River Valley. This cloth is not to protect the plants from hail and insects but to create an even temperature, high humidity, and shade similar to that found naturally in Sumatra. The use of tents greatly increases production costs. For instance, it takes 5,000 yards of cloth per acre, and most of it must be replaced annually. (Standard Oil Co. of New Jersey)

With these two developments, growers soon may be able to increase acreages.

Truck crops. In Massachusetts and Connecticut, truck farmers utilize the rich valley floor to produce vegetables for nearby urban centers. Some farmers grow a wide range of vegetables and others specialize in a single crop such as carrots or beets. In the hill towns, where the growing season comes later, farmers raise small quantities of fruits and vegetables for sale after the peak of local marketings, thus capitalizing on premium prices for off-season produce.

Figure 1-11. *Harvesting cranberries on Cape Cod. This mechanical picker is guided up and down the bog like a giant lawn mower. It prunes the vines as it harvests the berries, thus completing two operations at once. (Ocean Spray Cranberries, Inc.)*

Figure 1-12. *A government inspector checks potatoes during harvest in Aroostook County, Maine. Note the large size of the potatoes, their uniformity, and the number of potatoes in the row. (Agricultural Extension Service, University of Maine)*

Dairying. This is an important farm enterprise in most of the northern counties. Sales of dairy products amount to over $40 million a year. During the low production fall months, most of the milk is sold in fluid form in the urban centers of the Connecticut River area and in metropolitan Boston. In the spring, when milk is in surplus, a large proportion is used in manufactured dairy products. Improved roughage, together with the widespread use of artificial insemination and selective breeding, has assisted total milk production with fewer cows in the dairy herd.

Poultry. Poultry production is not as prevalent on the fertile fields near the river as in the foothills, where poultry enterprises are concentrated. Market eggs comprise about 58 per cent of the $17 million yearly revenue derived from poultry and poultry products.

CAPE COD CRANBERRIES

Cranberries, a native North American fruit, were brought by Indians to the first Thanksgiving in Plymouth, and Cape Cod sea captains used them to prevent dreaded scurvy. It was not until 1812, however, that Henry Hall of Dennis, Massachusetts, began experimenting with the cultivation of wild cranberries.[4]

Cranberries are harvested from early September through late October. Since the harvesting period is relatively short, especially if the season is late, many growers have to begin picking when the fruit is only partly colored. The longer the berries are allowed to remain on the vines, the deeper red and larger they become, and the higher their sugar content. Harvesting methods vary from one region to another. In New England the picking is done mostly with hand "scoops" that pickers push

[4] Cranberry culture is a highly specialized type of agriculture. Usually from three to four years elapse before a newly-planted bog bears a profitable crop and the grower can expect a return from his investment. The normal value of cranberry acreage is very high ($2,500-$3,500 per acre) when compared with the value of acreage devoted to other specialized types of agriculture. The marsh land used must be acid because cranberries will not survive on nonacid soils. Too-high soil fertility results in heavy vine growth with sparse setting of fruit. Covering the bog with a three-to-four-inch mulch of coarse sand lowers the fertility of the soil and helps retard the growth of weeds. Thus a source of sand must be located nearby. An ample water supply is necessary to flood the bog quickly to prevent frost or insect damage. It must be possible to drain the bogs fairly rapidly, by gravity or pumps, so that the vines will not suffer from lack of oxygen.

ahead of them as they move through the bogs on their knees. They use the wooden scoops in a rocking motion to comb berries from the vines.

New England produces approximately two-thirds of the nation's cranberries. Income from the first family bogs was used primarily as a means of raising the yearly taxes. Today the gross crop return exceeds $8 million. Cape Cod and southeastern Massachusetts lead the nation in production.

Aroostook potatoes. Northeastern Maine's Aroostock County is second to Idaho as a potato producer. The county's cool, moist growing season and easily-cultivated silty loam soil favor both high quality and high quantity yields.

In 1890 potato production in Aroostook County was estimated at one million bushels. From these small beginnings production has increased until now this county produces more potatoes than any other county in the nation.

The first potatoes were planted in the county for conversion into starch for the New England textile industry. After rail transportation was available, the emphasis shifted to producing for urban dinner tables. The starch industry, however, is still an important user of potatoes, consuming an average 5,000 tons per month.

Aroostook is pre-eminent as a certified potato seed producing area. The cooler climate enables the grower to control vine diseases better than can be done in warmer parts of the country. Aroostook Valley produces about 12 per cent of the nation's total potato crop. Average yields per acre are 480 bushels.

CANADIAN PLAINS

The chief agricultural products of the Maritime Provinces are hay, clover, potatoes, dairy products, oats, turnips, and apples. Agriculture is the main industry of Prince Edward Island. Prince Edward Island and New Brunswick produce 85 per cent of Canada's seed potato crop and export abroad about one-third of their output. The Annapolis Valley of Nova Scotia produces apples in quantity.

FISHING

NEW ENGLAND

Fishing has always occupied an important place in the economic and industrial growth of the region. The several thousand square miles of fishing grounds that parallel the coastline contain over 80 species of edible fish that flourish in the food-rich, cool waters on the continental shelf. Haddock, redfish, flounder, cod, whiting, pollock, and hake are the principal

Figure 1-13. The Annapolis Valley is one of the most scenic sections of Nova Scotia. (Nova Scotia Information Service)

Figure 1-14. Fishing fleet docked at Gloucester, Massachusetts. Gloucester is one of the leading fishing ports in the country. More than 23,000 fishermen are actively engaged in the fishing industry. Many methods of catching fish are utilized—seines, nets, lines, trawls, pots, harpoons, dredges, and tongs. (Massachusetts Department of Commerce)

demersal or bottom feeders. Herring and mackerel are pelagic, or surface, feeders; they are migratory fish characterized by great fluctuations in abundance.

The bulk of New England's fishing is a product of the banks. Average annual catches are 42 million pounds of cod, 189 million pounds of perch, and 161 million pounds of haddock. However, a substantial portion of the total is derived from New England's shoreline. The nation's greatest yield of Atlantic herring is in Maine. Small-boat fishermen, using mainly "stop seine" small-mesh nets to trap schools in coves or inlets, catch annually about 153 million pounds of herring worth around $6 million.

The shellfish industry, mainly lobsters and clams, provides a substantial portion of income and employment. Lobstering provides full- or part-time employment to more fishermen than any other single fishery, with Maine's lobster fishermen numbering about 5,000.

Clamming also is important both as full- and part-time occupations. Rhode Island leads in the hard-shell variety, producing about 3.2 million pounds valued at $1.1 million annually. Maine furnishes the bulk of soft-shell production with 5.5 million pounds worth $1.7 million.

Of the New England States, Maine and Massachusetts are foremost in fishing activities. Chief fishing ports are Boston, Gloucester, and New Bedford, Massachusetts, and Portland, Maine. These ports land about two-thirds of the weight and five-sixths of the value of all New England fish.

The small coastal villages are tuned to the ocean more than they are to the land. Village life here reflects the season's fishing just as surely as life in an inland village relates to the work on the surrounding farms.

Winter is the time for boat repairs and boat building, and mending nets or making traps, for the days are short and winter storms at sea are dangerous. Only the hardier fishermen go off to set the long lines far offshore for cod. Shrimp travel in enormous numbers along the bottoms of deep gullies on the sea floor, but usually for only a few days in April; they must be caught then or not at all. Hake pass along the coast, without stopping, in the same month. When they pass, the boats load up with tubs of long, baited, many-hooked lines and drive offshore through choppy seas for 50 miles or more to set them.

Lobstering continues day in and day out for several months. The work is arduous but assures a good living. Placing the traps is always a time of hope and excitement. For almost a week the boats go out with lobstermen aboard to sink the traps one after another along the line of ledges and islands, with each trap marked at the surface by a wooden buoy painted in vivid colors that identify its owner. Thereafter, throughout the summer, each boat goes out at least every other day (starting at dawn) to haul the traps, take the lobsters of legal size, throw out the small ones, rebait, and set again.

The herring man, on the other hand, gambles. He may make a small fortune in a fishing swoop or just as likely find himself bogged in debt to the canning company when the season is over. Herring are unpredictable. They promise no man an easy fortune.

Manufactured fishery products are even more important in New England than the catch. Processing includes packaging, freezing, canning, and curing by salting, drying, pickling, and smoking. Important by-products are fish oil, meal, animal food, fertilizer, and buttons. This manufacture, valued at more than $94 million, occurs mainly in the ports cited.

CANADIAN FISHERIES

The deep-sea fishing operations off Canada are in Atlantic waters covering the upland portions of the ocean bed between the outer edge of the shore fisheries and the extremely deep waters of the ocean. These "banks" cover an extensive area, ranging from the famed Grand Banks south of Newfoundland to the area off southwest Nova Scotia. Cod, haddock, herring, halibut, mackerel, and smelt are the major species caught. Lobsters, clams, and oysters are the most important shellfish. Canada's lobster industry leads the world in production. Canadian sardines are caught principally in southwest New Brunswick, where the largest sardine canning factory in the Commonwealth is located. Salted codfish is the principal product of the Newfoundland fisheries.

The coastline of New Brunswick is dotted with progressive fishing communities that derive their livelihood mainly from the 35 commercial species of fish and shellfish caught in abundance within a few miles of the shore.

A 50-foot tide carrying enormous quantities of plankton twice daily affects favorably the large sardine and herring industry of the Bay of Fundy. On the east shore of New Brunswick, Northumberland Strait is the world's richest lobster breeding ground. From the north shore of the province a large modern demersal fishing fleet exploits the prolific banks of the nearby Gulf of St. Lawrence.

Over 10,000 fishermen bring ashore an annual average of 225 million pounds of fish. New Brunswick lobsters, oysters, and clams from cold North Atlantic waters are renowned for their delicacy, and local sardines have an international reputation for excellent quality. Cod, herring, haddock, alewives, plaice, pollock, smelt, mackerel, and salmon also are caught in quantity. These are prepared for market in a variety of ways in efficient processing plants.

Modernization of fishing methods and processing facilities have improved the industry. Millions of dollars have been spent on boats and fishing gear and on processing and cold storage plants.

In a little more than ten years, the gross value of the fishing industry has nearly doubled. There still is ample room for expansion, particularly in the herring and groundfish industry, which offers great opportunity to fishermen and businessmen alike.

FUTURE

Electronic equipment and other technical innovations are causing great changes in the fishing industry. Methods of catching, processing, and marketing fish are improving considerably—echo sounders, filleting machines, precooked and breaded fish are examples. Despite a continual decline in the industry for over a decade, the emergence of a technological industry promises even richer rewards. Nature has been niggardly in giving the region metals, minerals, and oil, but has endowed it generously with an extended coastline, good harbors, and relatively short distances to rich fishing grounds.

TRANSPORTATION

NEW ENGLAND

The southern portion of the New England-Canadian Lowlands has one of the densest transport networks in the nation, with full rail, water, highway, and air facilities. However, the region suffers from several disadvantages in transportation that result in high unit freight costs. These are: (1) isolation at one corner of the country, (2) short hauls (averaging 130 miles compared to 230 nationally), (3) semi-monopoly of two railroads over the area's most densely populated parts, (4) the need to cover losses on commuter service, and (5) heavy terminal charges, diversity of routes, and diffusion of traffic. These disadvantages are offset to some extent by proximity to the Atlantic and the concentration of about one-third of the nation's population within a radius of 500 miles. Unfortunately, the rise of labor costs and other costs has so reduced local coastal shipping in recent years as to deprive New England of a substantial part of the advantages of tidewater location.

Rail. Railway mileage for all of New England totals some 7,500 miles, or 11.4 miles per 100 square miles (compared to 8.2 for the nation). The densest network serves the highly urbanized southern portion; in the north there are relatively few manufacturing sections, population is not dense, and traffic volume is light. With one or two exceptions, New England railroad lines serve directly almost no territory outside of New England; for freight traffic they depend upon the tonnage interchanged with their rail connections west and north and with steamship lines serving New England ports. The character of this freight tonnage is

peculiar to New England; in no other section of the country is so large a percentage of the tonnage made up of manufactured products. Outbound movement of raw materials is negligible. New England imports coal, iron, cotton, wool, and other materials for use in its manufacturing plants, and exports a large volume of manufactured goods. For every three carloads of manufactures moving west from New England, five carloads of raw materials move east into New England. This means a considerable movement of empty cars from the region, and consequent increased costs. Though freight traffic accounts for only two per cent of the nation's total, passenger traffic is relatively heavy, with nine per cent of the national passenger mileage.

Water. More than four-fifths of the region's water traffic is coastwise shipping, but both it and foreign commerce have declined greatly because of high labor costs.

Highway. New England, with two per cent of the country's area, has some three per cent of the nation's road mileage and five per cent of surfaced road mileage. Again, most of these are lowland routes. Trucking accounts for an estimated 29 per cent of total tonnage shipped to and from New England. If products of mines are excluded, 30 per cent of all commodities are moved by truck in the interregional trade, since only three per cent of items such as coal and coke use the highway.

Air. There are some 3,500 miles of airways, 230 air facilities (of which 90 are classified as airports with commercial service), and 20 military airfields. Boston is by far the most important regional point, both for domestic and foreign air carriers, ranking fifth in the nation and with well over 500,000 passengers annually. Although passengers constitute the preponderance of air transport, air express and freight have increased steadily and include manufactured products, fresh vegetables, fruits, flowers, and fish.

THE CANADIAN LOWLANDS

With a relatively small population somewhat removed from the heart of the Dominion, the Canadian Lowlands do not have the need for so dense a transportation network as that of the New England area. The two **great** transcontinental railway systems operating in Can-

Figure 1-15. Yarding (twitching) logs with a horse near Norway, Maine. Note the small size of the trees. Many acres must be logged in this area to produce any considerable volume of wood. (U.S. Forest Service Photo)

ada, the Canadian National Railways and the Canadian Pacific Railway Company, serve the region.

Air transport service. A high frequency of transcontinental and connecting flights operates passenger, mail, and commodity services across Canada from St. John's, Newfoundland. Trans-Atlantic flights are scheduled to London, Paris, and Dusseldorf.

FORESTRY

NEW ENGLAND

Since colonial days, when New England's straightest and tallest white pines were marked with a broad arrow and designated as masts and spars for the King's navy, the region's for-ests have constituted perhaps its most important natural resource. Even today about three-quarters of all New England carries some kind of forest cover, and the region's extensive lumber, pulp and paper, and furniture industries rely on local forests.

From the original cuttings by settlers to provide homes, fuel, and acreage for crops, the practice of logging became an enterprise for export as well as for the home market. Logging was and is still a winter activity with cuttings hauled over iced roads by sleigh to frozen streams. Of particular importance was timber for shipbuilding; the logs were floated downstream to shipyards in the spring. The completed ships then were used to transport lumber to many world ports. The coast of Maine was pre-eminent in this industry, with Bangor on the Penobscot River the chief center. Shipbuilding declined with the advent of steel ships but lumbering continued until the opening of the Upper Lake States in the late 19th century. Today, although forests still occupy nearly 75 per cent of New England's land area, their composition is vastly different from the virgin timber of early times. Small ownership predominates and all but five per cent is privately owned.

Indiscriminate cutting, together with the destructive action of fire, insects, and other forces, have depleted the productive capacity of New England's forests. Saw-timber stands comprise 46 per cent of the commercial forest area, but average only about 3,650 board feet per acre, or about one-third the original yield.

Lumbering. New England produces less than half of the 2.5 billion board feet of lumber that it consumes annually, since much of the saw timber occurs in stands of limited size or in inaccessible areas that make lumbering operations unprofitable. Total annual growth does exceed drain, but the deficit comes from such undesirable types as pole and sapling trees. Thus the average size of trees in the forest is decreasing and the proportion of less economically desirable hardwoods is increasing.

Sawmill operations are mostly small enterprises, often conducted by men of limited experience in the lumber business. Few large saw-timber tracts now exist. Small sawmill operators have neither the capital nor stability to engage in long-term ventures. Furthermore, lumber price levels fluctuate violently. Bulkiness and weight of the product further militate against building up a stable, long-term enterprise in a region of small land holdings and heavily exploited forests.

Pulp and paper. The pulp and paper manufacture comprises the largest forest industry with some 200 million cords of suitable wood. This represents nine per cent of the country's total, yet New England imports 25 per cent of its annual mill consumption of 2.3 million cords of pulpwood.

Paper and allied products industries have expanded outputs more than 25 per cent in the last decade. The rate slightly exceeds all the manufacturing growth in New England but falls short of the expansion rate in the United States' counterpart industry.

MARITIME PROVINCES

Forestry in Maritime Canada has reached a new record in the volume and value of its products, with an annual average exceeding $200 million. The largest part of this value is produced by pulp and paper mills, with the balance accounted for by lumber and other wood products.

The forests supporting this industry now cover about 16 million acres and are increasing in area as protection from forest fires improves. The volume of the forest growing stock also is increasing under better forest management, and it has been estimated that the potential yield is approximately three times the quantity now being utilized.

About two-thirds of the forests are made up of conifers or needleleaved trees, which are, in order of importance: spruce, balsam, fir, pine, cedar, hemlock, and tamarack (larch). The other third is made up of hardwood or broadleaved species, including birch, maple, beech, and poplar, with small quantities of elm, ash, oak, butternut, and basswood.

Nearly half the forested land is controlled by the Crown, which regulates cutting rights through timber licenses and stumpage permits. More than half the privately owned forests are in farm woodlots and other small holdings from which considerable quantities of pulpwood and saw logs are produced each year for sale to the highest bidder. The balance of the privately owned forests are in larger holdings controlled mainly by operators of forest industries.

MINERAL RESOURCES

NEW ENGLAND

New England contributes less than one per cent of the value of the total mineral output of the United States. There are no fuel minerals or ore deposits of commercial importance.

Limestone is quarried in all states except New Hampshire. Commercial deposits, centered at Rockland, Maine, although small, have been mined since 1732. Output is only 0.6 per cent of the nation's total.

MARITIME CANADA

About 40 per cent of Canada's coal comes from the collieries of Nova Scotia, and coal makes up about 74 per cent of the province's mineral output. Consumption has been decreasing in favor of oil and gas, lowering the value of Nova Scotia's coal production. Ninety per cent of the barite and 83 per cent of the gypsum in Canada are mined in the Maritimes.

New Brunswick's mineral output consists mainly of coal, structural materials, natural gas, and petroleum. Small quantities of copper, lead, silver, and tungsten are mined.

RECREATION AND TOURISM

NEW ENGLAND

In New England, vacation travel is second only to manufacturing as a dollar earner. Vacation business has more than doubled since 1939. It now totals more than $1 billion per year.

The Yankee states have their storied greens and monuments, old spired churches, 18th-century farmhouses, and museums filled with rare Americana. Colonial relics, together with lakes, woods, and shore—within a day's drive of a quarter of Anglo-America's population—are important assets to the recreation industry.

New England has many favorable factors making it a natural vacation land: moderate summer temperatures, up to 160 inches of snow in winter, over 2,000 miles of broken shoreline, more than 5,000 lakes, some 40,000 square miles of forest, and many points of historic interest. These attractions are easily available to concentrated New England via an extensive network of constantly improved highways. All sections of the region benefit from the recreational trade, with, for example, boating and fishing in all states, hunting in Maine, visits to historic sites in Concord and Plymouth, winter sports in the uplands of Vermont and New Hampshire, and summer beach home rentals from Maine to Connecticut.

New England's facilities for vacationers are growing. Lodging is provided by innumerable resort hotels, tourist homes, cabins, boys' and girls' camps, and more than 165,000 seasonal dwellings. Hunting, fishing, boating, swimming, picnicking, hiking and other outdoor activities appeal to old and young alike.

MARITIME PROVINCES

With its romantic history and its variety of beautiful scenery, Nova Scotia is one of the

Figure 1-16. This austere meeting house, built in 1832, dominates the Green in Old Sturbridge Village, Sturbridge, Massachusetts. It is one of 35 exhibition buildings in the re-created country town that brings to life the folkways of the New England of 150 years ago. (News Bureau, Old Sturbridge Village)

most colorful of Canada's provinces — a true paradise for sportsmen and tourists. Off the coast there is salt water fishing of all kinds, the greatest thrill being provided by big game fish, the swordfish and tuna. Inland there are countless rivers and lakes with large numbers of salmon and trout. For the hunter there are birds, small game, and deer. These attractions, in addition to mild temperatures modified by the sea, encourage the summer vacationist.

EDUCATION

Thirteen per cent of the nation's colleges and universities awarding higher degrees are located in New England. No other region can boast so many institutions of higher learning.

Few schools, if any, can match the academic reputation of Harvard, Massachusetts Institute of Technology, or Yale. Scores of major colleges and universities, teacher training institutions, small private colleges, and preparatory schools dot the New England landscape. These add revenue to the area's economy and enhance New England's position as a research center.

POPULATION

NEW ENGLAND

There are two distinct periods in the history of New England's population growth during the last 150 years. During the first half of the 19th century the northern portion grew more rapidly than the southern because of the north's agricultural, forest, and fishery resources. During the past 100 years the situation has reversed. The population of the southern lowlands rose to five times that of 1850, while in these same years the population of the northern lowlands increased only one and one-half times.

In 1809, New England accounted for 20.4 per cent of the nation's population — one in every five Americans lived in New England. By 1960, the corresponding percentage was only 5.9 per cent, about one out of every 16.

Table 1
*New England's Population**
(in thousands)

AREA	1800	1850	1900	1950	1955	1960
NORTHERN NEW ENGLAND . .	490	1,215	1,450	1,825	1,900	n. a.
SOUTHERN NEW ENGLAND . .	743	1,512	2,142	7,490	7,785	n. a.
TOTAL	1,233	2,727	3,592	9,315	9,685	10,427

*Source: U.S. Department of Commerce, Bureau of the Census.   (n. a. = not available.)

Table 2
*The Ten Largest New England Metropolitan Centers**

	CITY PROPER		METROPOLITAN AREA		INCREASE 1950 TO 1960
	1950	1960	1950	1960	METROPOLITAN AREA BY PER CENT
BOSTON, MASS.	801,444	682,303	2,410,572	2,566,732	6.5
PROVIDENCE, R. I.	248,674	206,352	760,202	810,145	6.6
HARTFORD, CONN.	177,397	161,077	406,534	522,735	28.6
BRIDGEPORT, CONN.	158,709	155,645	273,723	333,042	21.7
WORCESTER, MASS.	203,486	186,247	303,037	322,438	6.4
NEW HAVEN, CONN.	164,443	149,501	269,714	308,786	14.5
WATERBURY, CONN.	104,477	106,167	154,656	179,902	16.3
NEW BEDFORD, MASS. . . .	109,189	101,809	141,984	142,257	0.2
FALL RIVER, MASS.	111,963	104,000	137,298	137,420	0.1
LAWRENCE, MASS.	80,536	70,933	182,442	188,663	3.4

*Source: U.S. Department of Commerce, Bureau of the Census.

Figure 1-17. An aerial view of downtown Boston. In New England, all roads lead to Boston, the Hub. Located on Boston Bay, at the mouths of the Charles and Mystic Rivers, this important port has 40 miles of piers, docks, and wharves. It is the world's largest leather and shoe market and the largest wool market and the greatest fishing port in the United States. It is among the leaders in cotton and rubber goods and electrical apparatus. (American Airlines)

Of the 10,427,000 people dwelling in New England in 1960, approximately 90 per cent, or 9,384,300, were lowland inhabitants, largely concentrated in the three industrial states, —Massachusetts, Connecticut, and Rhode Island.

Prior to 1800, New Englanders were predominantly British, mostly of Puritan stock. Between 1800 and 1850, Irish and French Canadian immigration was conspicuous. Since 1850, every wave of European immigration has washed over New England—English Canadians, ans, Austrians, Poles, Italians, Russians, Swedes, Finns, Lithuanians, and Portuguese, to name a few.

Immigrants flocked to the urban centers and came into conflict with the older population. In many cities, the foreign born exceed the native born. This is especially true in the mill towns—Lowell and Fall River—and in Boston, the metropolitan hub.

Seventy-seven per cent of all New Englanders live in cities and villages. Yet there are very few large cities and there is no huge industrial metropolis. In 1960, only a dozen cities exceeded 100,000; sixteen had populations ranging between 50,000 and 100,000. Even Boston, the trade hub, ranked thirteenth nationally with less than one million (682,303). The Boston metropolitan area, however, ranked sixth, with 2,566,732.

The Boston Basin, a low plain surrounding the city, is thickly populated. Three million people live within a radius of 30 miles of Boston. Very few major markets have the size, services, and facilities of the Greater Boston area.

Rail and truck service enables the industrialist to obtain delivery to 18 major cities in eastern United States and Canada within three days.

Table 2 lists the population of the ten largest New England metropolitan centers and their growth or decline from 1950 to 1960.

In summary, significant shifts in New England's population from rural to urban areas and from central cities to suburbs were revealed in the 1960 U.S. Census. While this shuffling of population was taking place, total New England population rose 11.9 per cent in the decade 1950-1960. (See Table 3.)

Changes in population distribution are partially explained by the tendency for population to leave rural districts, especially those of northern Maine, New Hampshire, and Vermont, and settle in urban parts of these states and southern New England.

Many of the urban areas are concentrated in Connecticut and Massachusetts, and together these states accounted for 85 per cent of New England's 1,113,000 population increase over the last decade. In northern New England population increases tended to be concentrated around particular spots of economic activity, such as Burlington, Vermont, an industrial area, and Limestone, Maine, site of an Air Force base.

The movement of population from central cities to suburbs, first discernible in the 1940 Census, shows up strongly in the 1960 count. Twelve of the 20 Standard Metropolitan Areas in New England lost population in their central cities while their suburbs increased by substantial amounts.

Boston, the heaviest loser, displayed a trend other cities may experience in the future. Boston lost 15 per cent of its population, but the inner ring of cities around Boston also declined. Boston suburbs gained 156,160 people, but all the gain was in the outer fringe of the metropolitan area. Eight central cities in New England had population gains, but their average increase was only nine per cent, while their suburbs grew three times as fast.

The relatively greater rate of growth of the suburbs, even those adjacent to growing cities, reflects the desire of the population to escape from the more densely crowded areas. Somerville, Massachusetts, illustrates this type of decline. In 1950, Somerville was the most densely populated city in the nation, with 26,044 people per square mile. Between 1950 and 1960, it lost 2,040 people per square mile and is now in second place with a density of 24,004. New York City, whose population and density also declined, is in first place with 24,469 people per square mile.

Other densely populated cities in the United States, particularly in the East, had similar decreases in density during the last ten years. The 13 most densely populated cities in the United States in 1950 were again the top 13 in 1960, with slight changes in order of rank. All but one, however, declined in population per square mile. The average density of the 13 cities has dropped from 18,775 to 17,254.

Table 3
*Population of the New England States**

	1960	1950	PER CENT INCREASE	
			1950-60	1940-50
NEW ENGLAND	10,427,109	9,314,453	11.9	10.4
CONNECTICUT	2,514,897	2,007,280	25.3	17.4
MAINE	964,623	913,774	5.6	7.9
MASSACHUSETTS	5,114,558	4,690,514	9.0	8.7
NEW HAMPSHIRE	599,533	533,242	12.4	8.5
RHODE ISLAND	846,207	791,896	6.9	11.0
VERMONT	387,291	377,747	2.5	5.2

*Source: U.S. Department of Commerce, Bureau of the Census, preliminary figures.

Employment and population. There is a close relationship between population increases and growth in employment. The two states with the largest percentage gains in population are also the states with the largest increase in nonfarm employment. These states, Connecticut and New Hampshire, also had the largest increases in nonmanufacturing employment, and they were the only New England states with increases in manufacturing employment. In Rhode Island, whose percentage population growth was less in 1950-60 than the previous ten-year period, nonfarm employment declined 5.3 per cent and manufacturing employment 19 per cent.

New Hampshire's increasing rate of growth is concentrated in its southeastern counties, where there is industrial activity and a military installation. An influx of people into towns near Pease Air Force Base in Newington accounts for Rockingham County's increase of 39 per cent. In Hillsborough County, people have been attracted to the industrial cities of Manchester and Nashua and the surrounding towns.

The largest population gains in Massachusetts were in the arc of towns along Route 128, Boston's circumferential highway. The population growth of these towns may be associated with the development of industry along the highway and the movement of population from Boston.

More than three-fourths of Connecticut's growth was in three counties—Hartford, Fairfield, and New Haven. The growth in Hartford County is associated with employment in the rapidly expanding aircraft industry. Fairfield's growth is due largely to the county's proximity to New York City.

MARITIME PROVINCES

With only slightly more than 1,426,000 inhabitants, the Maritime Provinces possess more than nine per cent of Canada's total population. Over one-third of Nova Scotia's 723,000 people are concentrated in the metropolitan area of Halifax, the provincial capital and the largest Atlantic port, and in the metropolitan area of Sydney-Glace Bay, the main center of the mining industry. Another 20 per cent reside in the counties bordering Northumber-

land Strait. About 40 per cent of New Brunswick's 600,000 people are concentrated in the St. John River Valley. In contrast, almost half of Prince Edward Island's 103,000 people are on widely scattered farms, making a living mostly from the sale of seed potatoes, livestock and poultry, dairy products, and eggs.

Approximately 77 per cent of Nova Scotia's population is of British descent, 12 per cent of French, and four per cent of German descent. Certain districts in the province are almost entirely French and there are smaller French localities in several counties. The distinctly French areas are on the Digby-Yarmouth shore and in northwestern and southern Cape Breton in the counties of Inverness and Richmond.

After the founding of Halifax in 1749, England encouraged colonists to come to the new garrison. Several groups were organized in Germany; between 1750 and 1753 almost 2,000 Germans arrived in Halifax. The town was unable to support such population increase, although these new settlers were given all the provisions that could be spared. In 1753, 1,400 of these people moved 70 miles southwestward along the coast to the county of Lunenburg. Here a prosperous and almost self-contained community has thrived, retaining to this day interesting characteristics of German speech and folk customs.

With the founding and growth of Halifax, the migration of New England settlers between 1760 and 1767, and the coming of the Yorkshiremen, who settled chiefly in Cumberland County, Nova Scotia became firmly established as an English community. The English population was strengthened after the American Revolution by some 20,000 United Empire Loyalists. Shelburne was settled by Loyalists, who vainly hoped to make it a strong capital center. Besides the English there are sturdy strains of Scots and Irish. Fifty thousand Scots from the Highlands settled chiefly in Pictou and Antigonish counties or in Cape Breton; their descendants are still largely Scottish. "Highlands Games" are held annually at Antigonish and a "Gallic Mod" (festival of song and dance) is held in Cape Breton, where Gaelic, the old Celtic tongue, has survived even better than in Scotland itself.

Nearly 40 per cent of New Brunswick's people are French-speaking. Their Acadian back-

Figure 1-18. Aerial view of the Halifax harbor. Halifax is the chief wholesale distribution point in Nova Scotia for goods arriving both by land and by sea. It is the largest terminus for the Canadian National Railways system on the Eastern Seaboard. (Halifax Board of Trade)

ground has blended with that of the modern descendants of United Empire Loyalists. In this harmonious mixture of language and culture one finds the typical New Brunswick citizen of today.

Halifax (93,301), Nova Scotia's capital city, is one of the world's great ports. Ample in size, well protected, and open throughout the year, the harbor can handle heavy traffic. The 200-year-old city is steeped in history and tradition.

Besides being a major shipping point, Halifax is an industrial and educational center. There are 60 or more industries, among them shipbuilding; manufacturing of food, candy, and electronic equipment; and processing of fish. Halifax is the home of Dalhousie University, the largest university in the Maritimes; King's College; St. Mary's College; the Nova Scotia Technical College; and other educational and cultural institutions.

St. John, New Brunswick (52,491), is that province's largest city. It ranks second to Halifax as an Atlantic port, carrying nearly one-tenth of Canada's Atlantic shipping and about one-twentieth of its total ocean shipping. The Canadian National Railroad connects the port with Canada's major cities. With New Brunswick the main center for forest industries, large quantities of lumber and pulpwood are exported from the region. Fredericton, the provincial capital, has about 17,000 inhabitants.

Charlottetown (17,000) is the capital of Prince Edward Island. The Fathers of the Confederation first discusssed the union at the Charlottetown Conference in 1864. Today the city is the center of a rich agricultural hinterland and the home of Prince of Wales College.

2 | *Middle Atlantic Coastal Plain*

(Relief map copyright Aero Service Corp.)

THE Middle Atlantic Coastal Plain embraces parts of New York and Pennsylvania, most of New Jersey and Maryland, all of Delaware, and the northeastern tip of Virginia. It begins as a narrow strip at Long Island and widens to more than 100 miles in Pennsylvania and New Jersey.

SURFACE FEATURES

The topography is level to hilly, with hills mostly in the Inner Coastal Plain near the streams. Elevations range from sea level along the many tidal streams and bays to a little more than 300 feet in southern Maryland. The piedmont of New Jersey, generally hilly in its northwestern part, becomes rolling and then flat toward the south and southeast. The Palisades, cliffs that rise abruptly from the Hudson River to heights of 200 to 500 feet, stand at the piedmont's northeastern corner. The seacoast section extending from Sandy Hook to Cape May, a distance of 125 miles, is characterized by long stretches of sandy beaches, now occupied largely by summer resorts. Tidewater marshes become numerous to the south. Pine barrens, land covered with scrubby forests of pine and some oak, occupy the interior. The land is low and some of it is swampy. New Jersey's large cranberry bogs are located here.

The portion of New Jersey lying within the Middle Atlantic Coastal Plain drains into the Delaware River and Delaware Bay or into the Atlantic Ocean through the Passaic, Hackensack, and Raritan Rivers in the north and a number of small rivers and streams in the south.

The grain of surface configuration running northeast to southeast across New Jersey continues southwestward into Pennsylvania and Delaware and, at least in part, extends northeastward into New York.

In Delaware and Maryland the Coastal Plain Province includes more than half the land (including all of Delaware) and the greater part of the water. It lies between the ocean on the east and the fall line,[1] running from Wilmington, Delaware, through Baltimore, Maryland,

to Washington, D. C., on the west. It is divided into two parts by Chesapeake Bay. That part of Maryland east of the bay is known as the Eastern Shore while the land to the west is called the Western Shore.

The Eastern Shore, as well as most of Delaware, consists of flat, low, and almost featureless plains; the Western Shore is a rolling upland. On the Eastern Shore and in southwest Delaware the drainage is southwestward into Chesapeake Bay. In northern and eastern Delaware it is eastward into Delaware Bay and the Atlantic Ocean.

The Maryland-Delaware section contains within its borders a varied assortment of land and water areas of quite unusual nature. Maryland has a gross area of 12,327 square miles, of which approximately 9,891 are land and the remainder water, much of it tidewater. Chesapeake Bay covers 1,203 square miles; Chincoteague Bay, 93; and smaller estuaries and rivers, 1,054. In the tidewater reaches there are many marshes that afford a haven for migrating wild fowl; the rivers, bays, and estuaries abound with fish and contain excellent oyster beds. Delaware covers only 2,370 square miles, with a small proportion of water area and a topography less varied than Maryland's.

SOILS

The Coastal Plain slopes gently seaward, mostly in a series of somewhat parallel terraces extending inland along the bays and streams. The plain is composed of diverse material transported from the higher elevation of the Atlantic slope and deposited in layers or unconsolidated beds, which vary in texture from fine-grained silts and clays to coarse sands and gravel. The deposits are a mixture of marine, alluvial, and glacio-fluvial materials.

Sandy soils with little profile development are a characteristic of the Outer Coastal Plain in the region. Where surface drainage is good, these soils are arid because of excessive internal drainage. Such soils are found almost exclusively in forests.

Miscellaneous soils include those of the

---

[1] The fall line is the boundary between the crystalline Piedmont and the sedimentary Coastal Plain. Streams flowing to the sea have falls or rapids on this line, the crystalline rock being slightly higher and more resistant to erosion than the coastal sedimentaries. It is the upward limit of navigability for the larger streams and rivers and, therefore, the bulk breaking point for water-carried goods. The falls were often exploited as power sites and settlement in the area usually followed. Many important cities grew in string arrangement on the fall line. The list is rather impressive, including: Philadelphia, Baltimore, Richmond, and Washington, D. C.

Figure 2-1. An aerial view of New York City. Manhattan is in the center of the photograph, New Jersey is to the left, Queens to the upper right, and Brooklyn to the lower right. New York is the major port of America, with 40 per cent of the value of the nation's imports and exports flowing through its harbor. It is the hub of a vast transportation system, terminus of several of the country's railroads and highways, and focal point for the major continental and overseas airlines. The city is the financial capital of the world and the headquarters of the United Nations. (Port of New York Authority)

swamps, tidal marshes, and coastal dunes.

Because of parent material variation, soils have developed marked textural differences. The beds of sands, clays, and gravels of which the Coastal Plain is formed are generally thin along their western edge and become deeper toward the coast.

CLIMATE

Differences in climate within the region are quite marked. The northern half of the Middle Atlantic Coastal Plain has a humid, continental long summer climate, whereas the southern portion is humid subtropical. The northern extremity is well within the cyclonic belt and is subject to frequent storms that sweep across the Great Lakes and move seaward along the St. Lawrence Valley.

Temperature differences between the northern and southern parts are greatest in winter and least in summer. Nearly every station has registered readings of 100° F. or higher at some time and all stations have recorded temperatures of below zero. The average date of the first killing frost is October 20; the last killing frost in spring is April 25. Average January temperatures vary from 37° in southern Maryland to 30° in Long Island. The average July temperature has a somewhat narrower range— from 76° in the southern part of the region to 72° in New York. The frost-free season near the ocean approximates 190 days, and decreases to 150 days farther inland.

The average annual precipitation, 40 to 50 inches, has a July and August maximum of five inches or more each month, and an autumn minimum of three to four inches each month. Severe droughts are infrequent; periods of 30 days without rainfall during the growing season occur only during a third of the year. The relative humidity averages 70 to 80 per cent morning and evening, and 60 to 70 per cent in the afternoon; it is a little higher in summer and winter, and lower in spring and fall. This moderate humidity is a favorable condition for the many health resorts along the coast.

URBAN DEVELOPMENT

The Middle Atlantic Coastal Plain is predominantly a land of cities. Nowhere else in North America is there such a cluster of factories, skyscrapers, land and sea transportation routes, and people. Practically every type of industry is represented here, with products so diverse that it would be difficult indeed to think of many articles that are not manufactured in this region. Manufacturing and commerce dominate the economy, abetted by the area's nearness to: (1) raw materials, (2) markets, (3) fuel and power, (4) a supply of skilled labor, and (5) a well-developed system of transportation and communication.

Population density per square mile is greater on the Inner Coastal Plain than on the Outer Coastal Plain, with densities of 700 and 160, respectively.

THE GIANT METROPOLIS—NEW YORK CITY

The scale and variety of New York's economic activity make it unique among the cities of Anglo-America. Its business is of such magnitude a new standard of measure is almost required, for what is comparatively small by New York City standards would be huge in a community of average size.

The nearly eight million residents of New York City occupy only slightly more than 300 square miles. They comprise the largest and most concentrated consumer market in the country, as well as one of the most diversified in terms of tastes, skills, and economic status. The city also leads the nation in industry, banking, insurance, wholesale and retail trade, and specialized business services.

Although catering to the varied demands of its own population is a big business in itself, the city, to an even greater extent than most metropolitan areas, also exports a large proportion of its goods and services. It imports almost all its food. Many of its products—furs, apparel, millinery, scientific instruments, cosmetics, leather goods, and printed matter—are known throughout the nation and the world. New York's concentration of high-ranking specialized business services in such fields as law, advertising, engineering, research, finance, shipping, and other technical lines, makes it an ideal center for the head offices of large corporations.

STRATEGIC LOCATION—KEY TO NEW YORK'S IMPORTANCE

Soon after the completion of the Erie Canal in 1825, New York dwarfed all other cities of the nation. The basic elements making New York so important a community are: (1) its excellent location, (2) its unrivaled port and facilities, (3) its concentrated population with widely diversified skills, professions, and occupations, (4) its highly developed industry and commerce, and (5) its far-reaching network of transportation and communication.

Location. Situated on an arm of the sea at the mouth of the Hudson River and lying about midway between Boston and Baltimore, New York City is the terminus of the major sea, land, and air routes of the nation, the continent, and the world. The Hudson River links the Port of New York with the Great Lakes via the New York State Barge Canal system, which provides a cheap means of transportation for bulk commodities. No other Atlantic seaport enjoys so favorable a route to the interior. The Mohawk depression is the only break in the Appalachian Uplands, which otherwise continue without interruption from the St. Lawrence Valley to north-central Alabama. This almost sea level route owes its existence to the region's geology. The softer limestone rocks that lie between hard crystallines of the Adirondacks and Catskills have been eroded, creating an easy route through central New York. The Hudson, which lies at the eastern edge of this depression, is a drowned river valley. Land subsidence here permits ocean-going vessels to penetrate inland to Troy, a distance of 150 miles. From Troy the New York State Barge Canal links the Hudson River with Lake Erie at Buffalo. Because of cheap water rates, this 340-mile system handles the bulk of the interior's eastbound freight. Railroads parallel the canal; their rates are kept low by water freight competition. The more recently developed New York State Thruway, a toll express road following the same route, provides rapid service for passenger automobiles and trucks.

New York City dominates not only the trade of the interior but also coastal and foreign trade. The city is the funnel through which commodities flow from the New England fisheries and factories. From the South come an array of raw materials for processing, and oil and gas for power and domestic fuel.

Strategic location favors New York in foreign trade. Its position in the North Atlantic Basin facing Europe, the world's largest market, gives rise to an unequaled exchange of unlike commodities between the two continents.

THE PORT OF NEW YORK

The Port of New York is more than a bay for mooring ships, more than a single port city or community. It is an area of some 1,500 square miles, including large parts of two states, 17 counties, and over 200 cities and towns ranging in size from small villages to one of the world's greatest metropolises—an area containing more than eight per cent of the total population of the United States.

No other great world port has been as generously endowed by nature. The Port of New York is really a combination of ports. There are eight large bays, four straits (the Harlem and East Rivers and the two kills west of Staten Island), and four rivers (the Raritan, the Passaic, the Hackensack, and the Hudson).

Every day there are from 150 to 175 deepwater vessels using the facilities of the port's waterfront, which has 520 miles of frontage on navigable waterways. Only a small portion of this huge fleet of ships is in the passenger trade. The majority are cargo vessels.

The port now handles more than 40 per cent of the nation's waterborne trade, measured by value, and nearly 17 per cent of its tonnage. An average of 1,350 departures per month are made by vessels leaving New York for 130 foreign ports. Because New York usually is the last port visited by ships leaving the East Coast and the first port reached on arrival, considerable time is saved by shippers.

The port's system of waterfront rail terminals, interconnecting waterways, and flexibly-operated railroad lighters and carfloats enables freight to be transferred efficiently to and from ships anywhere in the harbor. Twelve railroads, including nine trunk line roads, connect the port district directly to all the major industrial sections east of the Mississippi River, and to all other areas of the United States, Canada, and Mexico, by means of a system of interlocking railroads.

Despite the costly cargo installations and the intricate organization of cargo handling, the genius of the port is geographical. Men made New York the great trade center it is today only after nature provided an amazing system of sheltered harbors and waterways. For the usefulness of the port lies mainly in its configuration—a huge landlocked area protected from the wildness of the ocean, yet close to the sea, and offering easy access to the interior.

It is true that, in the course of the four centuries since the harbor was discovered by Verrazano, some important geographical changes have been made by man—enlarging Governor's Island with earth from the subways, constructing the mammoth naval basin at Bayonne with fill dredged from the harbor, and removing obstructions to navigation in the East and Harlem Rivers. Since the early 19th century, too, the waterfront has been moved back 200 feet or more from the rivers to provide additional working space for ships; and the breakwater around the Erie Basin has been built up from ballast dumped by ships from all over the world.

But the genius of the port still lies in its unique combination of bays, estuaries, and rivers, and the short distance a ship has to travel from the open ocean. It is only seven

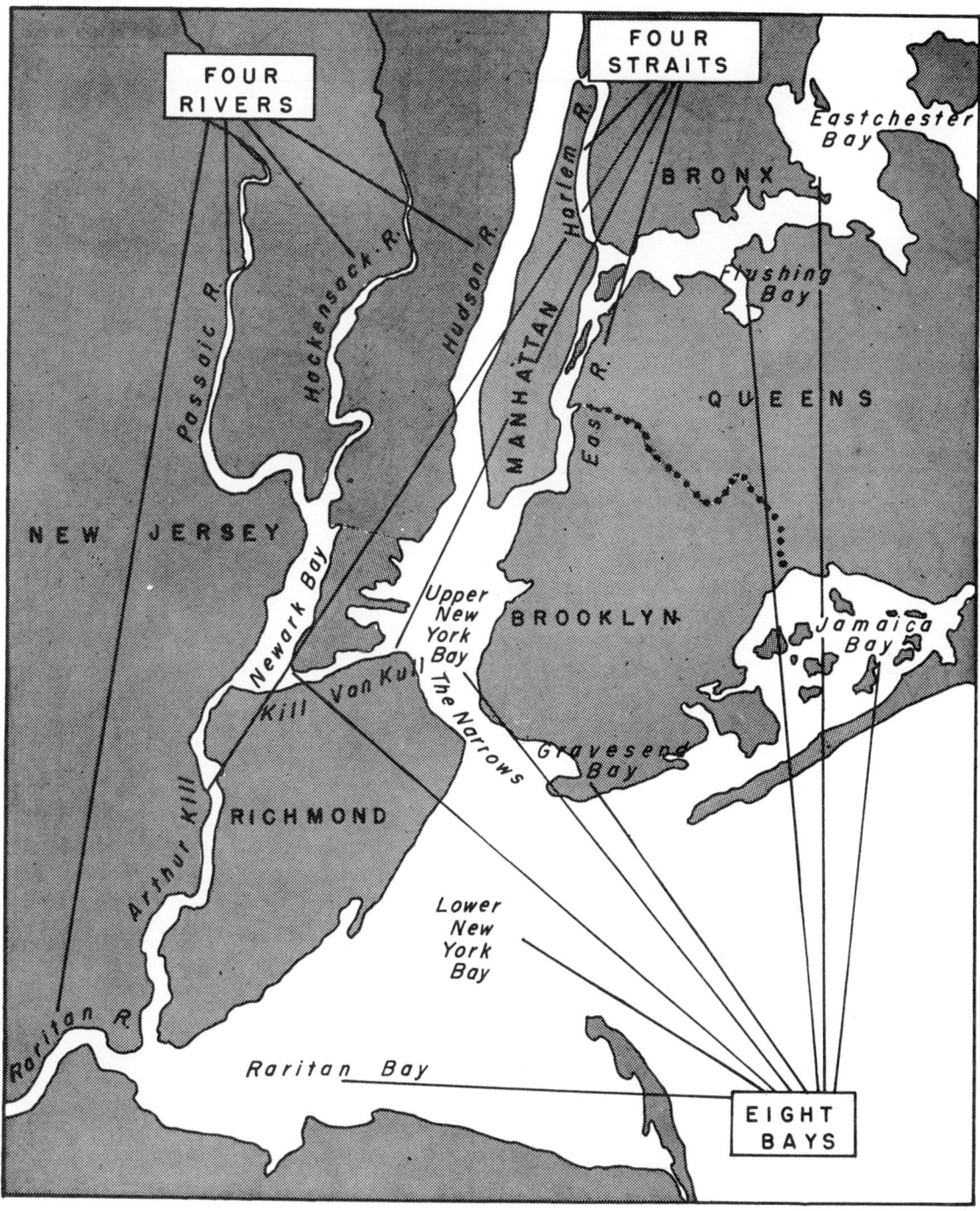

Figure 2-2. The Port of New York.

miles from the Battery at the foot of Manhattan to the Narrows at the harbor entrance. A ship can settle down to the long voyage to Europe, South America, or Asia in an hour or two from the time she leaves her pier.

Since every day in port is costly, the whole effort of the port organization is directed to-

ward getting a ship headed back to sea as swiftly as possible. It is a fundamental part of marine economics that anything speeding up the discharging and loading of a vessel is worth the expense. The romantic days of the rusty, plodding freighter are over; shipping cargo is big business now. Today the fast freighters from

Figure 2-3. Rush hour on a New York City subway platform. So great is the pressure of the crowd that people are jammed into subway cars like sardines in a can. (New York City Transit Authority)

America, England, northwestern and southern Europe, and Scandinavia are the ones that make good profits.

To the casual ferryboat or ocean liner passenger, the business of the harbor looks random and lumbering. Big ships slowly pass up and down on their schedules; but carfloats, oil barges, tugboats, and ferries swarm constantly through the turbid city water, sometimes callously bearing down on one another with an indifference that is alarming to the tourist. Everything appears to be cheerfully casual.

In point of fact, the port is organized by the necessities of its daily business. Every year there are more than 10,000 sailings out of the port, coastwise and foreign; this high figure is a tribute to New York's ability to keep things moving. Ships do not have to lie idle while awaiting attention ashore. Experienced pilots are always available at the mouth of the dredged channel, and there is a large fleet of tugs with trained docking pilots on call at any hour of the day or night.

The port includes about 200 piers equipped for deep-water vessels. Since the local fleet consists of about 2,500 tugs, lighters, barges and floating derricks, ships can discharge and load

cargo on the offshore side as well as directly to and from the piers. This system of double loading saves time. Tankers, which come here in great numbers from the Gulf of Mexico and the Persian Gulf, can discharge their cargo, take on return ballast, and put out to sea again in less than 24 hours. At the Port Authority's grain elevator pier in the noisy and cluttered little area of Gowanus Bay, ships can load 4,000 tons of grain in every eight-hour shift, or 12,-000 tons—capacity for the larger ships—in 24 hours.

The port is sweeping in size. It includes not only the major waterfronts, familiar to many people, on the Hudson and East Rivers, but also: Staten Island, where America's first free-trade area is located and where goods can be brought in duty-free for inspection; Elizabethport, where cotton, chicle, sugar, flour, and cocoa beans are stored and made into finished products; Edgewater, where crude sugar arrives from Brazil, Puerto Rico, and the Philippines; Port Raritan, where more than a thousand vessels appear every year with cargoes that include copper ore from Chile and Peru; the Port of Bayonne, with its drydock that can handle the largest ships in the world; Kearney, the home port for many colliers; and the Bronx, which has docks on the Harlem and East Rivers and on Long Island Sound.

AIR TRANSPORTATION

The metropolitan area has rapidly adjusted to the demands of the air age. Giant modern air terminal facilities meet the constantly increasing needs of travelers and shippers. The four airports operated and managed by the Port of New York Authority—La Guardia and New York International in New York, and Newark and Teterboro in New Jersey—serve more than ten million passengers annually.

Constant improvements are being made in these installations to anticipate the continued growth envisaged during the next decade. By 1965 alone, domestic and foreign travel is expected to increase to 13 million passengers. New York International Airport will handle all the overseas airlines and 37 per cent of the domestic passengers entering and leaving the region by air.

Impact of air transportation. New York's air passenger traffic exceeds that of any other urban center, with one out of four air travelers in the nation flying to or from the area.

Airports have made substantial contributions to the local economy through the employment and income opportunities offered. In addition to the Port Authority personnel, many people are employed by the airlines, service establishments, the Federal government, and other airport tenants. Over 10,000 persons are employed at New York International, 7,700 at La Guardia, and 2,400 at Newark Airports—at an annual payroll of approximately $105 million. In addition, numerous employment opportunities have been created by new and existing commercial and service establishments in communities surrounding the airports.

Helicopter service. Late in 1952, New York Airways began the first scheduled helicopter flights in the New York area. Today this carrier operates 17 round-trip flights daily between Newark, La Guardia, and New York International; all but three of these flights carry mail and freight. Interurban helicopter service is furnished to White Plains, New York; New Brunswick, Trenton, and Princeton, New Jersey; and Stamford, Norwalk, and Bridgeport, Connecticut. A heliport for midtown Manhattan is in the planning stage.

RAIL AND HIGHWAY TRANSPORT

Twelve railroads and 750 trucking firms expedite cargo movement in the port area. Railroad passenger and freight lines link the city with the nation's major trade centers. The New York Central and the New York, New Haven, and Hartford terminals handle most of the freight in Manhattan and the Bronx; branch lines serve Queens, Brooklyn, and Richmond.

A comprehensive highway, expressway, bridge, and tunnel network has been constructed within the past 25 years to handle increased urban traffic. The Major Deegan highway, which runs into the New York State Thruway, facilitates movement from the city to upstate points; an arterial highway permits motor travel along the periphery of Manhattan with quick access to Brooklyn, the Bronx, and Queens.

INDUSTRIAL PATTERNS

For many decades, trade and services have played a more significant role in the economy of New York City than in that of most other metropolitan centers of the country.

One of the most persistent legends about New York is that it is only a city of consumers and middlemen, an unproductive parasite that lives off the labor and substance of others, a buzzing market place where the goods of outsiders are exchanged (for exorbitant fees), a wasteful pleasure center where talents, services, and money are squandered without concern. In fact, New York is the greatest manufacturing center in the world.

There are many reasons for New York's primacy as an industrial center: (1) the location; (2) the port and harbor; (3) a large and highly concentrated population with widely diversified skills, professions, and occupations; (4) highly developed but essentially small and varied industries; and (5) a far-reaching network of air, land, and sea transportation and communications. The large population is especially important. It provides a great consumer market, an almost inexhaustible labor supply, and the need for secondary services to "mind the city's washing."

More than 3,500,000 persons are gainfully employed in metropolitan New York. Of that number about a million work at 300 different lines of industry in 42,000 manufacturing plants. They produce more goods, measured in dollars, than in any other manufacturing center in the world.

Every major manufacturing group is represented, but the heaviest concentration is in nondurable goods industries, which employ over 75 per cent of the area's manufacturing workers. Despite the concentration of employment in nondurables, there is a wide diversity of industry. This contributes an economic stability lacking in many other urban centers. Emphasis on production of consumer soft goods serves to cushion the shock of any economic decline, since the demand for such items is usually more constant than the demand for hard goods. For example, in Detroit the automobile industry accounts for 46 per cent of all employment. It would take 30 or more industries to use that percentage of the work force in New York. When people stop buying automobiles, Detroit is in trouble. People would have to stop buying nearly everything at once to have a comparable effect on New York, since the city accounts for 90 per cent of all fur goods made in the nation, 70 per cent of all millinery, 76 per cent of all women's outerwear, 41 per cent of all periodicals printed, 30 per cent of all apparel goods, 21.7 per cent of all printing and publishing, nine per cent of all leather goods, six per cent of all furniture, five per cent of all food production, and five per cent of all paper and allied products.

Small firms dominate. The average number of persons employed per establishment, 19 workers, is substantially below the national figure. Taken individually, the area's manufacturing enterprises are so diminutive that foreign visitors seeking the heart of American mass production hurry through New York and go out to see the giant automobile plants that dominate Detroit, the steél mills that darken the skies near Pittsburgh, or the sprawling aircraft factories of California. New York has nothing to match these industries, yet the combined output of its thousands of tiny shops is so much greater than that of other large cities that there is not even a close competitor.

These tiny shops are more representative of metropolitan industry than the huge enterprises with headquarters in the Empire State Building or Rockefeller Center. More than 235,000 separate enterprises exist in New York's five boroughs. Of these, only 500 businesses employ over 500 persons, and 210,000 are owner operated or have fewer than 20 workers on their payroll.

A major characteristic of New York City's manufacturing industries is that much of the production is carried on in rented lofts and other multitenant buildings. Of the 8,000 loft buildings in the city, 7,400 are in Manhattan. On the other hand, Manhattan has fewer than 1,000 of the city's 8,900 factory buildings, as distinguished from lofts.

The availability of lofts enables many small firms, particularly new enterprises, to avoid large outlays for plant sites and structures. Expansion is frequently accomplished by renting additional space—space that formerly may have been occupied by nonmanufacturing activities or was used for residential purposes. The high occupancy rate maintained in Manhattan's loft buildings and the continuing construction of new factories in many other parts of the city

are evidences of a sustained demand for manufacturing facilities.

Numerous firms have found suitable locations by renting quarters in industrial buildings especially designed for light manufacturing, with transportation connections, loading and unloading facilities, storage, power, and the like. Outstanding examples of such successful industrial undertakings are the Bush Terminal and the New York Dock Company developments in Brooklyn and the Port of New York Authority building in Manhattan.

Changes in zoning regulations permit the location of industrial laboratories and light industrial plants in some predominantly residential districts; this has kept industry within the city. A number of such plants have been constructed in various parts of Queens. Examples are the Sylvania Electric Company's laboratory and the Bulova Watch Company's factory, which have grounds open to the public almost as if they were municipal parks.

Increased industrial activity in the surrounding suburbs has proved to be of considerable benefit to the city itself. Although some industry has left New York to move into the outskirts, the many new and thriving firms established in suburban centers have strengthened the economy of the city on which they depend for business services. As manufacturing has shifted outward, compensating increases in nonmanufacturing enterprises in the city have resulted in more employment in the service and distributive industries. Studies of manufacturing firms that have moved to the suburbs show that the principal reasons for such moves are traffic congestion and high value of land—conditions related to the high level of activity in the city and the intense competition for space. The very success of the city is responsible for some of its losses.

The market of eight million residents is augmented by 400,000 daily commuters who work in the city's offices and factories, thousands of shoppers from the surrounding suburbs, and throngs of vacationists and business visitors who avail themselves of the vast variety of consumer goods for sale in the city.

THE GARMENT INDUSTRY

The largest single segment of New York's economy is the ladies' garment industry. This strange business, based on fickle feminine taste and requiring small capital outlay, provides jobs for 250,000 workers and has made New York a world fashion center. More than that, it has created a city within a city, the Garment Center—a crowded district bounded on the north by Forty-second Street, on the south by Thirty-fourth Street, on the east by the Avenue of the Americas, and on the west by Ninth Avenue.

Within this dynamic square, 4,000 manufacturers occupy 170 buildings. In their shops, $4 billion worth of coats, suits, dresses, underwear, millinery, furs, and other garments worn by American women are cut, shaped, pressed, packed, and shipped. The annual payroll amounts to nearly $1 billion.

The other branch of the garment industry is that devoted to clothing the American male; it supplies about 40 per cent of the national market. Eighty thousand workers, members of the Amalgamated Clothing Workers Union, and a thousand supervisors perform this task. Like the women's wear industry, it is one with a feverish pace and a rapid turnover. Today's boss may be a salesman tomorrow, a cutter the next day, and a boss again the next season.

Few industries are as ideally suited to a city where space is at a premium. Garment making lends itself readily to division of labor. Only small and relatively inexpensive equipment is needed, with little capital or risk required. But the most important factor of all is the unequaled local market—a metropolitan area population of more than 14 million, with a per capita income higher than the national average, in a climatic area demanding four seasonal wardrobe changes. What could be more advantageous than a site where clothes are made on the fourteenth floor and sold on the first?

PRINTING AND PUBLISHING

Linotype machines and printing presses are second only to sewing machines in New York's manufacturing industries. Printing and publishing trades employ 120,000 workers. With 5.2 per cent of the nation's population, this city produces 21.7 per cent of all printing and publishing manufactures. Forty-five per cent of the country's book publishers turn out about three-quarters of all books published in the United

Figure 2-4. Typical loft scene in New York City's garment district. Women operators using multipurpose sewing machines turn out clothing to suit every taste and every pocketbook. (Burton Berinsky Justice, International Ladies' Garment Workers' Union, AFL-CIO)

States. Fifty of the 80 national magazines with circulation of more than one million are printed in New York. In the newspaper field, New York is home to 150 general news publications (70 in foreign languages) and 24 specialized dailies.

OTHER INDUSTRIES

Machinery and metal products rank third in the city's industrial hierarchy. In order of importance, the list also includes: scientific instruments, chemical products, leather goods, paper products, furniture and wood products, and textile products.

FINANCIAL AND COMMERCIAL CAPITAL

Perhaps the best evidence of New York City's position as the trading and financial capital of the nation is the volume and diversity of its wholesale trade. More than in any other city in the country, its wholesalers function on a national or even international scale. Wholesale transactions aggregate over $38 billion annually, accounting for 20 per cent of all such trade in the United States.

The area around Wall Street contains the

world's greatest concentration of financial institutions, including: commercial, industrial, and savings banks; investment trusts; insurance companies; security dealers and underwriters; commodity brokers; exchanges; mortgage, loan, and installment finance companies; personal loan companies; and holding companies.

Nearly 30 per cent of all United States commercial and business loans granted by commercial banks is held by New York City banks, which supply funds to almost every type of industry. A large percentage of the total is granted to firms that have headquarters in the city and plants or facilities in other parts of the country.

Sharing in prominence with the great banking institutions in the Wall Street area are the nation's leading security exchanges. Investors and traders transact the bulk of their business in stocks and bonds on the New York Stock Exchange and the American Stock Exchange. These two exchanges account for more than 90 per cent (based on value) of all security transactions reported on all exchanges (registered and unregistered) in the country.

Insurance. Firms active in many phases of insurance maintain home offices in Manhattan. More than 21 life insurance companies, including three of the largest four, have their headquarters here; the fourth is located in the New York metropolitan area at Newark, New Jersey. In the fields of fire and casualty insurance, New York City is the home office for six of the 25 largest fleets (groups of companies under a common management); they account for over 25 per cent of the industry's business. New York also dominates in the field of marine insurance. Ranking first in the country in this phase of insurance, Manhattan is now second only to London internationally.

RESEARCH

New York's growing status in the fields of basic and applied scientific research is closely associated with its dominance as a financial center. More than 400 such facilities, engaged in full-time research in many fields, are located in New York. The metropolitan area also has many independently operated commercial laboratories that provide valuable technical and research services on a contract basis.

OUTLOOK

The continuation of present trends in industrial development and management may be expected to strengthen New York's position as the headquarters of American industry. Perhaps Manhattan's most significant trend is the change in economic emphasis toward a greater stress on business and professional services, finance, insurance, and real estate. Manhattan evidently is substituting office jobs for goods-processing jobs. It is replacing one-dollar-a-square-foot space by six-dollars-a-square-foot space in response to the shift in the pattern of economic activities. The city's economy is so massive yet so flexible, that it can absorb changes, adapt to them, and prosper through them. For the future, this size plus flexibility means a high level of economic activity based on the elements and considerations that have made New York what it is today.

POPULATION

New York City is a ferment of peoples. It contains people of 75 nationalities and racial groups. Of the nearly eight million who live there, two million are Jews—or nearly one person in every four. The two million Jews represent a great many nationalities—Russian, German, Polish, Rumanian, Austrian. There are 1,127,625 Negroes in New York. There are about 500,000 Puerto Ricans, about one million Italians, half a million Irish, and half a million Germans. There are 900,000 Russians, 150,000 English, 400,000 Poles, and quantities of Finns, Czechs, Swedes, Latvians, Belgians, Welsh, Greeks, and Dutch. Many Dutch families are descendants of early settlers. It is very hard to say how many Chinese there are. The official figure is 36,129, but there are many Chinese who are in New York illegally and who do not like census takers.

New York has about three million people who are natives but one or both of whose parents was born in a foreign country. It still has more than 1,750,000 residents who were born abroad. The collision and intermingling of these millions of foreign born people representing so many races and creeds make New York a permanent exhibit of the phenomenon of one world. The citizens of New York are tolerant not only from disposition but from necessity. The city has to be tolerant, otherwise it

Figure 2-5. Aerial view of Levittown, Long Island, a suburban community. Although this city owes much of its growth to its proximity to New York City, it has an important economic life of its own. (Ewing Galloway)

would explode in a mushroom cloud of rancor and bigotry. Every race problem in the world smolders in New York, but the noticeable thing is not the problem but the inviolate truce.

THE CITY'S PROBLEMS

In spite of extraordinary accomplishments, New York still has plenty of major problems—many of them not unknown in smaller communities. The problems of any big city are compounded and accentuated in New York by the great mass of people, permanent and transient, living off the facilities of a small area. Mass transit, sanitation, slum clearance, schools, the influx of nearly 500,000 Puerto Ricans since World War II—these are some of New York's big headaches.

Other headaches are traffic congestion, which is said to be costing New Yorkers over one billion dollars annually; the stubborn increase in crime, despite emergency police efforts; and the rising rate of the welfare rolls.

LONG ISLAND

Long Island extends a finger eastward into the Atlantic Ocean for some 120 miles from New York Bay. Its north shore, overlooking Long Island Sound, is the product of many deposits laid down during the last glacial period. Two of the most prominent deposits, now called *terminal moraines,* were concentrated at the southern edges of the ice sheet. These two diverging ridge-like hills give the east end of the island its "fish tail" appearance. The more southerly moraine comes from under the other moraine near Brooklyn on Long Island, and extends the length of the island as the Ronkonkoma Hills. The second moraine runs along the north side of the island as the Harbor Hills.

Some of the finer glacially deposited mate-

Figure 2-6. Duck farm at Flanders near Great Peconic Bay, Long Island. Long Island ducks have much more than a local reputation. The raising of poultry and poultry products, the second largest source of farm income, is highly developed. (NYSPIX-Commerce)

Since the beginning of World War II the industrialization of the Nassau-Suffolk area has been phenomenal. The production of aircraft and aircraft parts is by far the predominant industry; it employs almost one-third of all factory workers in the district. Grumman at Bethpage, Republic at Farmingdale, and Sperry Gyroscope at Lake Success are three of the state's leading firms in this field. Many smaller factories producing aircraft parts are situated in several nearby communities.

The manufacture of scientific and engineering instruments, the next largest industry, provides employment for 18 per cent of all manufacturing employees in Long Island. A world-famous plant at Great Neck produces high-precision aeronautical and marine instruments. Although individually small, there are numerous apparel shops in the area making such clothing as uniform caps, women's outerwear, and men's furnishings. Other important products include sheet metal goods, electronics equipment, toys, curtains, lace goods, canvas products, laboratory furniture, and marine fittings.

AGRICULTURE ON LONG ISLAND

Lucrative potato and vegetable crops are produced on the flat terrain of the island. Although Nassau County's vegetable farms have largely given way to suburban home developments in recent years, Suffolk County is less densely populated and still maintains its fundamentally agricultural character. Extensive acreage is devoted to truck farming; cauliflower, fresh beans, sweet corn, and cabbage are the leading products.

FISHING

The many miles of shoreline on Long Island Sound to the north and on the Atlantic Ocean to the south support a prosperous fishing industry. Fishing for clams, oysters, lobsters, and crabs is both a sport and a source of livelihood for the coastal inhabitants. About 34 million pounds of fish are marketed each season.

RECREATION

Few other densely populated areas offer the proximity of recreational facilities provided by Long Island. Most of the residential communities are either adjacent to a recreational

rial has been transported from the moraines and laid down as an outwash plain between the two moraines. The south shore has been greatly modified by wave action and currents. Headlands have been cut off and sandy debris has been strewn out in a series of bars and beaches pointing westerly, such as Fire Island, Long Beach, Rockaway Beach, and Coney Island. Nowhere does Long Island exceed 410 feet in elevation.

NASSAU-SUFFOLK

The Nassau-Suffolk district is the fastest growing region in New York State. These two counties occupy 87 per cent of the land area of Long Island, with the New York City counties of Kings and Queens to the west accounting for the balance.

center or are themselves resorts. Ready accessibility makes Long Island's playgrounds favorites for thousands of New York City's inhabitants who annually throng to its innumerable beaches, fishing piers, golf links, and 12 state parks.

THE CITY BELT—WEST OF THE HUDSON

At one end there is New York, at the other there is Philadelphia. Between, on either side of a thin railroad corridor linking them, live more than two-thirds of all the people in New Jersey. Here is the area of cities—Jersey City, Newark, Elizabeth, Camden, and the state capital at Trenton. This is the City Belt, where trains thunder over the busiest stretches of railroad tracks in the world, where heavy trucks and hundreds of thousands of automobiles each day grind away at cement and macadam on the highways and superhighways and turnpikes, and where factories and chemical plants combine to make New Jersey the seventh state in industrial development in the nation.

The upper half revolves around New York; the lower half has Philadelphia as its axis. This is the City Belt where "dormitories" for New York and Philadelphia have become a pattern. This is the land of industry, of city slums, of suburban housing developments, of progress, of noise, and of culture. This is the land Benjamin Franklin likened to a barrel "tapped at both ends."

Four bridges and two tunnels financed and constructed by the Port of New York Authority are in operation between New Jersey and New York City. Two bridges, the Goethals Bridge and the Outerbridge Crossing, were opened to traffic in 1928. Both the Bayonne Bridge and George Washington Bridge were opened to traffic in 1931. The Holland Tunnel, connecting Manhattan to Jersey City, was opened in 1927; the parallel Lincoln Tunnel, connecting Manhattan to Weehawken, New Jersey, was opened in 1937. These transportation arteries make the Jersey shore opposite Manhattan another economic borough. The northern counties are part of the New York metropolitan complex and share many of its problems—problems dealing with traffic and other aspects of growth and decay.

Located across Newark Bay from Jersey City, and eight miles from Manhattan, Newark is the metropolis of New Jersey, a port of entry and one of the world's great manufacturing centers. To the south of Newark is Elizabeth, the nation's leading producer of sewing machines. To the north is Passaic, the largest handkerchief center in the United States, and a center for the manufacture of woolen and worsted goods. Nearby Paterson, straddling the falls of the Passaic River, is noted for its silk, rayon, and woolen mills.

Figure 2-7. The Hudson River waterfront, lower Manhattan in the background and Jersey City in the foreground. (Port of New York Authority)

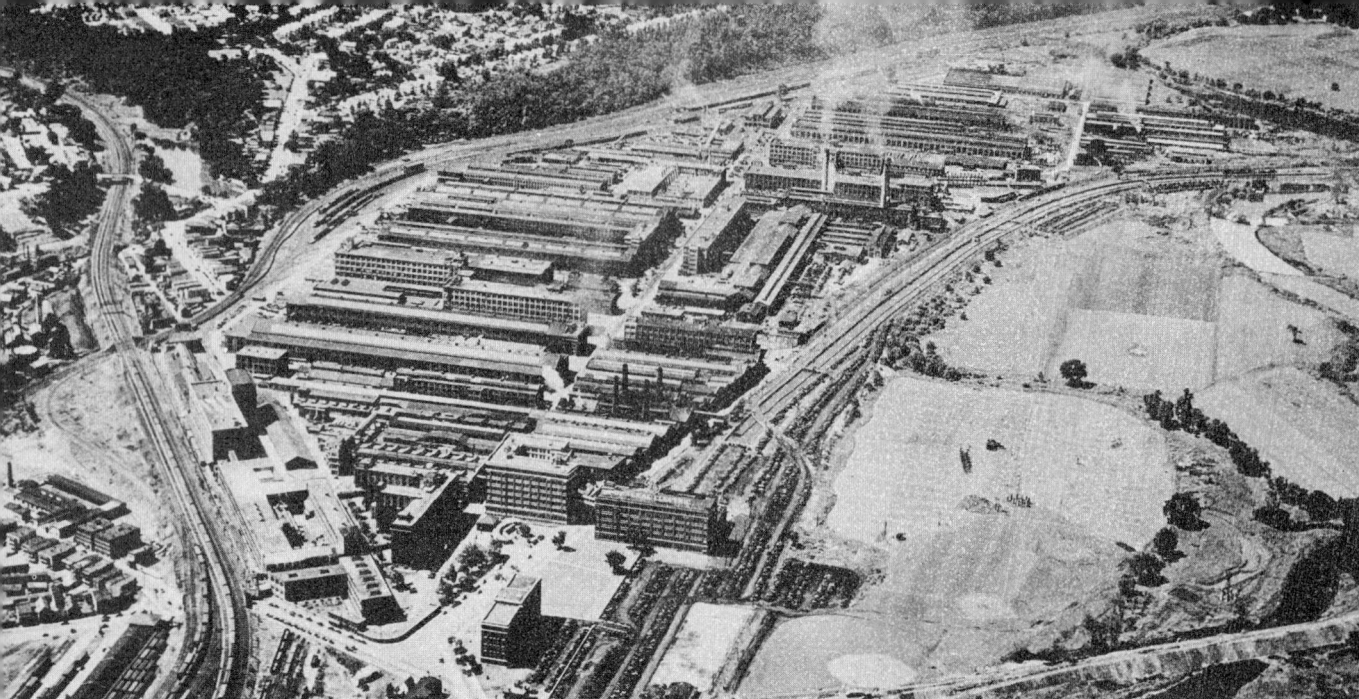

Figure 2-8. The Schenectady Works of the General Electric Company, Schenectady, New York. (Ewing Galloway)

THE HUDSON VALLEY

The Hudson Valley, an area of rich farms, industrial cities, and vacation areas, is the Northeast's natural gateway to the interior. Ocean-going vessels penetrate inland to Troy, and the major rail and highway routes converging upon New York City provide valley towns with ready accessibility to the city's markets.

THE LOWER HUDSON

More than half of the population within the Lower Hudson Valley lives in four large suburban cities: Yonkers, Mount Vernon, New Rochelle, and White Plains, with their economy closely linked to New York City. Manufacturing establishments produce nationally known brands of rugs, automobiles, copper wire, elevators, and hearing aids. Clothing manufacturing is the area's largest industry, employing about one out of every six factory workers. Textile mill products, primarily carpets and rugs, rank a close second to apparel in employment. Chemicals and allied goods are also well represented.

THE MID-HUDSON

The Mid-Hudson Valley's population has a greater proportion of its labor force dependent on agriculture, trade, and services than the areas previously mentioned. Its fertile soils support extensive fruit orchards, vineyards, and dairy farms. Apples, pears, plums, cherries, grapes, and currants are important crops.

Poughkeepsie, Newburgh, Kingston, and Hudson are the principal manufacturing and retail trading centers. The machinery industry is the most important source of manufacturing employment. Major products include electric typewriters, ball bearings, recording equipment, and gauges.

Brickmaking, centered around Kingston, owes its origin to the combination of large deposits of clay on the banks of the Hudson River and cheap water transportation to the New York City market. The manufacture of Portland cement near Hudson is another industry based on local water resources.

Numerous places of historic interest attract tourists, among them: the United States Military Academy at West Point, Washington's headquarters in Newburgh, the old Senate house in Kingston, the Hyde Park home of Franklin D. Roosevelt, and the magnificent estates along the Hudson above Poughkeepsie.

THE UPPER HUDSON

This section is dominated by Troy, located at the head of navigation on the Hudson River.

An important industrial city and the eastern terminus of the New York State Barge Canal, Troy claims national leadership in manufacturing men's shirts, engineering and surveying instruments, sandpaper, and emery cloth.

Albany, capital of New York, is located south of Troy on the west side of the Hudson. It is one of the most important inland ports accommodating ocean-going vessels.

Schenectady, located on the Mohawk River, 13 miles northwest of Albany, has been a noted center of the electrical industry since 1886. It has the world's largest plant for the production of electrical equipment and radio and television sets. It has extensive research laboratories, including a new $20 million atomic research laboratory at nearby Knolls. The city also is a major producer of electric and diesel locomotives, and has several smaller industries.

Gloversville and Johnstown, northwest of Schenectady, produce the bulk of leather dress gloves in the country. Lumber mills, machine shops, and tanneries are other major manufacturing enterprises.

THE DELAWARE VALLEY

The Delaware is a short river with a long history. It was controlled at various times by the Dutch, the Swedes, and the English. The river was the heart of Revolutionary resistance; its mention recalls many famous place names along the road to independence. Brandywine, Philadelphia , Trenton, Washington's Crossing, and Valley Forge are all in the Delaware River Basin.

The Delaware River flows generally south. Its irregular course alters the symmetry of Pennsylvania's otherwise almost rectangular shape. The river carves a boundary line first between New York and Pennsylvania, then between Pennsylvania and New Jersey, and finally between New Jersey and Delaware. It is an invaluable natural resource to these four states.

ECONOMIC IMPORTANCE

The economic importance of the Delaware Basin is out of proportion to its size. Fully five and one-half million people are now living in the area, about 430 to the square mile — ten times the United States average.

The Philadelphia metropolitan area contains two-thirds of the people of the Delaware Basin. Some of them are engaged in foreign and coastal commerce. A great many more work in the industrial establishments that produce manufactured products from raw materials assembled by waterways, railways, and highways converging in the heart of the metropolis. The workshops are almost innumerable.

As in all industrial centers, there are supporting and complementary activities of trade, banking, insurance, communications, utilities, and all the other services required to make an industrial metropolis function. Kilowatts to turn the wheels in mill and factory are extracted from coal delivered to power plants along the Delaware and Schuylkill; vegetables come from the flat, rich garden belt beyond Camden; dairy products come from Montgomery, Chester, and Berks Counties west of Philadelphia; potatoes, from Lehigh, Northampton, and Carbon Counties; poultry products, from the state of Delaware and the rich agricultural hinterlands of the piedmont.

The mineral wealth of the region is most heavily concentrated in the Lehigh and Schuylkill Valleys. Slate from quarries in Northampton County and from the Slatington deposits in Lehigh County account for half the country's output. For over half a century, these two counties have also been producing a very substantial part of the country's cement, made from a rich streak of limestone or cement rock. Here, beside great gaping cavities in the strata of limestone rock, are to be seen huge cement mills, which are the principal support of a dozen small towns extending from Martins Creek (near the Delaware River) to Egypt and Ormrod, west of the Lehigh River, and beyond. A large section of the great anthracite region also lies within the Delaware Basin.

SETTLEMENT

In a region as well endowed with natural resources and as highly diversified in economic activity as the Delaware Basin, one finds, as may be expected, a great variety of people and racial types. There are descendants of the original English, Scotch, Welsh, Dutch, Irish, and Swedish settlers, and the more recent Polish, Italian, Czechoslovakian, and Lithuanian

Figure 2-9. Independence Hall, with part of the new Independence Mall, Philadelphia, Pennsylvania. Philadelphia, noted for buildings of historical importance, has been undergoing extensive redevelopment in its downtown area. (Girard Trust Corn Exchange Bank)

Baltimore and Ohio and the Reading Railroads, did most to make industrial Philadelphia.

Planned as a "greene countrie towne," the city had a simple and humble origin. It began as a village with streets laid out at right angles in a two-square-mile rectangle on the narrows of the urn-shaped peninsula formed by the Delaware and the Schuylkill Rivers. The city has long since overrun the peninsula and spread north and south along the Delaware and west up the Schuylkill. About two-thirds of William Penn's company of 100 Quakers survived the Atlantic voyage to start the settlement of "brotherly love." Others followed; by the end of the next calendar year, 1683, Philadelphia had its first 400 permanent inhabitants. The population was about 35,000 when the Declaration of Independence was signed, and over a half million at the time of the Civil War. Population reached its peak in 1950 with 2,-071,605. The 1960 census showed a slight decline to 2,002,512—in keeping with a national trend of population shifts from the incorporated city limits to the suburbs. Philadelphia ranks today as the fourth largest city in the nation. Despite its age and its many people, it is still a "greene countrie towne"—at least more so than most other big cities. Rows of trees shade many Philadelphia streets, and the city has an abundance of parks and open squares.

groups. Successive waves of immigration brought heterogeneous peoples seeking not only religious freedom but also economic opportunity. Speaking many languages, representing many faiths, and skilled in many trades, they were absorbed by the Delaware Basin in its ever-expanding industrialism. The variety of people is still apparent in the valley and its tributaries.

THE PHILADELPHIA METROPOLITAN AREA

The main line of the Pennsylvania Railroad and the Delaware River meet in Philadelphia, and to both the city owes much of its growth. The Delaware made commercial Philadelphia; the Pennsylvania Railroad, together with the

DELAWARE RIVER PORTS

Maritime Delaware is the lowest third of the river—the section starting at Trenton. From there ports are found for miles on both sides of the river. For purposes of analysis, these ports may be grouped as follows: the port of Philadelphia, cross-river ports, down-river ports, and up-river ports.

The port of Philadelphia. The harbor and port of Philadelphia run along the west bank of the Delaware 23 miles downstream just below the mouth of the Schuylkill, and 8½ miles up both banks of the Schuylkill. The port of Philadelphia has almost 200 piers, wharves, and docks.

Ships laden with materials from the four corners of the world move into these piers, and without the lighterage required in New York and some other ports. From shipside, railroads and motor trucks extend the lines of commerce overland in all directions. A belt line railroad connects the extremities of the port with three trunk line railroads. The Reading Railroad reaches up into the hard coal region; the Pennsylvania Railroad goes over the mountains to Pittsburgh, Chicago, and St. Louis, north to New York City, and south to Washington; and the Baltimore and Ohio Railroad covers the same general territory as the Pennsylvania over a more southerly route. Hundreds of motor truck lines give one-day service as far as the Carolinas and Pittsburgh; over the Pennsylvania Turnpike, with relief drivers, they can reach Chicago in 20 hours.

Local warehouses provide ample storage facilities, dry or cold as required; local stevedoring concerns supply the labor; banks with foreign departments offer financing and foreign exchange facilities; various state and Federal agencies supply specialized services — navigation, weather, customs, health, and quarantine. The port has in abundance everything necessary to expedite commerce.

Cross-river ports. The New Jersey ports of Camden and Gloucester, across the Delaware River from Philadelphia, have less crowded waterfronts. Camden mills manufacture a wide variety of products for world trade—forgings, fountain pens, ships, and soup, for example. Gloucester, nearby, is a busy port of call for ships bringing in specialized products such as licorice and cork and is also industrial.

Down-river ports. Ships from Baltimore and other Chesapeake Bay ports take a shortcut through the Chesapeake and Delaware Canal and join the main stream of traffic to numerous ports on the lower Delaware. Some stop at Deepwater, New Jersey; others move up the little Christina River to Wilmington's harbor. Both Wilmington and Deepwater are chemical ports. The cargoes unloaded there are, petroleum, pyrites, and other mineral ores to be taken apart in the chemical plants. Farther upstream, and still in the state of Delaware, is Claymont, noted for chemicals and steel. Next door, in Pennsylvania, is Marcus Hook, noted mainly as a petroleum town, but with, however, a big rayon plant. Then comes Chester, Pennsylvania, whose shipyards build many of the tankers that haul petroleum and its products in and out of the Delaware. Still farther upstream is Eddystone, which should be re-

named Baldwin for all the locomotives it has built; and across the river on the New Jersey side is Paulsboro, where tankers, heavy with crude oil, call constantly.

Up-river ports. Freighters and motor barges going up the Delaware beyond Philadelphia carry cargoes of heavy raw materials—cryolite to chemical plants, pig iron and fuel oil to cast-iron pipe mills, oils and acids to textile and chemical factories.

Philadelphia is about midway between twelve downstream and nine upstream cities, towns, and villages with port facilities. These 22 localities have innumerable berthing places for ships. The port is a port of parts, geographically, but it is one continuous harbor, economically. Each section or locality is dependent, to some extent, upon every other section. This is apparent when you examine the papers of the ships to see what they carry, from what place they came, and where they are going.

MANUFACTURING

Unlike Pittsburgh, which is predominantly a steel city, or Detroit, which is automotive, Philadelphia has a great diversity of manufactures. Fully 87 per cent of all the country's manufacturing industries listed in the census "blue book" are represented in Philadelphia. There are between 5,500 and 6,000 manufacturing establishments; they are the mainstay of its economic activity. They employ the largest share of its working population. They keep three trunk line railroads and fleets of ships and motor trucks busy gathering raw materials and distributing finished products. They pay out hundreds of millions of dollars in wages, profits, and taxes, and support a large part of such complementary industries and services as banking, insurance, trade, utilities, and government.

Industry has expanded in all directions from Philadelphia, for industries show no respect for political and geographic boundaries. Industrial establishments are clustered along the Delaware River in adjoining Bucks and Delaware Counties and have crossed the river into Camden, Burlington, and Gloucester Counties in New Jersey.

Textiles. Textile mills of all classes flourish in the Philadelphia area. Although they employ ten per cent of all industrial workers—

more than any other group, they no longer occupy their formerly prominent place in the local industrial scene. Some textile plants have moved to the South. Other local industries, particularly the machine and metal trades, have grown to larger stature. Nevertheless, textiles still are a big family, including such major genera or subdivisions as scouring and combing plants that clean and prepare fibers for processing, yarn and thread mills that do the spinning, weaving mills that make only broad fabrics, and other mills that specialize in ribbon, braid, and related narrow fabrics. Other divisions are: dyeing and finishing mills, knitting mills, hat factories, and carpet and rug mills. Each contains further subdivisions. Knitting mills, for example, include full-fashioned hosiery, seamless hosiery, knit outerwear, gloves, and knit fabrics.

The heavy industries are assuming an ever-increasing prominence in the Philadelphia metropolitan area. The basic members of this large family group are the primary metal industries—the steelworks and rolling mills, the iron and steel foundries, and the smelters and refiners of copper, brass, and other nonferrous metals.

Iron and steel. The steelmaking capacity of the Delaware Valley is about 12 million tons, including the output of Bethlehem Steel at the valley's northern edge. The Midvale furnaces in Philadelphia, with an annual capacity in excess of 400,000 tons, make such heavy steel products as armor and ordnance, turbine and generator shafting, crankshafts, locomotive and freight car tires, forgings for cement, and mining machinery. Claymont, Delaware, has a mill with almost a half-million tons capacity, and with finishing facilities for the sheared steel plates used in shipbuilding and the manufacture of locomotive and marine boilers and fireboxes. Other iron and steel plants include an integrated mill at Conshohocken on the Skuylkill River, another at Phoenixville farther up stream, and a third at Coatesville on the Brandywine Creek.

U. S. Steel's Benjamin Fairless plant at Morrisville, Pennsylvania, across the river from Trenton, New Jersey, and the National Steel Corporation's plant near Woodbury, New Jersey, are new giants in the area's steel complex.

The Delaware Valley is becoming a new center of the steel industry because: (1) the high-grade (50 per cent plus) iron ore of the great Mesabi Range in Minnesota is running out; if estimates of remaining reserves are accurate, this source will be exhausted by 1965 or 1970; and (2) to replace Mesabi ore, the steel companies are importing ore from South America and Canada, especially the Venezuela and Labrador-Quebec deposits; this ore can be brought to the mills most economically by water transportation.

The location of an integrated mill on the riverside, such as the Fairless plant, affords advantages peculiar to the steelmaking process. The manufacture of a ton of steel requires four tons of raw materials—two tons of ore, one ton of coke, a half-ton of limestone, and about a half-ton of ferro alloys. In other words, roughly four pounds of raw material must be assembled and processed to make a pound of steel worth an average of about four cents. It is obviously advantageous for a steel mill to be located on a navigable waterway where the raw materials can be brought to the furnace in bulk by low-cost water transportation. Few other industries are as dependent upon navigable waterways as those of iron and steel.

The Delaware River offers natural low-cost transportation for all these bulk products. Deepening of the Delaware to a depth of 25 feet as far as the Fairless plant is already a Federal project, and there is every prospect that a 40-foot channel eventually will be dredged from Philadelphia to Trenton.

The valley's industries have been using twice as much steel as was produced in the area. In the past dozen years great numbers of new plants, many of them natural metal fabricators, have come to the Delaware Valley. Other plants have expanded. The result has been that almost half the finished steel used in the area has been shipped in from Pittsburgh, Youngstown, and Chicago. However, new local mills are drastically reducing the need to import steel.

Steel mills on the Delaware are in an excellent position to serve Eastern markets. The Middle Atlantic and the New England regions can be reached economically by coastwise water transportation. Interior markets within this area may be served by comparatively short rail hauls as well as by motor truck delivery over the new expressways.

Steelmaking capacity on the Delaware is also

situated favorably with respect to export markets. Foreign markets for American steel may be reached most economically by seaboard mills that can load finished steel directly onto ships.

Industry on the lower Delaware. Unlike southern Delaware, which is part of Delmarva's[2] great "broilerland," the northern part of the state is industrial. Wilmington is only 30 minutes south of Philadelphia by rail. More than just a way station on one of the heaviest traveled railroads, the city is two hours from New York and an hour and three-quarters from Washington, D. C.

Over a quarter million people live in the Wilmington metropolitan area. The largest group of working people is employed in the manufacturing industries — chemicals, leather goods, textiles, rubber, automobile assembly, fiber products, and papermaking machinery. A tour of the Wilmington industrial area may give the impression that Wilmington is a chemical city, because of the preponderance of chemical plants along this part of the river. In fact, the Delaware Chamber of Commerce calls the city the "Chemical Capital of the World." The statement is almost if not literally true. Despite the fact that Wilmington makes practically no chemicals, there are probably more chemists per square mile in Wilmington than anywhere else in the world. They work in the large experiment station of the Hercules Powder Company and in the still larger laboratories of du Pont's Experimental Station. The Atlas Powder Company also has its general offices and some plants in Wilmington.

Chemical companies are alike in only one sense—they make chemicals. Probably the most distinguishing feature of the E. I. du Pont de Nemours Company is its product proliferation. In only a very few major lines of chemical products is du Pont the largest producer (Nylon, discovered and engineered by the company itself is an example), but perhaps no other chemical company makes such a great variety of chemicals and chemical products. In a large number of major lines the company ranks second or third.

Wilmington is not 100 per cent chemical, it is also the Morocco and kid leather capital of the country, the country's largest center of vul-

[2] Delaware, Maryland, and Virginia.

Figure 2-10. *United States Steel Corporation's Benjamin Fairless Works near Morrisville, Pennsylvania. Located on a 3,939-acre site on the Delaware River, it is the largest steel mill ever to be built at one time. It handles the complete steelmaking process, from raw materials to finished products. (U.S. Steel Corp.)*

Figure 2-11. *The Chambers Works of the E. I. du Pont de Nemours & Company, Deepwater, New Jersey. (E. I. du Pont de Nemours & Co.)*

Figure 2-12. The Sparrows Point Plant of the Bethlehem Steel Company. Located 12 miles from Baltimore, on the Patapsco River near Chesapeake Bay, this mill uses Venezuelan iron ore and coal from nearby interior points. (Bethlehem Steel Co.)

canized fiber manufacturing, and the home of what is claimed to be the world's largest plant making braided rubber hose.

BALTIMORE: THE PORT AND CITY

The port of Baltimore is situated on a northern estuary of Chesapeake Bay, the Patapsco River and other streams. This port is 150 miles from the Atlantic Ocean via the Virginia capes. However, approximately 20 per cent of the deep draft ships putting in at Baltimore come through the Chesapeake and Delaware Canal. This route shortens the distance to the ocean by 25 miles. It is also a link in the Atlantic Intracoastal Waterway that extends from Boston to Miami. All main ship channels leading into the harbor are capable of handling deep draft ships, the depth varying from 35 to 39 feet at low tide.

At present, Baltimore's port facilities include some 300 piers, wharves, and docks. The shore frontage of the harbor extends for 45 miles, three-fifths of which is developed.

Almost all the large marine terminals are owned and operated by the trunk line railroads, with shorter lines connecting the terminals on the waterfront. Total investment in these facilities has been estimated at $200 mil-

lion, and employment at about 25,000 workers. A large part of these facilities is equipped to handle vast quantities of raw materials and semimanufactured goods. The facilities include grain elevators, coal and iron ore piers, and lumber piers. In addition, Baltimore has numerous United States Revenue and Customs Bonded Warehouses to facilitate the handling of imports. It also has 14 ship construction and repair yards employing approximately 13,700 workers.

Its inland location gives Baltimore the distinctive advantage of being the Atlantic port nearest the industrial center of the nation. Its hinterland, therefore, includes the Middle West, a large part of the Central Freight Association territory (that area east of the Mississippi River, north of the Ohio River, west of the Alleghenies, and south of the Great Lakes), and the Great Lakes region, as well as nearby territory. Connections are afforded by four railways: the Baltimore and Ohio, the Pennsylvania, the Western Maryland, and the Maryland and Pennsylvania. The advantageous location of Baltimore in relation to water, rail, and trucking transport has aided its development into a diversified center of production and trade.

Baltimore at the time of the 1960 census was

the seventh most populous city in the United States. It had approximately half of Maryland's population. For over two centuries the city has dominated the state's economic life. Probably the main reason for its paramount position is location, for Baltimore is the "compromise point" on the Atlantic Coast, neither too far north nor too far south. It is also the port nearest the grain-producing Midwest.

Early industries in Baltimore foreshadowed the future. Among the products were iron, copper, textiles, beer, umbrellas, and chrome ore. Shortly before the Civil War, important plants began to produce woolen fabrics, gas manufacturing and holder equipment, bichromate, fertilizer, and other products. To supplement the city's excellent maritime shipping facilities, enterprising businessmen promoted the nation's first railroad, the Baltimore and Ohio, to tap the riches of the Mississippi Valley.

IRON AND STEEL

Iron was one of Baltimore's early products. At first the ore was obtained within the state, but as the supply dwindled and transportation facilities developed, ores were brought into the state for smelting. In the course of this development, the first modern steel plant was built at Sparrows Point in 1889. Today this plant of Bethlehem Steel is one of the largest tidewater steel mills in the world. Many experts believe that as the ore supplies of America are depleted, Baltimore will become an even more important steel center, since it has been importing South American ore for many years.

For many years mills at Sparrows Point have been fed imported ore brought to Baltimore at lower freight rates than were charged for transportation of domestic ore. For some time Bethlehem Steel has imported small quantities of lateritic iron from Cuba and a much greater tonnage of ore from Chile. Bethlehem's most extensive source of foreign ore, however, is in Venezuela, where its El Pao open-pit mine has reserves estimated at 50 to 60 million tons.

Of even greater importance to the port of Baltimore is the decision by the United States Steel Corporation to make it the East Coast point of entry for its enormous Venezuelan iron ore discovery, possibly the richest and greatest iron deposit in the history of the world.

AIRCRAFT INDUSTRY

Although this area is not marked by the heavy concentration of aircraft producing plants found on the Pacific Coast, its two large plants, Fairchild at Hagerstown and Martin at Baltimore, account for around eight to nine per cent of the nation's total aircraft business.

OTHER INDUSTRIES

Baltimore has a score of industrial giants, some of which are the largest of their kind in the world, with others rating high in their respective fields. It is a leading producer of tin cans, bottle caps, spices, copper, stainless steel, bichromate, electric tools, high tension insulators, copper sulphate, paint brushes, weather instruments, and Christmas tree ornaments.

Baltimore's ship-repairing activity is extensive. Her shipping trade is legendary, as befits a maritime city that began its early life as the haven of the privateering fleet of the new nation. Later the Baltimore-built clipper ship was the outstanding vessel in international trade.

AGRICULTURE

The Middle Atlantic Coastal Plain, covering less than 12 per cent of the land area of the United States, produces about three per cent of the value of all farm products sold in the nation. It supplies, in value of products sold, ten per cent of all poultry and poultry products, eight per cent of all horticultural specialties, six per cent of all vegetables, nearly six per cent of all dairy products, 2.5 per cent of all fruits and nuts, and one per cent of all other products combined—forest products, field crops, livestock, and livestock products other than poultry.

This output is achieved with less than half the area devoted to farming, compared with about two-thirds for the country as a whole, and with fewer than five of each 100 employed persons at work on farms, compared with 12 out of each 100 nationally. The average value of output per farm worker in this region is $3,900, compared with less than $3,200 for the United States.

Variety is the word for the area's agriculture. Truckloads of produce pour into the world's

Figure 2-13. Typical of the substantial, efficiently run farms of the region is this farm in Milford, New Jersey. The farm derives its main income from the sale of milk produced by a herd of 40 pure-bred Holsteins. Poultry and hogs are a side line. (U.S. Department of Agriculture)

largest soup plant at Camden, New Jersey. The world's largest commercial truck farm enterprise, in Cumberland County, New Jersey, employs up to 6,500 people, who process 65 million pounds of vegetables yearly from seed to freezer.

It is true that the region's prominence in manufacturing tends to obscure its farm production somewhat, but this is not because of a lack of agricultural achievement or failure to recognize its success. Truck farms give New Jersey the name of "Garden State." The nickname "Blue Hen's Chickens" is likewise fitting for Delaware, for the state's Sussex County is the nation's leader in number of chickens sold and in value of poultry and poultry products. Surprising to many people is the fact that Lancaster County, Pennsylvania, raises more tobacco than any other county in the nation.

What are some characteristics of agriculture in the Middle Atlantic Region? First, much of the importance of agriculture is due to the area's dense population. Good highway and railway facilities lead to excellent markets in and adjacent to the region. About 20 million people live within its borders; inside its perimeter are the metropolitan areas of New York, Philadelphia, Baltimore, and Washington, D. C.

Cities are important to farming not only for their distribution centers, market places, and consuming populaces, but also for their influence on the types of farming prevailing within their orbit. For example, bulky, perishable products like vegetables, and products requiring relatively little land, like poultry and eggs, are produced close to cities—as is the case in New York, Delaware, New Jersey, and eastern Pennsylvania. Milk, another perishable product, is produced and shipped in from farms somewhat further away. Hogs, sheep, beef cattle, butter, and cheese are concentrated and may be shipped long distances at relatively little cost.

Agriculture in the Middle Atlantic Coastal Plain reflects these economic and physical factors. Nearly 60 cents of each dollar of products sold by farmers (compared with 22 cents nationally) come from the sale of chickens, turkeys, eggs, milk, and allied products. According to the Census of Agriculture, each dollar of sales for an average Middle Atlantic farmer would be broken down as follows: 31 cents from his poultry flock; 28 cents from his dairy; 13 cents from other livestock; 13 cents from such fields crops as tobacco, corn, and wheat; six cents from vegetables; five cents from his mushrooms, flowers, and greenhouse plants;

three cents from his orchards; and less than a cent from forest products.

THE BROILER PENINSULA

Delaware is part of the so-called Delmarva Peninsula, which includes the Eastern Shore parts of Maryland and Virginia, almost separated from the mainland by the bay waters of the Delaware and Chesapeake. This is still the country's pre-eminent broiler land.

A broiler is a 12-week old domestic fowl, exceptionally good to eat if grown for human consumption as tender meat. Formerly a luxury that was served only when the family had guests, the broiler is beginning to challenge pork as the poor man's meat.

Delaware is rather typical of the broiler peninsula; the state accounts for about 60 per cent of the birds produced. Numerous reasons are cited for the rapid rate of growth in the peninsula, but three stand out rather prominently. First, the area is near big Eastern markets that appreciate fresh-killed chicken meat. Delmarva broilers slaughtered in Georgetown, Delaware, on Thursday are the *pièce de résistance* of New York City menus on Friday. Second, World War II gave a sharp stimulus to the consumption of chicken, because red meat was scarce, rationed, and high-priced. Third, nature provided a short reproduction cycle, so that the broiler output may be stepped up quickly. Whereas it takes three to four years to increase the breeding and production of edible beef, one year to raise lamb and pork, it it takes only 15 weeks to make a broiler—from egg to pan.

TRUCK CROPS

The Middle Atlantic trucking region owes its existence primarily to three conditions: (1) The series of large cities extending from Washington, D. C., to Boston, Massachusetts, and affording the greatest market for fresh vegetables and fruits in Anglo-America. The population of this string of cities and adjacent towns exceeds 30 million—about 15 per cent of the total population of the United States and Canada. (2) Sandy to loamy soils that warm up rapidly in the springtime, are readily cultivated, respond well to fertilizers, and produce vegetables of high quality. On the other hand, these sandy soils are not as well adapted to hay or the small grains as the heavier soils inland. (3) A mild, semimaritime climate, having a long frost-free season and springs so warm that vegetables and small fruits may be shipped to the large urban markets one to three weeks in advance of the crops from inland districts at the same latitude.

More than 60 different vegetables are grown commercially each year in the Middle Atlantic Trucking Belt. Suffolk County, New York, and Monmouth County, New Jersey, are two of the foremost potato producing counties in the United States. Among the other truck crops, tomatoes lead; indeed, the acreage of tomatoes in New Jersey is almost as great as the acreage in potatoes. Three-fourths of the farms producing vegetables other than potatoes grow tomatoes. More than 300 million bushels of tomatoes are processed into pulp annually for soups, sauces, and puree, or are canned whole. Tomatoes are by far the chief product canned in New Jersey.

Vegetable production requires a large amount of labor per acre and therefore the acreage per farm is small. The long growing season makes it possible to double-crop much of the land. Truck farms vary from a few acres to 20 or more. The chief outlets for the truck crops of this area are the large Eastern markets and local canning houses. Truck routes extend to all the leading cities, and vegetables harvested in the afternoon are on the market the next morning to provide the consumer with fresh produce.

HORTICULTURE

Greenhouses are a familiar sight both on the main highways and the country roads of Chester County, Pennsylvania, one of the leading counties of the nation in the growing of cut flowers, potted plants, foliage, and green plants produced under glass. Greenhouses turn out $2¼ million of horticultural products each year, a sum considerably greater than the income derived from the sale of field crops other than vegetables and fruits.

Growers of cut flowers must be located near their markets because of the high perishability of their products. This is true particularly of roses. With all their beauty, rosebuds are delicate and cannot be shipped very far, unless by air freight. Because of their vivid colors and fragrance, roses are the favorite among cut flowers; they account for almost a million dollars, or nearly one-half, of the county's cut flowers produced each year.

Greenhouse operation is highly seasonal, both by nature and convention. Lilies go with Easter, poinsettias with Christmas. The peak periods for marketing cut flowers are Christmas, Easter, and Mother's Day; the grower of cut flowers must schedule his operations to have his crops maturing at the right time. Seasonality is reflected in prices commanded in the wholesale markets.

MUSHROOMS

About half of the country's annual 60 million pounds of mushrooms are grown within a 25-mile radius of Kennet Square, Pennsylvania. In this relatively small area, which runs across the curved boundary line of the state into northern Delaware, there are approximately 350 producers. Most of the plants, as the mushroom houses are called, are family owned and operated, with Italian and Quaker ownership predominating. Some are small ventures consisting of three singles or two doubles—a double being a house with four rather than two tiers under each roof. The larger producers often operate as many as 16 or 20 doubles; these are usually the most highly mechanized. Some growers specialize in mushrooms to the exclusion of everything else; others operate mushroom plants in conjunction with dairy farming, cattle feeding, or general farming.

Fresh mushrooms must get to the market within 24 hours after picking. Kennet Square growers, of course, enjoy accessibility to markets in New York, Philadelphia, Wilmington, Baltimore, and Washington. Nearness to a market is still an important factor in plant location, though now it is somewhat less urgent that formerly, because more and more mushrooms are being canned or made into soup.

DAIRYING

The climate, topography, and soils of the Middle Atlantic Region are particularly well suited to grassland dairying. The chief economic advantage enjoyed by dairy farmers, however, is the density of population in nearby markets. For this reason, most of the milk produced here goes to market for consumption as fluid milk, in contrast with the great North-central dairy region (the Michigan-Wisconsin area), where a much larger proportion of the milk goes to market in the form of manufactured products, such as butter, cheese, ice cream, evaporated milk, condensed milk, or powdered milk. Approximately three-quarters of the milk produced in the Middle Atlantic Coastal Plain goes to market as fluid milk in contrast with only one-third in the North-central dairy region.

Philadelphia is the largest fluid milk consuming market in Pennsylvania. The Philadelphia "milkshed" runs from the Atlantic Coast in New Jersey westward as far as Altoona, Pennsylvania. Delaware and Maryland dairy farmers also ship into the Philadelphia market, because these states are a natural part of the Philadelphia milkshed. The New York milkshed comprises a large section of Pennsylvania and overlaps the Philadelphia milkshed in part.

Fluid milk must get to market in a hurry because it is highly perishable. Where an individual farmer will ship his milk, then, depends upon which markets will accept his milk, what price he can get for it, and what it costs to haul it there. That is why milkshed boundaries sometimes seem to follow illogical lines.

NORTHERN PIEDMONT

This portion of the Middle Atlantic Region is a gently rolling plateau (uplifted peneplain) dissected by revived streams. Its valleys are not very deep. The weaker rocks have been cut down to a newer and lower peneplain. The topography provides good watersheds and drainage; limestone underlies the area, giving rise to a rich, productive soil, generally yellow to brown loams or silt loams.

Lacking minerals of importance, except limestone and building stone, with scant water power, and having no harbors except on its eastern edge, the Northern Piedmont is necessarily mainly an agricultural region; general farming and dairying prevail.

LANCASTER COUNTY TOBACCO— A SPECIALTY CROP

Filler tobacco for cigars is the big money

Figure 2-14. This farm in Marlboro, Pennsylvania, is a fine example of conservation farming. (U.S. Soil Conservation Service)

crop in Lancaster County, Pennsylvania. It pays the farmers' big expenses—the new tractor, another automobile, the hospital bill, or a big slice off the mortgage. Yet tobacco is a minor crop in terms of acreage, accounting only for about one out of every four or five acres tilled.

Partly because of tobacco, Lancaster has the largest cattle market this side of Chicago. Farmers buy and fatten cattle not primarily for additional farm income, but for the cattle manure to fertilize the soil. For some farmers, the profit derived from taking cattle as boarders on their way to the slaughterhouse is only incidental.

Lancaster's tobacco crop is a very small part of the country's tobacco crop, about 55 million pounds a year out of two billion pounds, or less than three per cent. High tobacco yields (up to 1,600 pounds per acre) are produced on small farms averaging less than 55 acres, only

a few acres of which are planted in tobacco.

Most farmers in Lancaster County use a four-year rotation cycle—tobacco, wheat, grass, and corn. This system not only preserves the fertility of the soil but also helps to prevent the soil from being blown away. It has other advantages, too: the corn provides both grain and fodder for cattle feed, the wheat provides bedding for the cattle, and the cattle provide manure for the fields.

The acreage given over to tobacco in any one year is governed not only by crop rotation, but also by prospective opportunities of making more money by producing other things, such as tomatoes or potatoes. Furthermore, the farmer also has to consider his other resources, such as labor, machinery, and capital.

APPLE ORCHARDS

A small but very important orchard belt runs through a cluster of Pennsylvania counties —

Adams, Cumberland, Franklin, and York — along the southern border of the state just west of the Susquehanna River. These counties have little in common other than the fact that they grow a lot of apples, and even the apple orchards differ from one county to another within this group. Two neighboring counties, Berks and Lehigh to the northeast, are also big apple producers.

The topography and soil are just right for apples and other fruit. The peaks and crests are forested with a mixture of soft and hard woods, and on the intermediate elevations— seldom over a thousand feet — the orchards stand. Fruit trees on the slopes and hillsides get the benefit of good air and water drainage. Cold air currents settle in the lowlands; apple blossoms escape the damaging effect of late spring frosts, and maturing apples have a better chance to avoid the hazards of early fall frosts.

Apple varieties produced here fall into two broad classes: those best for cooking (York, Rome Beauty, Rhode Island Greening, and Yellow Transparent) and apples for eating fresh (Delicious, McIntosh, and Winesap).

When harvesting time arrives, imported crews of apple pickers—mostly Puerto Ricans— move through the orchards with bags, boxes, baskets, ladders, trucks, and other equipment. Motor trucks loaded with field boxes of apples go directly from the orchards to the processing plants where the boxes are emptied onto a moving belt. Here they get the typical American mass production treatment — high speed, automatic assembly—winding up as canned apple slices, applesauce, apple juice, cider, vinegar, apple butter, or apple pie mix. Revenue is squeezed out of every part of the fruit—including the pulp, which yields dried pomace and is made into pectin for the manufacture of jellies. The entire process is scientific, sanitary, and swift. During the harvesting season, apples flow into the plants at a rate much faster than they can be processed; therefore the district has many large cold-storage warehouses out of which the plants continue to operate all through the winter and into the early spring.

The value of Pennsylvania's apple crop varies from $9 million in poor years to $20 million or better in good years. Pennsylvania is sixth in rank among the leading apple producing states. Washington is the undisputed leader, with a production of almost one-fourth of the country's total. New York ranks second and Virginia third; in recent years, California and Michigan have also forged ahead of Pennsylvania.

LIVESTOCK

About a half-million head of livestock go through the Lancaster market annually. This is a market where local farmers buy lean cattle shipped in from 37 states and from Canada.

The Lancaster livestock market grew right out of the corn fields that surround it. Its location is ideal for fattening Western and Southern cattle headed for the heavily populated Middle Atlantic Seaboard markets. Bred and grass-fed on the Western ranges and plains and in the hill country of the South, the cattle move into the Lancaster area where, on the "cafeteria principle," a final intensive corn feeding gives the proper fat and finish, after which the cattle are moved into the nearby markets. Radiating from Lancaster County is an area consisting of 18 counties in southeastern Pennsylvania and two in Maryland, where most of the stocker and feeder cattle going through the Lancaster market are converted into fat cattle. This area, sometimes called the "Eastern feeding district," is in reality a little corn belt. Each of these counties grows a tremendous amount of corn. Dairying is also important in this area, and a large part of the corn is converted into pork.

Cattle feeding is geared to the previously mentioned four-year system of crop rotation. By marketing his corn in the form of beef at the rate of about 16 bushels of corn required to produce 100 pounds of beef on the hoof, the farmer sells his corn at a higher price; at the same time a large part of the crop stays on the farm in the form of fertilizer.

Steer feeding in conjunction with the corn-tobacco-wheat-grass cycle is an unbeatable combination if the weather does not conspire against the farmer; this it seldom does in Lancaster. In fact, steer feeding in the county has assumed such large proportions that Lancaster farmers must supplement their huge local corn crop by purchasing from outside almost half as much again as they grow.

Lancaster's agriculture, for all of its wealth,

lags far behind its manufacturing industries, which produce two and a half times the wealth created on the farms. The county has a watch factory. It is the home of one of the world's largest linoleum factories. Other industries turn out leather products, textiles, ball bearings, television tubes, clothing, candy, jewelry, and cigars. Here is considerable diversity and stability.

FISHING

Nature has made the coastal waters of the Atlantic Plain a haven for shellfish. The drowned coast with its many bays, coves, estuaries, and shallow tidal flats is ideal for the propagation and culture of several shellfish varieties. Fresh water streams, which reduce salinity; relatively warm, shallow water; and weak tides further aid in making this area an outstanding producer of shellfish. Oysters and crabs are the most highly prized, bring the highest return, and engage the greatest number of fishermen. Mackerel, rosefish, salmon, and shad are also sought.

OYSTERS

Chesapeake and Delaware Bays historically have accounted for nearly one-half of the nation's oyster supply. Continuous fishing on natural beds, however, has caused a decline in oyster production. State governments were careless in enforcing laws designed to give oysters a fighting chance to maintain their population. Oyster gardeners themselves were careless in harvesting oyster clusters and in failing to return the small undersized oysters to the grounds. Upstream municipalities polluted the rivers with sewage, and industrial concerns poisoned the waters with factory wastes. As a result of such malpractices, along with the destruction caused by natural enemies of the oyster, some oyster beds have been almost totally destroyed.

Fortunately, oyster culture in New Jersey and Delaware is in a much better condition than in other oyster areas. This is because growers in Delaware Bay are partly dependent on the existence of public reefs from which to obtain seed for planting on privately owned beds. The state of New Jersey polices its seed beds and also maintains a laboratory with a corps of scientists who have made notable progress in helping growers to fight the oyster's natural enemies.

Oystering runs into money. A secondhand schooner, together with the necessary oyster gear, costs $20,000 to $30,000. A boat license of $3 per ton amounts to $100 to $200 depending on the size of the vessel. Then the oyster grower must pay $400 per acre or more for oyster grounds.

CLAMS AND CRABS

Clamming is carried on extensively in the waters from Long Island to Chesapeake Bay. Familiar to seafood gourmets are Cherrystone clams on the half shell. Cherrystone is a trade name used by the U.S. Fish and Wildlife Service to denote the size of the clam. Claw-like rakes with long handles are employed to dig for clams in the shallow waters near shore. Rowboats are used in deeper water.

The "soft shell," or Blue crab, is a highly prized shellfish in the Middle Atlantic Region. Chesapeake Bay abounds in this variety.

RECREATION

Visitors to the shore resorts of New Jersey spend between a quarter of a billion and a half-billion dollars annually. Although the resorts offer numerous attractions, the outstanding feature common to all is the climate. When the days get hot and sticky in the cities of the interior, it is always cooler and more comfortable at the shore. This is borne out by official records of the Weather Bureau, going back three-quarters of a century. The mean monthly temperature averages 53° F. throughout the year. It drops to an average of only 34° in the winter and rises to an average of only 73° in summer. Compared with New York, Philadelphia, and Washington, the temperature is usually six to ten degrees cooler during the summer and warmer during the winter. Another climatic factor favoring the seashore is the abundance of days with sunshine.

Summer vacationing is easily and quickly available to the millions of people living in the heavily industrialized New York-Philadelphia-Baltimore-Washington axis, the country's largest cluster of people. When a heat wave strikes Philadelphia, tens of thousands of people leave their places of business at the end of the workday and motor to the shore for a dip in the ocean. The market gardens, in the immediate hinterland of the seashore, supply fresh vegetables and fruits for the summer multitude, and commercial fishermen supply fish and other seafoods to add variety to seashore dining rooms.

THE SEASHORE COMMUNITIES

From Highland Beach, north of Trenton, New Jersey, to Cape May, at the state's southern end, there are more than 50 resort communities, ranging in size from less than 1,000 to over 50,000 permanent residents. Some communities have quaint names, like Ship Bottom and Love Ladies; others boast such famous names as Atlantic City and Cape May. Some of these communities, Asbury Park and Long Branch, for example, are at the water's edge on the mainland; others, like Toms River and Pine Beach, are a short way upstream; but most of them are on islands separated from the mainland by innumerable bays and inlets that dot the ragged New Jersey coastline.

The resort communities have many characteristics in common—bathing beaches, boardwalks, back bays, seagulls, hotels, restaurants, apartments for rent, and salt water taffy. Yet no two are alike, and each attracts its own particular clientele.

Cape May is the oldest and southernmost. Sitting on the very edge of the cape, the town has been host to a century and a half of patrons. In days gone by it entertained the country's leading citizens—presidents, congressmen, merchants, and socialites. It has charm, individuality, folklore, and tradition—old houses with "widow's walks" on the roofs where skippers' wives kept vigil for their husbands returning from year-long expeditions; a freshwater pond hard by the bay where British men-of-war and pirate vessels stopped to replenish their stores of drinking water, and legends of buried treasure cached by Captain Kidd.

Wildwood, just a short distance above the cape, is different. It is livelier and larger. Including the adjacent communities, Wildwood has a population of 10,000 permanent residents. Claiming the "World Finest and Safest Bathing Beach," this resort has been growing rapidly. Its growth is attributable to excellent bathing facilities afforded by a wide and moderately sloping beach, a variety of boardwalk amusements, and good fishing. It is only a short run from Wildwood to a number of excellent fishing banks off the coasts of New Jersey, Delaware, and Maryland. Many of the fishing boats are equipped with ship-to-shore communication facilities so that masters of the vessels may determine the best market for quick sales of their catch to representatives of the buyers waiting at the wharves.

Ocean City, further up the coast and within sight of Atlantic City, is a resort of still another type. With a permanent population of 6,000 that swells to an estimated 60,000 at the peak of the season, Ocean City takes pride in being "The Country's Greatest Family Resort." This grows out of the fact that it was started as a Methodist camp meeting, and in line with that tradition the sale of alcoholic beverages is still forbidden within the city limits. Placing somewhat less emphasis upon commercial forms of entertainment than its neighboring communities, Ocean City is steadily gaining in the size of its permanent population.

Atlantic City is in a class by itself. It has been described as "an amusement factory operated on the straight-line, mass production pattern." The belt is the boardwalk, along which each specialist adds his bit to assemble the finished product—the departing visitor, sated, tanned, and bedecked with souvenirs. Founded on sand, surrounded by water, and flooded with sunshine, Atlantic City is endowed with all the natural advantages that go with a seashore resort. What puts the city in a class by itself are the added attractions built in by its enterprising promoters.

Atlantic City entertains 12 to 14 million visitors annually. To take care of such numbers requires physical and entertainment facilities in the grand manner, and Atlantic City has them. It is a city of hotels—448 of them, big hotels with capacity of up to 1,000 rooms. In addition to the hotels there are about 1,600 guest houses. The Convention Hall is big enough to seat the entire population of the city. The boardwalk is one of the country's most famous fashion highways, where Easter styles go on parade each year.

Amusement and diversion facilities are al-

Figure 2-15. The Washington Monument towers above government buildings in Washington, D. C., a city of great beauty and charm and a mecca for tourists. (The Washington Post)

most endless—sports and entertainment compete with stores for space on the five large piers jutting out into the ocean. In addition to entertainment and recreational opportunities at the theaters, on the golf links, at the race track, on the dance floors, or in the night clubs, there are also fishing, yachting, boxing, wrestling, ice hockey, basketball, steeplechasing, surf bathing, and sun bathing.

By reason of its ideal climate and all its added attractions, Atlantic City is a great convention city. Americans are probably the world's greatest "conventioneers." Whether bankers, doctors, teachers, or diamond cutters, they all have their annual convention — and sooner or later they convene at Atlantic City, simply because the city has the facilities to house them, feed them, and entertain them. Atlantic City gets about 19 per cent of the country's annual conventions and can guarantee better than average attendance at convention sessions because conventioneers meeting there do not have as many cousins or other relatives to visit as they have when they meet in New York or Chicago or San Francisco.

THE NATURE OF THE RESORT BUSINESS

Founded upon the changing seasons of the year, the most obvious and obstinate characteristic of the resort business is its seasonality. The greatest influx of people naturally occurs during July and August. The month-to-month level of dollar volume of business by the producers of any or all of the various services shows a midsummer upsurge. The seasonality is revealed not only by the count at turnstiles of boardwalk amusements, but also by hotel occupancy rates, consumption of kilowatts, bank deposits, and volume of passenger car traffic over the Delaware River bridges.

But not all seashore resort communities roll

up their boardwalks for winter storage and go into hibernation after Labor Day. A study of the monthly composition of the total business volume of Atlantic City over a period of years shows that 25 per cent of the total is concentrated in July and August, with three-quarters of the total transacted during the remaining ten months. By various means, the season is extended beyond the peak months. Atlantic City extends its season by such attractions as the annual Miss America Pageant in September and the scheduling of conventions in off-season months. Reduced hotel and apartment rates also attract a considerable number of guests in the less-favored months of the year.

Off-season employment is provided in the maintenance of the bathing beaches, for sand, sea, and sunshine—the sources of the New Jersey shore's prosperity—also bring with them a major erosion problem. The shore line is forever changing, advancing here and receding there. It is a slow process that can be measured with the kind of stop watch used to time the movement of glaciers, but it is nevertheless very real to the seashore communities. Occasionally, though fortunately not very often, high winds of the North Atlantic storms whip the waters into an angry sea that rises up against the coast with considerable damage both to the shoreline and to shore properties. Over $30 million has already been spent in the construction of protective structures such as sea walls, bulkheads, and jetties. Jetties, built of quarry stone, and groins, built entirely of timber, are constructed at right angles to the shoreline so as to trap and hold sand, and create and build up beaches. The cost of beach-protecting structures is split fifty-fifty between the local communities and the state.

THE FUTURE

The growth of manufacturing has given rise to many industrial centers, making the Middle Atlantic Coastal Plain the most densely populated region of the United States. The big cities offer many advantages, among them being a wide choice of jobs, varied educational opportunities, many forms of entertainment, and a wide selection of manufactured goods and services. Great industrial concentrations, they are also centers of finance and commerce. Geographic location and markets will continue to favor expansion within this region. Such expansion will make it more difficult for government to solve the region's already serious problems. Too often the large Eastern city has been planless in pattern, uncontrolled in size, crowded and congested, and lacking in contacts with nature. The absence of planning has produced dirt and ugliness.

Only through large-scale planning, such as that now being sponsored by the Twentieth Century Fund to analyze urban problems from Washington, D. C., to Boston, can more people be absorbed into the urban landscape and still enjoy a reasonable living pattern. This calls for wholesale slum clearance, smoke control, zoning restrictions, and green belts on a scale unprecedented in America.

3 | *South Atlantic–East Gulf Plain*

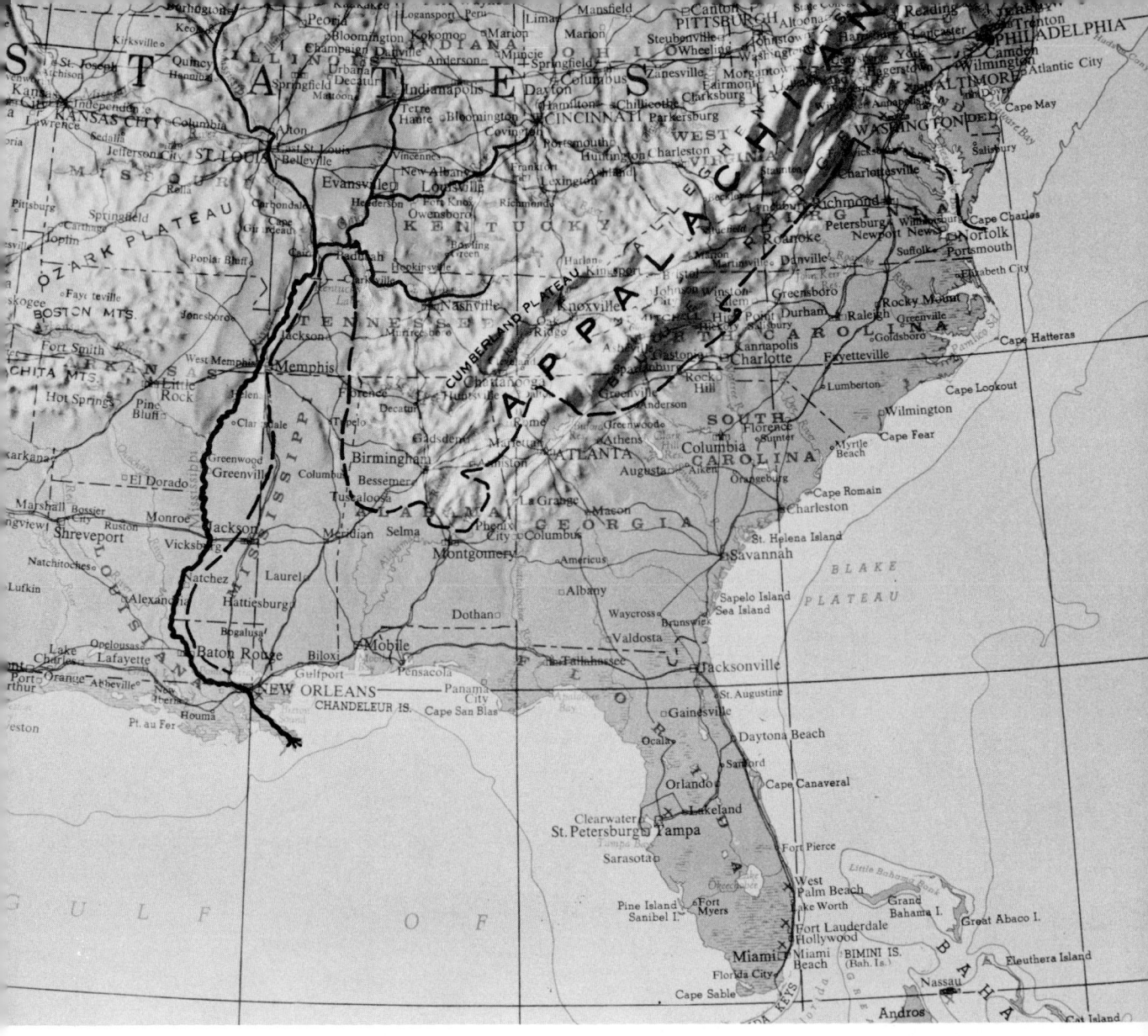

THE South Atlantic-East Gulf Plain consists of the eastern two-thirds of Virginia and North Carolina; almost all of South Carolina, Georgia, and Alabama; all of Florida; nearly all of Mississippi; a fringe of southeastern Louisiana; and a strip in western Tennessee.

SURFACE FEATURES

It is a region of comparatively low elevation. From the geological point of view, and also to a certain extent from the topographical, it is made up of two quite distinct portions. The part nearest the coast is almost flat, or having the gentlest possible slope seaward, and is unbroken by any elevations worthy of notice. Beyond this belt, to the west and northwest, is another belt, itself almost a plain, but more undulating than the region to the east and rising more rapidly westward, so that it forms almost a tableland at the base of the mountains.

THE ATLANTIC COASTAL PLAIN

This portion extends northeastward beyond the boundaries of the region to a width of zero at New York. Southward, it increases in width to 150 miles in North Carolina and 200 miles in Alabama. It embraces all of Florida and the Mississippi alluvial plain up to Illinois. The altitude of the inner edge is 750 feet in Georgia; less than 100 feet at Washington, D. C.; and 300 to 400 feet in southern Illinois.

The inner boundary runs generally against higher land. There is an abrupt rise of several hundred feet north of the Carolinas. Elsewhere the rise is less abrupt. The boundary between the "Piedmont" or "foot of the mountain" and the Coastal Plain is called the fall line because, in crossing it, streams develop rapids and falls as they descend from the harder rock outcrops to the softer sedimentary materials of the Coastal Plain.

All rocks of the Coastal Plain originally were sediments like those now forming on the continental shelf. A few of them are consolidated, but most of them are either poorly consolidated or not consolidated at all. Generally the strata dip seaward a little steeper than the surface slopes, creating formations that outcrop in parallel bands, the oldest (lowest) being farthest inland.

The seaward extension of the Coastal Plain, the continental shelf, has a gentle offshore slope to a depth of 600 feet. Its width ranges from five to 250 miles. It is covered with or composed of beds of sand, gravel, clay and marl (limy sediment sometimes mixed with mud).

The topography ranges from perfectly flat near the sea, where the erosion cycle has not yet begun, to maturely dissected, distinctly hilly, and even at places peneplained terrain near the inner margin. The local relief in some parts is 200 feet. The inner edge was first (longest) out of water, and is therefore most eroded. Moreover, it is only here that the altitude is sufficient to allow deep valleys. In general the relief increases from the coast inward.

Some streams flow almost directly toward the sea. Most tributaries are dendritic. The outcrop of a strong stratum may constitute a ridge between valleys. This ridge is generally a "cuesta" with a relatively steep scarp slope and a long gentle dip slope. The "inner lowland" on weak rocks at the foot of the scarp slope often is followed by a stream. Coastal plains thus characterized are "belted."

The seaward border is marked by: (1) many estuaries, (2) deltas (most of which still are only "mud flats") at the heads of estuaries, (3) bars and lagoons, (4) barrier beaches, (5) sand dunes, (6) salt marshes, and (7) fresh water swamps, such as the Great Dismal Swamp of Virginia.

In the embayed section north of Cape Lookout, subsidence of the land has drowned many valleys, making estuaries and islands. Local relief in this section rarely exceeds 50 feet.

The Sea Island section to the south has subsided less, but still enough to form the characteristic islands that give names to the section. The topography is that of a young plain near the coast. Erosion increases inland to maturity near the fall line, around which the local relief may reach 200 feet.

Florida is mainly a newly-emerged, uneven sea bottom with lakes and swamps (everglades). In the north-central part many basins are made by solution (limestone sinks). The "Keys" are a broken coral reef. A long barrier beach on the east encloses the so-called "Indian River."

The Gulf Coastal Plain is flat near the sea. Slight subsidence makes bays as at Mobile. Relief increases inland to several hundred feet at some points. Southern Alabama is typical "belted coastal plain" with Montgomery and Tuscaloosa in the "inner lowland." This is the "Black Belt" on weak chalky limestone, formerly one of the most important cotton districts of the United States.

The alluvial plain of the lower Mississippi and certain tributaries embraces large areas subject to overflow except where they are protected by natural and artificial levees.

PIEDMONT PROVINCE

The area between the Appalachian Mountains and the Atlantic Coastal Plain is called the Piedmont Plateau. Within the Southern States it consists of a strip through middle Virginia and North Carolina, and northern Georgia to central Alabama. It is a rolling to hilly region, the elevation varying between from 100 and 500 feet along the inner edge of the Coastal Plain to between 700 and 1,500 feet at the foothills. The Piedmont was a land area when the present region to the east and west, except the Blue Ridge Mountains, was still covered by the ocean. The soils have been formed from complex rocks, including crystalline igneous rocks, highly metamorphosed sandstone and shale, and unmetamorphosed sandstone and shale. The soils are mostly clays and clay loams, although some surfaces are sandy.

CLIMATE

All the South Atlantic-East Gulf Plain except the interior highlands and the southern tip of Florida is classed as a humid subtropical climate. It is characterized by abundant rainfall during all months and seasons; by maximum rainfall in the warm season; by tropic-like summer heat; by sharp, quick, summer thundershowers; by violent soil erosion; and by a cool, moist winter. Light snowfalls may occur occasionally during the winter. There are periods of fairly cold weather associated with winter cold waves that move into the realm from regions farther poleward. The number of frost-free days ranges from 200 in the northern portion of the region to 320 along the Gulf Coast, and many winters—sometimes several in succession—pass without frost or freezing in southern Florida. The average winter temperature is about 45° F. throughout the area. The average annual precipitation is 50 to 60 inches.

SETTLEMENT

At Jamestown, Virginia, English settlers established the first permanent colony in the New World (1607). In the days of early settlement this was a land of sickness, heat, famine, and Indian attacks; for in its floundering beginnings, the colony of Virginia depended on imported supplies and food traded or taken from the Indians. The colonists were extremely reluctant to engage in agriculture. Four years after the founding of Virginia, the government applied a rigorous regime of enforced agricultural labor and saved the colony.

The Coastal Plain, or "Tidewater," was the first area of settlement. It consists of four peninsulas averaging 70 miles in length and 10 to 15 miles in width, formed by Chesapeake Bay and the Potomac, Rappahannock, York, and James Rivers. This unknown physical environment presented many problems to the first settlers who came from the gray-brown forest soils of Western Europe. They were accustomed to a mild climate, with maximum precipitation of a gentle, drizzly nature, occurring during the winter months. In their new home they found, instead, subtropical red earth soils and an extreme climate characterized by high summer temperatures, high humidity, and copious rainfall of a thundershower type, most of it falling during the months of June, July, and August, but with no dry season. The small grains of Europe were unsuited to this climatic pattern. It was not until oriental staples—rice, tea, indigo, and cotton—were introduced that the colony prospered. The addition of tobacco as a cash crop and corn as a food rounded out the economy.

The cultivation of tobacco was begun in 1612. This was not the harsh native tobacco used by the Indians of the eastern woodlands, but the cultivated tobacco of the American tropics. During the 16th century Spaniards and Portuguese had introduced this Indian ceremonial plant to European trade and its seeds to European gardens. The use of tobacco spread rapidly into France and England. In both countries it was planted to some extent before the founding of Virginia. It is not definitely known how this tropical plant came to Virginia. Probably the very first plantings were of seed that had been brought from England.

Figure 3-1. Gullied area in Mecklenburg County, Virginia. Heavy thunderstorms, clean-tilled crops, and poor conservation methods quickly destroy the land. (U.S. Department of Agriculture)

Shortly after Virginia became a tobacco planting colony, English settlements were established in the smaller West Indies, most significantly in Barbados. The rapid growth of settlement and plantations soon crowded this and other islands, and an overflow of population was directed to South Carolina after 1670. Sugar cane; indigo; Barbados, or Sea Island cotton; and rice were introduced as plantation crops in the Charleston lowlands. Similar introductions were made around New Orleans in the 18th century. Florida entered only slightly into this plantation development, not because of unsuitable climate, but because of the lack of rich lowlands with deep soil.

THE PLANTATION SYSTEM

The need for labor able to stand the hot, humid atmosphere of the rice fields and cotton plantations resulted in the importation of the Negro. African slave trade seemed to be the best solution for the labor problem in the South. Eastern Asia was too remote and Chinese and Japanese laborers could not be secured as cheaply as laborers from Natal. Slavery did not pay even in the South where it survived and flourished, but it was less unprofitable than elsewhere in the colonies. If free labor had been available to do the work imposed upon the

Negroes, it would have been impossible for the system of slavery to stand up in competition with it. In only a few industries was the South able to work the slaves without absolute loss, and in these the method of work and type of organization were dictated by the difficulties inherent in getting a safe profit out of ignorant and indifferent bondsmen. Never did Southern capital produce as high a return as Northern; never was it as abundant; never was its possessor as free to take advantage of opportunity. The Southern planter owned his slaves, but in an equally true sense they owned him and bound him to a narrow repetition of unprofitable operations. Except in the great fields devoted to cotton, tobacco, hemp, rice, and indigo, and in the domestic work around the planter's home, slaves could not be used freely.

After existing nearly two centuries in the English colonies, slavery was, at the time of the framing of the Federal Constitution, on the road to extinction. Cotton proved to be the crop that made slavery profitable. The economic historians have shown that the fiber of the cotton boll was only an interesting curiosity until near the end of the 18th century. Not until Eli Whitney invented the cotton gin in 1793 did cotton become a profitable crop. Once it became possible to produce cotton at reasonable cost, its high adaptability for textile manufactures gave it a market. The plantation system developed in the cotton fields as a result of Whitney's cotton gin had an economic organization determined not so much by slavery as by Negro labor. Most of the slaves were useful only in the field; and there they were sent with white overseers.

The planter bought nearly everything he used. He purchased meal and pork for the slaves instead of raising it at little cost. He bought his clothing and theirs, and all the household equipment. And as he shipped most of his cotton directly from a nearby wharf to England, he tended to open an account with the proceeds. Every year the planter had to have his supplies regardless of the price of cotton. His mortgages grew as debts mounted against him.

There was still another consequence of the plantation system. The cotton planter stripped the fertility from his farms. He planted cotton, and only cotton, year after year. There was no rotation and no manure from livestock to be spread upon the fields. The best cotton soil was so fertile that for many years it continued to produce large crops in spite of this treatment, but the moment always came when the return began to diminish. Nothing in the history of American agriculture is less attractive than the plantation going downhill. The decline meant poverty for the planter's children and dissipation of land and slaves. Foreclosures came in their inevitable course, and too often what had been flourishing cotton fields reverted to wilderness. The small, poor, white farmer, who could and would live upon a few acres that had once been part of a plantation, had no surplus of either means or intelligence. The plantation era, with its soil destruction, passed over many an area, leaving it desolate.

KING COTTON

Cotton, the great crop of the South, is grown on about 900,000 farms. The average size of the crop is about 15 million bales of cotton lint, each weighing about 500 pounds, and more than six million tons of cottonseed.

The Cotton Belt was a name given to an area covering the greater part of the Southern States where geographical conditions were suitable for growth of cotton and where a large percentage of the agricultural population derived some or most of its cash income from the cotton crop. Though many still think in terms of a "cotton belt," and such a belt does exist to some degree, such great changes in the land economy of the South have taken place within the past 30 years that some qualification of the term is necessary.

Cotton is no longer the leading source of Southern farm income. Today's gross return from cotton represents slightly less than 25 per cent of total farm income; 30 years ago it accounted for about 50 per cent. Acreage reductions have affected the old Cotton Belt, but yield increases have offset acreage decreases; gross regional income from cotton is therefore about what it was 30 years ago. In 1939, for example, 13 million bales of cotton lint, each weighing about 500 pounds, were grown on about two million farms in the South; in 1960, 900,000 farms produced about 14.3 million bales of cotton lint.

The yield increases have come about mainly from: (1) a greater use of fertilizer, (2) a shift to higher-yielding areas, (3) a more careful selection of land on individual farms as well as in each area, (4) a more widespread use of improved varieties, and (5) the planting of larger legume crop acreages. Since these changes have affected the various production areas differently, considerable acreage shifts have occurred.

The South's decline as a cotton producing region results partly, of course, from healthy changes in its farm economy. Economic pressure and education are two of the important forces responsible for a more diversified farming system, one that places less reliance on cotton as the principal source of income. It is certain that these forces will continue to exert their effects. It is equally certain, on the other hand, that cotton will remain a basic component of Southern farm economy for many years to come. The relatively disadvantageous position of Southern cotton production, therefore, makes the need for increased efficiency even more acute than it is in other producing areas.

NATURAL ENVIRONMENT

Nearly all the cotton acreage in the South is in the South Atlantic-East Gulf Plain, the exception being the Red Prairie of Texas and Oklahoma. About two-thirds of the Cotton Belt

Figure 3-2. A field of cotton in the South Atlantic-East Gulf Plain Province. (National Cotton Council)

is a broad coastal plain composed principally of sedimentary material, bordering on and largely derived from two ancient and much eroded mountain masses, the Appalachian Highlands (including the Piedmont) in the east and the Ozark Highlands in the west. From these highland areas, rivers, bordered (especially along their lower courses) by swampy flood plains often several miles in width, radiate across the coastal plain. In the broad depression between these two highlands, the Mississippi River flows southward, dividing the Cotton Belt into eastern and western sections, approximately equal in area, in acreage of improved land, and in production of cotton.

SOILS

Cotton is grown on practically all well-drained types of soil in the Cotton Belt. Boll weevil infestation has altered the relative importance of finer and coarser textured types of soils, particularly in the Southeast. Though less fertile, the fine sandy loams, sandy loams, and loamy sands east of the Mississippi River are generally preferred for cotton raising to the loams, silt loams, and clays. The sandy soils allow earlier maturity of the plant and consequently avoid a part of the boll weevil damage that occurs on heavier soils, where the plants tend to more vegetative growth and are later in maturing, especially in wet seasons.

Among the more important soil regions for cotton are: (1) the sandy loams of the middle and upper Coastal Plain that extend across the eastern Carolinas, central and southern Georgia, western Florida, and southern Alabama into central Mississippi and Louisiana; (2) the sandy loams and red clay loams of the Piedmont Plateau; (3) the alluvial soils of the Mississippi and other river bottoms in Mississippi and Louisiana; and (4) silty soil that occurs on the loessial uplands or bluffs east of the alluvial valleys, principally in Mississippi.

CLIMATE

Although the most noticeable differences in the density of cotton acreage and variations in yield per acre are due principally to soil conditions, the outer boundaries of the cotton production area are determined almost entirely by climatic factors. The Cotton Belt has an average summer temperature of about 77° F. along the northern boundary. This temperature appears to be the limit beyond which commercial production becomes unprofitable. In the southern portion of the Cotton Belt the summer temperature is 80 to 85 degrees. Along the northern margin of the Cotton Belt the last killing frost in spring occurs, on the average, about April 10, and the first killing frost in fall

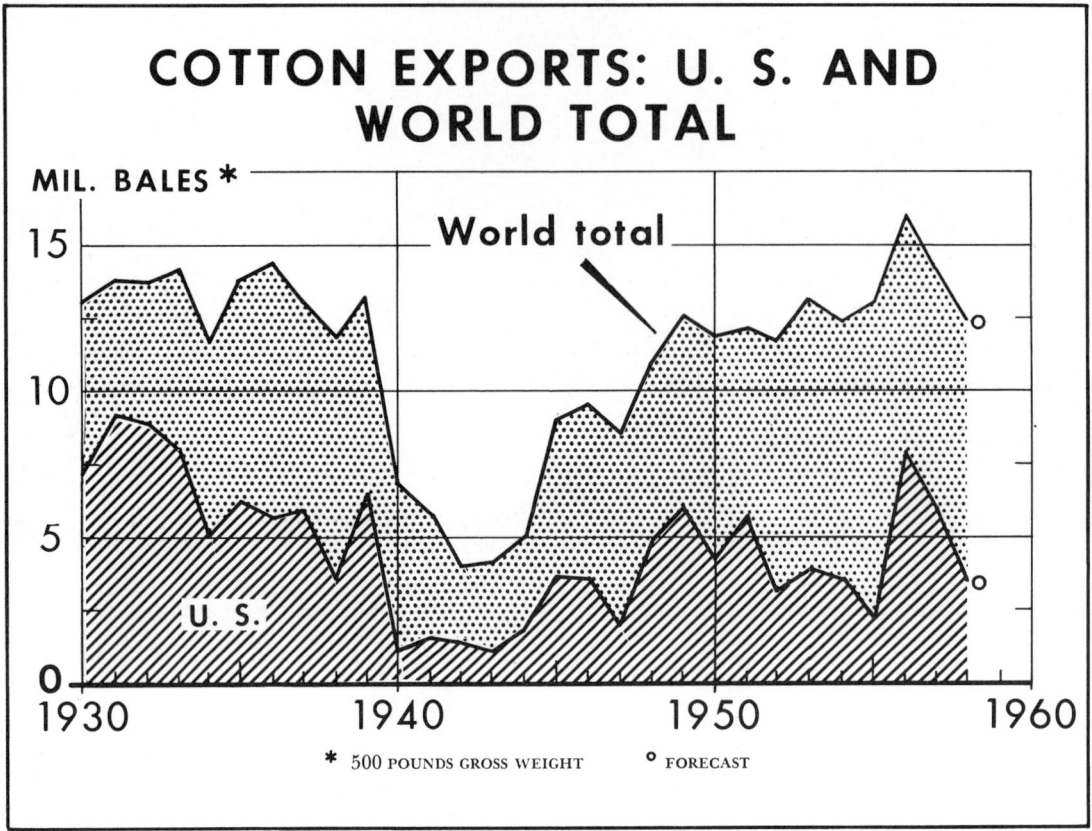

Figure 3-3. Competition in the world cotton market is increasing. The cost of American labor in comparison with that of other lands has damaged the relative position of the United States but it still ranks as a major exporter. (U.S. Department of Agriculture)

about October 25, so that the frostless season is about 200 days. In the southern portion of the Cotton Belt the last killing frost in spring occurs about March 10, on the average, and the first killing frost in fall seldom before November 25, the frostless season being 260 days or more in length.

The average annual precipitation in the Cotton Belt ranges from 23 inches in western Oklahoma and Texas to 55 inches in eastern North Carolina and 60 inches in southern Mississippi, but throughout much of the Belt it is between 30 and 50 inches. Spring rainfall ranges from six inches in western Texas to 16 inches in Arkansas and southern Mississippi, being heavier in the Mississippi Valley States than in Texas or the South Atlantic States. Summer rainfall is somewhat greater than that of the other seasons, especially in the southern and eastern parts of the Belt, reaching a maximum of 20 inches in southern Mississippi and in eastern North and

South Carolina. Autumn is the driest season of the year; nearly all the important cotton regions receiving less than ten inches of rain during the fall months. February and November are the wettest months in the Mississippi Valley States, in Alabama, and in northern Georgia. August is the wettest month in the Carolinas.

Weather conditions favorable to cotton. The best conditions for cotton production are found where a mild spring with light but frequent showers merges into a moderately moist summer (warm both day and night) followed by a dry, cool, and prolonged autumn. Weather too cool in the spring retards growth. Too much rain may cause the seed to rot rather than germinate, or later cause the development of surface roots at the expense of the deeper roots, with resultant wilting and shedding of leaves and bolls during drought in summer. May and June, particularly, are critical months when heavy rainfall, especially if accompanied by low temperatures, is very detrimental. Rainy weather in these months also interferes with cultivation. On the other hand, drought in the spring and early summer often kills the young shallow-rooted seedlings. A wet summer promotes vegetative growth, or "weed," at the expense of boll production, while drought stunts the plants, causes early maturity, and reduces the yield, as does a spell of cool weather.

METHODS OF MANAGING THE COTTON FARM

The character of the labor supply and the large amount of hand labor used in the production of cotton have developed systems of farm management peculiar to the South.

The plantation. From the time cotton became a commercial crop in the South until the Civil War, it was commonly grown under the plantation system. Strictly speaking, the term "plantation" was applied to a large farm operated under one management, with slave labor frequently directed by an overseer. After the slaves were freed the "cropper" system was established, and the plantation was then defined as a large tract of farm land operated under one management by wage hands and croppers. Under the cropper system there is much less supervision by owner or manager than was necessary with slave labor, and less than is necessary to operate the plantation with wage hands. The planter does not always have an overseer, although on farms most commonly recognized as plantations one is usually employed. The term "plantation" is often used colloquially, however, to designate any large farm employing a considerable amount of labor.

Wage hands. The owners of the plantations commonly operate a part of their land with the assistance of wage hands, the remainder being let to croppers or tenants. Wage hands are usually paid a stipulated cash wage per month and furnished with a house, firewood, and rations. On the upper Coastal Plain in South Carolina the wage hands are, in addition, frequently given two or three acres of land rent-free; they plant these acres on their own account, using the operator's work stock. The land is an inducement for them to remain on the farms through the season. Wage hands are employed principally to grow feed crops and keep up the farm, whereas croppers grow most of the cotton.

Croppers. Croppers are classed as tenants, but legally they are laborers paid by a share of the crop instead of cash. In the South they are regarded as a higher class than wage hands, but in some sections are called "half-hands" or "half-renters." Under the cropper system the common system is for the landlord to furnish the land, work stock, implements, feed, seed, and half the fertilizer, and to pay for half the ginning; all the crops are divided equally.

Tenant farms. It is almost impossible to draw a sharp line between tenants and croppers. In general, it may be said that the tenant is more nearly an independent farm operator. Where individual farms are rented on shares or for cash, little or no supervision is given the tenant. Most of the rented farms outside of the plantation regions may be designated as tenant farms. There are also some tenant farms scattered through the plantation region.

Share tenants. In renting on shares the landlord furnishes a part of the fertilizer, if any is used — commonly one-fourth of the cotton fertilizer and one-third of the fertilizer for other crops. The greater amount of labor required for cotton is the reason for granting the tenant a larger share for the cotton than for the corn.

Cash tenants. Some tenants pay cash rent for a part or all the land they operate. Frequently, however, instead of actual cash, the tenant pays a stipulated amount of lint cotton, usually two 500-pound bales, for enough land for a one-mule farm. In this way the landlord, and not the tenant, takes the risk on the price of the cotton he receives for rent. Such a tenant also may be called a "standing renter."

COTTON MARKETING

When cotton is harvested, it is hauled by wagon, truck, or trailer to gins where fiber is separated from seed. The separated fiber, or lint, is packed into bales at the gin and the seed either is run into the gin's seedhouse or loaded into trucks or freight cars. Modern gins are equipped with improved machinery for drying and cleaning the seed, cotton, and lint in ways that preserve the quality of the farmer's products.

At the gin the trade channels of cotton and cottonseed diverge. The lint goes to spinners who make it into yarn. If the seed is not taken back to the farms, it goes to the cottonseed oil mills for conversion into cottonseed oil, meal, cake, hulls, and linters.

Lint cotton from the gin is packed into bales that weigh about 500 gross pounds each. This type of bale is known as the uncompressed, or flat, bale. It is weighed, marked, and tagged at the gin.

The bale may then be sold immediately to the ginner or some other local buyer, or it may be left in the gin yard by the farmer for sale later. Sometimes cotton is hauled back to the farm or to a public warehouse for storage until the farmer is ready to sell, or it may be placed under government loan. In the Southeastern States some growers sell directly to spinners; others sell through co-operative associations.

Several types of buyers are engaged in buying cotton from farmers. Some are agents for large cotton dealers who supply cotton to domestic mills and to exporters. If the local buyer acts for himself, he usually sells to large firms. The services of a large group of cotton buyers, cotton merchants, exporters, and brokers are involved in bringing raw cotton from producers to spinners in this country and abroad.

When cotton is to be shipped from the local market, the bale is loaded on a freight car or a truck and shipped to a mill. Usually it is compressed first to occupy the least possible space in a freight car or in the hold of a ship. About 300 compress plants are distributed throughout the Cotton Belt.

COTTONSEED

Cottonseed is a very important crop, averaging more than four million tons annually, of which only about 500,000 tons are used each year for planting. The bulk of the remainder is sold to cottonseed processing mills, generally called oil mills, for the preparation of cottonseed oil, cottonseed cake and meal, hulls, and cotton linters.

The ginner accumulates a quantity of seed to sell to the oil mill. At the mill, cottonseed is kept in large storage houses from which it is conveyed mechanically, as needed, through the cleaning, delinting, hulling, separating, rolling, cooking, and pressing apparatus.

Cottonseed, as it leaves the gins, usually still has some lint on it — enough to interfere seriously with the later processes; the seed, therefore, is delinted immediately after it is cleaned. The fibers, when removed and baled like cotton (but in 600 pound bales) are called cotton linters. They are used in the manufacture of explosives, felts and waddings for upholstery and mattresses, and as a source of cellulose in the manufacture of rayon, varnishes, cellophane, films, and plastics.

Crude cottonseed oil is refined at local plants or at large refineries. Refined cottonseed oil is used mainly in making margarine, but it is also sold as salad and cooking oil and, after being hydrogenated, as vegetable shortening.

Cottonseed meal is valuable chiefly in the feeding of livestock. It generally is exported in the form of cake or slabs. Cottonseed meal is also used as a plant fertilizer. Some cottonseed cake, made entirely from perfectly sound cottonseed, is ground and sold as a flour for making bread and cakes for people who are not allowed to eat starches or sugar for health reasons.

Cottonseed hulls are made into a roughage feed. They also serve as a source of chemical compounds, such as furfural, which is used in making plastics. Thus all the contents of the cotton boll are put to use—the lint, the seed, and the seed hull.

MECHANIZATION

Cotton is one of the few field crops in American agriculture not completely mechanized, even though complete mechanization of cotton production is now possible. Mule power on the cotton plantation has been as characteristic of the system as sharecropper labor.

On the other hand, the broad expanse of level fields in the Cotton Belt is ideally suited to the operation of farm power equipment, and increasing numbers of operators are using tractors and mechanical pickers.

Attempts to mechanize cotton picking began in 1850; however, progress was slow until the 1930's. The first picker on a commercial scale was developed in 1941. By 1960 there were about 24,000 mechanical pickers in the United States. Most of them were in the Mississippi Delta and California.

Perhaps the greatest deterrent to complete mechanization is its high expense. Only big

Figure 3-4. Tobacco planted on contour in Virginia. Attention to proper soil conservation methods has resulted in increased yields. (U.S. Department of Agriculture)

operators can afford the necessary equipment. It takes about $35 an acre to mechanize farms in the clay hills of Mississippi. Tractors and tractor-drawn equipment are beyond the reach of many farmers. This is true especially of the mechanical pickers now on the market. A spindle-type picker and tractor, for example, often sells for $18,000 to $20,000.

The primary need in harvesting equipment is for a smaller, less expensive machine. Many cotton farms are too small to warrant the expense of machine and equipment. In Alabama, for example, although 69 per cent of the farms produce cotton, the average farm has only 10.6 acres.

Co-operative ownership of harvesting equipment is a possible means to mechanization. More efficient production will be brought about gradually by combining the smaller acreages into larger production units. It also will aid in conservation practices. No doubt cotton acreage east of the Mississippi River will continue to diminish as mechanization and conservation progress. The steady shift of cotton production to the West will continue unless prohibited by national agricultural policy and political considerations. Given a sufficient water supply, California could easily supply a third of total national cotton production.

TOBACCO—A DEMANDING CROP

Most tobacco is planted a little north of the cotton region. Nearly half the United States acreage is grown in North Carolina, although 20 other states also produce tobacco, the principal ones being Kentucky, Virginia, Tennessee, South Carolina, and Georgia. Though tobacco no longer is the great industry of the Middle South, it is still a chief money crop.

NATURAL CONDITIONS

Climate and soil probably influence tobacco more than any other plant. So marked are the influences of these factors that two regions rarely produce exactly the same type of leaf. The effect of slight differences is evident when comparing the tobacco of the Piedmont with that of the Coastal Plain. The leaf of the latter is whiter than the Piedmont, which grows a considerable quantity of mahogany leaf. The tobacco of the Coastal Plain ripens earliest because it lies farther south and nearer the ocean and the large amount of sand in the soil helps raise the temperature.

Climatic conditions. Climatic conditions affect the quality of the leaf as well as the general growth and development of the plant. The warmer regions tend to produce a smaller, heavier, more aromatic leaf. At ripening, cool nights with heavy dew are favorable; they cause the leaf to thicken and to mature rapidly with good body. The temperature must be such that the plant has a rapid uninterrupted growth; otherwise it does not cure well. A dry season results in a plant with a very thick leaf of close grain containing an excess amount of gum and having poor combustibility; these are qualities that make the leaf resistant to decay. Drought also prevents the leaf from filling out; consequently, it does not weigh as much as a normal leaf. Too much rain causes too rapid growth, and the plant shrivels and develops circles in the leaves. Other than this, wet weather produces characteristics opposite to those arising from dry weather.

In general the plant does best where it has a rapid uninterrupted growth; fairly high temperatures; and moderate, evenly distributed rainfall.

Soil. Under given climatic conditions the class and type of tobacco depend upon the character of the soil, especially its texture and physical properties. The mechanical condition of the soil and the absence of certain inorganic elements have more influence than the supply of plant food on the quality of the leaf. The grade of tobacco, as distinguished from the type, depends mainly upon the methods of cultivation and curing.

Both surface soil and subsoil are important. As a rule, a light-colored soil of low water holding capacity that is low in soluble mineral matter produces a large, thin leaf, light in color and body, and of fine texture and weak aroma. Heavier soils with much silt and clay have high moisture holding capacity and tend to grow a smaller leaf, darker and heavier in body, and with a strong aroma.

In the Coastal Plain, farmers prefer new lands for tobacco; in the Piedmont, old lands give a good quality when manures and fertilizers are used. New lands grow the brightest tobacco; old lands the darkest. The first crop on new land is very fine and more easily cured than the few succeeding crops, but it lacks the body and uniformity of color and texture of later crops. Some lands grow a good quality for a year or two but never again. This phenomenon is thought to be caused by an increasing compactness of the soil. The finest quality of tobacco seems to grow on old, worn-out fields that have

been abandoned for several years. These fields grow trees and bushes and may lie for 15 or 20 years without being used. They are so poor that nothing but tobacco can grow in their soil.

TOBACCO CULTURE

The culture of tobacco is difficult and demanding; tobacco has been called the most intensively cultivated annual crop grown on any large acreage. The seedlings, fragile and subject to many kinds of damage, are started in cold frames, then transplanted; between 5,000 and 10,000 plants are set out on each acre. A constant round of cultivating, topping, suckering, and spraying keeps the farmer and his family completely occupied until the tobacco leaves are mature. Then the ripe leaves are harvested and hung up for curing in the barn.

The life of the tobacco grower is not an enviable one. The work involved is disagreeable—hard, dirty, and in some respects unhealthy. Workers often contract skin irritations and sicknesses from the odor of the plants. Gum on the plants can adhere to the worker, too.

The tobacco plant is destructive to soil because it is a clean-tilled crop that induces erosion. Moreover, its root system has a tendency to suck rather than to hold the soil in place. In those areas where tobacco is grown almost exclusively, there is the most apparent poverty —not a poverty of money alone, but a poverty of culture, a poverty of soil, a poverty of good homes and social environment, and a poverty of health and of everything else that goes to make rural life an ideal mode of living.

It is obvious, then, that the continuous culture of tobacco is not without its problems. Common practice calls for resting shade tobacco land after four or five years when yields and quantity decline. Some fields remain in high production only two or three years. Rotation of crops may be employed if tobacco is grown in the right order in the rotation. If grown immediately after a legume or other soil building crop, the quality will be affected adversely. It is therefore necessary to grow a crop such as corn, wheat, or cotton before planting tobacco.

Types of tobacco are grouped largely according to three curing methods—flue-cured, air-cured, and fire-cured. The first two methods are the most widely used. Curing of tobacco is the

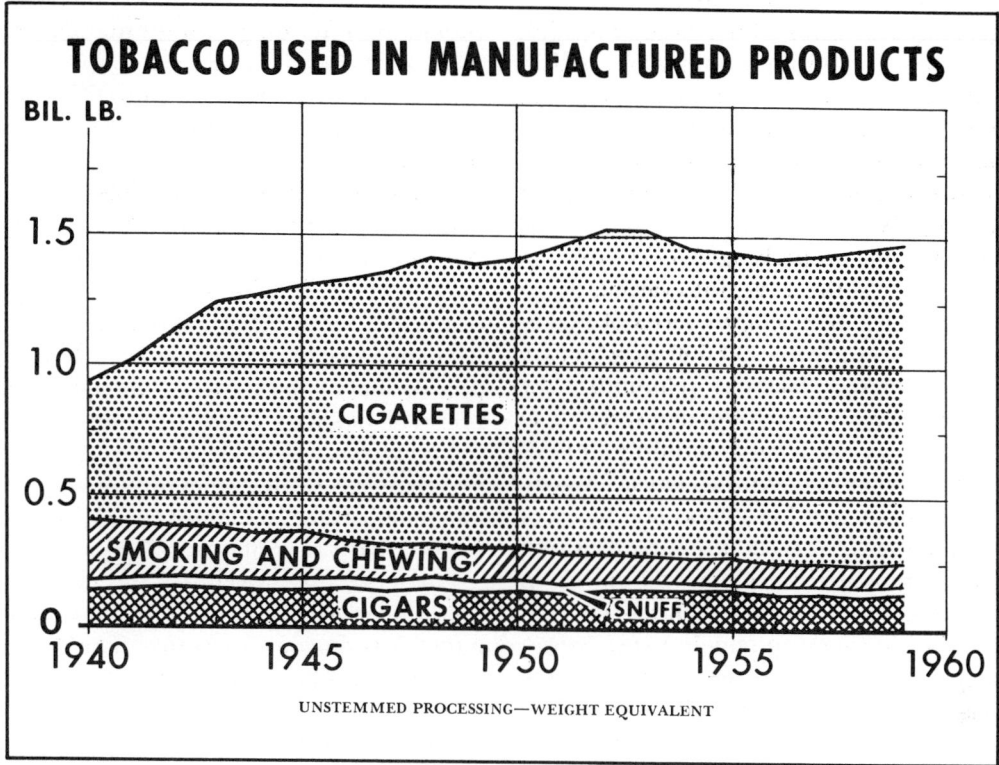

Figure 3-5. (U.S. Department of Agriculture)

tensest time of all. The weather during the curing period, especially for flue-cured types, may have a profound effect on the excellence and price of the leaves.

Flue-cured (bright) tobacco is produced in a curing process whereby in a barn small fires are started in furnaces in which a temperature of 90° F. is maintained until the leaf is properly yellowed. This takes from 24 to 36 hours. The next stage requires increased heat to around 130° for from ten to 18 hours; this removes the moisture as fast as it is given off by the leaf. Finally, the temperature is raised to a range of 160° to 180°, and maintained there until the stems are completely dry.

Flue-curing itself is a tricky, even dangerous, procedure in which many small errors can affect the value of the product—even burn down the curing barn. Because of high labor requirements and low capital outlay, tobacco farms tend to be many and small; the average size of flue-cured tobacco farms is about seven acres.

Air-cured tobacco involves very little labor in the curing process once the tobacco has been placed properly in the barn. The leaves are permitted to cure by air for a period of from 45 to 60 days. Precautions are taken against leaks and against hanging the tobacco too close to the tin roofs.

After the leaves are cured, the farmer begins the tedious and exacting job of sorting them for proper bundling and selling. Tied and packed, the leaves go to the warehouse sales floor. In about 170 auction markets in tobacco areas there are some 900 of these sales floors. Here a small knot of buyers from the major companies walk along aisles lined with baskets of tobacco while the auctioneer chants his sing-song and knocks down each basket in six to ten seconds time.

After the auction, the leaves are packed solidly into hogsheads and shipped to the storage facilities of the manufacturers. Here the hogsheads are opened, the tobacco taken out and completely dried, its moisture content accurately reintroduced by regulated steam jets, and its stems cut out by automatic machinery.

The tobacco then is repacked in the hogsheads and stored away for two to four years; during this time it passes through a certain degree of fermentation and other chemical changes important to its final taste and mildness. The huge quantities of tobacco stored in the sprawling brick warehouses of the great companies account for roughly four-fifths of the companies' total physical assets. At the peak season, the average inventory is about a 30 months' supply.

Drawing upon properly aged stock, tobacco companies process the leaves into various forms for the consumer. In a lengthy series of highly mechanized steps, some 90,000 production workers in different factories rehumidify the leaves, pass them into machines that spray them with hydroscopic (moisture retaining) liquids and with "casings" containing flavor ingredients that have ranged from chocolate to oil of juniper, and then feed them into shredding and cigarette-forming machines that roll out up to 1,500 regular cigarettes or 1,200 filter-tips each minute. In succeeding mechanized steps, the cigarettes are wrapped, sealed, labeled, stamped, and packed in cartons for shipping.

Wholesalers, jobbers, and salesmen distribute the products to some 1,300,000 retail outlets serving the public.

TOBACCO CENTERS

Durham, Raleigh, and Winston-Salem, North Carolina, and Danville, Lynchburg, and Richmond, Virginia, are the South's leading tobacco centers. Nineteen per cent of the nation's cigarettes are produced in Durham. About 50 million pounds of tobacco are auctioned annually at the Durham tobacco market. Raleigh is the wholesale and retail center for a wide territory devoted agriculturally to flue-cured tobacco. Lynchburg is one of the largest dark-tobacco markets in the country. Richmond is not only one of the greatest tobacco markets in the United States but also has various tobacco factories producing chewing and smoking tobacco, snuff, cigars, and cigarettes.

OTHER CASH CROPS

PEANUTS

Peanuts now occupy third place among Southern cash crops. The best soil types for peanuts have good drainage—sandy loam or fine sandy loam surface layers and friable subsoils. A large part of the commercial produc-

tion is concentrated in two distinct areas, although peanuts are grown throughout the area from Virginia to Texas.

The North Carolina-Virginia Coastal Plain is the oldest and most intensive peanut producing section in the United States. About half the cropland is used for peanuts, cotton, and tobacco and of this half approximately 70 per cent is used for peanuts. Soils are favorable for production and yields are high.

The Southern Coastal Plain in Georgia and Alabama has the largest peanut acreage and production in the nation. The agriculture of the area has long been based on a cash-crop economy. During the last 30 years, however, emphasis has shifted from almost complete reliance on cotton to major reliance on peanuts as a source of cash income.

For more than a century the peanut patch was only a source of nuts for the family to munch on during the winter. The growing of the crop on a commercial scale, either for nuts or for hogging, dates generally to the coming of the boll weevil.

It was logical for peanuts to replace cotton when the weevil made production of the latter crop too hazardous in the lower Coastal Plain. Cotton requires large amounts of hand labor; so does the raising of peanuts. Normally a laborer can pick about 150 pounds of seed cotton in a ten-hour day; with a yield of half a bale, a total of 40 hours is required to harvest an acre. An acre of peanuts can be harvested in about 32 hours. Since cotton yields high returns per acre, it was only by replacing it with another intensive crop, such as peanuts, that small farmers could make a living. Furthermore, the equipment used in growing cotton, mostly single row, mule-drawn implements, also could be employed in raising peanuts. With the labor and equipment already on hand, cotton farmers quickly shifted to the new crop.

Today peanuts are important in the Southeast, ranking high as a soil conservation crop, as human food, as feed for livestock, and as a money crop. They are planted for hog feed, for oil mills, and the confectionery trade. In recent years millions of pounds of peanuts have been crushed for oil, oleomargarine, and other compounds.

The most beneficial by-product of peanut-oil crushing is peanut cake or meal. High in protein, this is an excellent feed for all classes of livestock and poultry, equal in food value to cottonseed meal or linseed meal.

The big market for peanuts is oil. Under traditional agricultural practices, however, peanuts for oil cannot compete with such crops as soybeans, whose production has been mechanized. Steps toward complete mechanization of peanuts began in 1947. Machinery for planting and cultivating operations has been developed but the bottleneck in peanut production comes at harvest. Because of the threat of unfavorable weather a large number of man-hours per acre is required to harvest the peanuts as rapidly as possible.

SOYBEANS

Soybeans have been a major crop in the Orient for many centuries and have been grown in the United States since the beginning of the 19th century. Yet it was not until after World War I that this country experienced any increase in soybean production. Although the greatest increase occurred in the five Corn Belt states of Illinois, Iowa, Indiana, Ohio, and Missouri, this crop found favor in the South because production is easily mechanized and because it fits well into the cropper and tenant systems. The attention and publicity that have been given to the many new uses found for soybeans are the main causes of this steady increase. A few of these new uses are as food for people, as soybean meal for animals, and as soybean oil extracts — fertilizer, plastics, food products, soap, and paints and varnishes for commercial use. Soybeans are also a good cover crop, excellent for soil building and hay; they provide good pasture when used for grazing.

Soybeans are relatively easy to produce. In recent years, with the advent of more efficient machines, especially the combine, labor requirements for the crop have decreased tremendously. The average yield is 22 bushels per acre but many farmers produce as much as 30 bushels. Areas of greatest concentration are the Mississippi Delta, northern Alabama, and the Georgia-Carolina Piedmont.

Soybeans are a good rotation crop as they generally can be fitted into the farm program or provide an excellent crop for land that would otherwise be idle. No special machines are necessary for planting, cultivating, or har-

vesting. Generally a farmer uses the same breaking plow, disk, and harrow that he uses for other crops to prepare his seedbed. The beans usually are cultivated three times with the implements used for cultivating cotton and corn. Small grain combines may be used for harvesting in late October or early November.

THE LIVESTOCK INDUSTRIES

Grazing and livestock industries represent the greatest changes in the South's postwar agriculture. The number of livestock on farms, particularly the number of beef cattle, has increased rapidly since 1950.

Several factors have contributed to an expansion in the Southern grazing and livestock industries. Chief of these are: (1) more general use by farmers of recent technological developments; (2) advances in animal sciences, and production of feed crops, pasture, and other forage crops resulting from increased research and extension activities in these fields; (3) improved financial status of a large number of Southern farmers; and (4) an increasing consciousness of the real possibilities in livestock enterprises among farmers, farm organizations, and land-grant college personnel.

The general trend in numbers of livestock on Southern farms has not differed significantly from national trends. However, the relative increase in livestock numbers in the South since 1950 has exceeded the national average.

DAIRY CATTLE

The South has nearly 6.5 million dairy cattle. Mississippi, Tennessee, and Arkansas are the three leading Southern states, generally accounting for about 40 per cent of all dairy cattle in the South.

Partly because of the adjustment features of national farm programs and party by virtue of research work on the growing of feed and forage carried on by experiment stations, dairying seems to be getting its long awaited start on Southern farms. Many problems, however, remain for Southern farmers to solve before any large number of dairymen become efficient producers.

For the most part, low production rates are the results of poor herd sires and inadequate or uneconomical feed production programs.

Owners of small herds, who predominate, cannot afford proven bulls. Significant and rapid improvement in breeding, therefore, must come about largely by means of artificial insemination. This service is now available to many Southern farmers and calves artificially sired are beginning to replace mediocre cows in more and more herds.

About 49 per cent of all the milk cows in the South are on farms where there are only one or two cows; two-thirds are on farms where there are fewer than five. Dairying, therefore, is of little significance. Large commercial herds are common in Florida, however, where over a third of all milk cows are in herds of 50 or more. With the exception of Florida, the area is one in which commercial dairying has not yet developed enough to affect greatly the average dairy data for individual states or for the South as a whole.

BEEF CATTLE

About 11 per cent of the nation's beef and veal is produced in the South. Florida is the leading beef cattle producer. Over two million head of cattle graze on its pastures. Factors favoring beef cattle production are: (1) climate, (2) growth of native grasses and leafy crops, (3) available cheap lands, and (4) a ready nearby market.

Cattle raising is a major industry in central Florida where ranchers have transformed millions of acres of once worthless palmetto wilderness into rich grazing land.

Principal breeds successfully grown in Florida include Brahman, Aberdeen Angus, Herefords, Shorthorns, Polled Shorthorns, Red Polls, and Devons. Brahman sires are used extensively in crossbreeding with other breeds and with native range cattle in order to pass on inheritable qualities of adaptability to Florida conditions.

Neighboring states ship cattle to Florida for fattening. Approximately 1,100,000 acres of improved pasturage have been developed at a cost varying from $20 to $60 an acre. Some of Florida's improved pastures will support a head per acre. The average is one animal to three acres.

With the development of dehydrated citrus pulp, citrus molasses, and sugar cane "black strap" molasses, cattle feeding methods have changed radically. Pulp contains high nutritive values desirable for cattle diets; citrus and sugar cane molasses are excellent fattening and finishing feeds. All three are low in cost and available in large quantities.

HOGS

The number of hogs on Southern farms averages around 10.2 million head. Of this number, 52 per cent are on Georgia, Alabama, and North Carolina farms, where average corn yields are relatively good and large acreages of peanuts are grown.

POULTRY

Broiler production is an important industry in the Southeast, accounting for about 50 per cent of the commercial broilers in the United States. Associated with the growth of this industry are a number of important factors: (1) a demand situation favoring production of relatively low cost meat; (2) an area having a large number of farmers with limited alternative uses of land and labor; (3) a willingness on the part of individuals, feed dealers, processors, hatchery men, banks, and others to supply the capital necessary for large-scale broiler production; and (4) changes in technology of production and marketing that have reduced costs to the consumer.

The increase in hatchery capacity in the Southeast has paralleled the increase of commercial broiler production and is dynamic in nature. The heaviest concentration of hatcheries is in northern Georgia. Hatcheries in Louisiana are concentrated primarily in the rice area; in Mississippi, in the Tupelo and Jackson areas. Hatcheries in South Carolina are located mainly in the northwestern part of the state.

FLORIDA'S TRUCK CROP PRODUCTION

Florida is 1,500 miles closer to the large Eastern metropolitan markets than is California. Rapid highway and railway transit favors Florida growers, who can market early vegetables in New York, Philadelphia, Boston, and other cities at a time when they command the highest prices.

Technological changes are largely responsible for a phenomenal expansion in Florida vegetable production: (1) mechanization has provided more efficient production and harvesting techniques, (2) research has given rise to improved varieties and better fertilization practices, (3) more effective insecticides and fungicides have increased yields, and (4) market outlets have multiplied as both rail and truck transportation have become equipped with more adequate refrigeration.

The principal commercial producing areas are in central and southern Florida where some 365,000 acres of truck crops, mostly for fresh consumption, are grown on farms each exceeding 260 acres in size. In these large operations, economic use of specialized mechanical equipment encourages specialization. Producers in the Everglades tend to concentrate on beans, celery, sweet corn, and cabbage; they market these through co-operatives. By comparison, in the Plant City area, noted for its strawberry production, the average farm is about ten acres in size. Growers here market their crops mostly through the State Farmers Market, where relatively small lots are consolidated for shipment.

HIGH CAPITAL REQUIREMENTS

Compared with the capital requirements for most other crops, the proportion of working capital to fixed capital is very high for truck crops. It is estimated that on a 200-acre truck farm in the Everglades, investments in machinery, buildings, and equipment amount to about $200 an acre. Annual operating expenses on a 200-acre truck farm may exceed $100,000 —or $500 per acre.

The working capital needs of Florida farmers are increased by heavy applications of fertilizer required for the sandy soils. From one-half to two tons of a complete mixture per acre may be necessary for vegetable production, and applications of lime are needed periodically to correct the acidity of the soil. Continual drainage or irrigation operations necessary to maintain the desired moisture content of the soil cause severe leaching of fertilizers, particularly in the sandy areas. The very fertile muck soils of the Everglades are a sharp contrast. This land, consisting of partially decomposed vegetation, was held under water for centuries—a condition that prevented natural bacterial ac-

tion. Although high in nitrogen from an abundance of humus content, this soil requires large applications of fertilizers containing large amounts of phosphates and potash.

SEASONAL PATTERN

Because of the highly seasonal nature of vegetable crop production, the problem of availability of labor and credit at times when they are needed create difficulties for the growers. Ordinarily about half the year's labor requirements are concentrated in the harvesting period. At that time growers find it difficult to get enough help and have to depend upon transient domestic and Caribbean labor for most of their needs. The high cost of such labor and its undependability tend to accentuate rather than solve this particular problem.

Another serious seasonal handicap is the continual spraying and dusting required to control insects and diseases. Damp, cool weather during the growing period of tomato and Irish potato crops, for example, increases the danger of blight. As insurance against damage from this disease, frequent applications of insecticides and fungicides are made early in the season and continued on a regular schedule. Although some or all of these operations are performed by machinery, labor requirements connected with them are still substantial.

Most Florida producers seek those markets in which returns are greatest. Modern trucks deliver directly to small markets formerly serviced only through large wholesale terminals.

FLORIDA CITRUS INDUSTRY

Although mention of orange groves in Florida was made by Spanish and British settlers in the 18th century, the industry did not reach a commercial scale until 1884, when approximately 600,000 boxes of fruit were grown.

In 1886, the Florida citrus crop totaled, for the first time, one million boxes. The coming of railroads and improvements in communications made possible the development of citrus groves away from the waterways. Expansion was steady from 1886 to the freezes of 1894-1895; production soared to about five million boxes. It is interesting to note that California—still

Figure 3-6. Picking oranges in a Florida grove. Florida leads the nation in orange production. Its dominance is due to the popularity of frozen orange juice. Two-thirds of the Florida orange crop is processed into juice products. (U.S. Department of Agriculture)

far behind Florida at that time—produced only about 2,500,000 boxes a year. The freezes of 1894 and 1895 wrecked the Florida citrus industry. Production dropped to 150,000 boxes. Recovery of groves was started immediately after the freeze in most cases, but was interrupted by another extremely severe freeze in 1899.

Acreage in northeastern Florida, site of the first large citrus plantings, never again attained the extent it had prior to these three freezes, nor reached anything like the total previous production.

Early plantings had been made on locations selected primarily because of the character of the soil. Incoming growers knew little about problems of natural cold protection. The freeze

of 1894-1895 brought squarely into the foreground the problem of cold protection and resulted in a spread of the citrus industry to the south. This southward trend was speeded by the freeze of 1899, and the greatest area of the citrus industry today is in central Florida, where cold hazards are far less than those that faced early growers.

Development of increased production in succeeding years was based on new groves rather than rehabilitating old ones. By 1909-1910, the Florida citrus crop again exceeded five million boxes.

Citrus is grown to some extent in almost every part of the state but the commercial producing areas are concentrated in the central portion and in a narrow strip along the coast. Citrus groves cover slightly more than 500,000 acres, with oranges accounting for about 65 per cent of the total; grapefruit, 30 per cent; tangerines and limes, about five per cent.

A project designed to increase by 1,500,000 boxes the number of Florida oranges available for processing by the Minute Maid Corporation is under way in the St. John's River swamps west of Fort Pierce.

The Florida citrus industry presents one of the most varied economic patterns of all major agricultural enterprises. During the history of commercial citrus production, rapid expansion and technological changes necessitated far-reaching economic changes. Perhaps the most salient features of the present economic organization, however, are the widespread separation of grove ownership from grove operation, the importance of co-operative organizations, and the integration of the growing and processing functions.

The principal varieties of Florida oranges are Parson Brown and Hamlin, shipped mostly in October and November. Mid-season varieties are the Pineapple and Temple, shipped during January, February and March. Valencias and Lou Jim Gongs, late varieties, are shipped in the March to July period.

Citrus fruit consumption has increased greatly in recent years because of: (1) emphasis on vitamins generally, and especially Vitamin C, found so abundantly in Florida oranges and grapefruit; (2) processing and packaging of juice in liquid, powdered, and frozen forms, which permit a much wider distribution on a year-round basis; and (3) recognition of citrus fruits in any form as a staple food product.

SUGAR CANE

Sugar cane was one of the last staple agricultural crops to be introduced successfully in the South. Jesuits introduced the crop from Santo Domingo. Acadians later took up cane cultivation and spread its production westward. Commercial production became important after 1825.

Florida and Louisiana are the principal cane sugar growing areas of the mainland United States. There are about 50,000 acres of cane under cultivation in Florida, most of it in the Lake Okeechobee area.

Louisiana supplies about five per cent of the nation's yearly sugar requirement. Cane is grown on large mechanized plantations in the lower part of the state. Despite level topography and rich silty clay loam soils, the short growing season (nine months) makes cane production a gamble.

FORESTS AND FOREST INDUSTRIES

Forests make up one of the South's basic resources. Despite their rapid exploitation, forest lands now cover more than half the total land area of the South Atlantic-East Gulf Plain. Favorable climatic and soil conditions combine to make this extensive region ideal for timber growing. Much of the region's economic progress has come from natural wealth of merchantable timber stands.

More people in the South depend on wood products industries for their livelihood than on any other type of manufacturing. Although less so than in the past, lumbering still makes a tremendous economic contribution in every Southern state. Second only to textile manufacturing, lumber and wood products (excluding furniture) provide jobs for about one-sixth of total manufacturing employees. Scattered throughout the region and often located in rural areas, sawmill operations are a major source of cash income in many small communities. Southern pine accounts for two-thirds of the region's lumber output and also provides the raw material for other industries, such as naval stores and paper.

The basic process in manufacturing Southern pine is similar to that used for other types of wood. Trees are felled, limbed, and cut into suitable lengths. The resulting logs are then skidded to a central place where they are loaded on a vehicle and hauled to a sawmill. Here the logs are fed through a saw that reduces them to boards or planks of the desired thickness, after which they are conveyed to edgers and trimmers. The lumber is then ready to be air- or kiln-dried for seasoning purposes. Later, it is graded and sorted. Finally, in a planing mill, the rough, dry lumber is dressed smooth and sometimes processed further.

STRUCTURE

The nature of its timber resources has imposed special characteristics on the Southern pine industry. Generally of second or third growth and found principally in small scattered tracts, the timber stands in this region lend themselves best to small operations. Numbering about 11,000, small mills (those producing less than three million board feet annually) employ 96 per cent of the mill population in the South and produce almost two-thirds of the total lumber.

LOSS OF MARKETS

Known for its strength and nail-holding power, Southern pine has many sales outlets. Its most extensive use is in the building of homes but large quantities go into the production of boxes and crates; lesser amounts are used in railway construction and other industrial fields.

The industry recently suffered a declining market for its products. About one-half of this decline is attributable to the use of competing materials; the remainder to changes in size and architecture of homes with a trend to low-cost, slab-type construction.

Additional competition has come from brick, tile, sheet rock, concrete, and other forest products—paperboard, masonite, veneer, and plywood as well as from other types of lumber. Inroads by Western soft woods have been a particular source of difficulty to Southern pine producers. The severity of this competition is reflected by rising shipments of Douglas fir into the Southern pine producing states themselves, despite freight costs that are equivalent to as much as 50 per cent of the f.o.b. mill price per 1,000 board feet. Southern producers find it even more difficult to compete in Northern states, to which they once shipped large quantities.

The Western mills' ability to outsell Southern pine producers is attributable largely to lower costs. It takes from one-third to one-half fewer man-hours to log and manufacture 1,000 board feet of Douglas fir as it does to produce a like amount of Southern pine, because in the West, trees are much larger, volume per acre is higher, mechanization is greater, and the proportion of skilled workers is higher.

INCREASING COSTS

Rising costs in manufacturing Southern pine have made for additonal pressure, especially since wholesale pine prices have been held down. Loss of skilled labor to industries offering higher wages also has increased costs to pine producers.

Sawmill operators have made concerted efforts to reduce their work force by increased mechanization. The use of power chain saws has become more widespread and replacement of animals by tractors has continued. Even portable mills often have chain saws and tractors. At the larger mills, handling of materials is highly mechanized. Furthermore, within the last few years an increasing number of mills has installed debarking machines to strip the bark from the logs before sawing. The outside pieces of the log are made into chips for sale to pulp mills. Since this reduces the cost of producing the lumber by about four dollars per thousand board feet, sawmills having the equipment gain a considerable advantage over those that do not. A concomitant benefit of this development is reduction in waste.

Future markets for Southern pine will depend heavily on the level of housing construction and industrial activity and on scientific developments in lumber substitutes.

On the other side of the ledger are a number of favorable elements for the future. Although the productivity of recently-cut lands, especially on small private ownership lands, is still relatively poor in the South, improved management practices induced by tree farm and other programs are beginning to pay dividends.

Another favorable aspect is the average growth rate of Southern pine, which is greater than that of trees in most other parts of the country. Since the Pacific Northwest will eventually exhaust its virgin timber, competition from that area probably will diminish. Finally, greater development of new products made of Southern pine and creation of new markets for present products are foreseeable. One of the most promising developments of this type is the use of glued laminated construction. The Southern pine industry will undoubtedly continue to make a substantial economic contribution in this field.

PULP AND PAPER MAKING

The Southeast has millions of softwood trees (nearly two-thirds of its forest land) that provide a rich source of pulpwood.

The sulfate process, adaptable to the pulping of resinous woods, made possible the use of large acreages of Southern pine. Yielding a pulp of great strength, this process, first developed in Sweden, is known as the "kraft" process (the Swedish word for strength).

Pulp produced from Southern pine is used primarily for the manufacture of wrapping paper, bag paper, and paper-board, where its strength is an asset and its characteristic brownish color is no drawback. A rapid increase in the demand for paper as a packaging and shipping material, therefore, acted as a stimulus to the Southeast's pulp and paper industry. Techniques developed for bleaching sulphate pulp broadened its uses. Also, the adaptation of the groundwood process to Southern pine has led to the production of newsprint in this region.

With the necessary raw materials available in large quantities and stimulated by strong economic forces, the area's pulp and paper industry has grown phenomenally in the last 30 years. In 1930, the production of wood pulp, then concentrated in Louisiana, accounted for roughly six or seven per cent of the United States total. Today, about 54 per cent of our wood pulp comes from this area.

With the industry's expansion in the Southeast exceeding that in the nation, an increasing proportion of new capital expenditures has occurred here. There are more than 50 pulp and paper mills in the area, with the largest concentration in Georgia, Florida, Alabama, and Louisiana.

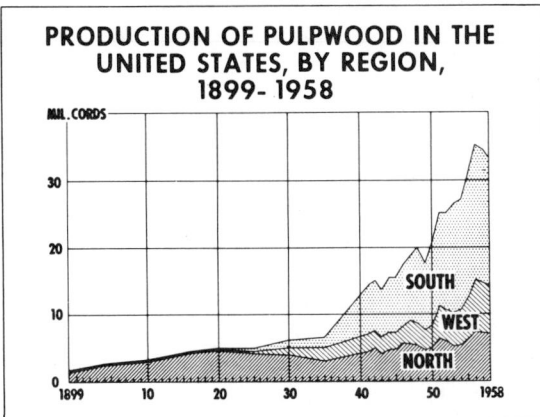

PRODUCTION OF PULPWOOD IN THE UNITED STATES, BY REGION, 1899-1958

Figure 3-7. (Bureau of the Census and Forest Service)

The pulp and paper industry has been the biggest boon to Florida's forest economy. The first major pulp mill was set up in Panama City, on the Gulf of Mexico, in 1931. Since then, many large companies have established pulp and paper mills in Florida. In fact, in 1960, Florida became the number one pulp state in the nation, with a total daily mill capacity of 8,280 tons. It replaced Washington, which had been the leader since 1939.

CYPRESS—THE LAST OF THE GIANTS

The ancients preferred cypress wood because it was straight and close-grained, soft and easily worked, and resistant to rot and decay. These qualities have made cypress a very popular wood in the United States.

Although the North American habitat of the bald or deciduous cypress ranges from Delaware to Texas and up the Mississippi River basin as far as Indiana, most of the great virgin cypress timber stands (trees 1,000 years old, eight feet thick at the base, and often 100 feet or more high) were in the tidewater and river swamp areas of the Atlantic and Gulf Coasts.

Southern mills produce about 146 million board feet, or $8 million worth of cypress lumber annually. Nearly half of this output is in Florida; about one-quarter of it is in Louisiana.

Despite a large decline in available supply, cypress lumber still is used to produce a wide variety of items. The highest grade of reddish-colored heartwood, which comes from large trees growing in the tidewater or deep-swamp forests and which is especially resistant to rot, is used to build shrimp boats along the Gulf Coast.

Lower grades of tidewater red cypress and much of the white or yellow cypress that comes from upland areas are used to manufacture interior trim, doors, sash, and blinds for homes.

With little basis for expecting artificial reforestation to be carried far, and with natural replenishment very uncertain, the prospect is that the cypress industry's supply of raw material will continue to dwindle as the drain from the forests exceeds the new growth.

NAVAL STORES

The naval stores industry (the production of turpentine, rosin, and pitch) has been an integral part of the Southeast's economy since the first colonists landed there more than 350 years ago.

The name "naval stores" was given to these products because they were used principally to calk boats, treat ropes, and in similar applications. Today, the term is a misnomer, for the uses of these products are many.

The United States normally supplies one-half the world's needs for turpentine and rosin, mostly by tapping second-growth longleaf and slash pines in southern Georgia and northern Florida. However, the naval stores belt extends along the Coastal Plain from the Savannah River to the Mississippi River.

THE PECAN INDUSTRY

Since 1846, when the pecan tree was first successfully propagated by grafting, pecan growing has been one of the principal horticultural industries of the South. Although pecans are a minor crop from the standpoint of total farm income, they contribute significantly to the income of several thousand farmers in the commercial growing area.

Between 1870 and 1890, seedling orchards were planted near Ocean Springs, Mississippi; Mound, Louisiana; Montgomery, Alabama; Albany, Georgia; and Monticello, Florida.

Prospects for profits in growing pecans naturally attracted speculators, and from 1900 to 1930, large acreages were planted by individuals and corporations for resale to potential investors. Many of the early ventures in pecan growing were not profitable because inadequate attention was given to soil fertility and moisture requirements. The pecan is a native of the fertile, well-watered soils of the Mississippi and other river deltas of the Southeast. Most of the orchards were planted on upland soils that had become low in organic matter, mineral nutrients, and water-holding capacity after many years of field crop production. Pecans will thrive on a wide range of soils but they usually require leguminous cover crops, fertilization, and insect and disease control.

FISHING

Fishing is one of the oldest industries in the South Atlantic-East Gulf Plain. Most fish are confined to the waters of the gently sloping portion of the ocean floor (called the continental shelf) or to bays and inlets of the coast. In these waters a greater variety of fish and shellfish abound than anywhere else off the shores of the United States.

The continental shelf is wide along much of the coast and far out along the Florida Keys. The deeply-indented bays, the coastal marshes and inland lagoons—especially those along the coasts of Louisiana, Mississippi, and Alabama —provide ideal growing conditions for oysters, as well as shelter for young shrimp and fish that come in from the open sea to grow to maturity.

Fish and shellfish add over $50 million to the Southern economy. In Louisiana, for example, fishermen derive more from their catch than the farmers realize from any crops except cotton, rice, and sugar cane.

SHELLFISH

Southern fishermen get the greater part of their income from shellfish. The latest comprehensive statistics place the value of shrimp sold by fishermen at more than $18 million.

Next to shrimp, oysters bring in more revenue than any other type of fish or shellfish. Louisiana, Alabama, Mississippi, and Florida oysters are worth about $5 million annually.

In contrast with other types of fish, most of the shellfish caught in Southern waters are processed before they are marketed. Oysters marketed fresh have their shells removed before shipping. Louisiana and Mississippi together can oysters valued at almost four-fifths of the total United States production. Biloxi, Mississippi, is the world's center for canned oysters.

Shrimp. Shrimp fishermen fall into two categories: (1) those who fish in the shallow bays, bayous, and lakes using boats only 35 to 45 feet long that cost from $3,000 to $6,000 each; and (2) deep-water fishermen who go out into the Gulf of Mexico some distance from the shore. The latter require boats at least 50 feet long, powered by a Diesel engine of from 125 to 175 horsepower, and costing around $25,000. Until recent years most consumers got their shrimp out of cans; practically all this canned shrimp came from the South Atlantic-East Gulf Plain. Louisiana and Mississippi marketed the major share, although shrimp canning was also important in Alabama and Georgia.

World War II limited production of canned shrimp because of a reduced labor supply and a shortage of cans. Therefore, a greater proportion of the catch was marketed either fresh or frozen. A decided consumer preference for frozen shrimp, cleaned and beheaded before shipping, continued after the war. Shrimp still are canned in considerable quantities but about three times as many are frozen.

Shrimp are frozen every month of the year, with the heaviest freezings coming during September, October, and November. Withdrawals from stocks are lowest during these months. Withdrawals are heaviest during March, April, and May, when the catch is light and when comparatively small amounts are being frozen.

FISH

The United States Fish and Wildlife Service lists almost 60 varieties of fish caught commercially off Southern shores. Seven varieties, however, account for 75 per cent of the total fish sales (excluding shellfish). Mullet, caught principally by Florida fishermen, yield about 28 per cent of the total returns. Other important varieties include Spanish mackerel, sea trout, menhaden, catfish, groupers, and red snappers. When four other varieties are added —drum, pompano, bluefish, and flounders—the list accounts for over 90 per cent of the total fish sales exclusive of shellfish.

Menhaden. The most important fish on the

basis of volume caught is menhaden, which amounts to 60 per cent of the volume of commercial catch of 180 million pounds annually. Most of the menhaden is taken from the waters off the Florida, Louisiana, and Mississippi coasts.

This fish is used primarily for the manufacture of meal and oil. Meal made from menhaden, very high in protein content, is fed to hogs and poultry. The oil has industrial importance in the manufacture of paints, varnishes, insect sprays, soaps, and as a lubricant for certain specialized uses. It also is used to fortify poultry feeds with vitamins.

At one time, menhaden-processing was concentrated in New England but because of the longer fishing season many of the newer plants are now in the South. Approximately 60 fish by-product plants, many of them processing menhaden, are found in Florida, Louisiana, and Mississippi.

Boats generally from 85 to 150 feet long, carrying a crew of around 20 men, supply the plants. Some of these boats venture as far as 100 miles into the Gulf, although occasionally large schools of fish may be found nearer the shore. Airplanes are sometimes used to spot the schools. When the boats arrive at the plants, they may be carrying as many as a million fish weighing approximately a pound each.

SPONGES

The sea provides another harvest along the Florida Gulf Coast in the sponges found near Tarpon Springs. The crop of sponges is valued at more than $3 million anually.

PROBLEMS OF THE FISHING INDUSTRY

The history of the fishing industry resembles that of many of the other extractive industries. Resources at first were close at hand and abundant and were exploited without much thought of complete utilization or of future supply. Most persons, if they thought anything about it, probably believed implicitly the old saying that when one fish is taken out of the sea, two others take its place.

Overfishing, water pollution, and industrialization, however, have cut production from bays, inlets, and sounds along many parts of the South Atlantic-Gulf Coastal Plain waters. New grounds and new devices for catching fish have had to be found. Technical advances have made fishing possible farther and farther away from shore, but the result often has been to make one fish swim where two swam before.

The Southern fishing industry has not been free from such troubles. The waters of some bays formerly yielding a good harvest of shrimp, oysters, and crabs, for example, have become so polluted that they no longer are productive. Overfishing in the inshore areas has reduced the supply of shrimp, and taking oysters without planting has reduced oyster production in some places.

Recognition of these problems has led state governments to start conservation programs and to regulate the industry in the hope of developing it on a sustained-yield basis. Interstate compacts help to enforce the laws. These activities promise to prevent recurrence of many past abuses.

Other problems, however, are facing the industry. Its development has been slow, partly because of a lack of knowledge and partly because of a failure to apply existing knowledge. Exploration in the South Atlantic and Gulf waters has been comparatively limited. Little is known of the fish that grow there—where they are found in greatest numbers, their life cycles, how large a fishing industry they can support, and what conservation measures are necessary to keep the industry on a sustained-yield basis. There is also a lack of knowledge of the most efficient methods of utilizing the fish. Development of a wider market and reduction of its seasonal character, as well as solutions to some production problems, are other obstacles still to be overcome by the fishing industry.

TRAPPING

Fur trapping is an old industry in the South. The fur trapper preceded even the explorer in colonial America. Muskrat, mink, raccoon, and other such fur-bearing animals long have been means of livelihood for people in the bayou and swamp lands of southern Louisiana. Today, over $3½ million annually is realized from peltries in that state. Muskrat alone accounts for nearly $2 million of this total.

Figure 3-8. Phosphate operations in central Florida. The modern dragline scoops up a carload of ore at a time; a high-pressure water system washes the mineral and floats it to a processing plant. (Hedrich-Blessing)

MINERAL RESOURCES

PHOSPHATE

Florida is the nation's largest producer of the phosphate rock used in a wide range of industries. Florida's total production of phosphate rock has an annual value exceeding $50 million. Most of it comes from the "land pebble" district in Polk and Hillsborough Counties in west-central Florida, where the rock is surface dredged by huge draglines. Hard-rock and colloidal phosphate are found in Citrus and Marion Counties in north-central Florida. Raw phosphate rock is used in the manufacture of fertilizers, sugar juices, jellies, preserves, beverages, medicine, rust-proofing compounds, baking powder, and many other products. Most recently, phosphate-derived insecticides have yielded dramatic results.

MANUFACTURING

Southern states produce only about 22 per cent of the nation's manufactured products—much less than their proportion of land area and population. Never in its history, however, has the South had a period of industrial growth and diversification comparable to that of the past ten years.

THE CAROLINA PIEDMONT REGION

The Piedmont region of the Carolinas furnishes an outstanding example of the industrial progress that has given rise to the "New South." This area is growing faster in manufacturing production than the United States as a whole; manufacturing increased five times in value since the beginning of World War II as compared to 4.5 times in the entire United States.

Although the Piedmont contains only about 50 per cent of the population of North and South Carolina, it accounts for over three-fourths of all manufacturing workers and wages, almost 80 per cent of the value added by manufacturing, and 63 per cent of all manufacturing enterprises in the two states.

The industrial structure of this area is based on three industries: textiles, tobacco, and furniture. In each of these fields the Piedmont enjoys world leadership.

The most dramatic aspects of industrial progress in the Piedmont are the new multi-million dollar plants and the numerous expansions of old ones since 1945. Not too many years ago a new factory here that cost a few million dollars was a relatively rare occurrence; today the industrial strides of the Piedmont are measured by multi-million dollar installations and expansions. The old college town of Rock Hill, for example, made the nation's headlines when the Celanese Corporation of America surveyed its advantages and decided upon it as the location for its new $40 million rayon yarn plant. Operating at capacity, this textile giant will employ 5,000 workers (almost one-fourth the total population of the town in 1947) and will augment the annual payroll of a formerly one-industry county (cotton manufacturing) by $8-$9 million.

In addition to having the most modern and efficient machinery, many of the new textile plants are pleasant to look at—architectural exhibits of a new industrial age that stresses the

aesthetic in factory appearance. Far from creating the dreary factory towns so characteristic
of the older, heavily industrialized areas, such
plants as the new nylon throwing mill of the
Duplan Corporation in Winston-Salem, the
$13 million Grace bleachery of the Springs Cot-
ton Mills, and the rural textile spinning plant
built by Deering, Milliken and Company in
McCormick, South Carolina, are positive contributions to the appearance of the areas in
which they are located.

Textile diversification. While increasing
the number of new large plants, the Piedmont
is gradually diversifying its industrial structure
and forging ahead of other areas in industries
founded on recent technological advances.
Camden, South Carolina, is a good example;
long famed as one of the South's leading pleasure resorts, it is the site of a huge new du Pont
plant for the manufacture of Orlon, one of the
newest synthetic fibers.

Industrial leaders in the Piedmont are fully
aware that in order to maintain leadership in
the textile industry, Piedmont plants must be
able to turn quickly to production based on
laboratory-made fibers. The rayon industry affords a good example of the flexibility of the
region in this respect. Burlington Mills, which
got its start in North Carolina, is the world's
largest weaver of rayon goods, with plants in
20 communities scattered over the Piedmont of
North Carolina. Williamston, South Carolina,
is one of the latest entrants in this field with a
new $4 million filament rayon weaving plant.
All told, there are rayon plants in over half the
21 counties comprising the Piedmont region of
South Carolina.

Diversification in the Piedmont's textile industry has progressed in another very desirable
direction. In the past the emphasis was much
too heavy on semifinished items such as yarn
and gray goods. Now, as a consequence of new
construction and expansion of finishing facilities, the Piedmont is leading the South to a
ranking position as a supplier of finished textiles. King Cotton's domain has been invaded
more recently by the woolen and worsted industry; probably this invasion is the most significant textile development in the South during the postwar period. Again, the Piedmont
is in the van, with mills recently established in
McCormick, Johnston, Greenville, and Union,
South Carolina.

Although such developments have produced
economic conditions in the Piedmont superior
to those of other comparable Southeastern
areas, a still-greater industrial diversification
must be achieved to raise per capita incomes to
the national average. Progress is, however, being made—illustrated by the recent growth in
the important metalworking industries, including large plants of the Western Electric Company in Winston-Salem and Burlington, and
in food products, agricultural implements, fertilizer plants, paper and container products,
apparel, and chemicals.

It is along such lines that new opportunities
must be created and realized throughout the
South. The Carolina Piedmont has an abundance of raw materials supplied by its forests,
farms, and mines, capable of servicing a wide
range of local semifinished and finished goods
industries such as synthetic boards, cement,
plastics, paints and varnishes, glass and china
ware, firebrick, apparel, and food products.
The list might be extended considerably but
the point is that all too many of the raw materials still are shipped out of the area, to be
brought back in the form of processed goods.
Certainly many of the raw materials could be
utilized economically in the region of their
origin.

Today, with all its industrialization, the
Piedmont of the Carolinas has only one city
with a population over 100,000; but there are
many small cities and towns strung along the
network of highways that weaves the region
and its three million people into an integrated
pattern of mutually-dependent economic interest.

In effect, the Piedmont is a huge, continuous market extending 275 miles north and
south, attracting the attention of hundreds of
national distributors operating out of such natural distribution centers as Charlotte, Greens-
boro, Winston-Salem, Durham, Columbia, and
Greenville.

Furniture manufacturing. High Point,
North Carolina, is the pivot of a vast Southern
furniture industry. Within a radius of 125
miles, 38 per cent of the nation's bedroom
furniture and 40 per cent of its dining room
suites are made.

FLORIDA'S NEW INDUSTRIAL PLANTS

More than 400 new industrial plants, representative of American industry, have been added to Florida's economy since 1956. The most rapid development is taking place in labor-oriented metalworking industries, especially electronics, aircraft, and missiles.

Industrial activity in Florida extends over a wide range—from ships and paper to cigars, food, and novelties. The long list of products manufactured in Florida includes, among many others, building materials, brooms, truck trailers, communications equipment, glass, frozen and other food products, machines, containers, clothing, hardware, paint, chemicals, and furniture.

Among the largest manufacturing plants are the Glenn L. Martin guided missiles and electronic components plant south of Orlando, the Pratt & Whitney jet aircraft engine development and testing plant west of West Palm Beach, and the Kraft Foods citrus concentrate plant in Lakeland.

Industrial engineering and research, too, are enjoying unprecedented growth, for Florida's climate attracts engineers, scientists, and other skilled personnel.

WOOL MANUFACTURING

The history of industrial development shows that manufacturing in a region passes through several broad stages. In each stage the type of manufacturing that predominates results from efforts to combine most profitably the region's factors of production. The most profitable combinations, of course, vary from time to time.

In the early stages, the processes used are likely to be those requiring comparatively large quantities of raw materials and unskilled labor, both abundant in relation to capital and to labor and managerial skill. Processes that are simple and those that involve only the first steps of transforming raw materials into finished products, therefore, are generally the rule. In the later stages, both labor and management possess skills too valuable for use in merely the simple types of manufacturing. As development advances, the processes in which these skills are important to success become more profitable than those in which only an abundance of unskilled labor or raw materials is important. Manufacturing, therefore, becomes more complex and carries along further

the process of transforming raw materials into finished products. The closer development approaches maturity, the more influence technological advances, capital equipment, and the skill of management and labor have in governing the type of manufacturing that is carried on in a region.

Although the South has by no means reached industrial maturity, postwar developments in many manufacturing fields are similar to those found in the later stages of manufacturing. One example is made up of the recent entrance of Southern textile firms into a more complex type of manufacture, that of woolen worsteds; the building of new plants in the South for that purpose; and rumored plans for the erection of additional mills.

Wool manufacturing has been carried on in the area for more than a century. During most of that time, however, it lay almost dormant. The development of complete wool manufacture came about slowly. Of the 1,800 complete sets of wool machinery reported for the United States in 1845, only four were in the Southeast. In addition, there were scattered throughout the region many small carding mills that processed wool brought to them by local farmers, whose families then spun the yarn and wove the cloth. Most of these mills employed only one or two workers. The clothing that equipped many Confederate soldiers was made on household looms and in village workshops.

Expansion of wool manufacturing in the South did not occur on a large scale until about 1900. The greatest growth, however, has taken place since 1945. Today the South produces as much as 14 per cent of all the men's woolen work and dress trousers made in this country, although manufacture of men's suits and coats is still concentrated in the New York, Rochester, Boston, and Philadelphia areas, which together account for 55 per cent of the country's suit manufacture and 65 per cent of its overcoat production.

Southern expansion in the manufacture of worsteds marks only the beginning of an expansion similar to the one that took place in cotton textile production.

THE GARMENT INDUSTRY

One of man's oldest occupations, the making of clothes, has been expanding rapidly in Southern states in recent years. Scarcely a

Figure 3-9. The Martin Aircraft plant at Orlando, Florida, illustrates the trend in the design of new factories—campus-like facilities that add beauty to the community. (The Martin Co.)

month goes by without several announcements of new plants being set up. Many of these plants, as well as those already established, are comparatively small; taken together, however, they add up to one of the South's largest manufacturing enterprises. These new plants have created new jobs, increased output, added to income, and thereby broadened the South's economic base.

To develop and expand this industry, both local and national savings have been tapped. Many of the larger plants, those employing between 500 and 1,000 workers, have relied almost completely upon local capital and retained earnings. Beyond this, "national" money has flowed into the area, some of it representing a complete shift from apparel centers in the North. Probably of greater importance, however, have been the opening of branch plants by companies that were established elsewhere. Many of the firms transferring operations to the South have come from the great apparel manufacturing centers of New York, New Jersey, and Pennsylvania.

More than 830 plants produce a wide variety of clothes but generally there is a tendency for clothing manufacturers in this area to concentrate on men's and boys' wear, particularly work clothes such as overalls and shirts. In a recent census year, men's and boys' wear ac-

counted for two-thirds of the value added by apparel manufacturing in this area.

Besides the concentration on particular types of garments, there has been a tendency for the industry to concentrate in some states rather than in others. Georgia, for example, accounts for almost a third of total apparel employment and is followed by Mississippi, Alabama, Louisiana, and Florida.

In the Northeast, apparel manufacturing is normally found in the crowded metropolises. In the South, however the apparel industry, or "needles trade," generally has sidestepped large cities to settle in small towns. More than 40 per cent of all apparel producers listed in the manufacturing directories of the Southeastern States are located in communities of less than 10,000 population. In Florida and Louisiana, however, most of the plants are in the larger cities, but together these two states account for only a small share of the region's apparel output.

Although several reasons might be given as to why garment producers have chosen to locate in small towns, possibly the most valid is the abundance of cheap labor in these places. This is particularly important, for about 55 per cent of total value added by apparel manufacturing in the area represents labor cost as opposed to 40 per cent in most other manufacturing concerns. Estimates show that even with today's high-speed machines, about two-thirds of an employee's time is taken up with handling and manipulating the garments. Stitching itself takes but a few moments; far more time is spent in picking up the parts, placing them together properly, putting them under the needle, bringing down the machine attachments that hold the pieces in place, and starting the machine. Besides these, other operations such as fitting and pressing require hand work.

Special programs like Mississippi's BAWI—Balance Agriculture with Industry—have contributed to the rise of the apparel industry in small communities. To attract new business, municipalities with little or no industry offer such special inducements as low rentals of plant space and special tax benefits. In Mississippi, apparel and shoe manufacturing concerns have been more inclined to take advantage of these inducements than have other producers.

RAYON

Considerations that enter into a manufacturer's decision to locate in a specific area are numerous. Sometimes tax concessions or other types of special inducements are important but more often industrial location is the result of adjustments to basic economic forces. Frequently these forces are difficult to isolate and they vary among different types of businesses. Nevertheless, students of industrial location found that the primary attractions for most plants are markets, materials, or labor, or a combination of these factors. The influence of these considerations on plant location is particularly well illustrated by the rayon industry.

Rayon and acetate are made from cellulose as distinguished from the more recent discoveries of nylon, acrylic, polyester, and other non-cellulosic fibers made from petroleum, coal by-products, other minerals, or proteins. Until recent years, rayon and acetate have enjoyed a meteoric growth in this country. Output rose from 400,000 pounds in 1911, to over 1.5 billion pounds in 1960, and accounted for one-fifth of total mill fiber consumption. Among man-made fibers, rayon and acetate remain the overwhelming choice of consumers, their consumption being about four times as large as that of noncellulosic fibers.

The Southeast has shared in this growth and is now an important producing region of rayon and acetate. Since World War II, almost all the new rayon plants have been built in the South, so that today the area accounts for more than 50 per cent of the nation's total productive capacity of rayon and acetate.

Factors affecting location. Because tremendous amounts of pure water are needed in the manufacture of rayon and acetate, availability of water is often the principal factor in determining a site. One viscose yarn producer, for example, uses 20 million gallons of water daily. This high demand explains why rayon plants are generally found near rivers or large streams.

Their location is further influenced by the proximity to supplies of cellulose in the form of refined cotton linters and wood pulp. Most Southern plants now use cellulose made from wood pulp almost exclusively, because it is cheaper and, according to many observers, technically superior to cotton linters.

Another attraction has been the availability of chemicals. Many important producers of sulfuric acid and caustic soda are located in Alabama. These plants supply most of the chemical needs of Southern rayon producers.

Nearness to Alabama and Kentucky coal is another advantage, for coal is a source of steam as well as power to rayon producers. Cheap electricity, on the other hand, plays little or no part in attracting them because the factories generate their own electricity. Combining in-plant facilities with commercial power assures a dependable power supply, a consideration that is important because the nature of rayon production makes power shutdowns extremely costly.

Availability of labor also influences plant location. By locating principally outside the major cities, rayon firms have been able to draw on workers from rural areas and nearby small communities.

RAMIE

This is a relative newcomer among fibers grown in this country, dating to 1945, when some 1,600 acres were planted in Florida on an experimental basis by various individuals and firms.

Ramie belongs to the hemp family and grows

Figure 3-10. Aerial view of the Chemstrand Corporation's nylon filament yarn plant situated on a 2,000-acre tract 12 miles north of Pensacola, Florida, shows shipping docks, the textile spinning area, an office building (left), and the chemical intermediates (right). It is the world's largest plant for making nylon from raw materials to the finished yarn in one continuous operation. (Chemstrand Corp.)

as a weed in tropical and subtropical climates in many parts of the world. Its stalk can reach a height of ten feet and a diameter of three-quarters of an inch. The ramie plant is a perennial, it grows from root segments and matures in from 60 to 70 days. Under favorable circumstances it yields three or four cuttings a year with little cultivation.

Interest in the plant focuses chiefly on the long white fibers that lie embedded in gums just beneath the thin outer bark. The fiber has been known and used for more than 6,000 years but it still plays a negligible role in the world's markets. In a way, therefore, ramie is both man's oldest and newest natural fiber.

When properly processed, ramie is long and lustrously white. It is several times stronger than cotton—stronger in fact than any other vegetable fiber known. When wet, ramie is from 30 to 60 per cent stronger than it is when dry; it does not shrink and it strongly resists rot as well as the ravages of sea water. Though it is highly absorbent, ramie fiber dries quickly. It is light in weight. Moreover, it can be spun and woven into fabrics that are as coarse as heavy canvas or as sheer as the filmiest silk. Little imagination is needed to foresee a very large and diversified demand for such a product.

The industry has progressed substantially in the past few years. In Florida alone twice as many acres of ramie were planted in 1960 than in 1950, and more are being prepared for planting. Successful decorticating machines are enabling a number of concerns to make commercial shipments.

The Pearch-Florida Ramie Products Corporation has a plant at Belle Glade, near Palm Beach. A newcomer to the industry in the 'glades is the Peter J. Schweitzer Company of New York. This company is interested in ramie primarily as a source of raw material with a high cellulose content for the manufacture of cigarette paper. The yield of pure cellulose from the flax straw now being used for this purpose is about 40 per cent, but the yield from ramie will be twice as much.

Another center of ramie development in Florida is in and around Zellwood, near Orlando. In this locality the oldest operation is that of the Institute New Plants and Products, Inc.

The outlook. The general outlook for the ramie industry reveals a bright future on the demand side. Manufacturers are voicing increasing interest in ramie and even the general public is learning something of its possible role among consumer goods. On the supply side, however, the industry still faces serious problems. Some of them are technical though these are less serious than they have been. Other problems are economic and organizational in character.

Attaining lower growing and processing costs, the heart of the industry's economic problem, rests upon a careful weighing of new technical advances and the adoption of those that promise the most efficient operations.

There remains an organizational problem, the sort of problem new industries always have to face; it is caused by an industry's various segments losing step with one another. An example of this type of problem was presented by the cotton industry in its early days. Cotton, like ramie, was only an Oriental product in the 18th century. Again, like ramie, it caught the

fancy of the people. Before that time it had been produced laboriously by hand in the Orient and then exported to England. To satisfy the enthusiastic demands for cotton, however, the production of large quantities in England itself was needed. The lack of technical facilities for spinning and weaving on a large scale proved to be as much of a handicap to cotton as the difficulty in decorticating (husking) has proved to ramie. Little by little, however, inventions invaded one segment and then another of the cotton industry—spinning, weaving, carding, ginning—with the result that at different times at least one of them was out of pace with the rest. Many years passed before cotton flowed efficiently from the American plantation to the gin and on through the English mills.

The ramie industry is now in a somewhat similar position. At present more ramie is being grown than can be processed with the existing facilities. If no means of decorticating the

Figure 3-11. Miami Beach, Florida, boasts a mild year-round climate and is a summer and winter attraction to more than a million people annually. The sprawling structure in the center of the picture is the new 15,000-seat convention hall. (Miami Beach News Bureau)

Figure 3-12. Aerial view of the Alabama State Docks, Mobile, Alabama. The Alabama State Docks represent the first complete state owned and operated plant in the United States for the interchange of freight between land and water carriers. There are also a number of privately owned docks and terminals in the port. (Mobile Chamber of Commerce)

matured crop is available, it can only be cut down and left on the ground, with a total loss of at least that particular cutting. If, on the other hand, as construction materials become more abundant, a great expansion of decorticating and degumming facilities should develop, the new plants might be handicapped by a shortage of raw materials. This would mean idle plant capacity, and idle plant capacity usually means high costs and the possibility of unprofitable operation. Obviously the best interests of all persons concerned require that all the different segments of the industry keep in step as closely as possible if loss in one branch or another is to be avoided.

THE TOURIST INDUSTRY

Few regions in the nation excel the Southeast in the number and variety of tourist attractions. The whole periphery is ringed by vacation areas and centers of tourist traffic. In many cases these already are highly developed, in others they are merely potential resources, the future of which will depend upon the wisdom, energy, and imagination displayed by public and private agencies in their development.

Of all the vacation areas in the Southeast,

Florida is by far the most important. The whole state is virtually one great playground. Enjoying an unusually favorable climate, spangled by its 30,000 lakes, washed by the Atlantic on its eastern shore and by the waters of the Gulf along its western shore, the state of Florida has exercised for centuries a powerful attraction on people seeking health and recreation. The Florida of the '60's has no one tourist season; golfing, swimming, fishing, and plain relaxation are catered to the year 'round. Miami, Marathon, Palm Beach, and Ft. Myers, to name a few, are places that mean warm sun, white beaches, and fun to millions.

Northward from Florida, the islands lying off the Georgia coast already attract considerable numbers of tourists and vactionists. Their full possibilities, however, are yet to be developed. Westward from Florida, the Gulf Coast provides another natural vacation area. Alabamans dream that some day Baldwin County will rival Miami, Gulfport, and Biloxi as a vacation center.

Evidences of the nation's historic past are perhaps more numerous in Virginia than anywhere else in the region. Thousands annually visit Williamsburg, where the old Courthouse, the Capitol, Public Gaol, Raleigh Tavern,

Ludwell-Paradise House, Governor's Palace, Wythe House, Magazine, and Guardhouse have been restored. Other historically significant places are Monticello, home of Thomas Jefferson, and Jamestown, site of the first permanent English settlement in America. Numbered among North Carolina's historic attractions are the Fort Raleigh national historic site on Roanoke Island, where the first English attempt to found a colony in America was made by Sir Walter Raleigh, and the County Courthouse at Charlotte, where the Mecklenburg Declaration was signed. In South Carolina are located the home of John C. Calhoun on the Clemson College campus and old Fort Jackson, where the first shot of the Civil War was fired on Fort Sumter.

Seashore, mountain, and health resorts, some catering to the budget minded and others to the wealthy, are to be found throughout the region. Outstanding on the coast are Virginia Beach and Ocean View (Norfolk), Virginia; Carolina Beach, Morehead City, and Wrightsville Beach, North Carolina; and Myrtle Beach, South Carolina. Virginia Beach offers an excellent sand beach, two miles of concrete boardwalk, and numerous recreational facilities.

The Southeast has a large financial stake in the tourist trade. Florida claims four to four and a half million tourists a year who spend about $700 million annually. This exceeds the value of Florida's manufactured products and the annual production of its forests, mines, or fisheries. Obviously the tourist business is the state's most important industry.

Mississippi claims that about $200 million is spent annually on travel and recreation within the state. In Louisiana, tourist expenditures are estimated at $100 million a year, an amount in excess of the value of the state's entire cotton crop; 80 per cent of this is said to be spent in the New Orleans area. Tourist expenditures in Georgia are estimated at $105 million a year and in Alabama at $50 million. The magnitude of the tourist trade is such as to raise to a position of major importance in the South's industrial pattern any industry that caters to it. Quite clearly the tourist industry should be a matter of concern to all the states within this region. It is an industry well worth cultivating.

POPULATION

Industrial expansion in the South Atlantic-East Gulf Plain has given rise to large population gains since the Federal census of 1950. Florida's growth is currently the fastest of any state east of the Rockies, with a population of 4,951,560 (1960).

POPULATION CENTERS

Mobile, Alabama (202,779). Alabama's only seaport, Mobile is situated on the west side of the Mobile River near the head of Mobile Bay. The bay is about 27 miles long and averages eight miles in width; its entrance is between Mobile Point and Dauphin Island.

Mobile is an important industrial and commercial center. The largest manufacturing operations of the city are pulp and paper production, bauxite reduction, cement, woodworking, fertilizer mixing, textile manufacturing, chemicals, naval stores extraction, petroleum refining, and the manufacture of asphalt and asbestos roofing.

Montgomery, Alabama (134,393). Montgomery is a center of agricultural trade within a radius of 125 miles. Located at the edge of the Black Belt, it is a great cotton market with hundreds of thousands of bales sold each year. Montgomery is the largest livestock market and the center of the largest dairying section in the Southeast. In recent years there has been a tremendous development of hydroelectric power in the district and, as a result, the city has become a manufacturing center.

Miami, Florida (291,688). This is the largest city in the state and the commercial and tourist center of south Florida. Some of the city's resort attractions are the seven miles of ocean beach, yachting and boating in Biscayne Bay, and exceptional salt water fishing from the causeways and the ocean pier or in the Gulf Stream, 20 minutes offshore. Large game fish include marlin, sailfish, tuna, dolphin, and amberjack.

Jacksonville, Florida (201,030). The main gateway to the Florida Peninsula is this city situated in a great double loop of the St. Johns River, the nation's longest north flowing river, where it turns east to the sea, 20 miles from the Atlantic Ocean. It is a world port and the financial, industrial, transportation, and com-

Figure 3-13. Atlanta, the capital and largest city of Georgia, is an important communications center. (Atlanta Chamber of Commerce)

mercial center of Florida. The city has the largest naval stores yard and the largest wholesale lumber market on the southern Atlantic Coast. Jacksonville is also a popular summer and winter tourist city.

Tampa, Florida (74,970).   Situated on Hillsborough Bay at the mouth of the Hillsborough River, the city has an excellent harbor with a 30-foot channel to the Gulf of Mexico. It is a gateway to Central and South America.

Atlanta, Georgia (487,455).   This city is one of the great financial and industrial centers of the Southeast and an important railway, highway, and air transportation center. Its many industrial plants manufacture more than 30,000 different commodities, including cotton goods, cottonseed oil, furniture, machinery, flour, and fertilizers.

Savannah, Georgia (149,245).   Savannah is one of the most beautiful and historic cities of the South. It is located on the Savannah River, only 22 miles from the Atlantic Ocean. This city, which is noted for its splendid harbor, has had a rapid industrial growth in recent years. Its industrial plants now number more than 300 and the city is the center of the expanding Southern pulp and paper business. Through its modern port pass a variety of commodities, including: paper and paper goods, petroleum, sugar, lumber, cotton and cotton products, naval stores, fertilizers, peanuts, and tobacco.

Charlotte, North Carolina (201,564).   The metropolis of the Carolinas, Charlotte is one of the major distributing points in the Southeast. Although noted for the diversification of industries, Charlotte's major industrial occupation is textiles.

Norfolk, Virginia (305,872).   Situated on the Elizabeth River and Hampton Roads, Norfolk has one of the finest harbors in the world.

Figure 3-14. The Norfolk & Western Railway coal piers at Norfolk, Virginia. The port's facilities for handling cargo are among the finest in the United States. (Norfolk Chamber of Commerce)

Its waterfront bristles with almost 200 piers, wharves and docks. Serving the city and its waterfront are nine trunk line railroads whose tracks crisscross 21 states. In addition, some 50 motor carriers and four scheduled airlines operate in and out of Norfolk.

Waterfront facilities include many piers and shipside warehouses for general cargo, along with specialized structures for handling such commodities as liquids, coal, bulk and bagged fertilizer materials, heavy or extra-length freight, and for performing extensive ship repair work.

Norfolk's harbor, with a channel 40 feet deep, is accessible to the largest ships. Norfolk and Portsmouth are twin cities separated only by the Elizabeth River and connected by tunnel and bridge. A tunnel connects Norfolk with Hampton and Newport News across Hampton Roads, and another tunnel, of tremendous importance to the area's growth, is under construction between Norfolk and Cape Charles on the eastern shore of Virginia.

Norfolk and Portsmouth together form one of the most important naval stations in the nation. The naval station at Norfolk is the country's largest operating base.

Richmond, Virginia (219,958). Richmond is an important industrial and commercial city. It is one of the great tobacco processing centers, producing chewing and smoking tobacco, snuff, cigars, and cigarettes. Other leading industries of the city in order of importance are manufacturing paper and paper products, printing, publishing, engraving, and the manufacturing of steel, iron, and machinery.

4 | *Mississippi-West Gulf Plain*

THE Mississippi-West Gulf Plain includes the extreme southeastern corner of Missouri, most of the southern and eastern thirds of Arkansas, the western portion of Tennessee immediately adjoining the Mississippi River, the northwestern third of Mississippi, all of Louisiana west of the Mississippi River, and the southeastern third of Texas. The Mississippi-West Gulf Plain evidences sufficient differences in structure and relief to be divided into (1) the Mississippi Delta Subregion and (2) the Coastal Plain Subregion.

THE MISSISSIPPI DELTA

SURFACE FEATURES

The Mississippi Delta is the alluvial plain of the Mississippi Valley. It stretches from Cape Girardeau, Missouri, to the Gulf Coast, and it includes the flood plain, the deltaic plain, and the loessial terraces.

The elevation increases northward from sea level at the Gulf of Mexico to about 320 feet above sea level in Missouri. The surrounding loessial terraces rise 20 to 50 feet higher than the flood plain. The flood plain consists of low meander belts of ridges and intervening irregular flood basins.

Most of the surface features reflect the depositional activities of running water. The ridges and basins of the upper part of the deltaic plain are somewhat more uniform than the flood plain, with the ridges standing higher above the general surface. The lowlands often are covered with water. Between ridges the lowlands give way to coastal marshes and bays, and the marsh areas are affected by wave action.

The entire alluvial plain is slightly more than 650 miles long, 25 miles wide between Natchez, Mississippi, and Sicily Island, Louisiana, and 125 miles wide in the latitude of Helena, Arkansas. Average width is 70 miles.

CLIMATE

The climate of the Delta is determined by the continental and marine tropical air masses that invade the area. There are no relief features to obstruct air flow, and elevation is a minor factor. The average water temperatures of the Gulf along its northern shore range from 64° F. in February to 84° in August, so that air moving northward is warm and humid.

In summer the prevailing southerly winds provide a moist, tropical climate. When the atmospheric pressure decreases westward from the Atlantic Ocean, a condition favorable for afternoon thundershowers occurs. When the pressure distribution is altered so as to bring westerly to northerly winds, periods of drier and hotter weather interrupt the prevailing moist condition. In the colder season the area is subject, in periods of varying length, to tropical air and cold continental air alternately. Though warmed by its southward journey, the cold air occasionally brings large and rather sudden drops in temperature.

From December to May the water of the Mississippi River averages colder than the air temperature in this latitude, a condition favoring river fogs, particularly when southerly winds prevail with slight barometric gradients. However, the river water is not too cold to ameliorate conditions near its banks during unusual cold spells, as the average water temperatures at New Orleans of 47.5° F. in January and 47.1° in February show. In the more southern sections, lakes also serve to modify the extremes of temperature and to increase fogginess over limited contiguous areas.

The average growing season ranges from 200 days in the extreme north to 320 days in the south. There are occasional winters in the extreme southeast without any freezing temperatures or killing frost.

The average annual precipitation ranges from slightly below 46 inches in the northwest to over 60 inches just north of Lake Pontchartrain. Droughts occur at times in the growing season but long periods without rain are seldom experienced.

Local storms, including hailstorms, tornadoes, and other wind storms of small area, have occurred in all seasons but show somewhat more frequency in spring.

SOILS

The constant migration and shifting of the channels of the Mississippi and Ohio Rivers over the years and the overflows from many tributaries have largely determined the pattern of the surface soils. Alternation of silts, sands, and clays is characteristic of an alluvial profile.

The soil types along the old stream channels generally are fine sandy loams. The broad, flat basins are mostly clay soils, and the intermedi-

Figure 4-1. Confluence of the Mississippi and Ohio Rivers near Cairo, Illinois, at the northern extremity of the Mississippi-West Gulf Plain Province. The Ohio River is to the right, the Mississippi River to the left. Note the flat terrain and the meanders of the Mississippi. (Henry Moreland, Cairo, Ill.)

ate areas between the basins and the ridges are silt loams and silty clay loams.

Until recently, the stream channels were inadequate for their water load and large areas were flooded frequently. Damage to crops and property was tremendous, but the alluvial deposits maintained and replenished an already fertile soil.

Today an elaborate levee system and the straightening of stream channels have reduced the possibilities of floods. Probably in no other area in the United States is the conflict between too much water and too little water as pronounced as it is in the Mississippi Delta. Excess surface water seriously handicaps winter-growing crops in winter and spring, interferes with land preparation for row crops planted in the spring, and often retards the growth of young plants.

AGRICULTURE

Cotton, soybeans, corn, oats, wheat, barley, alfalfa, sugar cane, rice, and pastures occupy more than 96 per cent of the open land in the Delta.

Cotton leads all other crops. It is grown profitably on most of the soils that have good internal drainage or where surface drainage can be provided. The Delta in Arkansas, Louisiana, Mississippi, and Missouri is a specialized cotton producing area that is adapted to mechanization. The topography is level. The soils are deep and productive. Rainfall usually is adequate but droughts may occur locally during critical growing periods causing many cotton farmers to turn to irrigation. The acreage of cotton has increased relative to the national total from about 13 per cent of the total acreage in the 1930's to nearly 17 per cent in the 1950's. Production has remained at a high level. The Delta presently accounts for more than 20 per cent of the nation's cotton production.

The greatest cotton acreage occurs in the Yazoo, a great basin formed by the Mississippi River on the west and the Yazoo River on the east. This is a crescent-shaped area about 70 miles across at the widest point and extending 200 miles from Memphis on the Tennessee border to Vicksburg, Mississippi, on the south.

It embraces 6,500,000 acres of rich land, the rich soils in some instances being 170 feet thick. About 4,500,000 acres are given to crops; the area supports a $200 million annual cotton and cottonseed economy. Agricultural diversification has moved apace, with about 750,000 acres in cotton, 600,000 acres in corn, 160,000 acres in wheat, 500,000 acres in soybeans, and 46,000 acres in rice.

Soybeans now rank second to cotton in value. They grow equally well on fine sandy loam to clay soils. The small grains—barley, oats, and wheat—are particularly suited to this region. All three grains, especially barley, require good surface drainage.

More sugar cane is grown in the Delta than in any other part of the United States except Hawaii. The acreage is concentrated largely in the lower part of Louisiana. Rice is adapted to clay and silty clay soils and to silt loams that have a compacted layer. It is grown on about 20 per cent of the Delta farms as a rotation crop. The crop sequence is rice for one to two years followed by lespedeza, soybeans, or pasture. One new and apparently promising rotation in some parts of Arkansas consists of two years in rice and one to two years of water fallow. A water level of two to four feet is maintained during the fallow period and a crop of fish is produced, restoring nitrogen to the soil.

Pastures occupy ten to 15 per cent of the open land in the Delta. Their acreage has expanded rapidly in the past decade. Most of the expansion has been on the silty clay and clay soils, except in places where a three- to five-year rotation with other crops is practiced.

THE COASTAL PLAIN

This subregion lies to the west and southwest of the Delta. It encompasses most of south-

ern Arkansas, western and southwestern Louisiana, and all of Texas east of the Balcones escarpment running from the Rio Grande near Del Rio to San Antonio and then northeastward to Austin and (with less definite markings) to the Red River north of Dallas.

SURFACE FEATURES

Across most of southern Arkansas the Coastal Plain is rolling to slightly hilly, with elevations varying from about 200 to 700 feet above sea level. The lowest measured elevation in Arkansas, 58.9 feet above sea level, is in this region. It occurs at the point where the Ouachita River crosses the Arkansas-Louisiana state line. Small farms predominate here. Much of the land is used for timber production.

The Coastal Plain in southwestern Louisiana and in southeastern Texas is a long narrow band of marshland lying generally within 50 to 70 miles of tidewater and almost paralleling the coast of the Gulf of Mexico. The topography appears to be flat over wide areas but the land slopes gradually to the Gulf. The maximum elevation above sea level is slightly more than 100 feet, although most of the area is less than 50 feet above sea level.

Inland from the coastal belt, the rolling terrain (50 to 700 feet above sea level) slopes gently upward from the Gulf Coast. The land

Figure 4-2. Sugar cane planting in Louisiana. Louisiana sugar could not compete with sugar imported from the tropics, where the yield per acre is greater, were it not for the tariff on imports. (Louisiana State Department of Commerce and Industry)

Figure 4-3. A rice combine in Louisiana. Rice production in Louisiana is highly mechanized; diking, plowing, planting, and threshing are done by machines. (Louisiana State Department of Commerce and Industry)

in its virgin state is covered with loblolly, long-leaf, and shortleaf pine on the uplands, and hardwoods in the alluvial valleys.

SOILS

The soils in Louisiana (and also in extensive sections in Texas) are deep, medium in texture, and slightly permeable. They were formed from material carried by fresh water to the sea and deposited. These sediments later were uplifted and subjected to soil-forming processes under a grass cover.

CLIMATE

The climate is humid subtropical, with an average annual rainfall ranging from 58 inches in Louisiana to 34 inches in Texas. The average January temperature is 55° F. and the average July temperature is 83°. This region averages 286 days between the last frost in spring and the first frost in fall. Extremely hot weather and extremely cold weather seldom occur.

AGRICULTURE

About 90 per cent of the Louisiana Coastal Plain is in cultivation, compared to only 25 per cent in Texas. Rice production dominates the Louisiana and eastern Texas part of the Coastal Plain. In the extreme western part in Texas, the main crops are cotton, grain sor-

ghums, and corn. Some rice is grown there also. The Texas rice belt is a strip of land about 75 miles wide extending along the Gulf Coast from the Louisiana line west to about Lavaca Bay. A rice crop requires from 40 to 45 inches of water at Beaumont on the east to 38 inches at Edna on the west. It is necessary to irrigate the crop heavily to meet seasonal needs. Some rice growers use wells for irrigation, but most of the water is pumped from the Neches, Sabine, Trinity, Brazos, and Colorado Rivers, all of which cross the district. The allotted Texas rice acreage in 1960 was about 422,000.

From the planting of presprouted seed by airplanes to harvest by combines, rice is the most mechanized of the major crops grown in the United States.

Cattle are raised in conjunction with the major crops. Approximately 75 per cent of the Texas Coastal Plain is in pasture. Vegetable crops and dairying are important in small areas near cities.

Southeast Texas has an important "broiler" industry. Processing plants in such poultry centers as Nacogdoches, Center, and Gonzales find a ready market in San Antonio, Houston, New Orleans, and other urban centers within the region.

South of the poultry belt to the Mexican

border is an area of specialized crop production that may be divided into: (1) the Coastal Bend around Corpus Christi, (2) the Winter Garden, (3) the Lower Rio Grande Valley, and (4) the rangeland in between. The average rainfall varies from 18 to 32 inches, but wells and some streams and lakes yield irrigation water—the lifeline for intensive crop production.

The Coastal Bend. Cotton and grain sorghums are the principal crops. Acreage controls on cotton have resulted in a big increase in grain sorghum production. Otherwise the present $40 million cotton crop would be much greater, and the grain sorghum and corn acreage, now valued at $20 million, would be much less. Most of the cotton and grain sorghum produced goes into the government loan program.

Vegetable production amounts to about $2 million a year, even though many farmers are getting away from vegetables to save moisture for field crops.

Beef cattle are an important part of the economy. The type of stock has changed radically—from rangy longhorns to blocky British breeds to Brahman crosses. There are also many registered herds of Santa Gertrudis, Aberdeen-Angus, and Herefords in the area.

Some 200 grade-A dairy farms market about $10 million worth of milk for fresh consumption annually. Many dairymen who once used Jerseys are switching to Holsteins, which produce more gallons of milk per cow.

Corpus Christi is the market outlet for many of the Coastal Bend's products because of its storage and port facilities and its mushrooming population (167,690 in 1960).

The Winter Garden. Centered upon Crystal City and Carizzo Springs, the Winter Garden is the result of a long growing season, fertile soil, excellent irrigation water from the Carizzo sands beneath the surface, and a land boom that began in the early 1900's.

The boom brought people south to plunge into the highly speculative vegetable business. The largest expansion was from 1910 to 1930; then the boom declined rapidly. Today the amount of land producing Winter Garden vegetables remains fairly stable, and much of the boom land has become range again.

Onions are the big money crop, with about 9,500 acres planted; they bring growers about $4 million a year. Spinach is the second largest crop. A monument to "Popeye the Sailor" and a sign in downtown Crystal City proclaiming it the "Spinach Capital of the World" attest to the importance of this vegetable.

Cauliflower, lettuce, carrots, peppers, beets, and snap beans are produced in quantity and are marketed in fresh or processed form in Chicago and Eastern centers. The big fresh outlets, however, for Winter Garden vegetables are the supermarkets in Dallas, Fort Worth, Houston, and other Texas cities.

Cattle bring the largest income from livestock, although there are sheep and goats on some of the ranches. Some cattle are in "contract" feed lots, but most are sold at local auctions or on the central markets.

The Lower Rio Grande Valley. The valley is a sort of world in itself, separated from other highly populated sections by mile after mile of ranch land. Its agriculture moves at fever pitch and marketing is a gamble. There is no way of foretelling at planting time what prices will be paid for crops. Disaster in competitive areas may cause prices to skyrocket, but overproduction may cause prices to slump below the cost of production.

Although agriculture is its mainstay, the valley is versatile. Manufacturing brings in an estimated $100 million a year. Each year, too, oil and gas contribute $60 million, shrimp and commercial fishing $25 million, and national defense installations $40 million.

Cotton, valued at $60 million to $80 million a year, leads all other crops. Vegetables (26 kinds) account for $30 million; fruit, $14 million; cattle, $11 million; and poultry, eggs, and milk another $4 million.

Carrots, cabbage, and onions dominate the vegetable crops. The valley is recognized as the nation's winter carrot basket. Tomatoes, beans, beets, cantaloupes, watermelons, sweet corn, and lettuce also are produced abundantly.

The relative importance of citrus fruit is somewhat misleading in valley economy, with 6,500,000 boxes valued at slightly more than $13 million annually. Production reached a peak in 1948, when 28 million boxes were picked from 14 million trees. A severe freeze the next year, followed by an even more devastating freeze in 1951, wiped out ten million trees. Farmers bulldozed the dead trees aside, planted cotton, and harvested 600,000 bales.

But citrus is making a comeback, and many young orchards have been established, at a cost of $400 to $700 per acre. About 70 per cent of the new trees are grapefruit trees and 30 per cent are oranges. Almost all the new grapefruit trees planted bear red-fleshed fruit. Most of the fruit is crated and shipped to Northern markets; the remainder is processed.

Even though cotton, fruit, and vegetables are the big money crops in the valley, the growing importance of livestock cannot be overlooked. With the abundance of grain sorghum and the increase in corn production, commercial cattle feedlots are increasing in number.

FORESTRY

On the Coastal Plain, forests are predominantly pine—including longleaf, slash, loblolly, and shortleaf varieties. There are also bottomland hardwoods along the many rivers and cypress and tupelo in the swamps.

Rainfall is heavy, usually averaging about 60 inches along the Gulf Coast but dropping off gradually from the Mississippi westward to the treeless prairies. Logging is relatively easy and inexpensive except in the swamps and deeper river bottoms or during periods of prolonged rain. Tree growth is generally rapid. The large private holdings of the South are located mostly in the Coastal Plain and in the rolling uplands of Texas, Arkansas, Louisiana, and Mississippi. A warm climate, abundant rainfall, and a long growing season assure excellent conditions for both the establishment and growth of trees. Most soils are reasonably well drained and can store water and plant nutrients. Throughout the region, trees are the paying crop for 57 per cent of the land. With proper attention, this could be one of the most productive timber regions in the nation.

The Delta embraces about 32 million acres. Its forest is composed largely of hardwood species, and growth is rapid. Annual floods are the rule in this area but the water does not remain on the land long enough to affect growth or regeneration adversely. The annual floods, however, are obstacles to logging, which must be done in the summer and early fall. In some years this period is shortened materially by the summer rains. The heavy, large timber obtained from the Delta forests requires heavier and more expensive logging equipment than is ordinarily needed in the pine forests of the South.

There are wide variations in the fertility of Delta soils. Many of the soils, however, are quite fertile, and clearing for agriculture has gone on in the past. There may be some additional clearing in the future for this purpose. However, it seems probable that 40 to 50 per cent of the area will remain in forests. Ownership tracts are medium to large. There are a number of sawmills that own more than 500,000 acres. Large farms or plantations are more typical of the area than small ones and many of them include forest lands in excess of 1,000 acres.

The Delta is a productive timber area where, with good management, tree crops can be made an increasingly important part of the local economy. Although the Delta's forest is least understood by foresters, it has the potential to furnish substantial employment and income to the people, and many useful forest products to the nation.

Forest industries rank next to agriculture in their contribution to the economy of the region. In nearly every community, operating units of the forest industry employ workers, buy products, and pay taxes. The contribution is so general and of such long standing that most people assume it will remain forever, not realizing that the timber resources on which the industry depends might play out some day.

In the latter part of the 19th century, the South felt the effect of the nation's expansion. Large mills were constructed. Lumbermen mowed down the virgin timber on a liquidation basis. The financial arrangements of that day were predicated on the rapid and the complete removal of the standing trees; the concept of timber as a crop was neither understood nor accepted by the industry. Gradually the original stands were cut over and, by 1935, the good virgin timber had been cut.

Hundreds of big mills had to quit. Smaller mills that cut smaller trees and required less volume per day to operate took over. They cut the remnants and the second growth that had reached merchantable size since the first operation.

The pulp industry is the newest large forest industry. Thus far, it has concentrated on production of kraft paper in the region. The first newsprint mill in the South, built by the Southland Paper Company at Lufkin, Texas, started production 1940. A second mill was put in operation in 1948. Since that time several additional mills have been built.

The pulp and paper industry has stimulated business. Communities where pulp mills have been built have prospered. The industry has invested millions of dollars and manufactures products that add many millions more to the income of the region.

Among other products obtained from the forests forming an important part of the raw material for the forest industry are poles, piling, crossties, fence posts, fuel wood, pipe bowls, handles, and furniture.

FOREST MANAGEMENT PRACTICE

Only about one-third of the larger owners utilize good cutting practices—selecting trees to be cut and leaving enough trees to assure reasonable stocking and improved succeeding stands.

The Crossett Lumber Company of Crossett, Arkansas, illustrates how many operators follow sound cutting rules. This company is now co-operating with the Arkansas Forestry Commission in organized protection of its 500,000 acres under the Clarke-McNary Law. Besides the fire crews and equipment available through the regular state organization, the company provides extra crews and equipment, as needed, to the state's fire patrol chief.

Trees cut from the forest are utilized thoroughly in an integrated set of mills that produce lumber, pulp, chemicals, and lesser products. Nonmerchantable trees are destroyed by girdling or poisoning. Bare lands are replanted to trees. Foresters direct all wood operations; a forester is in charge of each block of 50,000 acres.

FISHING

The Gulf of Mexico's coastal waters yield thousands of tons of seafood in large variety and of superior quality worth millions of dollars annually.

Shrimp, which constitute about three-fourths

Figure 4-4. One of Galveston Island's "mosquito fleets." Galveston is noted for its commercial and sport fishing. (Galveston Chamber of Commerce)

of the entire marine crop, are caught in the bays and offshore Gulf waters, with the heaviest concentration in the Port Isabel-Brownsville, Texas, area. Ten large processing plants line the industrial channel in Port Isabel and almost every day shrimp boats come in to unload their catch. The shrimp are graded and sorted into seven to ten different sizes by a huge grading machine, packaged and frozen within moments of being unloaded, and are soon on their way by refrigerated trucks to the big market centers of the nation.

Oysters are taken in the shallow waters of the Gulf. Crabs also abound in the coastal waters, but the commercial crop has never been large. Speckled trout, redfish, croaker, red snapper, mackerel, and drum are other salt water species caught. Game fish, such as tarpon and amberjack, are favorites with sports fishermen.

From fresh water streams within the region come catfish, crawfish, carp, sunfish, pike, turtles, frogs, shrimp, and crabs. Most of these are noncommercial, but they contribute to the area's recreation attractions.

TRAPPING

The southern part of Louisiana is famed for

Figure 4-5. A drilling scene in Louisiana bayou country shows one of the more remote areas where oil and gas producing operations are being extended. (Phillips Petroleum Co.)

the millions of fur pelts taken there every year. The large area especially adapted to the raising of fur-bearing animals makes Louisiana one of the leading states in the nation in this respect. Muskrat, otter, mink, raccoon, opossum, nutria, and other fur-bearing mammals abound. From a commercial standpoint the muskrat occupies the place of greatest importance.

Most of the trapping in Texas is carried on in a desultory manner, becoming active in first one community and then another, and depending on natural reproduction for the game supply. In the vicinity of Beaumont, however, the muskrat production is carried on under a range management program.

MINERALS

The character of minerals found in a given region is often related to its geologic history and therefore to the types of rocks in which the minerals are found.

The relatively flat lying, poorly consolidated rocks of the Gulf Coastal Plain contain asphalt, bauxite, clay, sand, gravel, lignite, fuller's earth, bentonite, iron, gypsum, chalk, marl, ocher, natural gas, petroleum, sulphur, and brines containing salt and bromine.

FUELS

Petroleum and natural gas have provided much of the energy which has made possible the industrial development in the Mississippi-West Gulf Plain. Right now the coast area embraces 30 per cent of all United States oil reserves and 34 per cent of the natural gas. It is the site of 20 per cent of the country's crude oil production and 32 per cent of its refined gasoline. Here are 50 out of the 400 United States refineries. Here also are manifold dependent industries—one industry, for example, boasts 93 per cent of the world's total production of oil drill bits. Here is the starting point of one of the world's largest pipelines—2,250 miles from the Rio Grande Valley to New York City. This carries natural gas and, with two other lines (one in Illinois, the other in Virginia), gives the Gulf Coast a national natural gas market.

Petroleum. Texas' first great oil gusher was brought in at Spindletop in 1901. So great was the flow of oil from this field that it was producing 94 per cent of the state's oil production by 1902. Texas production jumped from 836,039 barrels in 1900 to 4,393,658 in 1901; in 1902, Spindletop alone produced 17,421,000 barrels.

In rapid order other fields in the district were

discovered. The east Texas field, biggest of them all, began production in 1930. The success of this field, drilled on land condemned many times by geologists of the major companies, was followed by the largest leasing campaign in the history of the industry.

Following the east Texas discovery there was a succession of major discoveries in widely separated parts of Texas. They were grouped largely, however, in the Gulf Coastal and west Texas areas.

Louisiana is the third largest oil producing state after Texas and California, and is second only to Texas in natural gas production. Oil is produced in 59 of the state's 64 parishes. Southern Louisiana inland fields produce 65 per cent of the crude oil obtaind in Louisiana. Offshore fields now account for 21 per cent of total production, and northern Louisiana fields for only 14 per cent.

The southern part of the Gulf Coastal Plain of Arkansas contains all the oil producing fields of the state. Arkansas currently produces an average of 30 million barrels of oil and gas condensate annually. It is ranked twelfth among the 32 producing states in estimated proved reserves of crude oil, natural gas liquids, and total liquid hydrocarbons, and is considered to have about one per cent of the United States' total.

Offshore drilling. Along the Texas and Louisiana coast there are about 30 million acres of submerged land under which there may be oil. Nearly three million of these acres have been leased in Louisiana—at an average of $35 an acre. Some acres have gone for as much as $2,000 each.

Geologists estimate that there are from ten to 15 billion barrels of oil underlying the Gulf of Louisiana, within the 14-mile limit, and at certain points in Louisiana the Gulf extends as far as 75 miles before exceeding 100 feet in depth. Obviously, Texas geologists claim, still more oil underlies the Texas Gulf. It is a significant addition to our national reserves.

The Gulf, however, has yet to be conquered. So far, 35 petroleum companies (some are groups of companies united to lighten the financial load involved) have invested over $1¼ billion in Gulf waters prospecting and drilling. For many, it will be ten or 14 or 20 years

before they start to get it back, if then. But the challenge of the continental shelf, the last great known untapped reserve within the United States, keeps them drilling and hunting. Partial settlement of the Federal-state argument over ownership of the Gulf in 1953 touched off new interest that has mounted steadily since.

To date, oil is being produced in the Gulf from three general types of bases. Growing in popularity are the mobile drilling platforms that may be anchored to the bottom by means of a submerged barge and pilings or caissons; everything needed to produce a well and house a crew is contained on the decks or in storage.

A second type of base is a combination drilling platform and drilling tender. Some tenders are self-propelled and others must be towed to the drilling site.

Figure 4-6. This oil well is 40 miles from land in the Gulf of Mexico. Set over water 85 feet deep, the 690-ton platform supports a self-contained unit of drilling rig, supplies, crew's quarters, and helicopter landing deck. (Phillips Petroleum Co.)

The third base is the self-contained platform. It is expensive to build and cannot be moved. When one of these units goes into place it usually forms the base for drilling as many as seven or eight wells directionally. It also may be used as a foundation for oil storage.

Producing the undersea oil is one thing—transporting it to shore is another. Lack of transportation facilities has held back production. Only about 175 miles of underwater pipeline have been built to handle the offshore oil, but the picture is brightening. Recently a corporation was formed with a capitalization of $150 million to build two pipelines across the Gulf, from Texas to the Mississippi, and construct from them feeder lines to tap all known fields in the Gulf.

The oil lies imprisoned against the impervious flanks of "salt domes," which are mountains of rock salt thrust up from immense depths by pressure, bending and rupturing the shallower, oil-bearing strata of subsequent ages of Mississippian mud and sand (themselves 60 million years old). Or the oil may be trapped by the faults and distortions caused by the dome's thrust, sometimes miles from the dome itself. Nothing shows on the surface, everything must be found by geophysical methods, and locations must be marked by electronics. The oil itself lies two to three miles below the bottom of the Gulf in a great group of salt structures that is the extension of those below Texas and Louisiana inland, the source of some of the nation's most productive fields.

Natural gas. The expansion of the natural gas industry in recent years has been an economic asset to the Mississippi-West Gulf Plain. Until the middle 1920's, natural gas production and marketing was considered a local utility. In 1926, the first big pipeline in interstate commerce was built from the Monroe field in Louisiana to the East. Before the depression caused a slackening of pipeline building in the 1930's, gas from the region was going to about 20 other states.

There was no extensive pipeline building until after World War II, when the operation was resumed with great activity. By 1950, a number of large, high-pressure pipelines had been built from the Mississippi-West Gulf Plain fields to other sections of the country from coast to coast.

Texas leads all other states both in reserves and production of natural gas. Louisiana follows, and Mississippi and Arkansas are minor producers.

Lignite. Texas has very large lignite deposits. They are found generally throughout eastern Texas. The easy availability of this fuel, obtained by the strip mining process in many instances, and its nearness to large industrial centers favor its use. Burning lignite in powdered form in large-scale power production is a proven process that adds to lignite's potentiality as a fuel.

A high grade lignite has been used for a number of years in the production of activated carbon at Marshall, Texas. In July, 1951, the Aluminum Corporation of America began to use lignite in large quantities in the production of aluminum. Since then, other aluminum producers have been attracted to the region to avail themselves of the cheap power offered by lignite.

NONMETALLIC MINERALS

Many kinds of nonmetallic minerals are found in the Mississippi-West Gulf Plain. Among those playing a significant role in the region's rapidly expanding industry are salt and sulphur.

Salt. There are records of salt being mined in the state of Louisiana as early as 1817, and today its place in industry is growing rapidly. In the chemical field, salt is used in the manufacture of sodium sulphate, soda ash, caustic soda, and hydrochloric acid. In the textile industry it is used for setting dyes, and it is also used for curing hides; in the manufacture of glass, paper, steel, brick, and tile; for refrigeration; for softening water; and for pickling. In the household, salt is used in many ways, including the seasoning of food.

Three of the world's largest rock salt deposits and three large mines and plants, with an aggregate capacity of 1.5 million tons per year, are located in Iberia Parish at Avery Island, Jefferson Island, and Weeks Island. These rock salt deposits contain the highest grade of sodium chloride in the world, averaging 99 per cent pure in the natural state. Nearly 15 per cent of the nation's salt is mined here.

Salt mining is the oldest mineral extraction industry in Texas. There has been continuous

Figure 4-7. Sulphur production in Beaumont, Texas. Hot water is pumped underground (left) to melt the sulphur. The molten sulphur is brought back to the surface and discharged from giant vats to solidify in the open and be shipped as a solid or it is discharged from the vats directly to ships as a liquid (right). (Texas Gulf Sulphur Co.)

extraction of salt from the Lower Rio Grande Valley for more than 200 years. Most of the salt production comes from salt domes, or salt stocks, found at many places beneath the surface of the Coastal Plain. From deposits at the tops of these salt domes comes all the Texas sulphur, and from reservoirs around them comes much of Texas oil.

Sulphur. Texas is the leading sulphur producing state, with an annual output of 2.6 million tons. Sulphur deposits on the tops of coastal salt domes were first discovered in Louisiana in 1870, and in Texas in 1901. Sulphur is recovered by the Frasch process, in which superheated water is forced into the porous limestone formation, melting the sulphur and forcing it to the surface.

At the surface the sulphur is carried in liquid form to giant vats at the shipping points, where it is discharged from the pipes and allowed to solidify. These vats when filled are solid blocks of sulphur, usually approximately 80 feet wide, 30 to 40 feet high, and from 600 to 1,200 feet long.

Four major sulphur producers—Texas Gulf Sulphur, Freeport Sulphur, Jefferson Lake Sulphur, and Duval Sulphur—recently formed the Sulphur Export Company to market sulphur abroad.

Louisiana also has large sulphur deposits, and three new Gulf Coast deposits are being developed. One new mine, the Jefferson Lake Sulphur Company near Lake Charles, is now in production.

Because of its wide use in the chemical industries, sulphur is of great significance to the future industrial development of the region. About 80 per cent of all sulphur goes, in the initial manufacturing process, into sulfuric acid, and about 15 per cent into sulfurous acid. The greatest uses of sulphur are in the making of white sulphite paper pulp, fertilizers, explosives, bleaching and dyeing materials, and various acids and chemicals.

A $23 million project to permit shipping of sulphur in liquid rather than in solid lump form has been started by Freeport Sulphur Company. The program will spell substantial savings for makers of sulfuric acid, fertilizer, rayon, steel, and other items, who until now have had to melt sulphur after delivery. Today there is a growing preference among sulphur users for deliveries in liquid form, to lower material handling costs in their plants. Liquid users also will have fewer problems of loss in handling and contamination from moisture, scale, and other foreign solids.

Diamonds. One of the few places in the world and the only place in North America where industrial diamonds are found in the rocks in which they were formed is in Arkansas. Here, two and a half miles southeast of Murfreesboro, is the Prairie Creek peridotite area —roughly triangular in shape and containing approximately 73 acres. This is the site of an old volcano, a volcanic neck, of the same type that yields diamonds in South Africa.

Peridotite is a dark, fairly coarse-grained rock. Some of it was broken into smaller pieces as it was moved up into the volcano, and this broken material, when cemented into rock, is called peridotite breccia. Some diamonds have been found in the peridotite, but most of them have been taken from the peridotite breccia or from the thin soil overlying this type of rock. Approximately 48,000 stones, with an average weight of one-quarter carat, have been produced since the discovery of diamonds in the area.

Figure 4-8. Ore ships unload bauxite for the Reynolds Metal Company's Sherwin alumina plant near Corpus Christi, Texas (foreground). After the bauxite is refined to alumina it goes to the San Patricio aluminum plant (background) and to other Reynolds reduction plants across the country. The bauxite for the Sherwin plant is mined in Jamaica, Haiti, and British Guiana. (Reynolds Metal Co.)

METALLIC MINERALS

One of the largest and most stable mining ventures in Arkansas is in aluminum-bearing bauxite. The Republic Mining and Manufacturing Company crushes ore dug from nearby mines at its mill a few miles southwest of Little Rock. Then the moisture is removed. That part of the bauxite intended for the manufacture of aluminum is shipped to a reducing plant in East St. Louis, Illinois, where it is converted into alumina. Alumina is shipped to mills in the East for manufacturing into metal and metal products. A portion of the ore is calcined in the town of Bauxite and sold for use in chemicals and aluminum abrasives.

Arkansas produces more than 95 per cent of the bauxite mined in the United States, all of it from this area; the output amounts to over 400,000 tons annually. Estimated reserves of recoverable quality ore (32 per cent or higher) are placed at 40 million long tons. Most mining has been by open pit stripping.

MANUFACTURING

The Mississippi-West Gulf Plain has the world's most extensive industrialization for a subtropical region. New industry is going up at a rate some 45 per cent above that of the nation as a whole. This industrial upsurge is largely the product of research, mainly in such highly technical lines as chemicals, petrochemicals, synthetic fibers, and light metals—industries that would be nonexistent but for the laboratory. Although much of this research stems from the North, it is plunging the South, almost without intermediate stages, into an advanced state of technology. And in this changed climate the region is beginning to build its own research facilities for future growth.

The significance of the development and continued growth of these basic industries is that the materials produced are used in the manufacture of finished goods. It is reasonable to expect, then, in the immediate future, an extensive growth of industries that will use these processed resources.

The area is ideal from a raw material standpoint, for it has power, salt, gas and ethylene products, and deep-water transportation.

ALUMINA AND ALUMINUM

Most of the nation's domestic bauxite is

mined in Arkansas, and two Mississippi-West Gulf Plain cities, New Orleans and Baton Rouge, are major ports of entry for bauxite imported from Surinam, Jamaica, and British Guiana.

During the past several years, the Aluminum Company of America, Reynolds Metals, Kaiser Aluminum and Chemical, and Olin Revere Chemical have completed or put under construction more than $440 million in new and expanded facilities in the Mississippi-West Gulf Plain, changing the area into one of the nation's major alumina and aluminum producing regions.

The area now has plants with capacities to process over 1.9 million tons of alumina annually, over 55 per cent of the nation's total alumina production facilities. Aluminum reduction plants in the Mississippi-West Gulf Plain now have capacities totaling more than 350,000 tons annually, over 25 per cent of the United States total.

With the rapid expansion of alumina and aluminum reduction facilities in the area, new aluminum processing plants are locating in the South to convert the aluminum ingots into finished and semifinished goods. Already aluminum fabrication and processing is a multimillion dollar industry here.

Among the aluminum processing plants that have been built in the Mississippi-West Gulf Plain in the last five years or so are: General Motors, $3.2 million aluminum casting plant adjacent to the Reynolds Metal reduction plant near Corpus Christi, Texas; an $800,000 facility of the Standard Rolling Mills at Newport, Arkansas, to produce aluminum foil; an aluminum shutter plant of the Moreland Manufacturing Company at Camden, Arkansas; the Texas Metal processing plant at Magnolia, Arkansas; and the Woodlin Metal Products plant at Texarkana, Arkansas.

Recently, the Kaiser Aluminum and Chemical Company completed a new $3 million billet casting unit at its Chalmette, Louisiana, reduction plant. The output of this new facility, plus billets available from Reynolds' Gum Springs and Jones Mill plants in Arkansas, provides billets suitable for extrusion press and wire forming operations, and should prove an attraction to aluminum processors of this type.

At Gramercy, 40 miles up the Mississippi

Figure 4-9. The Humble Oil Company refinery at Baytown, Texas, near Houston. Both the Houston-Galveston Bay and Beaumont-Port Arthur areas possess refineries with a total crude oil capacity in excess of 700 million barrels per day. Other important refining centers are Baton Rouge, Lake Charles, Corpus Christi, and New Orleans. (Humble Oil and Refining Co.)

River from New Orleans, Kaiser recently completed a $70 million alumina plant, its third big installation in this area. A few miles north, at Burnside, the Ormet Corporation, a joint venture of Olin-Mathieson and Revere Copper and Brass, constructed a $54.5 million alumina plant on a 4,000-acre tract.

PETROLEUM REFINING

The Mississippi-West Gulf Plain has the largest refining capacity in the world. Almost a fifth of the crude petroleum produced in the United States comes from fields in this region.

Figure 4-10. The Texas Eastman Company, Longview, Texas, manufactures polyolefin plastics and chemicals. It is typical of the huge investment in new petrochemical plants in the region. (Texas Eastman Co.)

Obviously, the Gulf Coast has compelling attractions for the petroleum industry: (1) Up to 75 per cent of all claimed petroleum reserves in the United States lie within easy pipeline reach of the area; (2) water transportation is immediately available to ship products to lucrative markets in the eastern United States or abroad or, by the Intracoastal Canal, up the Mississippi River to Chicago and the Midwest; (3) the flat Texas-Louisiana terrain is ideally suited for the construction of the underground pipelines necessary to move petroleum raw materials and intermediates easily from plant to plant; and (4) salt domes and fresh water are immediately available (it takes 1,600 gallons of water to refine a single barrel of crude oil).

THE PETROCHEMICAL INDUSTRY

When World War II exposed the United States' supply lines to enemy action, Washington looked about for safe sources of the raw materials that were needed for fuels, explosives, plastics, and other uses. Chemists found these raw materials in a source that was barely developed—the gases associated with oil fields. From the hydrocarbons in these gases they found ways to manufacture many standard chemicals and some that were totally new. They coined a name for this phenomenon of the 1940's—the petrochemical industry.

Petrochemicals, made by rearrangement of the hydrocarbon molecules, supply the antifreeze for your car, the fuel for rockets that rise into space, the rigid plastic of the comb in your pocket, and the softer plastics that are wrapped around food in the supermarket. As chemists experiment with the molecules, they create new forms with new uses.

The petrochemical industry made the Gulf Coast its home because it found there a tremendous source of raw material and, in the oil refineries, a reservoir of technically trained

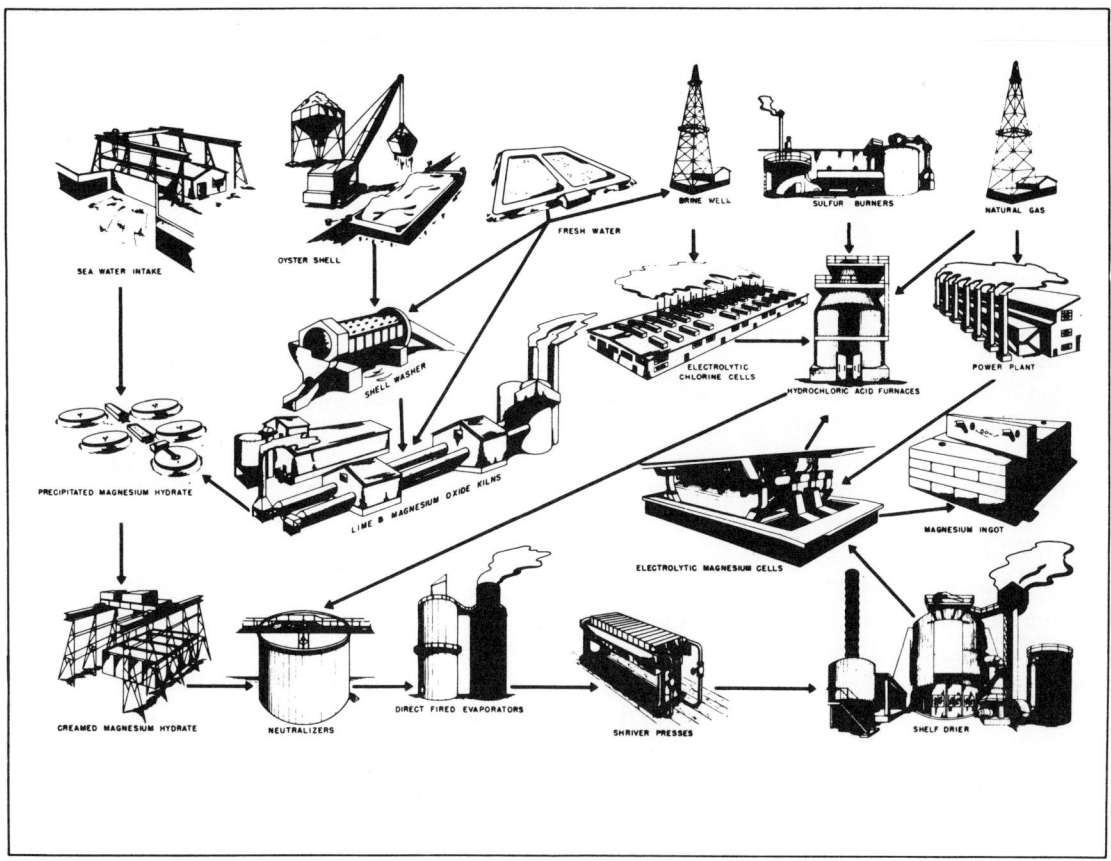

Figure 4-11. This diagram shows how the Dow Chemical Company produces magnesium from sea water. (Dow Chemical Co.)

men ready to move into this new field. Today the Houston area is the location of about 85 per cent of the productive capacity of the entire petrochemical industry of the United States. Some 32 major plants are interconnected by many hundred miles of pipeline in a network so complex that the area has been described as a "spaghetti bowl."

The complex network is necessary because one plant's waste product may be another's raw material. For example, an oil refinery may remove sulphur from a "sour" crude oil and sell the sulphur to a nearby chemical manufacturer. Almost every new plant that goes into operation has some waste or by-product that an existing plant can use. If an existing plant cannot use it, its mere availability may be the incentive for the construction of still another kind of plant that can.

This symbiotic boom still goes on; the entire stretch from Baton Rouge south past New

Orleans is becoming one huge chemical plant, linked by webs of pipelines, strings of tank cars, and fleets of barges. Among the new and prospective arrivals are: W. R. Grace's Polymer Chemicals Division (an $18 million plant at Baton Rouge), Dow Chemical (a $54.5 million chlorine and caustic soda plant at Plaquemine), and Wyandotte Chemical (a $28 million layout for similar production across the river from Dow at Geismar).

These facilities will add new basic and intermediate chemicals to the growing list of the Mississippi-West Gulf Plain's processed resources. Caustic soda, chlorine, ethylene and propylene oxides, hydrochloric acid, vinyl chloride monomer, butadiene, ethylene, nitric acid, ammonia, petroleum, waxes, methanol, methylethyl, ketone, polyethylene, bromine, adipic acid, kralastic, and acrylonitrile are some of the products now produced here.

These products in turn have thousands of

uses in the manufacture of many types of plastics and plastic products, synthetic rubber and products, alcohol, antifreeze, dyestuffs, pharmaceuticals, resins, synthetic fibers, insecticides, explosives, detergents, and other items.

In recent years, the petrochemical industry in the Sabine area has grown to such proportions as to become a strong rival of petroleum refining in value of products produced. Located only a few miles from Beaumont is the world's largest butadiene plant. From petroleum gases, it produces butadiene that is converted into synthetic rubber by two nearby rubber producers. Other chemical plants here produce fertilizers, plastic and nylon base materials, and additives for poultry feeds.

MAGNESIUM

Begun before World War II, stimulated by wartime demands, and sustained at high level of production since the war, the Dow Chemical Company plant at Freeport, Texas (on the Gulf Coast 60 miles from Houston), extracts magnesium, bromine, and more than 100 other chemicals from sea water.

An evaluation by the Dow Chemical Company listed a number of advantages of its site: (1) The sea water is high in dissolved salts containing magnesium and bromine; (2) there is plenty of natural gas, a source of chemicals and fuel; (3) there are many subsurface salt domes, a ready source of brine; (4) in nearby Galveston Bay there are enormous deposits of oyster shell, useful as a source of lime; (5) the area has sulphur mines; (6) low-cost water transportation is available, both by barge and by deep-water vessels; (7) salt water that has been processed can be discharged from the plant without affecting the incoming supply; and (8) there are adequate supplies of fresh water.

In extracting magnesium, sea water is pumped through screens into a flocculating tank and mixed with calcined oyster shells to form magnesium hydroxide. This is filtered and treated, in rubber-lined steel tanks, with hydrochloric acid, a process that converts it to magnesium chloride. A series of evaporating and drying operations follow, after which the material is fed into electrolytic cells, where it is reduced to metallic magnesium. With its purchase of the government's Velasco, Texas, plant

near Freeport in 1957, Dow now produces almost all the nation's magnesium.

PULP AND PAPER

The Mississippi-West Gulf Plain accounts for 15 per cent of the nation's pulp mill capacity. Products include newsprint, kraft paper, food board, pulp, hardboard, wrapper paper, liner board, paperboard, and machine-coated printing paper.

The new $57 million plant of the International Paper Company at Pine Bluff, Arkansas, is the area's first newsprint mill. It began operation in 1958, and has a capacity of more than 130,000 tons of newsprint and 165,000 tons of kraft board annually.

POPULATION

The Mississippi-West Gulf Plain, largely composed of the states of Texas, Louisiana, and Arkansas, has experienced approximately a 14 per cent increase in population in the last decade. Texas shows a gain of 24.2 per cent; Louisiana, 21.4 per cent; Arkansas has decreased by 6.5 per cent, largely because of an exodus from rural to urban centers outside the region. The increase in population in the Texas and Louisiana portions of the region is a response to the demand for highly trained technical personnel.

POPULATION CENTERS

Houston, Texas (938,219).   Houston is not only the South's largest city but also ranks seventh nationally. It is connected with the Gulf of Mexico by a deep-water channel and is one of the nation's leading seaports and chemical centers. Cotton, lumber, oil, and shipping are important. Principal industries include petroleum refining, cotton compressing, warehousing and shipping, tool and oil field equipment manufacture, meat packing, chemicals, synthetic rubber, steel, ship construction, paper and cement, iron and steel fabrication, grain elevators, rice milling, container making, cottonseed oil, paints, clothing, baking, furniture, brewing, and food processing. Houston is a leading educational and medical center, with Rice Institute, University of Houston, Baylor Medical College, University of Texas School of Dentistry, and Texas Southern University.

San Antonio, Texas (587,718).   Third in population among Texas cities, San Antonio is the commercial, civic, and cultural center for a wide area of south and southwest Texas. In many ways it is a city of contrasts, with centuries old historic buildings—the Alamo is one —standing amidst great modern structures. Its most important industries are garment manufacturing, cement, furniture, meat packing, food processing, and railroad repairing.

Near San Antonio are four Air Force bases: Lackland, the largest in the United States; Kelly, one of the world's largest repair and supply depots for aircraft; Brooks, home of the School of Aviation Medicine; and Randolph, a Strategic Air Command unit for training aerial tank crews.

Austin, Texas (186,545).   The capital city of Texas is a cultural, political, and educational center. Important industries are cottonseed oil, Mexican food products, furniture, stone processing, foundry products, brick, and pottery. The University of Texas is located here.

Corpus Christi, Texas (167,690).   The retail center for a rich farming area, Corpus Christi has varied resources—oil and gas, farming, shipping, manufacturing, commercial fishing, and the tourist trade. Among the larger industries are: manufacture of corn products utilizing grain sorghums, petroleum refining, chemicals, Portland cement, food processing, and cottonseed oil. Corpus Christi is a deep-water port connected with the Intracoastal Canal. Its excellent beaches and its boating and fishing attract many tourists. The Navy's largest air training station is located here.

Beaumont, Texas (119,175).   A shipping center, Beaumont is also noted for rice milling and oil refining—Spindletop, where oil was first discovered in Texas in 1901, is located here. Ports of Port Arthur, Beaumont, Orange, and Lake Charles comprise what is known as the Sabine Customs District, whose annual combined cargo tonnage frequently exceeds that of any other district in the nation with the exception of the Port of New York.

New Orleans, Louisiana (627,525).   The South's second most important city, New Orleans is located on the Mississippi River, 110 miles upstream from the Gulf of Mexico, and is the natural and logical gateway to the mid-

Figure 4-12. Houston, Texas, is the center of a great petrochemical industry, a cotton shipping port, and the collection point of a huge rice crop. (Houston Chamber of Commerce)

continent area of the United States and to the markets of Central and South America. Second in the nation in cargo-dollar volume, the New Orleans port handles annually more than $1.5 billion worth of exports and imports.

Eight major railroads, 11 airlines, and more than 120 motor freight lines link the city with the nation's major metropolitan centers.

Physically, the port of New Orleans is a 25-mile developed area of the Mississippi River, with about 20 miles of wharves and other waterfront facilities. More than 70 steamship lines schedule regular sailings from New Orleans to major world ports.

The city has a widely diversified economy: aluminum, asbestos products, binder twine, cement, chemicals, coffee, cotton, fertilizer, food processing, petroleum refining, shipbuilding, cottonseed oil milling, and rice milling.

Figure 4-13. Aerial view of the central business district of New Orleans looking toward the Mississippi River and the Greater New Orleans Bridge—the longest cantilever span in the United States. (Bureau of New Orleans News)

Baton Rouge, Louisiana (152,419). Baton Rouge is a center of petroleum refining and chemical manufacturing along the Mississippi River north of New Orleans. It also is a trade market for a large agricultural region and the seat of Louisiana State University.

Shreveport, Louisiana (164,372). The state's second largest city, Shreveport is a commercial, industrial, and financial center for a section yielding cotton, lumber, petroleum, and natural gas.

Little Rock, Arkansas (107,813). Little Rock, the capital and chief city of the state, is in a fertile farming area producing cotton, grains, and timber. It is a manufacturing center noted for cottonseed oil mills, lumber products, and furniture. Large bauxite deposits, coal, natural gas, petroleum, and clay are recovered in the vicinity.

Memphis, Tennessee (497,524). Memphis, the largest city in the state, is a market for cotton, cottonseed products, hardwood lumber (it is the nation's leading hardwood center), grain, livestock, and oil. Memphis also is a railroad center and port on the Mississippi River.

Part II | HILLS AND MOUNTAINS OF EASTERN ANGLO-AMERICA

The hills and mountains of eastern Anglo-America stand out clearly on a physical map. The hills are lands of moderate relief, but with a low percentage of near-level land; the mountains are areas of high relief with a low percentage of near-level land. Although the economy of the area has been influenced to a large degree by that of the adjoining plains, a greater similarity in land use may be noted from one hill and mountain area to another within the region than between it and the nearby plains. Nevertheless, one cannot deny the economic interdependence of the Northeastern Uplands on the New England-Canadian Lowlands, for example, or the relationship of the Middle Atlantic Coastal Plain to the Appalachian Mountains, Hills, and Valleys.

Landforms greatly influence human geography. Differences in accessibility, climate, soil types, stages of development, and the like cause great variation in population density and distribution. Physical barriers often are a deciding factor in lines of migration and movement, which may have a bearing, then, upon the degree of isolation or contact within a particular area. Thus, upland dwellers tend to be more provincial, conservative, and independent. Travel is more difficult. Industries, if any, are few. Agriculture is handicapped by lack of arable land in acreage large enough for the use of machinery.

Because of their many economic and physical similarities, the hills and mountains of eastern Anglo-America have been treated as a unit rather than in relation to the adjacent lowlands.

5 | *Northeastern Uplands*

(Relief map copyright Aero Service Corp.)

THE Northeastern Uplands encompass the extreme north-central tip of New Jersey, the areas east of the Hudson and north of the Mohawk River Valleys in New York except the plains bordering Lake Erie and Lake Ontario, all of Vermont except the extreme northwest corner, all of New Hampshire other than the southeast segment, most of western Massachusetts, the western third of Connecticut, the inland half of Maine, the eastern half of Quebec, all of Newfoundland and Anticosti Island, and the Notre Dame Mountains of New Brunswick.

The region from the Adirondacks to northern Labrador is a rough land in places; it has a long and interesting history. The southern portion of this region is near the cradle of Anglo-America; yet, unlike its lowland neighbors to the east, most of it remains virtually unsettled.

The growing populations of these adjacent Lowlands cannot be ignored, however, for they have brought about many changes in the Uplands. Although they still demand the products of forest and mine, their main contribution to the Uplands' economic and social scene comes during vacation periods, principally summer, when they seek rest, relaxation, and relief from heat and humidity. The Adirondack, Taconic, Green, White, and Berkshire Mountains are among the vacationists' favorites in the United States. Farther north, in Canada, the Gaspé Peninsula's Shickshock Mountains and the Highlands of New Brunswick are perhaps not so frequented by temporary occupants from the Lowlands, but the Laurentides and other uplands of southern Quebec are popular winter sports areas.

SURFACE FEATURES

The Northeastern Uplands are treated separately here because their landforms are different from their neighbors. In general the land is steeper, with longer slopes and more local relief than in the surrounding Lowlands. In most places local differences in elevation exceed 1,000 feet. In New York's Adirondack Mountains, for instance, this relief may be more than 4,000 feet, as near Lake Placid, Elizabethtown, or Mt. Marcy. Here many lakes and swamps are nestled between steep hills and mountains as high as Whiteface (4,872 feet)

or Marcy (5,344 feet). The heart of the Adirondacks is perhaps not spectacular. Near Raquette Lake, for instance, the typography is best described as knobby. There are a few steep hills and the area abounds in lakes and swamps.

ADIRONDACKS

The unique surface configuration within the Adirondacks is partially attributable to the ancient granites and other extremely hard rocks making up these mountains. During the geologic era when the Applachians were upraised, the Adirondack area was uplifted like a dome, then eroded by streams for thousands of years. Subsequently, huge masses of ice moved over the entire area, removing all vestiges of soil and loose rock from the mountain summits and leaving smoothed and bare granite behind. Much of the material eroded by the glaciers from the mountain tops and sides was deposited later in the numerous valleys, filling them to great depths. Many glacially formed depressions in these valleys are now the sites of the lakes for which the Adirondacks are famous. Because of the hardness of the rocks, the Uplands have retained many of their glacial-scoured characteristics.

The boundaries of the Adirondacks are not everywhere well defined. In the south there is a joining with the Catskills in the vicinity of the Mohawk River. The western boundary is the most difficult to determine, since the Black River and some of its tributaries have eroded through the rolling upland surface of Tug Hill "Plateau," increasing locally both relief and degree of slope. Therefore, it is necessary to move the boundary away from the base of the Adirondacks and to include within the Northeastern Uplands a small area west of the Black River. On the north, the Adirondacks gradually become the St. Lawrence Lowland. The sharpest breaks are perhaps along the eastern boundary, especially in the northeast and southeast, where steep mountains look down upon Lakes Champlain, George, and Sacandaga. Near Lake George this area connects with the remainder of the Northeastern Uplands.

NEW ENGLAND

To the south, the rather low but fairly steep Taconic Mountains straddle the boundary be-

Figure 5-1. Mt. Washington (6,288 feet) and the Presidential Range from Intervale, New Hampshire. (New Hampshire State Planning and Development Commission)

tween New York and her three neighboring states to the east—Vermont, Massachusetts, and Connecticut. Near Bennington, Vermont, for instance, the land is rough to rolling, with a local relief of 2,300 feet. Mt. Greylock (3,505 feet), in the northwest corner of Massachusetts, has the highest elevation and greatest relief (2,900 feet) in the Taconics. To the south, local relief is progressively less and the slopes, in general, less steep. This terrain continues southward almost to New York City. An off-shoot crossses the Hudson at West Point and enters northern New Jersey, where local relief approximates 1,000 feet.

East of the Taconics lie the Berkshire Hills of Connecticut and Massachusetts. These rise to the north to become the Green Mountains of Vermont. Although not a rugged range, these mountains are cut by some very steep-sided canyons. Mt. Mansfield (4,393 feet), in northern Vermont, is the culminating peak.

As is the case in most parts of the Northeastern Uplands, lakes and swamps are much in evidence in certain places.

The surface of eastern Vermont is not as high and steep as that of the Green Mountains. Local relief tends to be slightly more than 2,000 feet, and much of the terrain varies from undulating to rugged relief. In western New Hampshire the topography is even more subdued, with local elevation differences of about 1,500 feet. In the north, however, the White Mountains, topped by Mt. Washington (6,288 feet), have a maximum local relief of 5,200 feet, and are very rough, with many steep slopes. The Saco River gorge, for instance, is up to 3,000 feet deep at Crawford Notch.

The White Mountains continue into Maine and might be thought of as being connected to Mt. Katahdin (5,267 feet). This is an unusual peak, for near its summit is a large area of tableland. Much of the upland surface in this vicinity appears to be rather subdued. The mountain's south and east slopes are long and steep, however.

Upland Maine has a variety of landform features in addition to its many lakes and swamps. In places the terrain is knobby or rolling, but it may be rough, with short, steep slopes. In a few areas the local relief is less than 500 feet but it tends to be over 1,500 feet in most places. The least known part of the state is in the northwest — north and east of the Boundary Mountains. This is truly a land of lakes and swamps. Poorly drained areas are found away from and above streams as well as near them. These and other evidences of glaciation abound. Rocks and stones of a variety of shapes and sizes cover the surface for miles and miles, except where farmers have attempted to clear land for plowing. Many of these rocks are too large to have been carried by streams or currents. The fact that they were glacially deposited is further proved by the fact that a small percentage of them are types not found within a hundred miles of their final resting places. The same glaciers removed most of what little soil might have existed in the Uplands before the Ice Age, so that now the soils, if any, are thin and infertile.

EASTERN CANADIAN UPLANDS

The Northeastern Uplands continue northward across the international boundary into southeastern Quebec and northwestern New Brunswick until they are interrupted by the St. Lawrence Lowland. Beyond the St. Lawrence Lowland is a much larger but far lessser known part of the Uplands. This area includes most of eastern Quebec and all of Newfoundland-Labrador.

North of Vermont, the Sutton Mountains form a short extension of the Green Mountains. The relief here, about 3,000 feet, is unusually high for Quebec, although there are several other ridges and summits of considerable relief. Several other smaller isolated masses are scattered between New England and the St. Lawrence, but in general, as one proceeds toward the river, slopes become gentler and there is less relief.

A core of upland connects southern Quebec to Gaspé, where the steep north slopes of the Shickshock Mountains look down upon the mouth of the St. Lawrence. Towards the south, the upland surface, still strongly rolling, grades down to Chaleur Bay.

Northern New Brunswick, which is inadequately mapped, is much like adjacent portions of Maine and Quebec. As in most of the Northeastern Uplands, lakes and swamps are common and the general surface configuration is strongly rolling. Steep slopes tend to be near the many streams that have eroded rather deep, narrow valleys through much of this area.

Two hundred and fifty miles east of Gaspé, across the Gulf of St. Lawrence, lies Newfoundland, the world's tenth largest island. This is, except for northern Labrador, the most rugged part of the Uplands, for not only is the surface rough, but the climate is severe, the soils thin, and the vegetation sparse. More than half the island is barren, covered only by mosses, bogs, and lakes.

The Long Range comprises the western and roughest portion of Newfoundland. South of the Strait of Belle Isle, the coast of the Gulf of St. Lawrence is particularly steep and rugged, with a rolling upland surface dotted with lakes and swamps, abruptly sloping down 1,500 to 2,500 feet to the sea. A steep bluff overlooks the Atlantic side of northwestern Newfoundland, too. To the east this land is less rugged, but still rough, with a much-indented coastline. Lakes, bogs, swamps, and streams are everywhere. Steep slopes near the coast are not as common as in the northwest.

Nearly half of Newfoundland's population lives on the edges of Avalon Peninsula, at the island's southeastern extremity. Here, too, are lakes and swamps and poor soils. Local relief is generally less than 1,000 feet, while it is over 2,500 feet in many places in the northwest. Rocky and inhospitable, this peninsula offers little in the way of making a living from the land. People here look to the sea.

Labrador, a part of the mainland to the north of the Strait of Belle Isle, belongs to Newfoundland politically. Its northern portion is the roughest area in Provincial Canada east of the Rockies. The rugged and alp-like Torngat Mountains, with at least one summit 5,500 feet above sea level, are near the boundary of Quebec, just south of Hudson Strait. Elevations become lower southward, and much of the southern half of Labrador is rolling upland country with many lakes and swamps.

Eastern Quebec, north of the St. Lawrence, is much like southern Labrador, with certain areas somewhat rougher than others, such as in the Laurentides or Mont Tremblant Provincial Park, where local relief is over 1,000 feet and steep slopes are common. The interior upland, which has not been mapped adequately, is best described as having a rolling surface broken here and there by steeper sloping summits and rich in lakes and bogs.

NATURAL VEGETATION AND SOILS

This region is of such wide latitudinal extent that vegetative types tend to be belted according to distance from the southern boundary at New York City. There are significant differences caused by elevation changes, too, and in parts of the region exposure to prevailing winds or the sun is important in conditioning the type of vegetation to be found. In the far north and along the coast of Labrador the so-called tundra prevails. This moss- and lichen-covered barren is similar to vegetation above timberline on high mountains in western Anglo-America. Protected locations sometimes support dwarfed trees, and wild flowers flourish during the short spring. Much of insular Newfoundland also has tundra-like plant life.

South of the tundra belt are thin, stunted conifers, particularly balsam fir and black spruce. These trees grow taller and become more numerous as one moves southward, and other varieties, such as jack pine, white spruce, and white pine, become important. Deciduous trees mixed with needleleafs are to be found near the St. Lawrence, and this mixed forest type continues to the region's southern limits. Typical varieties are maple, birch, and aspen, and these often are associated with white pine (the best timber tree in the region) as well as hemlock and other conifers.

Good soils exist only in pockets like those found near Lake St. John or along streams. The long winters retard whatever soil development normally might occur, and the parent rock, usually hard, crystalline material like granite, is not readily conducive to soil formation.

CLIMATE

The Northeastern Uplands is a land of great climatic extremes. Lying in middle latitudes, it comes within the influence of constant conflicts between cold, dry air masses flowing out of the great subpolar region to the northwest and the warmer, moisture-bearing, tropical marine air from the south. The tendency of most of the general cyclonic disturbances to skirt the polar front puts their paths of movement through this region and results in a more or less regular succession (twice a week) of storms of snow or rain, with two- or three-day periods of fair weather, typically with warm west or southwest winds in summer and cold northwesterly winds in winter, intervening.

Continental influences prevail because the general movement of air masses in these latitudes is from west to east. By the time winter air has moved eastward across snow-covered interior Anglo-America, it is bound to be cold. Therefore winter temperatures here are far colder than those on the continent's west coast at the same latitude where maritime influences are at work. By the same token, summers in the Uplands are warmer than one might expect.

In the Taconic Mountains of Connecticut, January temperatures average about 25° F., which is about the same as the south coast of Newfoundland, many miles to the north. In Newfoundland, the influence of the sea provides a warmer climate than might be predicted on the basis of latitude. In the high mountains, such as on Mt. Washington, and in the north, temperatures average well below 0°, with —50° readings on the coldest days.

Summers are very short in northern Quebec and Labrador, although some days are quite warm. In the uplands south of the St. Lawrence, summers are longer, but nowhere is summer the dominant season. In the far south, average July temperatures are about 72°; in the north they are below 50° and frosts are to be expected even in July. With the exception of a few coastal locations in Newfoundland, summer is the season of maximum precipitation. Summer rains are supplemented significantly by winter snows, however, and these usually pile up depths of 100 inches or more in the south half of the region. The deep winter snows of the more accessible parts of the Northeastern Uplands attract thousands of skiers and other winter sports enthusiasts each season.

Total annual precipitation is high in the south and east. St. John's, Newfoundland, receives about 55 inches a year and southeastern Connecticut only five to ten inches less. The total gradually decreases towards the north until it may be as little as 15 to 20 inches in northern Quebec. The higher elevations, such as in the Laurentides, receive substantially more precipitation than the surrounding rolling uplands.

No climatic discussion of this region would be complete without mention of the frequent winter storms, with their high winds and biting cold. The area is visited by most of the storms that cross the continent and by others that form in the eastern half of Anglo-America. Fog, too, plagues fishermen, especially over the Grand Banks, a shallow area in the Atlantic off the southeast coast of Newfoundland.

FORESTRY

The Northeastern Uplands have old granitic rocks that are very hard, high in coarse crystals of quartz, and very low in lime. The soil material that comes from them is stony, sandy, and low in fertility; the agriculture of the Uplands is poor. Timber and scenery are therefore the most valuable resources, and the cool climate and annual precipitation make forest cover the natural vegetation of the region.

LUMBERING

Lumber is a bulky commodity, unprofitable to ship. But the Northeastern Uplands have an advantage over many other parts of the country because of their proximity to the biggest wood pulp market in the United States and to a heavily populated region needing lumber for housing. On the other hand, the fact that much of the timber grows in inaccessible places, so sparsely populated as to be lacking in roads and railroads, poses a problem.

Much of the more accessible forest has been cut or burned. Some has regrown in assorted less desirable hardwoods instead of the conifers that once covered it. Some has been farmed or close cut and then abandoned. Considerable acreage is in small lots, unprofitable to cut.

Northern New England. Maine has the largest per capita forest acreage in the nation. Some 16,783,000 acres, over 80 per cent of the state, are in forest land, and 97 per cent of this forest land is privately owned. Harvesting trees and manufacturing wood into useful products have been this state's principal industries for more than 300 years. The estimated value of all finished wood products exceeds $500 million and industries using wood are the state's largest employers.

About 85 per cent of New Hampshire is covered by forests and farm woodlands. The largest area, the White Mountain National Forest, is under the protection of the United States Forest Service to insure a permanent timber supply.

White pine predominates in the farm woodlots in the southern and eastern parts of the state. It is especially valuable lumber for building purposes. Many of the New England structures that remain today are monuments to the durability and usefulness of white pine, the wood that built New England.

In central and northern New Hampshire are mixed hardwoods of good quality—spruce, fir, and some pine—cut for lumber, furniture, veneer, and a wide variety of other products. The spruce, fir, hardwoods, and—more recently—pine, are used extensively for pulp.

Two-thirds of Vermont's total land area is classed as forest land. Of this, over one-half bears hardwoods, notably beech, birch, and maple; the remainder is covered by pine and other softwoods. Vermont forests yield millions of board feet of lumber, fuel woods, pulp, and excelsior wood annually.

Northern New York. The Northeastern Uplands project into New York State to include the Adirondack Mountains and the Tug Hill Plateau to the west, and the Taconic Mountains east of the Hudson River. The Adirondack Forest Preserve, about 2,200,000 acres, includes approximately half the Adirondack region between Lake Champlain on the east and the Black River Valley on the west.

Canada. The Northeastern Uplands of

Canada favor the growth of timber. Commercial forests extend from the United States border in the south to latitude 52° in the north.

The Appalachian Highlands are rather heavily wooded except where villages and new settlements break the apparent monotony of the timber stands. Eastward from the Chaudière Valley the trees are mainly softwoods; spruce and balsam fir are the most common species in the Notre Dame Mountains, except on special sites where cedar is substituted, while on the forest-covered plateaus and mountains of the Gaspé Peninsula, east of the Matapedia Valley, dark-green coniferous stands are brightened by the clear green foliage of white birch. Close to the United States border, hardwoods—aspen, white birch, yellow birch, and maple—predominate. West of the Chaudière Valley, with the exception of the Lake Megantic region, hardwoods are again more common.

Many prosperous sawmills exist in the Highlands zone, and the forests are leased to sawmill operators and to the pulp and paper plants of lumber dealers, some of whom supply the United States market. However, considerable stretches of forest lands are owned in small parcels by local farmers or are demarcated for their use as township forest reserves.

The uplands of northern New Brunswick are mantled with conifers or needleleaved trees —spruce, balsam fir, pine, cedar, hemlock, and tamarack (larch). Hardwood or broadleaved species including birch, maple, beech, and poplar, with small quantities of elm, ash, oak, basswood, and butternut, dominate in the southern uplands.

The greatest forest wealth lies within the Laurentian Plateau (Quebec) that forms part of northern Canada's extensive softwood belt. White pine once reigned supreme, but it was so extensively exploited during the past century that it has been virtually eliminated in many areas. In the openings created by cuttings, mixed stands of spruce and balsam fir have sprung up (although there are some pure stands of spruce) to cover the immense Laurentian territory. Hardwood stands of white birch and aspen occasionally occur between the softwood forests, adding variety to the landscape. The many rivers flowing south from the Laurentian Plateau into the St. Lawrence River have made accessible much of this vast

forest land whose products are the basis of Quebec's pulp and paper industry.

About two-fifths of Newfoundland is covered with commercial forest. Both coniferous and deciduous families alternate with barrens in the interior, where large herds of caribou and moose are found. The most accessible timber lies within the watersheds of the major streams. The hinterlands of White Bay in the northwest and the Bay of St. George in the southwest are also important timber districts.

FOREST PRODUCTS

Pulp and paper. Companies engaged in the manufacture of pulp and paper lead all other types of forestry enterprises in the Uplands. They control the largest area of land, employ the most foresters, and have the greatest financial stake in sustained-yield forestry. Their programs date from the turn of the century.

Quebec produces more than one-third of all Canada's pulp and paper products. Within its boundaries are stands of 50 million cubic feet, or about half of Canada's coniferous trees. In addition to this supply of raw material, Quebec has an unparalleled waterways system to carry logs to the mills and to supply the mills with the hydroelectric power than runs the paper-making machines. Deep, swift rivers wind through the forests; the winter's cut of pulp logs is thrown into streams to ride with the spring freshets down to the pulp and paper mills on the St. Lawrence, the Saguenay, and other rivers. Manufactured pulp, paper, and by-products from the mills are loaded directly into the holds of ocean-going freighters and carried via the St. Lawrence to the sea and the markets of the world.

The government of Quebec administers the forest lands in the public interest. Great care is exercised to ensure that new growth will always exceed the cut and that losses to fire will be held at a minimum. Every ten years, companies harvesting the pulpwood crop must make an inventory of their timber limits under lease and draw up a long-term plan for cutting. The plan must be submitted to government foresters for approval. In addition, plans for each season's cutting must be approved in detail by provincial forestry engineers. Consideration of such things as the age of the timber stand, soil conditions, drainage, and the possibilities of future forest growth in the area govern the methods of cutting to be employed. In the late summer and early autumn, woodsmen begin to move into the forest, setting up camps and cutting roads through the brush for the haulage of logs and supplies. Their season's operation plans may call for selective cutting, a thinning out process that leaves certain types and sizes of trees, or for clean cutting, taking everything out in strips when there are certain trees, such as black spruce, that cannot survive a thinning operation.

The pulp and paper industry of Newfoundland dates to the first decade of this century when a paper mill was erected in Grand Falls on the Exploits River. A second and larger mill was built at Corner Brook on the Humber River in 1923. Water power developed on these rivers provides the electricity to operate the mills and to serve the domestic needs of the surrounding districts. These mills together produce about 1,900 tons of paper a day. Raw materials such as fir and spruce are found in considerable quantity in the principal river valleys.

In addition to the pulp and paper industry, the forests of Newfoundland provide raw material for a large, modern birch mill and an equally modern pressed board plant, both of which are working at full capacity. Other forestry products are fuel wood, lumber, and staves for the cooperage trade supplying barrels and casks for the fishing industry.

Several paper companies operate large-scale enterprises in the Northeastern Uplands. The most notable are Great Northern in Maine; Eastern Pulpwood in Maine and New Brunswick; International Paper in New York, Vermont, New Hampshire, and Maine; and Finch-Pruyn in the Adirondacks.

Ownership of large forest properties in the Uplands has changed appreciably during the past two decades. Pulp and paper companies are the strongest and most stable owners. The large investments in pulp and paper mills can be liquidated only over long periods of time; such investments make necessary a continuous supply of timber. Many of the companies are enlarging their holdings. Others are attempting to stimulate good forest practices on the part of private owners who control land tributary to their mills.

In spite of the large proportion of forest in the New England Uplands, the area is presently producing less than half of the 2.5 billion board feet of lumber annually consumed in the adjoining Lowlands. One-fourth of the 2.3 million cords of pulpwood used yearly must also be imported. Paper consumption per capita has increased drastically in the United States in the last century until it is now over 400 pounds per capita. With coniferous forests running short and the size of trees in the forests diminishing, the pulp users in New England are filling the gaps by importing from the South, the Great Lakes States, and Canada.

The one hopeful note for the Uplands, which produce most of the pulp, is the expansion into the use of hardwoods. Since coniferous forests tend to be replaced by hardwoods after cutting or burning, this new use would make profitable the growth of hardwoods, which are unsuitable for saw logs. Hardwoods may be utilized in the manufacture of opaque paper and in the making of corrugating medium, the middle ply of cardboard used in containers.

The use of hardwood pulp is somewhat limited at present because of the neutral sulfate semichemical process employed. No economical method of controlling the pollution resulting from this process has been found, and paper companies within the region are hard pressed to satisfy the New England Interstate Water Pollution Control Compact and local ordinances.

Christmas trees. Balsam fir and spruce Christmas trees traditionally have been shipped from New England to all major Eastern cities. Most of the trees have been cut on abandoned farm land in New Hampshire, Vermont, and Maine, and in the higher elevations in Massachusetts. Such trees, growing in the most favorable locations, receive sunlight from all sides and are generally balanced, compact, and free of dead limbs.

For decades the natural seeding of old farm land provided an annual supply of many million trees for the Christmas market; dealers were able to purchase trees on the stump for a few cents apiece. This situation has changed gradually during the last two decades as the best quality trees were cut out in many areas and the abandoned fields grew up to forests.

Figure 5-2. A farmer's sugar house at the edge of his orchard, Chittenden County, Vermont. Armed with a bit and bitstock, a hammer and an axe, and with team and sled nearby to haul the sap buckets, the farmer begins his tapping. He bores an inch and a half to two inches into the wood and pounds the spout snugly into the opening. Often before the whole bush can be tapped, the first buckets are full of the clear, slightly sweet, water-like liquid that is maple sap, of which 45 to 50 gallons are required to make one gallon of maple syrup. (U.S. Department of Agriculture)

As a result, the prices of most kinds of Christmas trees delivered at roadside in northern New England have doubled during the last six or eight years.

Many areas in the Uplands provide ideal growing conditions for balsam fir and spruce. Balsam fir, especially, are desirable because they hold their needles for a long time, are easy to pack and ship, and have a good color and a pleasant odor. These trees can be produced not only by planting, but also by pruning and thinning trees that seed naturally on old fields.

New England could control the Atlantic market if a tree of high quality were produced. This means planting, controlling disease, culling poorer grades, and avoiding overcrowding. Christmas tree growing can be a profitable business for those resident landowners who are prepared to grow and merchandise a high quality product.

Maple syrup and sugar. Maple sugar is an important crop locally in this region. From one to two months a year the sugarbush is the center and spirit of all the life on the Uplands farms.

The maple sugar and syrup industry has shown considerable decline since the early part of the century. This decline has not been regular, for some rises occurred during periods of strong prosperity. The drop in the amount produced is caused by increasing use of a combination of cheap substitutes and by rising labor costs. Maple syrup, often mixed with corn and cane syrups, usually shows steadier prices than maple sugar. Retailing for as much as 80 cents a pound in some areas, maple sugar has become a luxury most people rarely enjoy. Vermont is the leader in the industry.

Almost three-quarters of the syrup is sold in the spring, but summer, fall, and winter sales as syrup, creams, or candies usually net a greater cash return.

AGRICULTURE

Upland agriculture is, at best, likely to be a marginal enterprise. Commercial crops may be grown only where market orientation offers sufficient advantage to cover the cost of overcoming climatic and soil discrepancies between regions. As soon as transportation voids this advantage the crops cease to be grown except for local markets.

The two main commodities of the area are dairy and poultry products. Both of these do better on the Lowlands, but high prices and great demand encourage their existence on a commercial level throughout the region. Pastures are planned, seeded, and rotated as well as possible to avoid the purchase of feed. Grain is imported from the Midwest and supplements local hay and silage corn. Grass silage is also used. Along with various grasses, oats, barley, and rye are grown for hay. Most of the milk moves to the Boston milkshed in fresh form for daily consumption.

DAIRYING

With more dairy animals than people, 66 per cent of Vermont's agricultural income is derived from the sale of milk and milk products. The Vermont farmer gets a larger share of his income from dairying than do farmers in any other state in the nation. Vermont accounts for 40 per cent of all the milk produced in New England. Nearly two-thirds of it is shipped to southern New England or New York as fluid milk or cream. The rest is sold locally, used on farms, or processed in country plants.

Although dairying is the most important farm business in every Vermont county, its concentration is greatest on the gently rolling hills and plateaus in the north-central part of the state. Farms are small, averaging 141 acres in size. Sixty per cent of them have less than 18 cows. Holsteins, Jerseys, Guernseys, and Ayrshires are the chief breeds.

New Hampshire's dairy industry, too, is a profitable agricultural enterprise. With hay lands and pastures offering an economical source of summer and winter feed nutrients, dairymen are able to establish a sound and permanent agriculture. Because of the high quality of the dairy herds with respect to production, good growth, and general breed type, New Hampshire dairymen have always enjoyed a ready market for their surplus animals in supplying replacement needs of neighboring states in southern New England.

POULTRY

The cool, dry air of the Uplands provides a healthy climate for the production of poultry and eggs. Although the industry is dwarfed by comparison to that of the Lowlands, it has grown steadily for many years, and the outlook for the future is for continued growth. The poultry industry is becoming even more efficient with modern methods and much breeding research. Most of the laying chickens are sex-linked crosses, line-bred to get higher egg production. The most prominent of the regular breeds is the New Hampshire Red, which is also an excellent meat chicken.

GENERAL LIVESTOCK

The raising of beef cattle, sheep, swine, and horses is a supplementary enterprise. Beef cattle raising is increasing, with the establishment of select purebred herds. Climate and topography are ideal for sheep; labor requirements are small and extensive equipment is not necessary. Sheep produce two sources of income, wool and lambs, and nearby markets for these are among the best in the world.

SEED POTATOES

The cooler climate and, at the higher elevations, the relative absence of insects that cause the spread of leafroll and other virus diseases, make the upland fields of this area ideal for the production of seed potatoes. They are used partly as foundation stock for future seed crops and for sale to table stock growers.

SMALL FRUITS AND BERRIES

Small fruits are grown commercially. Most berries and small fruits, however, have fallen to levels that barely can supply local needs, including roadside stands selling to tourists. Only blueberry production has risen considerably above home market demands. Blueberries constitute a rather important industry; they are grown on cut-over forest land. Production varies with the stand, the age of the plant, the season, and many other factors; it can range from almost nothing to nearly 1,000 quarts per acre.

Blackberries and grapes are grown commercially to a limited extent. The acre yield of these fruits is low, however, compared to that in the more favorable sections of the country.

MINING

ADIRONDACKS AND NEW ENGLAND

The Adirondack Mountains of New York and the New England Uplands are poor in minerals. With the exceptions of iron and titanium, most of the minerals are in such small quantity and are produced with such difficulty that if they occurred anywhere else in the country, they would probably not be worked commercially. Even though many of these minerals are relatively close to market points and refineries, the difficulty of transportation alone has kept some of them from being used. Subzero winter temperatures inhibit year-round operations in some areas; in others, no one is willing to invest the necessary capital for transportation of ores to market.

Beryllium is produced in limited quantities in Maine and New Hampshire only because government purchasing plants help the small producer.

Copper is mined both by open pit and underground methods. The mine at Elizabeth in Orange County, Vermont, produces about 800 tons of ore per day. Gold and silver are also recovered in small quantities from smelting operations.

Manganese deposits occurring in northern Maine rank among the largest in the United States. But, like all domestic manganese ore, it compares very poorly with the high quality ores found in such places as the Soviet Union, India, Ghana, Brazil, and the Republic of South Africa.

Iron ore is found chiefly on the slopes of the Adirondack Mountains in New York. As mines in the Great Lakes area are forced to use lower-grade ores, these deposits are coming into more favorable competition since they are closer to Pittsburgh. Now being worked are Republic Steel Corporation's properties at Lyon Mountain, near Plattsburgh, and Mineville, near Port Henry; the deposits of the Jones and Laughlin Steel Corporation at Benson Mines; and the titanium-iron mines of the National Lead Company at Tahawus. Containing from 25 to 35 per cent iron, these ores are beneficiated at the mines into concentrates of 68 per cent iron and then sintered.

QUEBEC HIGHLANDS

The Highlands of southern Quebec produce an immense variety of minerals that have given rise in several localities to large mining operations. Copper, lead, zinc, gold, and chromite are all mined in this area. Copper ore occurrences have been reported from many places. What may become an important producer of medium grade copper ore has, in recent years, been prospected at the headwaters of the York River, in Gaspé. Latest report by Noranda Mines, Ltd., a large Canadian company that holds an option on Gaspé copper, is that at least 70 million tons of copper ore can be mined profitably during the next 43 years. This

is an extraordinary life expectancy for a copper mine. The vast Arizona copper field in the United States, geologically similar to the Gaspé find, has a life expectancy of only 23 years.

Noranda plans call for construction of a smelting plant and refinery on the spot. Power will be tunneled under the St. Lawrence River from the new hydroelectric plant on the north bank near Havre Saint Pierre. Provincial authorities are planning a model mining village to accommodate an initial population of at least 1,000 persons.

The Canadian National Railways will construct a line to connect the copper field with the present Gaspé terminus, which is also the most accessible port. Docking facilities for importing smelter coal, probably from the United States, will be constructed in Gaspé Bay, a sheltered deep-water inlet so spacious that it was used as an assignation depot for entire convoys during World War II.

Lead and zinc also are known to exist in this eastern peninsula, and small quantities of these metal ores are being produced southeast of Ste. Anne des Monts. Chromite, a substance with many industrial uses and from which chromium is obtained, has been mined sporadically at several localities in the vicinity of Richmond.

Nonmetals include limestone, marble, talc and soapstone, granite, roofing slate, marl, peat, petroleum, and asbestos.

Asbestos. Of all the mineral substances contributing to the wealth of Quebec, none is as important as asbestos. Discovered in 1876, the deposits, until a few years ago, were mined by open pit methods; today the larger producers have gone underground, using mining methods initiated in the large copper mines of the southwestern United States. East Broughton, Thetford Mines, Black Lake, Coleraine, Asbestos, and Norbestos are fiber producing centers from which over nine million tons of asbestos-bearing rock are mined each year and sent to defibering plants.

INTERIOR QUEBEC AND LABRADOR

Interior Quebec and Labrador are made up of hard crystalline rocks extending from the St. Lawrence River northward over the rest of the province to its limit at Hudson Strait. Indeed, Quebec contains more of the vast, min-

Figure 5-3. The Arvida plant of the Aluminium Company of Canada, Ltd., is one of five smelters operated by the company in Canada. Arvida, with a capacity of about 700 million pounds of aluminum, ten per cent of the world's production, is one of the world's largest aluminum smelters. (Aluminium Limited)

eral rich Pre-Cambrian Shield than any other province. The area has already yielded such metals as gold, silver, copper, zinc, lead, iron, molybdenum, tungsten, and titanium, as well as several commercially important industrial minerals, such as apatite, asbestos, fluorspar, garnet, graphite, silica, magnesite, mica, and pyrite.

Whether north, south, east, or west, some part of every section is a storehouse of minerals. The inland country of the Laurentian Shield until recently was populated only by a few isolated groups of Indians whose sole occupation was fur trapping.

An industrial invasion that began some 50 years ago has been drawing wealth from the forests, rivers, and mines of the Laurentian Shield. In less than 30 years, some 20,000 square miles have been settled in the southern part of the James Bay watershed, where new mining centers and farms support a population of 120,000 inhabitants. The settlers supply farm produce, wood, and labor; and the operating and prospective mines provide jobs and a market.

Labrador iron ore. The most publicized mineral area at the moment is that section of Ungava and Labrador called the Labrador Trough. This covers a northwest-trending stretch of country, about 40 miles wide and 350 miles long, extending from the headwaters of the Hamilton River to beyond the Koksoak River. Geologically, the area is similar to the famed Mesabi iron district of Minnesota. Its sedimentary formations hold thick beds of high-grade iron ore, the total dimensions of which are not as yet known.

Geologists have long been aware of the vast iron ore riches in the trough straddling the border of Quebec and Labrador. When geologist A. P. Low talked about the deposits 50 years ago, Mesabi was just coming into its own and nobody was interested in the sub-Arctic wilderness. In 1937, when Quebec geologist Joe Retty came out of Ungava with a more detailed report of high-grade iron ore, Mesabi was still king. But as war demands cut deep into Mesabi, Retty's reports became more interesting. By 1942, Hollinger Consolidated Gold Mines, Ltd., of Montreal, was ready to gamble $5 million on Ungava. Since then exploration drills have been biting into the northern earth.

The Hollinger development came at a propitious time, for American steel companies were beginning to be disturbed by the approaching exhaustion of Mesabi's high-grade ore and the increasing demands of an industry pressed by civilian and military needs. Teams prospecting the trough area have found over 40 deposits of ore averaging between 55 and 65 per cent iron, with one deposit alone containing an estimated 20 million tons.

The M. A. Hannah Company of Cleveland, Ohio, one of the biggest iron ore suppliers in the United States, holds 40 per cent of the stock in the Hollinger ore. Together the companies organized Hollinger-Hannah, Ltd., and interested six American steel companies in the venture (as the Iron Ore Company of Canada, Ltd.) that has become one of the greatest developments ever attempted by private citizens of any country.

The Iron Ore Company of Canada is an example of the nature of Canada's boom. It demonstrates why there are few mad rushes of men staking claims, erecting mushroom towns, and getting rich overnight. It takes more than a pan and a pick to operate in the 20th century. Only a rich individual can stake a claim as large as Hollinger's. Even to reach the mine site in the Ungava region of northeastern Quebec, 358 miles of railroad had to be built from Seven Islands, the little fishing village on the St. Lawrence which serves as the outlet for Ungava's ore. A temporary townsite has been constructed at Burnt Creek in Ungava to accommodate railroad and mine workers until a permanent town can be constructed for the 1,500 workers needed to work the mine and for those who provide services for them. A dam is being erected across the rapids of the Ashua-

nipi River, near Burnt Creek, to supply the new town and the mine with power.

Following the expenditure of over $250 million and nearly four years of unceasing effort, the Iron Ore Company of Canada made the first shipments of iron ore from its new Quebec-Labrador properties in June, 1954. Approximately 2,119,000 long tons were produced, of which 1,782,000 tons were shipped from the port of Seven Islands to steel mills in the United States and Canada; nine-tenths was shipped by tidewater and the remainder by way of the St. Lawrence River. The company eventually expects to arrive at an annual output of 20 million tons.

The 400 million tons of proved ore on the Hollinger-Hannah property seems to be only a hint of the potentialities of the Quebec-Labrador area. Five other companies are working or hold concessions in the Labrador Trough, where close to 600 million tons of high-grade ore occur in an area 80 miles square between the Leaf and Larch Rivers, which flow into Ungava Bay 300 miles northwest of the present iron ore center at Burnt Creek. The greatest problems facing development are: (1) how to maintain a reasonably comfortable existence in one of the world's severest climates, where high winds blow constantly, and where the cold is fierce in winter (and the mosquitoes worse in summer) and (2) how to ship ore out and supplies in through waters choked with ice most of the year.

NEWFOUNDLAND

The province of Newfoundland has extensive mineral deposits. The total value of mineral production annually exceeds $40 million. Iron ore is mined from the huge Wabana deposits on Bell Island by Dominion Wabana Ore, Ltd., a subsidiary of Dominion Steel and Coal Corporation, Ltd. Essentially all operations are submarine, extending in some sections about four miles out under the Atlantic Ocean. High-grade hematite ore reserves have been estimated at as high as four billion tons. Production of iron ore from Wabana mines that can be shipped directly exceeds two and one-half million tons annually. Approximately one-third of the output goes to Sydney, Nova Scotia; the remainder to West Germany and the United Kingdom.

The remainder of the province's metal production—zinc, lead, copper, silver, and gold—comes from the operations of the Buchans Mining Company, Ltd., near Red Indian Lake in central Newfoundland.

Newfoundland's copper output will be increased substantially as a result of developments in the Notre Dame Bay area on the north coast, where the Bathurst Corporation, Ltd., and the Maritimes Mining Corporation, Ltd., jointly are preparing two copper properties for eventual production, one at Tilt Cove on the west side of the bay and the other at Gull Pond, 50 miles to the south. Exploratory drilling has outlined over two million tons of ore averaging 2.2 per cent copper.

OTHER NATURAL RESOURCES

WATER POWER

The potential power available from the falls and rapids on the St. Lawrence River and its tributaries provides a wealth of water power capable of furnishing a dependable flow of low-cost hydroelectric energy for the development of the forest industries and mines in the more remote areas.

Low-cost hydroelectric energy is fundamental to the industrial activities of Canada and is the basis upon which its essential industries have been built. The pulp and paper industry ranks highest in the use of hydraulic and hydro-electric power. Mining and its attendant metallurgical industries are also large users of hydro-electricity, particularly in the final processing of aluminum, of which Canada is a very large producer.

QUARRYING

The Northeastern Uplands are underlaid with old, hard rocks—granite, marble, slate, and soapstone—used for building and decorative purposes. Quarrying occurs in many parts of the area.

Granite. This is the principal stone quarried in the Uplands. Vermont's granite, with a superior color and texture that make it popular for use in monuments, leads in value. The state's granite activity is centered in Barre, at the famous "Rock of Ages" quarry. New Hampshire's quarries are around Concord, on the slopes of the White Mountains, and in the

Figure 5-4. *Rock of Ages Quarry, East Barre, Vermont. This 350-foot deep, 20-acre granite quarry has been called one of the man-made wonders of the world. More than 100 granite manufacturing plants are located in the Barre-Montpelier area. (Rock of Ages Corp.)*

southwest section of the state near the borders of Vermont and Massachusetts. Production is small, accounting for slightly more than four per cent of New England's total. Valuable gray and white granites of high quality have been obtained from quarries in Quebec—at Mt. Johnson in Iberville, at Beebe, Stanhope, St. Gerard, and St. Samuel. The stone is used for the construction of prominent buildings in Quebec and elsewhere.

Marble. Vermont leads the nation in the production of marble. Quarries near Rutland and Proctor on the west flank of the Green Mountains are without rival in the United States. Marble from this area varies in color from pure white to gray, pink, and even green, and is used extensively for construction and interior decoration. Large marble deposits are quarried for building and ornamental purposes at Philipsburg, Quebec. In marble, the original materials have been recrystallized. As a result the rock takes a high polish that makes it desirable for monument work.

Slate. For many years slate was a primary material for roofing because of its durability and fireproofing qualities. It is now being replaced by synthetic materials and sheet metal. Two of the more important slate producing areas are those near Monson, Maine, and along the Vermont-New York border. The Monson area produces a black variety of high quality that is in demand for electrical panels and blackboards. Vermont slate occurs in several colors and is used primarily for roofing. For over a half-century, roofing slate also was quarried at New Rockland, west of Richmond, Quebec.

FISHING

Newfoundland has been famous for centuries for its fishery resources. The "inshore" fishing, which takes place in the narrow belt of coastal waters off Newfoundland, is almost unique. Huge quantities of fish are caught in open "trap boats" within a short range of the shore. Cod predominates, but herring, salmon, and lobster fishing are also carried on extensively. The gear used includes traps, gill nets, trawls, and hook and line. Caplin, squid, and herring are the chief baits.

Newfoundland is surrounded by a number of large "banks," or submarine plateaus frequented by fish, the most famous being the "Grand Banks" of Newfoundland, greater in area than the island itself. The average depth over the Grand Banks is 200 feet. Here, for centuries, fishermen from Canada and many other countries have fished. The great fleets of "bankers," or line fishing vessels, have almost disappeared; Canada and Portugal are the only countries still retaining boats of this type. In their place have come fleets of large trawlers, many of them operated from European bases; and some of them among the largest fleets in the world. The Newfoundlanders have, during the past decade, increased their trawler fleet to a considerable degree, and it is an important producer for the frozen fillet trade.

Fish oils and fish meal are by-products of cod and other types of fish. There is an important whale fishery, which produces oil and meal. The seal fishery, prosecuted on the Arctic ice in the first half of the year, is valuable for its fur and leather products and also for its oil.

A recent trend in the inshore fishery is toward mechanically equipped vessels for long lining, Danish drag trawling, and midwater trawling. This departure into methods that have proved successful in other fisheries will make possible the extension of fishing in areas from ten to 50 miles offshore. Experiments on this equipment, carried out on a commercial scale by the Fisheries Research Board of Canada and the government of Newfoundland, have proved successful in some areas and are being extended to areas not fished previously.

Fairly extensive experiments in purse seining of herring on a commercial scale and the recent departure into commercial experiments with midwater herring drag seines, argue well for capitalizing on the potential deep-sea herring fishery off Newfoundland's shores.

THE RESORT AND VACATION INDUSTRY

The rapid growth in recreational activity that has taken place within the life span of the present generation springs from a complex of social forces. The advance of an industrial economy brought urban concentrations of population, revolutionary changes in production techniques, shorter working days and more leisure hours, cash incomes on a more universal scale, faster and more comfortable transportation, a greater need for relief from the specialized routine of daily affairs, and a more general recognition of the value of leisure time pursuits.

The Northeastern Uplands possess a number of assets for recreation. The southern portion is easily accessible from the urban centers of the

Figure 5-5. Skiers at Snow Valley near Manchester, Vermont, bask in the bright spring sunshine between runs on the trail. Many sports enthusiasts are lured to resorts like this on weekends and holidays. (Vermont Development Commission)

industrial Northeast. Its rugged topography, cool climate, heavy snowfall, lakes, streams, trails, and campsites make possible a variety of activity. Its town halls, churches, commons, and shaded villages are rich in historical tradition. Its small towns, cleared farms, and vast forest wilderness are inviting retreats from urban life.

The "recreation industry" has mushroomed with the postwar boom until it now leads all other economic enterprises. The number of summer and winter visitors has been increasing rapidly. Large numbers of people have bought vacation homes. The greatest growth has been in the small cabin and motel type of establishment. However, even permanent residents who have large houses frequently rent rooms, and large bedrooms in ski areas often become dormitories on winter weekends.

Many summer tourists return as regular visitors and there has been a considerable growth in the number who establish permanent residences after retirement. Such development may offer opportunities for the use of marginal land in some places, since poeple of retirement age generally prefer small acreages, and are usually not dependent on income derived from the land.

The central and southern parts of the Northeastern Uplands have the heaviest concentration of recreational facilities. The areas north of the White Mountains have not been reached by large numbers of summer residents, mainly because of the easier accessibility of desirable sites closer to the urban centers of southern New England.

The Adirondacks contain hundreds of mountain peaks, 46 of them over 4,000 feet

Figure 5-6. Business section of Petersborough, New Hampshire (population 2,963). Such small towns are characteristic of the Northeastern Uplands. (Dan Eneguess, Petersborough)

high, to make the area a famous vacation land. Lake Placid is the scene of international winter events. Saranac Lake is a world-renowned health center. Hunting, fishing, and skiing make this section a year-round playground. The largest of the numerous ski centers is the state development on Whiteface Mountain.

Winter sports are becoming increasingly popular in the Berkshires of Massachusetts and the Green Mountains of Vermont. Snow trains run from New York City to the better areas where many ski trails and other facilities have been developed.

The White Mountains of New Hampshire form one of the most popular mountain resort regions. Scenically, the area is most famous for its notches, especially Franconia and Jefferson. Most of the mountains may be climbed by foot trail, and some by cable car or motor road. Numerous lakes and streams afford good fishing. There are eight ski trail centers, over a thousand miles of foot, ski, and horse trails, and a number of overnight shelters for hiking and skiing parties.

The Uplands of northeastern Canada are also becoming more important as a vacation area. Fishing and hunting have for many years provided healthy recreation for the area's residents. Now, more and more, its rivers, lakes, and forests are visited by fishermen and hunters from other countries, but especially from the United States. The forests abound with deer, bear, rabbits, and birds, and the streams and lakes are well stocked with a wide variety of game fish. Camping, boating, picnicking, hiking, and swimming provide many recreational outlets.

POPULATION

The Northeastern Uplands have always been sparsely populated. This area was, and continues to be, a region of marginal living based chiefly on mining and agriculture, each operated in small, uneconomic units. In times of emergency or extreme prosperity people here have been able to make a fair living. At other times (and today increasingly, as cheaper transportation brings in the same products produced more economically elsewhere) people have had difficulties making ends meet. The worst farming areas were abandoned when the inhabitants no longer could scratch out a living from them.

Yet growth in population for the past 150 years has climbed from a total of 490,000 in 1800, to approximately two million today. As a state, Vermont followed the trend rather closely; its population increased rapidly during the first 50 years of the period and then leveled off through the past century. Where there has been growth, most of the increase is in medium-sized urban areas and in small towns. There are no metropolitan districts in the Uplands.

6 | *Appalachian Mountains, Hills, and Valleys*

(Relief map copyright Aero Service Corp.)

THE Appalachian Mountains, Hills, and Valleys Province lies south of the Mohawk Valley in central New York State and extends southwestward for 1,100 miles to central Alabama, where it terminates on the South Atlantic-East Gulf Plain. On the east the province merges with the Piedmont; on the northwest it abuts the Allegheny Front; on the southwest, the Cumberland Plateau. Elevations within the region are not high, but considerable local relief has historically presented formidable barriers to westward movement. Parts of 11 states (south-central New York, east-central Pennsylvania, western West Virginia, northwestern Maryland, western and southwestern Virginia, western North Carolina, the extreme northwest corner of South Carolina, the southeast corner of Kentucky, eastern Tennessee, the northern tip of Georgia, and the northern third of Alabama) lie within this region.

SURFACE FEATURES

Complicated as the structure of the Appalachian Province is, it has a definite geological unity. The ranges all belong to an ancient system of uplift or disturbance, and have not been invaded, broken up, or covered by volcanic materials of recent date—in both these respects a most marked contrast to the Rocky Mountain System.

Geographically the Appalachian Province may be subdivided into: (1) the Blue Ridge Mountains and (2) the Appalachian Valley.

BLUE RIDGE MOUNTAINS

The Blue Ridge is the first mountain range inland from the Atlantic Coast. It extends from southern Pennsylvania to northern Georgia. Most of it lies in western North Carolina but parts of it spread into Pennsylvania, Virginia, Tennessee, Georgia, and South Carolina. North of Roanoke Gap the subregion averages ten to 15 miles in width. Its greatest width, 70 miles, is at the south end. There the name Blue Ridge applies only to the first ridge seen from the Piedmont section. This is also the divide that limits the Ohio drainage basin.

North of the Roanoke River, this province (called Blue Ridge in Virginia and South Mountain in Maryland and Pennsylvania), consists of generally rounded mountains of

gentle slope and fairly even skyline when seen from a distance. Several parallel ridges separate steep valleys in the southern portion. These ridges flatten out toward the north to form a long, sweeping curve across Pennsylvania in a southwest to northeast direction. The ridges stand from 1,500 to 3,000 feet above sea level, with the top an old imperfect peneplain, older of course than the lower adjacent peneplains.

South of the Roanoke River, the older peneplains become less perfect and monadnocks on them are more abundant. In western North Carolina peneplanation was barely begun along the larger streams. This part of the province consists mainly of subdued mountains rising 1,000 to 3,000 feet above the peneplain or 3,000 to 6,000 feet above the sea. Twenty to 25 peaks rise above 5,000 feet; eight, above 6,000 feet. Mount Mitchell at 6,684 feet is the highest point in the eastern United States.

Main streams run northwest from the Blue Ridge in deep valleys separating mountains into groups bearing local names (Bald, Smoky, Unaka, Iron, etc.). Near their heads these streams run in flat-bottomed valleys one to four miles wide, the mere beginnings of the older peneplain, now raised 2,000 to 3,800 feet above the sea. The rejuvenated streams (those that have had their rate of fall increased) have cut so deeply in their lower courses as to destroy the old, flat bottoms; but rejuvenation has not yet reached their heads.

APPALACHIAN VALLEY

The Appalachian Valley is a great lowland that extends from central Alabama 1,100 miles northeast to the Hudson River. It is not a single valley but a composite of many valleys bordered on both sides by higher land; it varies in width from 30 to 90 miles. Within this lowland are many mountain ranges parallel to its trend. The section from the Hudson River to southern Virginia is occupied mainly by mountains, except for a strip ten to 20 miles wide on the east side often known as the "Great Valley." This strip is called Shenandoah Valley in Virginia, Hagerstown Valley in Maryland, and Cumberland and Lebanon Valleys in Pennsylvania. In the southern section the ridges are generally lower, fewer, and more widely spaced.

The rock structure consists of limestone,

Figure 6-1. A spring scene along the Blue Ridge Parkway in Virginia, near the Peaks of Otter. The parkway, which follows the crest of the Blue Ridge Mountains, connects the Shenandoah National Park in Virginia with the Great Smoky Mountains National Park in North Carolina and Tennessee. (Virginia Department of Conservation and Economic Development)

shale, and sandstone beds laid down when seas covered the interior United States. The Blue Ridge and Piedmont were above water and received no sediment. All strata are now tilted, in some places vertically. Weak rocks of limestone and shale underlie the valleys. Most of the mountains are of resistant sandstone.

The valley floor is the youngest peneplain, generally smooth or gently rolling, but at places imperfectly developed and elsewhere eroded by streams. This valley floor is about 500 feet high near the Delaware, Susquehanna, and Potomac Rivers, and in central Alabama, but rises to more than 2,000 feet in southern Virginia, where it was lifted unequally since peneplaining. In general, the highest parts of the valley floor are the most hilly, partly because they were less perfectly peneplained and partly because of erosion since uplift.

The mountains rising above this valley floor are generally long, nearly straight, even-topped, forested ridges with occasional water gaps where transverse streams cut across; there are also wind gaps, which are notches not cut down to the stream level. Common altitudes of crests are 1,000 to 2,000 feet above the valley floor, 1,500 to 3,000 feet above sea level. Many neighboring ridges have similar heights, their tops

representing the older peneplain. In the mountainous parts of the middle section most valleys are narrower than the ridges. The opposite is true of the southern section.

The present stream valleys are cut into the valley floor (the youngest peneplain) from 50 to 500 feet, according to its altitude, making it locally very hilly. Some larger streams have broad valleys that are the beginnings of a still newer, hence lower, peneplain. In the northern and southern sections the master streams are longitudinal. In the middle section the master streams are transverse, all flowing toward the Atlantic except the New-Kanawha, which joins the Ohio.

CLIMATE AND NATURAL VEGETATION

Considerable climatic contrasts occur within the province because of the latitudinal distance from north to south (ten degrees) and the range in elevation (1,000 to 3,000 feet). The northern portion is humid continental; the southern, humid subtropical.

HUMID CONTINENTAL CLIMATE

From Maryland through Pennsylvania into central New York State, the mountain belt is not rugged enough to have anything like a true mountain type of climate, but it does have many of the characteristics of such a climate in modified form. The mountain and valley influences on the air movements cause somewhat greater temperature extremes than are experienced on the Coastal Plain, and the daily range of temperature increases somewhat under the valley influences. The growing season varies from 130 days in the mountains to an average of 165 days in the valleys. The average annual precipitation for the whole section is 40.74 inches. The seasonal snowfall is moderately heavy (about 54 inches) and fields are normally snow-covered about three-fourths of the time during the winter season.

The mean temperature of the northern section decreases about six degrees from south to north. In the northern highlands the summer mean is about 67° F. and the winter mean about 24°. Temperatures of 100° or higher occur in the southern counties of Pennsylvania, for example, nearly every summer season, and midwinter temperatures of 20° to 25° below zero are occasionally recorded in the northern highlands.

HUMID SUBTROPICAL CLIMATE

From northern Virginia southward the principal climatic characteristics are: (1) rigorous but not severe winters; (2) warm summers, except at the higher elevations in the Blue Ridge and Great Smoky Mountains; (3) a rather heavy annual snowfall in the western part of the section; (4) usually ample precipitation; and (5) abundant sunshine. Dry or wet spells of long duration are infrequent. The average seasonal snowfall ranges from about 15 inches in middle Virginia to about 24 inches in the Shenandoah Valley and 3.3 inches in the Tennessee Valley.

FORESTS

Forests of spruce, fir, and northern and central hardwoods characterize this region, with hardwoods predominating. The principal species are oak, maple, pine, gum, beech, and poplar.

Each year the forests provide the raw material for pulp and paper, lumber, railroad ties, veneer, firewood, furniture, excelsior, piling, and many other products.

SETTLEMENT

The bulk of the peoples now living within the Appalachian Mountains, Hills, and Valleys are descendants of early settlers who were crowded off the better lands of the Coastal Plain and Piedmont. Many of them preferred a life of hunting, fishing, trapping, and subsistence farming on their own land to one of toil for wages on the cotton or tobacco land of others.

Geography conditioned travel and settlement within the region. By 1700, settlement had reached the fall line in most parts of the English colonies. In those colonies southward from New York the settlers above the falls were already well on their way inland.

Above the fall line and running roughly parallel to the seacoast lay a barrier to expansion in the form of the Appalachian system, with its multitude of parallel river valleys. Here, for a thousand miles, extending from northern Alabama to the watershed of the St. Lawrence, the advance into the interior of the continent was impeded, or deflected into such channels as nature had provided. Many of the eastern valleys of this system are cut across by rivers emerging from the higher ranges, and the interior valleys themselves carry the head-

Figure 6-2. Panoramic view of the Great Smoky Mountains in Great Smoky Mountains National Park. The Great Smokies are a range of the Appalachian Mountains extending along the North Carolina-Tennessee boundary. They are remarkable for their large tracts of hardwood and red spruce. (National Park Service)

Figure 6-3. The rich farmlands of the Shenandoah Valley of Virginia resemble a giant crazy quilt. The valley, about 110 miles long and 20 miles wide, extends southwest from Harper's Ferry, West Virginia, between the Allegheny and Blue Ridge Mountains. It is drained by the Shenandoah River. (Virginia Department of Conservation and Economic Development)

waters of great rivers. The tributaries of the Potomac, Susquehanna, Shenandoah, Juniata, Ohio, and Tennessee Rivers interlock sources and share these parallel channels. The settlers who passed the fall line and climbed the eastern ridges to the first series of valleys, found in this valley system a land that answered their needs for a new frontier. Until after the Peace of Paris in 1763, the families that ascended above the fall line into the Piedmont and the mountains moved north and south rather than farther west.

A long search for a central route to the interior soon followed. The question facing westward moving settlers was how to get out of the Great Valley. The approach into the valley was simple enough through southern Pennsylvania, which affords the best approaches to the junction of the Allegheny and Monongahela Rivers where the Ohio is formed. Here is the gateway to the Ohio and Mississippi Valleys. By way of either the Potomac or the

Susquehanna, in this latitude, the settlers easily advanced from tidewater to the foothills of the Appalachians. Both these rivers cut across the easternmost of the mountain valleys.

At the southern extremity of the Appalachians the mountain buttress is the source of the Savannah, Chattahoochee, Coosa, and Tennessee Rivers. During the colonial period, this was the northern limit of the territory of five Southern Indian tribes. These tribes forced settlers to go around them on their westward trek.

With the hostile Iroquois nations in control of the corridor route through what is now central New York and the five tribes blocking the southern route, there was not much pressure from white population at either the northern or southern end. Thus the middle portion became a focal point for penetration westward to the Ohio and beyond.

The Cumberland Gap is the only good break through the Appalachian system. It is an old wind gap in the Cumberland Front or Ridge, 1,315 feet above sea level, in the northeast corner of Tennessee.

MINERAL RESOURCES

ANTHRACITE COAL

All coals consist of the altered remnants of plants. The extent to which alteration has proceeded is a measure of the rank or maturity of the coal, and, other things being equal, the older the coal, the higher its rank. The hardest coal is anthracite, which yields under 15 per cent (sometimes as little as four per cent) of inefficient volatiles. It burns with a blue flame, is almost smokeless, and yields 15,000 to 17,000 B.T.U.'s per pound.

Almost all the hard coal in the United States is concentrated in a 480-square-mile area in five northeastern Pennsylvania counties—Lackawanna, Luzerne, Carbon, Schuylkill, and Northumberland. Three anthracite regions—the Wyoming, the Lehigh, and the Schuylkill—are drained by the Susquehanna, Lehigh, and Schuylkill Rivers, respectively. Most of the coal comes from the Wyoming region.

Mining anthracite is a highly skilled, hazardous occupation. The veins of coal are sometimes thin, often irregular, usually steep, and eventually deep. Most of the shafts are dark, damp, dirty, and dangerous.

Coal is dug (if not stripped) out of the mine, hauled to the surface breaker where bone, slate, and other impurities are removed, and sorted into eight different sizes for market. In these processes, machinery is being used more and more for such operations as undercutting, loading, cleaning, grading, and, more recently, stripping.

Markets. Except for its brief use as a blast furnace fuel in the pre-coke era of a century ago, anthracite has found its chief outlet as a fuel for household heating. Located near New York City and Philadelphia, and connected by nine railroads with the heavily populated seaboard from Boston to Washington, the region is admirably situated for markets.

From small beginnings a century and a quarter ago, production expanded more than tenfold during the canal building decade that ended in 1837. Hard on the heels of the canal era came the railroad building epoch, its first phase characterized by the construction of short lines connecting Eastern metropolitan areas. Thus, anthracite gained access to still larger markets and production increased phenomenally from 1850 to 1910. After 1910 the market grew at a slower rate, and production hit its peak of almost 100 million tons in 1917. Since that time the trend has been downward, despite the fact that there is still plenty of coal in the ground—enough to last 240 years at the present rate of consumption.

The decline was caused by the competition of other heating fuels—coke, gas, and especially fuel oil—a competition that continues to this day. Gas and oil are the most serious rivals because they give the householder completely automatic heating. Such competition has resulted in a steady drop in tonnage ever year since 1950 when 44,076,703 tons were mined. By 1960, production had fallen to 21,171,142 tons. Between 1946 and 1955, mining employment decreased from 79,000 to 38,000, and its downward trend continues.

The anthracite coal section is heavily populated as a result of early settlement and, until comparatively recent years, rapid growth. The million people now living in the five counties

Figure 6-4. The Cumberland Gap in the Cumberland Mountains, from the Tennessee side. The Gap, a natural passageway through the mountains, has an honored place in history. Through it passed the Wilderness Road, the main artery of the great migration that extended the western boundary of the United States to the Mississippi River. (Tennessee Conservation Department)

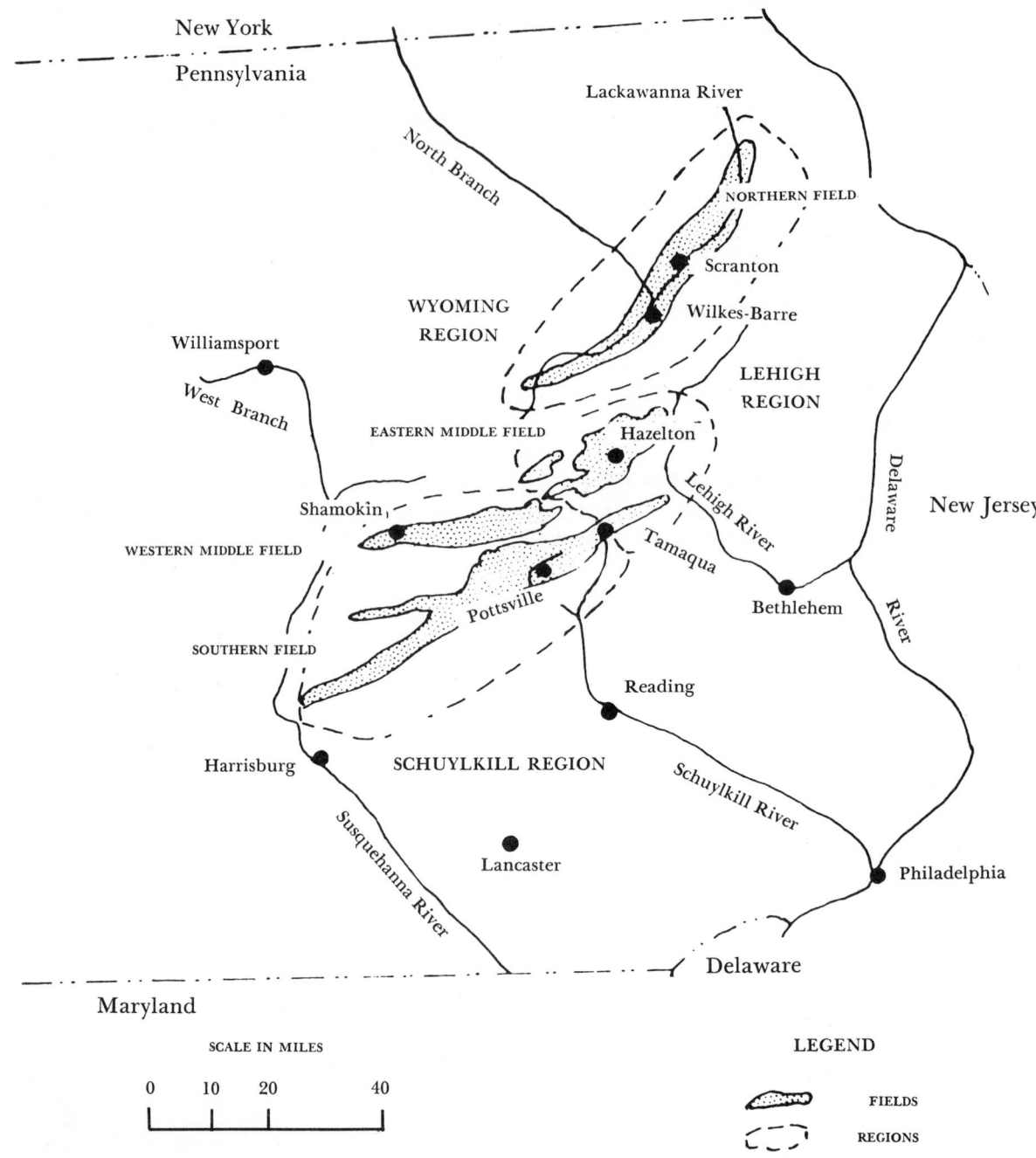

Figure 6-5. The anthracite coal area of northeastern Pennsylvania, one of the world's largest hard coal deposits. (U.S. Bureau of Mines)

include a large number who are of Welsh, Italian, and Polish origin. Scranton, the area's biggest city, is the fourth largest in Pennsylvania, ranking after Philadelphia, Pittsburgh, and Erie. Other prominent mining towns are Wilkes-Barre, Hazleton, Tamaqua, Shamokin, Pittston, and Pottsville.

Communities throughout the anthracite region are making heroic efforts to survive. The Northeast Pennsylvania Industrial Commission, set up to attract new industries to the area, has succeeded in creating 12,000 new jobs.

Meanwhile, the Anthracite Institute has labored to retard the extension of natural gas lines into the anthracite marketing area. It conducts laboratory research to find new uses for hard coal as well as to improve present usage.

BITUMINOUS COAL

Soft coal mining is one of the most important industries within the Appalachian Mountains, Hills, and Valleys Province. Pennsylvania, Maryland, West Virginia, Virginia, Tennessee, and Alabama have sizable bituminous operations. West Virginia has the largest reserves with 116 million tons; Pennsylvania has 75 million; Alabama, 67 million; and Tennessee, 25 million. Only Maryland has small reserves, slightly more than one million tons.

The coal is mostly of good quality, both high- and low-volatile, and is used for domestic and industrial purposes, including metallurgical, steam, and coking applications.

IRON ORE

Sedimentary iron ore beds outcrop in the Appalachians from New York southwestward to Alabama. Although iron ore mining has been carried on in several places throughout the region, large-scale production has occurred only in Alabama. Vast deposits of iron ore in the Birmingham and Gadsden areas lie near coal and fluxing materials used in the iron and steel industry. Only Minnesota and Michigan produce more iron ore tonnage than the Birmingham district.

SLATE AND MARBLE QUARRYING

Slate is widely used in the form of granules for surfacing, for prepared roofing, and in the form of slate flour for the manufacture of linoleum and of fillers in paints. Dimension slate is quarried, slabbed, and split to size for making cemetery vaults, billiard table tops, and electrical apparatus. About three-fifths of the United States' supply of slate is quarried in Pennsylvania between Bangor and Slatington.

Alabama, Georgia, and Tennessee produce fine marble. Tennessee marble, world famous as an interior decorative material, is quarried in the Knoxville area. Alabama has a vein of marble 35 miles long, but the only profitable operations are in Sylacauga. Here the greater portion of the ornamental marble used in buildings, memorials, and homes in the Western Hemisphere is quarried, sized, and polished. Sylacauga marble is accepted as the nation's white marble standard because of its cream-white appearance.

NONFERROUS METALS

Tennessee is a major producer of copper and zinc ores in the South. The copper ores are smelted to blister copper at Copperhill, near Ducktown, but all subsequent refining and fabrication are done outside the state. Sulfuric acid is recovered in this smelting of the copper ores. Normally the annual acid output is about 500,000 tons, the bulk of which is used by the state's large phosphatic fertilizer and rayon industries.

The zinc mining industry of eastern Tennessee, centering near Knoxville, is one of the largest in the eastern United States and annually produces about 1,500,000 tons of ore, none of which is smelted or refined in the area. Zinc also is mined at Austinville, Virginia, where the New Jersey Zinc Company produces about two per cent of the United States total.

OTHER NONMETALLIC MINERALS

Clays, shales, cement rock, sands, and gravel occur throughout the whole area. Limestone and dolomite mines are located in the Blue Ridge and Great Valley sections and near Birmingham. Most of the limestone goes into production of steel, crushed stone, lime, and Portland cement; dolomite is used as crushed stone. Some of the more important uses of crushed stone are for road stone and in concrete aggregate, furnace flux, and agricultural lime. The considerable output of fire clay in western Maryland is used mainly to make bricks for furnaces.

Cement. Cement manufacturing is widely distributed throughout the Appalachian Province. The Lehigh Valley, however, is the area of greatest concentration. In the cement industry it occupies a position somewhat comparable to that of Pittsburgh in steel.

The first cement mill was constructed in 1872, at Coplay, Pennsylvania, where rock outcrops contained the essential ingredients—lime, silica, and alumina—for making natural cement. This was made simply by quarrying,

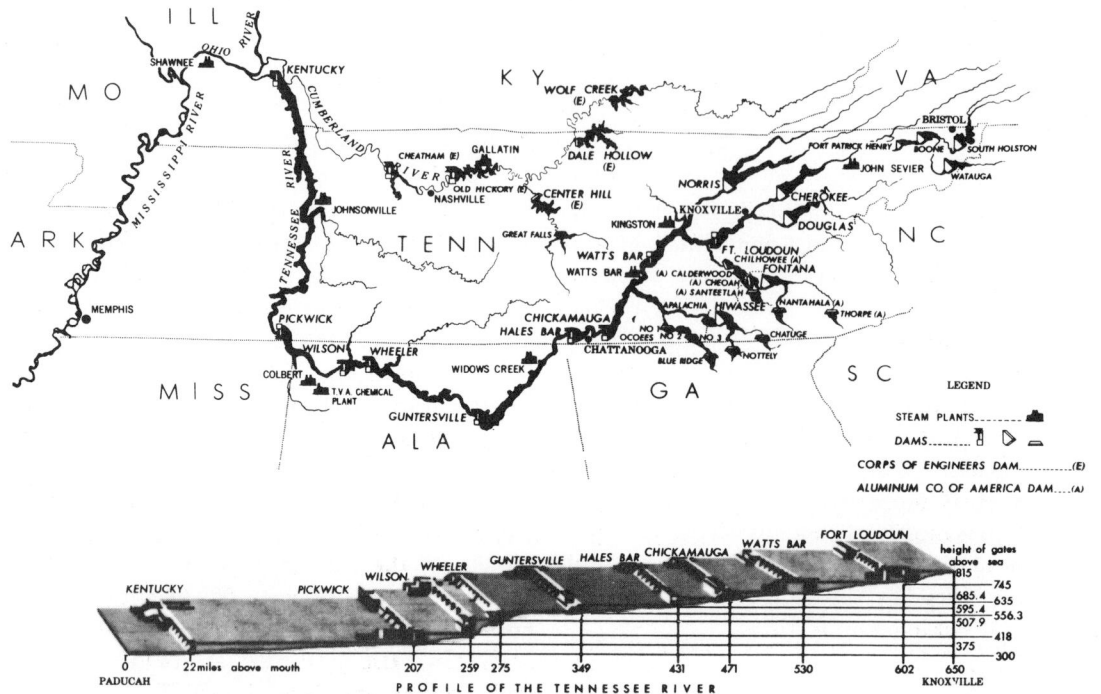

Figure 6-6. Map of the Tennessee Valley showing the location of dams in the T.V.A. system. (Tennessee Valley Authority)

crushing, and firing the stone. Soft coal from the Pennsylvania fields was used for fuel, which is consumed in tremendous quantities for power to crush the rock and in firing the furnaces. The region's location near the Atlantic Seaboard with its large metropolitan centers provided a ready market.

By 1900, the Lehigh Valley district was producing almost three-fourths of the nation's cement. Although it still makes more cement than any other region in the country, its share of the national total has dropped to 15 per cent. The establishment of regional mills to serve markets more economically affected producers in the Lehigh Valley. Decentralization of the industry was facilitated by the adaptation of fuels other than bituminous coal. Some of the Southern and Western mills fire their furnaces with either oil or gas, whichever can be obtained cheaper. High transportation costs also exert a strong influence on the industry's location. Under ordinary circumstances, shipping charges limit the market to a radius of 100 to 200 miles.

Mills in the Lehigh district have a combined capacity of 30 million barrels of cement annually, but their price advantage is confined to a territory that consumes only about eight million barrels. They compete on a substantially equal basis with the Hudson Valley producers for another eight million barrel market in the New York City area. Disposal of the rest of the cement the Lehigh Valley mills are equipped to produce is a difficult problem. In the absence of a delivered-price system, producers in the Lehigh district are virtually excluded from most of the New England market, and they cannot go very far south or west before they encounter local competition they could meet only by cutting mill prices.

THE TENNESSEE VALLEY AUTHORITY

Created by Congress as a United States government corporation charged with carrying on a widespread and unified program of natural resources development, the Tennessee Valley

Authority was instructed to develop the Tennessee River system to control floods on the Tennessee and lower Ohio and Mississippi Rivers, to provide a navigable channel from the mouth of the river to Knoxville, Tennessee, and to generate electric power. It was also directed to engage in activities for the agricultural and industrial development of the Tennessee Valley, to operate facilities built in World War I at Muscle Shoals, Alabama, and to aid in the national defense.

When President Franklin D. Roosevelt, on May 18, 1933, put his signature on the act creating the Tennessee Valley Authority, he envisioned a far-reaching electrical network based on water power. Today the T.V.A. makes full use of water power, but it is also the world's largest buyer of coal, with three-fourths of its power produced by steam.

President Roosevelt looked to electrical energy to revitalize the life of the valley. He saw the power of the Tennessee River furnishing cheap and abundant energy for cities and towns and for rural co-operatives. This goal has been achieved. But today T.V.A. sells nearly 60 per cent of its power to the Federal government, most of it to an agency whose name whould have had no meaning in 1933— the Atomic Energy Commission.

Thus T.V.A. has moved into a field of extensive preparation for defense, into a new and almost unimaginable world. To the force of water running to the sea and the energy extracted from coal, will someday be added the power of the atom. Several atomic power plants already are operating or are under construction, although their power production costs still exceed the more conventional methods.

Figure 6-7. The Tennessee Valley Authority's Hiwassee Dam on the Hiwassee River in western North Carolina. This multiple purpose dam impounds a lake 22 miles long, with a shoreline of 180 miles. The dam is 307 feet high and 1,376 feet long. It has a generating capacity of 117,100 kilowatts. (Tennessee Valley Authority)

Figure 6-8. The Tennessee Eastman Company, Kingsport, Tennessee, manufactures cellulosic plastics, fibers, and industrial chemicals. (Tennessee Eastman Co.)

Water power, once harnessed, is cheap, and it will be a long time before the waters of the Tennessee system cease to turn the turbines in the dams. The cost of steam power, too, is being reduced steadily. But if Congress should ever order T.V.A. to harness the atom, it will be ready.

POWER DEVELOPMENT

Since 1933, T.V.A. has constructed and placed in operation 17 dams on the Tennessee River and its tributaries. It also operates Wilson Dam at Muscle Shoals and five dams purchased from a private power company. Under an agreement with the Aluminum Company of America, T.V.A. directs the operation of five of their hydro projects, so that 27 dams now operate as a single integrated system.

The T.V.A. power system generates about 61 billion kilowatt-hours of electricity a year. Nearly one and a half million consumers use T.V.A. power, five times as many as had electricity in the same area in 1933. Ninety-five per cent of the region's farms are electrified, compared with 3.5 per cent in 1933. T.V.A. also sells large amounts of power directly to big industries, including light metals and heavy chemicals companies.

T.V.A. does not market electricity at retail rates, a restriction that has encouraged the growing interest of municipalities and co-operatives in acquiring local distribution systems.

The organization of T.V.A. is unique: It is a government body that possesses the flexibility and initiative of private enterprise. It receives its funds from Congress, but is free to initiate its own policies and execute its own program on its sole authority.

T.V.A. has caused considerable controversy. Proponents believe that it can provide power more cheaply than can the private utilities. Opponents of T.V.A. believe that the vaunted "cheapness" of public power is not cheap but subsidized. Private electric companies point out the fact that tax exemptions are the biggest factor in the government's low rates. Private utilities say that, on the average, 18 per cent of their gross revenues, amounting to more than 3 mills per kilowatt-hour, go to Federal and local government in taxes. Thus taxes alone boost private rates above the government's selling price.

FERTILIZERS AND FORESTRY

At Muscle Shoals, T.V.A. operates the chemical plant built during World War I in the development and experimental production of new and improved fertilizers, particularly phosphates. T.V.A. phosphates are used widely for practical test demonstrations with the state land-grant colleges and extension services.

T.V.A. also carries on a broad forestry program in co-operation with Federal, state, and local agencies, with the aim of promoting sustained-yield management of the forests and woodlands that cover more than half the area of the Tennessee Valley. More than 450 selective cutting demonstrations have been established, most of them on farms.

NAVIGATION

Nine T.V.A. dams along the mainstream of the river assure a navigation channel for vessels of nine-foot draft traveling between cities as far east as Knoxville, Tennessee, and the Gulf Coast and inland river ports of 20 states. River traffic ton-mileage is about 60 times as great as it was before T.V.A.

FLOOD CONTROL

Ten large storage dams on the principal tributary streams hold flood waters in check and team with the main river dams to regulate heavy storms. T.V.A. reservoirs have up to 12 million acre-feet of storage space reserved for flood control alone at the beginning of the flood season. This makes possible the reduction of floods in the valley and aids in control of lower Ohio River and Mississippi River floods.

In addition to the major benefits, a chain of lakes on the main river and the reservoirs behind the storage dams on the tributaries provide outstanding recreational assets, including boating, swimming, and fishing.

Eight of the dams built by T.V.A.—Pickwick Landing, Chickamauga, Watts Bar, and Fort Loudon, on the main stream, and Norris on the Clinch River, Douglas on the French Broad, Cherokee on the Holston, and Watauga on the Watauga—are located in Tennessee.

INDUSTRY AND NATIONAL DEFENSE

The products of mines and quarries support a variety of manufacturing industries within the region, from handicrafts to light processing, ceramics, chemicals, furniture, aluminum, and heavy steel goods.

Mountain crafts mastered by mountain people of eastern Tennessee in their days of isolation from the world still flourish. Most of the hand-made fabrics, pottery, brooms, dolls, wood carvings, and other articles are made in the Great Smokies. Gatlinburg, Tennessee, is the handicraft capital of the nation.

Tennessee Valley power has attracted many manufacturers to that region. Between 1933 and 1960, several large industries located there. The Aluminum Company of America was a pioneer in the area, building hydroelectric dams and factories years before T.V.A. was created. Today, the Alcoa, Tennessee, plant covers 135 acres of manufacturing space.

The Atomic Energy Commission selected the T.V.A. site at Oak Ridge, Tennessee, for its three nuclear plants because of available blocks of hydroelectric power. The Oak Ridge National Laboratory is one of the largest research centers in the nation. It is engaged in nuclear research and development, with emphasis on fundamental studies in support of applied technology. Four of the country's atomic reactors are in operation at the laboratory: the Graphite Reactor, constructed in 1943; the Low Intensity Testing Reactor; the original

Figure 6-9. Oak Ridge National Laboratory, Oak Ridge, Tennessee. One of the Atomic Energy Commission's major research centers, the laboratory employs about 4,200 people and is engaged in virtually every aspect of nuclear energy research. It is operated for the AEC by the Union Carbide Corporation. (Atomic Energy Commission)

"Swimming Pool" Reactor; and the Oak Ridge Research Reactor, which began operation in 1958. The laboratory is also heavily engaged in the "Sherwood Project," which is the development of energy sources by fusion in thermonuclear-type reactions. In addition to being the nation's chief source of stable and radioactive isotopes, the laboratory serves as a nuclear education center for academic, industrial, and government representatives.

T.V.A. industries related to national defense, huge as they are, constitute only part of the picture of industrial expansion in the valley. New plants for making synthetic fibers have been built by du Pont, American Enka, Monsanto, and American Viscose. The Electro Manganese Corporation at Knoxville, Tennessee, is the largest producer of electrolytically pure metallic manganese in the United States.

The growth of manufacturing in the T.V.A. area, as in the southeastern part of the United States generally, has been affected by: (1) expansion of the nation's whole industrial economy, (2) availability of power and raw materials, (3) plentiful labor supply, and (4) good transportation and communication facilities.

T.V.A.'s multipurpose dams, its forestry and agricultural aids, and its service to industry have helped make it possible for the people in the area to increase their per capita income 624 per cent since T.V.A. began; in the nation, the increase has been 441 per cent. Since 1929, there has been a net increase of more than 1,600 manufacturing and processing plants in the Tennessee Valley.

MANUFACTURING IN OTHER AREAS

SYNTHETIC FIBERS AND PLASTICS

These products are significant props in the economy of western and southwestern Virginia. For years this state has led the nation in their manufacture. The larger operations include: du Pont's elastic fiber and rayon acetate processing plant and Dawbarn Brothers' plastic yarn plant, both in Waynesboro; Imco Container Corporation, maker of plastic bottles for cosmetics, at Harrisonburg; American Viscose Corporation's plant at Front Royal; and Burlington Mills' many facilities—a weaving plant at Vinton in the suburbs of Roanoke, a nylon

hosiery plant in Salem, a weaving plant in Radford, a dyeing and finishing plant in Dublin, and nylon hosiery plants in Marion and Chilhowie.

IRON AND STEEL

Within a 25-mile radius of Birmingham, Alabama, are large deposits of iron ore, coal, and limestone. The availability of these raw materials, plus the presence of a market for steel products, led to the establishment of mills in that area, and the successful manufacture of steel by the Carnegie Company and others brought the construction of open hearth furnaces. In 1905, the Republic Iron & Steel Company and the Tennessee Coal, Iron & Railway Company consolidated. Two years later, the U.S. Steel Corporation acquired the operation. Since then it has poured millions of dollars into the Birmingham district, constructing many plants at Birmingham and Gadsden to produce an ever-widening range of finished steel products. Total annual steel capacity slightly exceeds five million net tons.

GLASS MANUFACTURING

This industry is widely distributed throughout the region. The Chattanooga Glass Company at Chattanooga, Tennessee, is the world's largest manufacturer of soft-drink bottles. Corning, New York, leads in the manufacture of technical glass in volume and diversification, including laboratory and pharmaceutical apparatus; marine and railroad signals; home and industrial lighting ware; tubing for fluorescent, neon, and incandescent lighting; and the famous Steuben Ware. Other important glass centers are Athens, Tennessee, and Asheville, North Carolina.

MISCELLANEOUS INDUSTRIES

A variety of industries has been attracted to the anthracite coal centers at Wilkes-Barre and Shamokin, Pennsylvania. The industries include silk mills, sheet metal works, shirt factories, woodworking, building materials, and the manufacture of sport shoes. The Radio Corporation of America has a large semiconductor and materials division facility at Crestwood Industrial Park near Wilkes-Barre. Altoona, Pennsylvania, is the home of the car shops of the Pennsylvania Railroad. It is also the center of a wide array of manufacturing industries.

AGRICULTURE

In general, this is one of the poorer agricultural regions in the United States. Much of the land is hilly or mountainous. A little less than half the total farmland is cropland. About a third is woodland. The average farm has about 50 acres of cropland and less than 20 acres of other land that may be used for pasture. The small average size of farms and the steep and irregular topography in many parts of the region militate against the adoption of large-scale operations.

Climate, soil, and topography are more favorable to hay in the northern part of the region than to other crops. Milk cows are the logical choice to convert large quantities of roughage into usable food for the large urban areas of the Northeast, particularly New York City. The relatively cool summers, the rainfall, the topography of much of the land, and the character of the soils favor commercial dairy enterprises. Big barns and silos are outstanding features of most farmsteads, and milk receiving stations are comparable with cotton gins in the South or grain elevators in the Middle West.

Ranking after dairying is poultry, especially in the southeastern part of New York. Commercial poultry farms in this area buy most of their grain instead of raising it themselves, so that little land is needed with this type of farming. Many farms are elaborately equipped for the production of eggs, chickens, or turkeys.

General farming prevails throughout the greater part of the Appalachian Mountains, Hills, and Valleys Province. Exceptions are the northeastern dairy area and the Cumberland fruit, poultry, and dairy section. The leading field crop in total acreage is corn. Wheat, barley, oats, and clover occupy large acreages. Livestock—milk cows, beef cattle, swine, and sheep—are distributed widely.

The Blue Ridge Subregion lies mostly in western North Carolina, but parts of Virginia, Tennessee, Georgia, and South Carolina are within it. Farms are small. The average farm is about two-thirds the size of farms in the rest of the region and its cropland is about one-third as much. This is an important dairy sec-

Figure 6-10. Farms in the forest and forests on the farm—a view of the Alleghenies in Centre County, Pennsylvania. (U.S. Forest Service)

tion, with the emphasis being on grassland farming. Burley tobacco is the leading cash crop. Corn, small grains, and forage crops do well. Temperature and moisture conditions are favorable for the production of high-quality vegetables. Mountain City, Tennessee, is a major market for green beans. Cabbage is another important crop. Some lettuce is grown in the Georgia part of the subregion.

Farming throughout the upper Tennessee Valley is characterized by small general and part-time farms. Much of the farming is on a subsistence basis. A wide diversity of crops is grown, with emphasis on corn, small grain, tobacco, and hay. Irish potatoes, strawberries, cabbage, and fruits are important crops in certain counties. Dairying, poultry, and truck gardening have developed around major urban centers. Range-type livestock production occurs in some counties that are remote from markets. Forestry is a major land use in many counties but agriculture continues to play the dominant role in determining the level of farm income.

Soils in the Appalachian Valley Subregion are derived chiefly from limestones and shales. In general, the higher the lime content of the underlying rock, the more productive the soil. Where shales form the bedrock, the soils fre-

Figure 6-11 Farmland erosion in western Virginia—a good example of poor conservation methods. This scene is common in the Southern uplands, where man tills the soils instead of planting tree crops. (U.S. Department of Agriculture)

quently are less well drained, the subsoils tend to be yellowish, rather than red, and the soils may be shallow or nonexistent.

Forage crops, notably lespedeza, clover, and alfalfa, are relatively important here and so is the number of livestock, particularly cattle and sheep.

A considerable acreage is in apple orchards in the northern part of the subregion. The four leading varieties of apples are York, Imperial, Delicious, and Winesap. Winchester, Virginia, is a center of apple growing and packing.

Farther west, the Appalachian valleys produce manufactured milk, burley tobacco, and some truck crops; cattle and sheep are grazed on the hillsides.

RECREATION AND TOURISM

Every year thousands of tourists are attracted to the region, which offers great variety in outdoor recreation. The Finger Lakes in the New York section, a result of Pleistocene glaciation, are a scenic attraction. Other water bodies and varied landforms in the area are within easy reach of the densely populated lowlands. Within a few hundred miles of the Atlantic Coast are the Blue Ridge and Allegheny Mountains, with the beautiful Shenandoah Valley between them. The Skyline Drive along the crest of the Blue Ridge within Shenandoah National Park connects with the Blue Ridge Parkway to form a continuous mountain-top drive across the state of Virginia. Scenic wonders of this area include limestone caverns, the Natural Bridge, and the Breaks of the Cumberland.

The Great Smoky Mountains National Park is one of the nation's most popular tourist attractions. It is on this "roof of eastern America," embracing an area 54 miles long and 19 miles wide, that tourists see 29 peaks more than a mile high and 16 more than 6,000 feet high. The heavily forested slopes, cascading streams, and many waterfalls provide impressive scenery. The lakes and lakeshores of the Tennessee Valley Authority offer boating, swimming, fishing, camping, and other outdoor activities.

7 | Hills of the Ohio and
Tennessee Basin

(Relief map copyright Aero Service Corp.)

THE Hills of the Ohio and Tennessee Basin Region encompasses parts of 11 states: southwestern New York, Pennsylvania west of the Appalachian Mountains, most of West Virginia, the eastern half of Ohio, the extreme northwestern tips of Maryland and Virginia, the southern third of Indiana, almost all of Kentucky, central Tennessee, the northwestern third of Alabama, and northeastern Mississippi.

SURFACE FEATURES

In general, the Hills of the Ohio and Tennessee Basin Region is a partly or wholly dissected plateau with a northwesterly slope. On its southeast, or higher side, the area is limited almost throughout by an escarpment called the Allegheny Front in Pennsylvania and West Virginia, and the Cumberland Front in Tennessee. It also is limited by an escarpment on the west side in Kentucky and Tennessee and on the north in New York, Pennsylvania, and Ohio.

The several parts of this province differ in elevation, in degree of dissection, and in their underlying rocks. A part also was glaciated. Two sections on the high and deeply dissected eastern margin are always called mountains— the Allegheny Mountains and the Cumberland Mountains. The strata are somewhat folded, even making ridges within the plateau province. Most of western Pennsylvania, West Virginia, eastern Ohio, and eastern Kentucky is maturely dissected. The highest elevations are in the central part of West Virginia, where much of the land lies between 1,500 and 3,000 feet; the maximum elevations exceed 4,000 feet. Local relief may be 500 to 1,000 feet on the east and south but diminishes toward the west and north. The escarpment on the north, 500 to 1,000 feet high, overlooks the Mohawk Valley, which is a strike valley not as low and smooth as the Hudson Valley or the plain south of Lake Ontario. This escarpment extends west to northeastern Ohio, overlooking the Eastern Interior Low Plains. At the south end is the Cumberland Plateau, in which large areas of nearly flat upland remain between young valleys—except at the southern extremity.

The Bluegrass Subregion consists of two separate areas, one in Kentucky, centering on Lexington, and the other in east-central Tennessee. Their outstanding feature is the soils of high phosphate content, which largely accounts for the abundant growth of bluegrass and other pasture plants that are considered characteristic of this general subregion.

The Tennessee portion of the subregion, referred to as the Nashville Basin, is mostly level; its average elevation is about 600 feet. It is surrounded by the Highland Rim, which is several hundred feet higher in elevation. Outliers and ridges of the Highland Rim are numerous at the border of the basin. Major drainage systems are the Cumberland River, which empties into the Ohio, and the Duck River, which empties into the Tennessee.

The Kentucky part of the subregion has elevations up to 1,000 feet. A belt of rough land of higher elevation, called the Knobs, encircles the subregion in Kentucky except in the north, where the Ohio River is the boundary. The major drainage systems are the Kentucky and Licking Rivers, which empty into the Ohio. Stream dissection is deep along the Ohio and Kentucky Rivers. The elevation of the Ohio River in northeastern Kentucky is below 500 feet. Much upland adjacent to the streams, particularly in the northern section, is unsuited for cultivation. The land in the central portion (inner Bluegrass) generally is smooth.

The Pennyroyal Subregion in southern and southwestern Kentucky is undulating to rolling. Near streams and sections of underground drainage it is hilly or karsted (a limestone region in which most or all of the drainage is by underground channels, the surface being dry and barren). Mammoth Cave Park is in this area noted for caverns. The limestone area of the western Pennyroyal is undulating but some small parts are rolling or even hilly. Subsurface drainage has created limestone sinks and karst terrain in much of the area. The eastern Pennyroyal is an upland, higher than the rest of the subregion, and has a great variation of relief. Most of the terrain is rolling, some is undulating; in places it is hilly or karsted and, near streams, may be rough or precipitous. There are wide bottoms along the Cumberland River.

SOILS

The soils are relatively shallow, acid, and low in natural fertility. The bedrock is mostly sandstones and shales, with limestone occurring occasionally. The rock is usually horizontally bedded, although some tilting of strata occurred near the eastern end of the province.

Because the mantle of parent material over the sandstone and shale is shallow in most places, even moderate erosion in cultivated fields can be serious. The preferred uses for much of the land are for pasture, hay, or forest.

Reddish-colored soils occupy the broad till-mantled hills of the Allegheny Plateau in New York State where glacial action has mixed red and gray shale and sandstone. The dominant soils are very strongly acid and low in fertility.

Soils in the unglaciated parts are fair where topographically favored, such as in the smoother parts of the Ohio Valley, but beds that cap the plateau, being mainly siliceous, generally are not good soil makers.

The inner Bluegrass Subregion of Kentucky contains some of the most fertile soils in the province. Limestones, many of which are phosphatic, represent the dominant rock formations. Shales occur also, often interbedded with limestone. Surface soils are brown silt loams, and subsoils are reddish-brown silty clays of good structure and drainage. A thin deposit of glacial till occurs in the extreme northern portion in Kentucky. There is evidence of shallow loess in places near the Ohio River.

In the central part of the Nashville Basin are soil series low in phosphate. Similar soils are present in Kentucky, where they have more random distribution.

The soils of eastern Ohio generally are rather thin but respond well to fertilization and care. Soils of the valley bottoms are usually more limited in extent. Silty loams derived primarily from shaly rock are characteristic of the area. They are deficient in organic matter and lime content, and require moderate to heavy fertilization.

CLIMATE

The Hills of the Ohio and Tennessee Basin Province lies within the humid continental climatic region. Even in the southern portion of the province the uplands experience the variable weather associated with the higher middle latitudes.

The northern Georgia and Tennessee portions of this province are not in the path of any of the principal storm tracts that cross the country; instead they come under the influence of the storm centers that pass along the Gulf and then up the Atlantic Coast, and also of those that pass from Oklahoma northeastward to the Great Lakes and then to the coast of Maine. Weather changes are therefore frequent compared to the remarkably stable conditions of the far Southwest, but not nearly as frequent as in the Lakes Region and the Northeastern States.

Very changeable temperature conditions prevail in winter. In Georgia the daily maxima are very rarely below 32° F. Owing to its high altitude, northern Georgia is comparatively free from oppressive heat.

Zero temperatures occur, on the average, about once a year over the lowlands in Tennessee, but they are comparatively frequent in the mountains. Occasionally the temperature falls considerably below zero. Maximum temperatures exceeding 100° are very rare. In the highlands the conditions of heat and humidity are modified somewhat, the nights being cooler and the air movement greater.

Kentucky's climate generally is temperate. Sunlight, heat, moisture, and winds are all in moderation, without prolonged extremes. Rainfall is abundant and fairly regular throughout the year, usually as short showers. Heavy snowfalls are rare. The seasons differ markedly yet warm to cool weather prevails, with extremes of heat and cold occurring only in short spells.

Topographic characteristics considerably modify the latitudinal control of the climate of West Virginia, with the result that marked variations in temperature and precipitation occur, not only among the mountain, plateau, and hill areas, but also between different parts of the same counties. The seasons are nearly of equal length, and strongly contrasted. In most sections of the state the winters are moderate to rigorous and severe only occasionally, except in the mountains. Cold waves occur on an average of three times during the winter, but severely cold spells, as a rule, last only two or three days.

The northern portion of the region in southeastern Ohio, western Pennsylvania, and southern New York falls entirely within the humid continental climatic regime. With its adequate precipitation and marked seasonality, this climate has been considered among those most stimulating to human activity.

Because hilly topography permits uneven heating of land surfaces and allows colder air to settle to lower points, local differences in climatic conditions are more apparent than differences on an area-wide basis. Although the northern one-third of the area is slightly cooler and drier than other portions, the differences involved include a temperature range of only about six degrees and a precipitation variation of some six inches.

The annual temperature range is marked but not excessive. The average January temperature for the area is 29.3° F.; the July average is 72.6°. Extremes of —28° and 109° have been recorded, but average annual extremes range from —10° to about 90°.

The growing season lasts from 130 to 140 days in New York and Pennsylvania, 140 to 150 days in Ohio, 130 to 180 days in West Virginia, and 180 to 190 days in Kentucky and Tennessee.

The total precipitation varies from 38 to 40 inches in New York, Pennsylvania, Ohio, and the northern sections of West Virginia, to 50 or 55 inches in Tennessee. Summer maximum is the rule but the rain is not well distributed. Evapo-transpiration is high, and drought periods in some sections—Kentucky, for example—are frequent. Snow blankets much of the northern portion of the region during December, January, and February.

NATURAL VEGETATION

Forests mantle the Hills of the Ohio and Tennessee Basin Province. Red, black, and white spruces; balsam fir; white, red, jack, and pitch pines; Eastern hemlock; maple; oak; beech; birch; and aspen predominate on the Allegheny Plateau in New York and Pennsylvania and in the uplands of central West Virginia. Eastern Ohio, the extreme western portion of Pennsylvania, the western half of West Virginia, and most of Tennessee lie within the

Central Hardwood Forest. Several species characterize the area. In the northern portion oak, hickory, ash, elm, maple, beech, black walnut, pine, and cottonwood occur; the southern portion contains red and black gums, Eastern red cedar, and yellow poplar, in addition to oak, hickory, ash, black walnut, and beech.

Private ownership is divided almost equally between individual farmers and industrial concerns, utilities, and other organizations. No commercial forest stand of consequence is in virgin condition and most are in need of better management. All forest land in the region can grow merchantable timber.

SETTLEMENT

The westward flow of population has been characteristic of American growth since the period of early settlements. To be able to acquire land cheaply was an attraction to the settlers on the Atlantic Coastal Plain. In the middle of the 18th century came an early wave that poured the Germans and Scotch-Irish into the Great Valley. Poverty, religious persecution, and the devastation that followed war were among the special causes, along with the systematic advertising of the attractions of the Pennsylvania and Virginia lands extending to the Ohio Valley.

There were essentially three focusing points for the routes through the Appalachian barrier: the Forks of the Ohio, the Cumberland Gap, and the Valley of East Tennessee. Pennsylvania, Virginia, and Carolina trappers first made their way into the Ohio Valley about 1701; they followed the Roanoke River in Virginia to the New River Gorge and then moved along the Kanawha River to the Ohio. Later, other settlers followed the Juniata River westward across Pennsylvania to its headwaters at Fort Bedford and to the Loyalhanna, which flows westward to the Conemaugh River. They followed the Conemaugh to the Allegheny to the Ohio. Still later, a more direct route was taken from Harrisburg to Carlisle to Shippensburg to Fort Bedford at the upper end of the Juniata River. From there, settlers traversed the same route as before to the Allegheny River; this latter route became known as Forbes Military Road.

In taking up new land in the Hills of the Ohio and Tennessee Basin Province, the qualities of the soil for agriculture played a dominant role; settlers also considered the possibilities of grazing, the wealth of nearby forests, and the availability of a good supply of water. Coal and iron ore were discovered in various areas within the region by 1750. These were industries allied to agriculture..

In 1775, Daniel Boone crossed the Cumberland Gap. Westward movement was then under way. The Kentucky Blue Grass area was settled by Maryland and Virginia settlers; the Nashville Basin by people from North Carolina. Statehood came rapidly; Kentucky was admitted to the Union in 1792; Tennessee, 1796; and Ohio in 1803.

AGRICULTURE

Agriculture, one of the oldest occupations in the province, began with the Indians, mainly in the northern portion of the region, long before the white man came. In a very limited way the early Iroquois tillers grew Indian corn, common beans, pumpkins, squash, artichokes, gourds, and tobacco. Maple sugar was produced in quantity; from the forest such products as groundnuts, leeks, and wild onions were gathered.

The agriculture of the early white settlers was equally primitive. Progress in clearing land occupied mainly by dense virgin forests was painfully slow. The frontier was pushed northward and westward only a few miles a year. It was not until after 1800, that urban markets for farm products began to develop, stimulating the expansion of agriculture as a more specialized and commercial enterprise and encouraging the use of better tools and more scientific methods.

The Erie Canal, opened in 1825, brought steadily increasing quantities of foodstuffs to Eastern markets from the new states. The development of the railroads, which shortly followed the canal's opening, meant even better transportation. By 1860, changes in the region's agriculture because of freight competition definitely were under way.

More emphasis was given to bulky and perishable foodstuffs that, because of large and growing nearby markets, partly could escape Western competition. Pork, lamb, cash grains, and wool began to decrease in importance in relation to milk, poultry, market hay, and—somewhat later—fresh fruits and vegetables.

DAIRYING

Dairying, as in the Appalachian Mountains, Hills, and Valleys Province, is the major agricultural enterprise in the plateau areas of New York, Pennsylvania, and northeastern Ohio. The investment in a typical commercial dairy farm exceeds $25,000, about half of which is in land and buildings and the balance rather evenly divided between livestock and machinery. The principal building is the barn, which houses cattle and provides storage for hay and other feeds. Adjuncts to the barn, conveniently located, are the silo and the milk house. In addition there is likely to be a hen house, a machinery storage shed, and a building for the machine shop. Farm buildings are electrified to run such laborsaving devices as a water pump, milking machines, a milk cooler, a hot water heater, a hay hoist, and perhaps a gutter cleaner. Thirty-five to 40 head of stock are usually kept, about 25 of which are likely to be cows in milk. The farm machinery inventory includes a tractor, plows, a harrow, a grain drill, a corn planter, a fertilizer spreader, a sprayer, wagons, and a truck. In addition, a hay baler, forage chopper, or combine are not unusual.

Surrounding the farm buildings is the land, perhaps 150 acres in extent in the larger operations, in addition to woodland. About 75 acres are in crops, mostly hay, oats, and corn silage, and another 75 acres in pasture. Cash receipts annually on such a dairy farm ordinarily amount to about $9,000 or less, the principal item for sale being the 80,000 or so quarts of milk delivered to a nearby dairy plant. The chief expense items are concentrate feeds purchased and machinery costs, including depreciation. Although home-grown grains supply straw for bedding and a certain amount of high-energy feed for the dairy cows, farmers purchase the bulk of their grain and additional proteins. Most of these products come from Western States.

POULTRY

Ranking next to dairying is poultry. Like

Figure 7-1. General farming along the Susquehanna River in north-central Pennsylvania. Note the rolling hills in the background. (U.S. Department of Agriculture)

the dairy cow, the chicken is well dispersed throughout north-central and southern New York, western and southwestern Pennsylvania, and northeastern Ohio. Poultry returns total more than ten per cent of farm cash receipts; the money comes mainly from the sale of eggs, although the raising of broilers, turkeys, and ducks for market are important ventures.

SHEEP

Ohio has long been known for the quantity and quality of its wool; the state now produces more wool than any other state east of the Rockies. As is typical of all Ohio agriculture, sheep are raised on the general farm. But few Ohio livestock men keep only sheep. Formerly most Ohio sheep were of the Merino breed, but an increasing number of the mutton breeds now are found. In many counties the winter feeding of Western lambs has become a sizable enterprise.

GENERAL FARMING

General farming continues throughout much of the central and southern portions of the province. Potatoes and vegetables are grown on about seven per cent of the cropland. Irish potatoes are cultivated on some of the better drained soils on the broad ridges in Steuben and adjoining counties in southern New York.

Many of West Virginia's farms are small and therefore comparatively easy to maintain. Livestock and livestock products account for three out of every four dollars of the farm cash income. Poultry production is also important. Corn, wheat, oats, barley, buckwheat, hay, and a variety of fruits are grown on most farms. Kentucky's farm economy, long based principally on tobacco, corn, and beef production, has experienced a shift in recent years to a greater dependence upon a wider variety of

Figure 7-2. Broadleaf burley tobacco growing on terraced and contour planted fields south of Georgetown, Kentucky. About one-third of the tobacco grown is produced by tobacco tenants on a half-share basis. A tobacco tenant differs from an operating tenant in that the former rents only the tobacco land, whereas the latter rents an entire farm. (U.S. Department of Agriculture)

income producing elements. Tobacco, however, remains king. Strong emphasis is being placed on dairy products, swine, broilers, soybeans, and fruits and vegetables. Tennessee agricultural income is derived almost equally from crops and livestock. The national census lists more than 52 different crops grown in Tennessee. Leading in extent and value within this region are corn, tobacco, small grains, potatoes, and soybeans.

Many large residential farms, particularly near Lexington, Kentucky, and Nashville, Tennessee, are devoted primarily to grassland and meadow for production of light horses and other registered livestock. The high phosphate content of the soils on most of these farms encourages a vigorous growth of bluegrass and white clover.

TOBACCO

Burley tobacco, a thin-bodied tobacco, generally very light in color when cured, is grown for chewing tobacco, cigarettes, and smoking mixtures. It is a specialty crop in the Bluegrass Subregion of Kentucky, the Nashville Basin of Tennessee, and in the Ohio River counties bordering Kentucky. It is grown mainly on silt loams of limestone origin be-cause of the crop's demand for highly fertile soils.

Kentucky is second only to North Carolina in total tobacco output, accounting for about 20 percent of the national total. Three classes of tobacco are produced: light air-cured, fire-cured, and dark air-cured. Yields are high, averaging 1,598 pounds per acre. Production costs exclusive of family labor, management, land and investment for burley tobacco amount to $265 per acre; the range in average costs varies from $303 for the inner Bluegrass to $196 per acre in the lower Ohio Valley. Receipts from burley tobacco average $840 per acre.

The tobacco production period extends from March, or earlier, to December, and frequently into January. In the total of 309 hours of labor utilized per acre for the usual tractor operated farm, peak periods occur with the jobs of transplanting (33 hours), cutting and housing (42 hours), and stripping burley tobacco (135 hours). These peak periods usually come about June 1, from August 15 to September 15, and in November and December.

Early settlers from North Carolina and Virginia brought the tobacco plant across the Appalachian Mountains and continued its culture along the navigable streams of western

Kentucky. This Kentucky area was the first center of tobacco production in the state and became known as the "Black Patch," from its concentrated production of dark tobacco. During the Civil War, burley tobacco was introduced into Kentucky and its production spread rapidly throughout the central part of the state and into adjoining states. High calcium and phosphorous soils, the development of railroads and other transportation facilities, and the fact that burley found a good market in cigarettes as well as in smoking and chewing tobaccos, contributed to its rapid rise. As production of burley grew, production of dark types declined. A decrease in the use of snuff and other tobacco products made from dark types also contributed to the shift.

Burley is now the predominant tobacco type throughout eastern and central Kentucky. Dark fired and dark air-cured tobaccos are grown along with burley in the western part of the state.

Tennessee ranks fifth nationally in tobacco production and is exceeded only by North Carolina, Kentucky, Virginia, and South Carolina. Tobacco is grown throughout the middle and eastern areas of the state. Four types are grown. Two are air-cured—burley and dark air-cured; two are fire-cured—eastern dark-fired and western dark-fired. Burley occupies the greatest acreage.

Only a small percentage of the land within the tobacco area is planted to tobacco itself. Farms in the belt average 190 acres in size. Of this acreage only five per cent is in tobacco, and six per cent in corn; 16 per cent, or nearly all the remaining crops harvested, is used for hay and small grain. Pasture occupies most of the tillable land and 60 per cent of the total acreage.

MINERAL RESOURCES

COAL

The United States has one-third of the earth's reserves of coal. Nearly 80 per cent of the reserve, on the basis of heating value per pound, is bituminous and subbituminous. These ranks of coal are distributed all over the United States—about one-third east of the Mississippi River, one-third in the interior, and one-third in the Northern Great Plains, Rocky Mountains, Gulf, and Pacific areas.

The Hills of the Ohio and Tennessee Basin Province contains the nation's most valuable deposits of high-grade coking coal. These reserves, enough to last a thousand years at current rates of consumption, make possible an abundance of cheap power. Power stations may be located close to the mines or along the many streams that cut below the surface of the coal beds, in which case the stations are supplied economically by barge.

Over the years there have been wide variations in production in the several states. West Virginia, Pennsylvania, and Kentucky are the leading coal producing states, in the order named. For nearly quarter of a century, West Virginia has led the nation in its output of high-grade bituminous coal. Mineable coal is present in 44 of the state's 55 counties and underlies more than 55 per cent (nearly 25,000 square miles) of its land area. Bituminous coal mining is the principal mineral industry in Pennsylvania, despite a 21 per cent decline in output since 1957, its lowest point since 1898. Present annual production is about 85 million tons of coking coals, with a volatile content of 20 to 43 per cent. Pennsylvania coal production has followed closely the ups and downs of national coal output. More than 500 years' supply remains at the present rate of consumption. Kentucky has large coal reserves. Less than four per cent of the total estimated deposits (123 billion tons) has been depleted. Ohio's reserves are small but the eastern part of the state is an important coal mining area. Tennessee, with small coal reserves, is a minor producer.

Coal mining methods. There are wide differences within the region in production, number of mines, uses of coal, average value per ton, men working, days worked, and output per man-day.

The bituminous coal industry has bet heavily on its own future. By great capital investment in complex and costly new equipment, it has succeeded in raising its efficiency to the point where the price of coal at the mine has remained relatively stable over the last decade.

Mechanization has made enormous strides. With the aid of giant machines, the coal miner produces an average of 10.73 tons per working

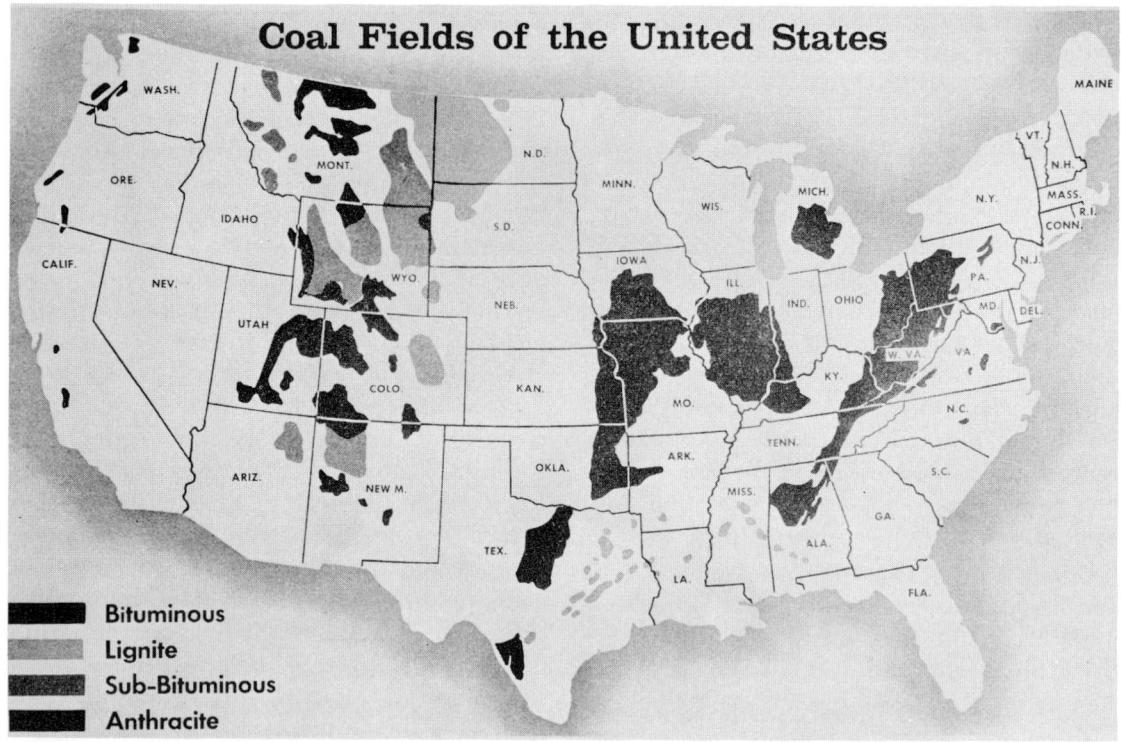

Figure 7-3. As indicated by this map, most of the nation's high-grade coking coal is found in the Hills of the Ohio and Tennessee Basin Region. (National Coal Association)

day in all mines, strip and underground. This is more than twice as much as he produced in 1942.

Intensive mechanization has occurred not only at the mine but in the processing and preparation plant, in storage facilities, on the grate where coal is burned, and even beyond, in the handling of ash.

Underground, where 73 per cent of the coal is still mined, machines have replaced hand and pick mining in all but some smaller mines. Some coal continues to be cut, drilled, blasted, and loaded by hand, but the quantity produced by this method is declining rapidly. About 85 per cent of the underground coal production now is cut by machines. About the same amount is loaded by mobile machines that scoop up the loose coal with a pair of steel arms and pass it over their backs to moving belts or shuttle cars on built-in conveyors. Another 11 per cent of the underground output is produced by continuous mining machines that eliminate the separate steps of cutting, drilling, blasting, and loading.

Surface mining, also called strip or open pit mining, has increased rapidly within the region since World War II. It is feasible only where the coal seam is relatively close to the surface of the ground. Two basic steps are involved: removing the soil and rocks (called the overburden) above the coal seam, and loading the coal into trucks for transfer to the preparation plant. Giant power shovels and drag-lines are used to remove the overburden. One of the largest of these shovels weighs 5,790,000 pounds and chews out a 105-ton bite—70 cubic yards—of earth and rock every 50 seconds, uncovering coal at the rate of two million tons a year.

After the coal seam is exposed by the big shovels, its surface is cleaned by scrapers, rotary brushes and other equipment. Then the coal is loaded into trucks by smaller power shovels of the size used in ordinary construction work.

Strip mining is no small job. The overburden averages more than 41 feet in depth. The uncovered seam averages about 4.9 feet thick.

Auger mining, another method of coal production, was developed recently, as an offshoot of contour strip mining, to increase coal recovery. Often in hilly areas the coal seam continues under overburden too thick for profitable removal. After the final stripping cut in the open mine leaves the face of the seam exposed, huge augers, from 16 to 20 inches in diameter, bore horizontally into the seam as far as 200 feet. The loosened coal flows along the auger and onto a conveyor that dumps it into a truck. The augers are mounted on a movable frame that moves down the high wall from hole to hole. Though sites for auger mining are limited, productivity is some 17 per cent higher than in strip mining, and three times the underground average. Only a few hundred augers are in operation but they produce nearly 25 tons of coal per man per day.

Transportation. Moving coal to market is a massive job. Most of the task falls on the railroads. They haul about 78 per cent of the output of the bituminous coal industry. About ten per cent moves to market by river barge, another ten per cent by truck, and the remaining two per cent is used at the mine or transported short distances by conveyor belt.

Although some of the earliest shipments of bituminous coal were made by river barges, major movements by this method awaited the growth of large consumers on water, particularly the steel industry on the Monongahela River near Pittsburgh and, in more recent years, the aluminum industry in the Ohio River Valley and the Tennessee Valley Authority installations in the Tennessee River Valley. Like rail shipment, river shipment is not necessarily to a final destination. A considerable tonnage, particularly in the Cincinnati area, is transshipped from the Ohio River to its ultimate destination by railroad or truck.

An important development in shipping bituminous coal has been the trucking of coal from mines to railroad sidings or to waterways for further shipment. This relatively new use of trucks made possible the opening of many small mines and even of some of the larger strip mines.

Because of the importance of costs, pipeline transmission of coal in water has been developed by the Consolidation Coal Company to carry coal 108 miles from Cadiz in eastern Ohio to the East Lake power plant near Cleveland. Specially prepared coal is crushed and mixed with water to form a slurry that flows through the pipeline. The mixture is pumped through the 10¾-inch line at three to four miles per hour, the same speed used for pumping oil. At the receiving end the coal is separated from the water, heated, and dried for use.

Uses. Most of the region's coal produced is burned for heat and power production—to generate electricity and to provide process heat, motive power, and heat for domestic use. Approximately one-quarter of the coal mined is made into coke for metallurgical purposes and, as by-products of the carbonization process, into coal chemicals. Almost one and a half tons of coal is needed to produce the one ton of coke that, in turn, is needed to make about one and a quarter to one and a half tons of pig iron. Bituminous coals having acceptable properties and characteristics are carbonized at high temperatures to produce coal tar and light oils, which serve: (1) as raw materials for such or-

Figure 7-4. Men placing permissible explosives in a hole in a coal face preparatory to blasting. Note the roof bolts above the heads of the men. With more efficient means of digging coal have come better ways of roof control to supplant much of the old timbering method. Roof drills bore into the roof. Then long expansion bolts are inserted to bind several feet of the overlying strata together. This reduces the hazard of roof falls. (Bureau of Mines, U.S. Department of the Interior)

ganic chemicals as synthetic rubber, detergents, plastics, photographic materials, flavor and perfume chemicals, explosives, and medicinals; and (2) after comparatively slight processing, as wood preservatives, disinfectants, animal dips, and road and building materials.

PETROLEUM AND NATURAL GAS

The American oil industry began in 1859 with a shallow, spring pole well near Titusville in northwestern Pennsylvania. It was financed, rather inadequately, by a small, adventurous group in New Haven, Connecticut, who believed that petroleum had a use and a future. The drilling was supervised by a former railroad conductor, "Colonel" Edwin L. Drake. After many trials and tribulations, the Drake well struck oil at a depth of 69½ feet. It was not a big well but its results were stupendous; it launched an industry now among the world's largest.

Oil production boomed in the Pennsylvania fields after Drake's discovery. Production, by 1863, was up to 2.6 million barrels; in 1870, it was 5.3 million; in 1874, it hit 11 million; and early production peaked at 31 million barrels in 1891. Since that time crude output has declined steadily in the Appalachian Province, except for a brief period during World War II when the use of secondary recovery methods resulted in a second peak of more than 35 million barrels. The Bradford-Allegheny field, lying in Pennsylvania and New York, ranked forty-first in leading fields in 1960. Production from this field totaled 6,459,000 barrels, bringing production since discovery to 683 million barrels. Most wells in the province are now extremely small, averaging between an eighth and a quarter of a barrel per day. The oil is high grade, has a paraffin base with few impurities, and consequently commands the highest price of all petroleum. It is of particular value in the making of high-quality lubricants.

The utility of natural gas was known and commercially exploited in the United States long before Colonel Drake drilled his oil well in 1859. Pennsylvania today ranks eleventh among the states in natural gas production and eighth in total dollar value of production, showing a decrease in both quantity and value since 1957. West Virginia ranks seventh in production, Kentucky twelfth. New York and Ohio, the only other producing states within the province, have minor outputs.

OTHER MINERALS AND WATER

Many other industrial minerals are produced in quantity in the province. The list includes: brines and rock salt, which play a major role in brick, terra-cotta, tile, and stoneware items and in high-fusion clay for firebrick and furnace linings; limestone; and sand and gravel. Limestone is a raw material that is the foundation of diverse industries. It is used as dimension stone in construction, as low-cost crushed stone, in steel and chemical manufacturing, in glass factories, in paper and cement mills, and as a soil conditioner. Sand and gravel have wide uses in the construction industry. High silica content sand is washed and crushed for special industrial uses, particularly glass manufacture.

The Hills of the Ohio and Tennessee Basin Province also possesses a large supply of industrial water, a major consideration for manufactural growth. The region receives 40 per cent more precipitation each year than the national average. This precipitation is distributed with a surprisingly high degree of uniformity, both geographically and seasonally. Further, there is a high degree of natural stream flow regulation, for despite the region's tremendous urban and industrial development, it remains 52 per cent forested. There is a constant increase in the effectiveness of stream flow regulation through the construction of flood control and multipurpose reservoirs in all the major drainage basins.

INDUSTRIAL DEVELOPMENT

THE IRON AND STEEL INDUSTRY

Two out of every six tons of steel produced in the United States are poured and finished at mills clustered around Pittsburgh, Youngstown, Wheeling, and along the Ohio River. The region's share of the nation's ingot capacity has remained unchanged since 1954. At that time the Chicago district replaced it as the leading iron and steel center. On a product basis, however, mills here are equipped to turn out more than one-half of the country's pipe, tubing, and galvanized flat products and 45 per

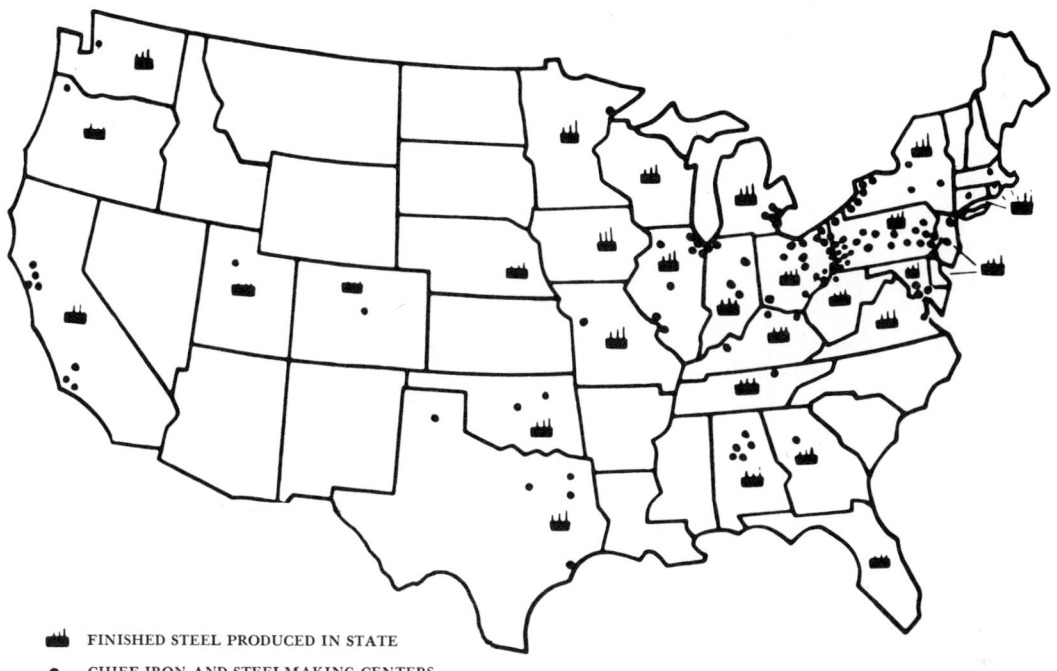

FINISHED STEEL PRODUCED IN STATE
CHIEF IRON AND STEELMAKING CENTERS

Figure 7-5. Distribution of steel companies in the United States. Twenty-seven states have steel-making facilities; 84 companies produce ingot steel; 255 companies finish steel. Note the great concentration in the northeastern part of the country. (Iron and Steel Institute)

cent of such important finished mill products as cold-finished bars and hot- and cold-rolled sheet and strip.

PITTSBURGH

The Pittsburgh steel district accounts for 17.4 per cent of the nation's steel. Only the Chicago area, with 19.2 per cent, surpasses it.

Pittsburgh's location, which includes the fact of its nearness to coal, has made it a titan of industry. The city exists because two great rivers, the Allegheny and the Monongahela, come together at the "Point," the apex of the city, to form the Ohio. The result is a marvelous system for the collection and assembly of vast quantities of the bulky raw materials, namely iron ore, limestone, coal, and coke, needed to make steel. Transportation is supplied by fleets of barges and by trunk line railroads.

The lack of level land has forced a large majority of the basic industries up the Allegheny and Monongahela, almost without a break for distances of 40 and 25 miles, respectively, and

down the Ohio for 30 miles. Pittsburgh is the heart of an industrial empire, but its limbs sprawl along the banks of its rivers into many other communities.

The strategic location at the junction of two rivers early led to bringing together at Pittsburgh the materials for making hardware and other iron products. The up-river areas furnished adequate supplies of coal and iron ore. During the early part of the 19th century most of the pig iron manufactured in western Pennsylvania was made in local charcoal furnaces scattered throughout that portion of the state. Later, coal became the major fuel and furnaces were constructed near coal mines further to the south and west. The pig iron usually was brought to Pittsburgh by river, and rolled, forged, or recast in the city. Necessary coal for working the iron was brought from nearby mines, often by water.

When the market for raw iron became primarily industrial, as contrasted with a previously agricultural demand, it was necessary to

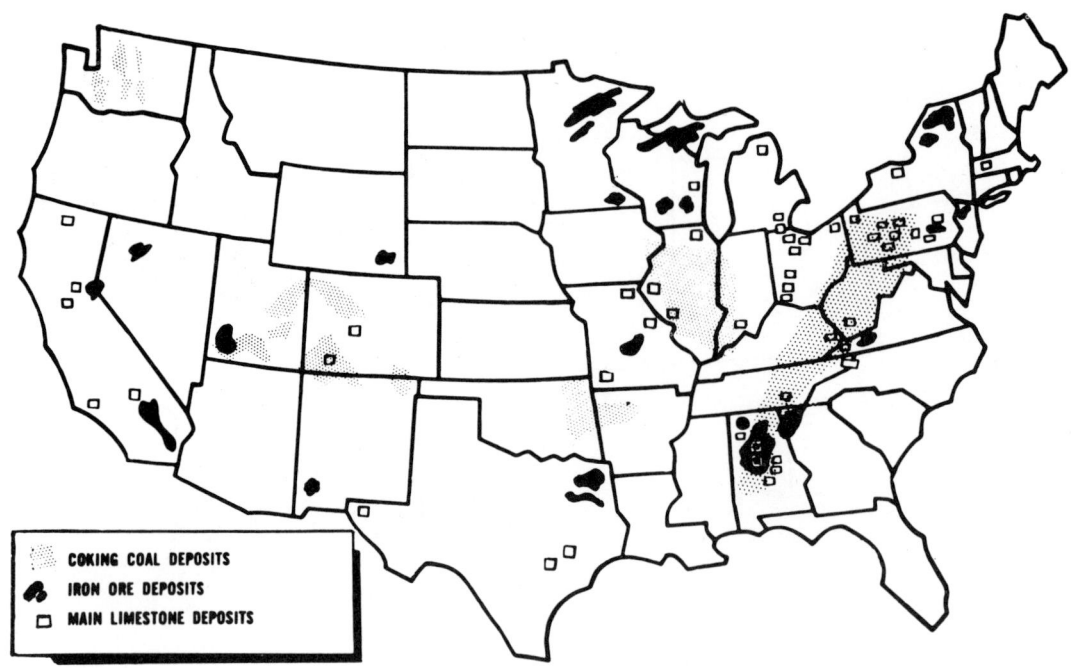

Figure 7-6. Location of some basic steelmaking raw materials in the United States. This map shows why the steelmaking industry is concentrated east of the Mississippi River. (Iron and Steel Institute)

produce large amounts of cheap metal of uniform quality. By 1850, the nature of the market for pig iron was changing; the requirement for smaller amounts of high-grade bar iron to be used in local forges or foundries was being supplanted by a requirement for large quantities of cheap iron to be made into industrial products at the factory. This change forced the rolling mills in Pittsburgh to control production of pig iron itself. After 1860, therefore, blast furnaces were built in connection with the local rolling mills. In order to produce good quality iron consistently, these plants found it advantageous to use the high-grade iron ore of the Lake Superior region. Thus the iron industry first became integrated in Pittsburgh, where Connellsville coking coal was used with Lake Superior ore. The main geographic advantage of the city as an iron producer was its location near large supplies of high-grade coking coal and near enough to Lake Erie to obtain the necessary supplies of ore at relatively low freight costs.

Since the Civil War period, the growth of iron and steel manufactures in the United States has been prodigious. The Pittsburgh area took an early lead as the center of this industry and for decades enjoyed an almost complete monopoly in iron and steel production. Other factors, however, soon began to offset many of the favorable advantages once held by this district. Perhaps Pittsburgh's greatest asset was its nearness to coal, for Pennsylvania bituminous has always been dependent to a large extent on an industrial market, especially the railroad and steel industries. The downward trend in these industries, with the added influence of a pronounced increase in the economy of combustion, led to a slowing-up in the rate of growth in coal output. Less dependence of other regions on western Pennsylvania coal for manufacturing steel caused other steel centers to rise and expand and eventually to challenge the supremacy of the Pittsburgh district in iron and steel production.

In spite of increased competition from other

steel centers, the relative importance of the several geographic characteristics of Pittsburgh —low-cost fuel, power, raw steel, and water transportation—has changed little in the past three-quarters of a century. Nearness to coal and comparative proximity to the Great Lakes remain of crucial importance. The production of primary metals, chiefly steel, continues to dominate; blast furnaces account for about 17½ per cent of national pig iron capacity. Steel rolling mills in the Pittsburgh area turn out every line of steel products, ranging from heavy structural components to fine wire. Some steel is also made into forgings and castings. Other commodities include coal chemicals, ferroalloys, and titanium products.

Most of the steel mills are in Allegheny County; several of these each employ more than 5,000 people. Smaller plants in the primary metals group, employing from 500 to 1,000, produce zinc, sheet copper, brass, bronze, and aluminum basic shapes.

The comparative position of the Pittsburgh district in iron and steel manufacturing will depend on the extent to which local producers take a leading part in exploiting new markets, in recovering their relative position in old markets in which the area once was much stronger, and in increasing their share of sales in markets in which the area has been comparatively weak.

Aluminum. Although bauxite ore from which aluminum is made is not mined in the Pittsburgh district, the Aluminum Company of America, by far the largest unit in the industry, always has had its home office there, along with one of its larger fabricating plants.

Glass. Pittsburgh is the city of glass as well as of steel and aluminum. This is because the sand of which glass is made and the coal or natural gas used for fuel in its production have been abundant from the start. Glass plants, large and small, are scattered up and down the three rivers, but the largest producer is the Pittsburgh Plate Glass Company.

Westinghouse Electric. It was in Pittsburgh in the early 1870's and 1880's that George Westinghouse started to manufacture the air brake and the railroad signals he had perfected. Because the signal system required electric controls, he soon found himself making electrical equipment; the vast Westinghouse

Figure 7-7. Pittsburgh's "Golden Triangle," where the Monongahela (right) and the Allegheny (left) join to form the Ohio River. Pittsburgh, Pennsylvania, is handicapped as well as blessed by topography, for the city occupies one of the most irregular and uneven sites of any upon which a great city is built. Ten per cent of its surface is in slopes of 40 per cent or more. The lowest elevation, at river level, is about 700 feet, and many of the more than 1,200-foot-high hills within the city are steep, barren, and unfit for habitation. (H. J. Heinz Co.)

Figure 7-8. The Jones and Laughlin Steel Corporation steel mill in Pittsburgh is one of the country's oldest and largest mills where light steel is the major product. It is on the north bank of the Monongahela River, along which it extends for nearly a mile. (U.S. Department of Agriculture)

interests have been in Pittsburgh ever since.

From its giant plant, Westinghouse ships each year more than 20,000 carloads of basic electrical equipment, much of it tailor-made. Among the products are motors for industrial use and electrical equipment for mine cars and railroad trains.

H. J. Heinz Company. One of the comparatively few large industries within the city limits of Pittsburgh itself is the H. J. Heinz Company. Heinz is the largest maker of ketchup in the world, the second largest maker of canned soups, and one of the four largest makers of baby foods. There are from 120 to 127 varieties, not just the fabled "57," and the chief products, besides those mentioned above, are baked beans, pickles, spaghetti, and condiments.

YOUNGSTOWN (MAHONING-SHENANGO VALLEYS) DISTRICT

Situated about midway between Cleveland and Pittsburgh, the Youngstown metropolitan area is even more specialized than Pittsburgh in steel production. Youngstown is the third largest steel center in the country and one of the oldest of the major American steel centers. About nine per cent of the nation's pig iron and steel capacity is located here. Finished steel is largely of the flat rolled variety used in automobiles and appliances but some heavier items are also rolled in Youngstown mills. In the city and its environs, steel works and rolling mills manufacture pipe and tubing, sheets, strips, rod and wire products, and plates and shapes. Ingot molds are produced at Hubbard. Mills in Warren and Niles turn out flat rolled steel and pipe. Furnaces and steel mills in and near Sharon produce pig iron, steel sheets, strip, pipe, and tubing; foundries in Sharon and elsewhere in Mercer County turn out ingot molds and miscellaneous castings.

JOHNSTOWN

At the junction of the Conemaugh and Little Conemaugh Rivers about 60 miles east of Pittsburgh is the Bethlehem Steel Corporation's Johnstown mill. The city, in the center of an area producing both iron ore and bituminous coal, probably has contributed more than any other city to the development and technology of the steel industry. This congested valley, a miniature Pittsburgh, presents a striking picture of intensive industrial use.

THE OHIO VALLEY

The Ohio River, beginning at Pittsburgh with the confluence of the Allegheny and Monongahela Rivers and winding south and west 981 miles to the Mississippi at Cairo, is technically the property of Kentucky, West Virginia, and Pennsylvania, but it flows past three other states—Ohio, Indiana, and Illinois. Narrow and bordered by mountains at the beginning, the Ohio Valley is crammed with steel mills, coke ovens, power plants, and brick kilns for its 40 miles in Pennsylvania. For another 60 miles, West Virginia and Ohio duplicate the Pennsylvania industrial pattern on a somewhat smaller scale. Then the cities and towns, narrow ribbons of humanity pressed between the river and the Allegheny foothills, begin to separate; long stretches of open farmland intervene. The countryside is essentially rural with only a sprinkling of metropolitan centers to dominate the hundreds of miles of river— Wheeling and Huntington, West Virginia; Cincinnati and Steubenville, Ohio; Louisville, Kentucky; and Evansville, Indiana.

Space, coal, and power have attracted new industries and given rise to expansion of old facilities in the Ohio Valley to the tune of $7.5 billion since 1950. The Ohio now surpasses the Rhine, Europe's "chemical river," in chemical plant investment; nearly three times as much steel is produced on the Ohio as in the celebrated Ruhr Valley, and over three times the coal. The Ohio's fissionable material plants rival those at Oak Ridge. A group of power companies has invested over half a billion dollars in new facilities to supply these Atomic Energy Commission plants, and nearly three times as much to keep pace with the demands of private users. Within the past few years the aluminum industry has made a significant break away from Northwest sites offering cheap hydroelectric power to Ohio River sites based on coal. Producers believe savings in transportation that result from having the metal produced nearer its markets will more than offset the two mill per kilowatt-hour higher cost for coal over water power. Among the new aluminum producers in the Ohio Valley are: (1) Alcoa's 150,000 ton smelter near Evansville, In-

Figure 7-9. The Tennessee Valley Authority's Kentucky Dam is of tremendous value for flood regulation purposes to the lower Ohio and Mississippi Rivers. Located on the Tennessee River, near its mouth in Kentucky, the dam creates a reservoir with a capacity of more than six million acre-feet of water. By regulating the flow of the Tennessee River at the Kentucky Dam, crests on the Ohio and Mississippi can be lowered as much as four feet. The dam has a generating capacity of 160,000 kilowatts of electricity. (U.S. Department of Agriculture)

diana; (2) Kaiser Aluminum's $216 million Ravenswood, West Virginia, facilities, with an annual smelter output of 220,000 tons; and (3) Olin Mathieson's $120 million (120,000-ton) aluminum smelter near Clarington, Ohio.

The Atomic Energy Commission has invested $1.7 billion in three plants: a uranium processing plant at Fernald, Ohio, and gaseous-diffusion plants at Paducah, Kentucky, and Portsmouth, Ohio. To supply the diffusion plants, there are four new power plants located at Joppa, Illinois; Paducah, Kentucky; Madison, Indiana; and Cheshire, Ohio.

Salt, over a hundred feet thick in places, along the upper Ohio Valley attracted chemical industries to the area. To producers of chlorine and chlorine products, few places offer as many advantages as the Ohio Valley. Brine deposits, salt, and the water essential to chlo-

rine operations are abundantly present. Chemicals valued at a third of a billion dollars are produced, mainly in new plants at Calvert City, Kentucky, home of the Pennsylvania Salt Manufacturing Company's sulfuric and hydrofluoric acid operation, and in New Martinsville-Moundsville's $70 million chemical facilities—both in the vicinity of Parkersburg and Marietta—and in the expansion of the existing billion dollar complex on the tributary Kanawha, around Charleston.

Steel industries along the Ohio River have expanded plants by nearly $1 billion since 1956, an increase primarily represented by the expansion up-river of National Steel at Weirton, West Virginia; of Wheeling Steel from Steubenville, Ohio, south; and that of Jones & Laughlin Steel at Aliquippa, Pennsylvania. Down-river there is Armco's $75 million facility at Ashland, Kentucky, and the $90 million expansion of Detroit Steel at Portsmouth, Ohio.

The Wheeling-Steubenville metropolitan area, which is located along the upper Ohio River a short distance west and south of Pittsburgh, is made up of two Ohio counties and four West Virginia counties. Steel mills are the largest employers in all six counties. Well over 5,000 workers are employed by mills in Weirton, Steubenville, and Benwood; they produce structural steel, tin plate, sheets and strip, and galvanized sheets and pipe. Riverside locations make possible the use of low-cost barge transportation on the Ohio River for the industry's bulky raw materials, most of which come from outside the area, as well as for its heavy finished products. The river also furnishes water for industrial processing and cooling.

Traffic on the Ohio River. More than 80 million tons of shipping traveled the Ohio in 1960—50 per cent more than passed through the Panama Canal and 50 per cent more than is anticipated annually for the St. Lawrence Seaway in its first years of operation. The importance of the Ohio River as a commercial route may be attributed to: (1) its proximity to the nation's largest soft coal deposits; (2) its all-water connection, via the Mississippi, with the very large petroleum reserves of the central South; and (3) the industrial growth of the country, particularly that portion lying generally to the north of the river. The value of the river as an inexpensive avenue for bulk commodity movement could not have been realized without a stabilized flow of water and a guaranteed minimum channel depth. The Federal government, recognizing this requirement at the turn of the century, assumed the responsibility for the full canalization of the river in the interest of furthering interstate commerce. Today the river is canalized and channeled for its entire length, with a controlling depth of nine feet. The river is navigable all year. Its chief tributary in Ohio, the Muskingum, also is canalized to permit navigation from Zanesville in central Ohio to the Muskingum's junction with the Ohio at Marietta.

Tributary streams of the Ohio River—the Tennessee, the Cumberland, the Green, the Kentucky, the Big Sandy, and the Kanawha—and the so-called headstreams, the Monongahela and the Allegheny, add some 1,340 miles of navigable channel with nine-foot draft.

A modernization program of the Ohio, now under construction, will reduce the number of dams and locks from 46 to 19 to insure speedier, more efficient passage for barge tows.

The chief port on the Ohio River is Cincinnati; other important ports are East Liverpool, Steubenville, Wheeling, Marietta, Portsmouth, Louisville, and Paducah.

Binghamton, New York (75,941). The Binghamton area is one of the more highly industrialized districts in the state. Excellent transportation facilities provide ready access to regional and national markets. The triple-city zone of Binghamton, Endicott, and Johnson City is a center of trade and industry, producing business machines, cameras, film, electronics equipment, aviation trainers, and shoes.

The confluence of four rivers in the vicinity of Binghamton served to stimulate the early development of the area. With the building of the Chenango Canal and the Erie Railroad in the middle of the 19th century, Binghamton became the hub of a communications network midway between New York City and Buffalo. As additional railroad lines were developed connecting it with other sections of the state and nation, Binghamton became an important industrial and distribution center.

Elmira, New York (46,517). The central position of the Elmira area makes it a crossroads for a number of major railroads and highways, and Cayuga Lake, one of the Finger Lakes, gives it access to the New York State Barge Canal system. Cargo moving between Cayuga Lake and the Barge Canal consists mainly of salt, cement, and oil. Three railroads, the Erie-Lackawanna, Pennsylvania, and Lehigh Valley, converge on Elmira, and three serve Hornell, an important railroad repair center. The largest concentration of industry is found in Elmira, which, as far back as 1845, was the location of one of the country's earliest manufacturers of fire engines. Today this city is a center of heavy industry, producing, in addition to fire-fighting equipment, machines and metal products of all kinds—business machines, gears, valves, precision tools, coaster brakes, starter drives, trucks, electronic devices, metal castings, and small arms.

Nearly all the manufacturing activity in Corning, a city named after a maker of foundry products, is accounted for by the glass industry. The manufacture of glass, which began on a small scale in 1868, is today so large that Corning is nationally known as the "Crystal City." Corning specializes in the production of such glassware as electric light bulbs, radio tubes, cooking utensils, experimental glass, optical and chemical ware, and beautiful cut and engraved table and decorative glassware.

Canton, Ohio, metropolitan area. Canton is noted for its leading manufacturers, which include: Automatic Steel Products, Inc., the world's largest manufacturer of automobile pulleys; the E. W. Bliss Company, producer of mechanical and hydraulic metalworking presses; the Hoover Vacuum Company; and the Timken Roller Bearing Company. In Canton proper are located the integrated steel works and rolling mills of Republic Steel Corporation.

In addition to those in the metals field, there are a number of important plants in Canton producing fabricated rubber products, ceramics, dental equipment, structural clay products, paperboard boxes, petroleum products, women's apparel, and pharmaceutical preparations.

Massillon, located just west of Canton, manufactures industrial machinery, heat exchange apparatus, stampings, steel castings, bolts and nuts, and roller bearings.

Akron, Ohio (290, 351). The rubber industry accounts for more than half of Akron's manufacturing employment. It arose by chance in 1870 when Benjamin Franklin Goodrich answered an advertisement of the Akron Board of Trade. Akron has been known as the rubber capital of the world since 1910. It is one of the more specialized industrial cities in the country.

The Akron rubber industry employs more than 50,000 people, or one-fifth of the nation's total employment for the industry. Products include motor vehicle tires and inner tubes, synthetic rubber, reclaimed rubber, and a large variety of fabricated rubber goods.

Aircraft parts, machinery (including precision tools and special industrial machinery), ordnance equipment, cereal breakfast foods, sporting and athletic goods, gray-iron castings, millwork, pottery products, and machine shop products are also important in this area.

Cincinnati, Ohio (502,550). The metropolitan area of Cincinnati, straddling the Ohio River at the southwest corner of Ohio, had a 1960 population of 1,067,669. The city is the cultural and in some ways the economic capital of the Ohio River.

Cincinnati has long been known for its machine tool industry, but in the period since World War II the production of automobiles, automobile parts, aircraft engines, and truck trailers has grown so rapidly that the manufacturing of transportation equipment now is as important as the long-dominant machine tool industry. Two of the major automobile manufacturers have large plants in the area, each of which employs more than 3,000 people.

Virtually every kind of metalworking machinery, with its accompanying tools and dies, is manufactured in Cincinnati, as well as a variety of special purpose machinery and equipment. Machine tool plants employing more than 500 persons each turn out valves, laundry machinery, and power transmission equipment. Fabricated metal plants, employing between 500 and 1,000 each, manufacture plumbing supplies and metal containers.

The chemicals and chemical products group contains one of the largest plants (Procter and Gamble) in the area; it employs about 6,000 in the production of soaps, detergents, toilet articles, and vegetable shortening.

In addition to river traffic, several important railroads, running both east-west and north-south, converge on the area. Cincinnati is a terminal point for some of them.

Geographically, Cincinnati is an attractive community. Until 1900, it was compressed into a small level area called the basin—the flood plain of Mill Creek fronting the Ohio River for two miles. Then came the electric streetcar and the automobile, making it practical for the city to climb the steep, 400-foot hills that rim the basin. The city spilled over into the surrounding rolling hills and wide valleys.

Today more than 500,000 people are scattered over Cincinnati's 75 square miles, making it one of the more widely-dispersed large cities in America. It has many fine parks on the hills overlooking the valley of the Ohio.

Louisville, Kentucky (390,639). Louisville is Kentucky's largest city. Its location on the falls of the Ohio River made it a bulk breaking point. Because goods had to be unloaded and carried around the falls, Louisville early became an important market, distributing point, and railroad center. Traditionally noted for whiskey and cigarette production, much of the postwar growth in Louisville has resulted from the transfer there from other cities of the General Electric Company's entire household appliance output. More than 15,000 workers are employed by this new General Electric facility.

Furniture, distilled products, and large tobacco plants still are major props of Louisville's industrial economy. Other types of manufacturing include aluminum sheet, rod, and extruded products; ordnance; explosives; aircraft parts; automobile parts; and butadiene for synthetic rubber.

Lexington, Kentucky (62,810). Lexington, capital of the Bluegrass, is the principal marketing and processing center for the burley tobacco area of Kentucky. Although Lexington does not produce finished tobacco products for immediate consumption, burley tobacco is sent out of the area in semifinished state, ready for blending into cigarettes with other varieties of tobacco.

About two-thirds of nonfarm wage and salary workers in Lexington are employed in wholesale and retail trade, government, and the service industries. Agriculture provides employment for about 3,500 people. The University of Kentucky, located at Lexington, an important educational center, is also of economic significance to the area. Surrounding Lexington are picturesque farms noted for their thoroughbred horses.

Nashville, Tennessee (170,874). Lying in the fertile, productive Nashville Basin on the Cumberland River, Nashville is Tennessee's commercial and industrial city and port of entry. Its location on a north-south route, combined with its basin-like structure, has made Nashville a focus for many railroads and highways.

The city has diversified industries: shoe manufacturing (General Shoe Corporation, with headquarters in Nashville, is one of the leading shoe manufacturers of the world), cotton, flour and feed, lumber, brick, snuff, chemicals, foundries, meat packing plants, stone and cement works, printing and publishing, rayon mills, cellophane, and fertilizer industries. Nashville also claims to have the largest titanium plant in the United States. Such a list suggests a wide industrial base and is in keeping with the rapid growth in manufacturing throughout the South.

8 | *Ozark-Ouachita Highlands*

(Relief map copyright Aero Service Corp.)

THE Ozark-Ouachita Highlands, with a total area of more than 50,000 square miles, lie mainly in southern Missouri and northern Arkansas, but extend westward to include parts of eastern Oklahoma and the southeastern corner of Kansas. The Shawnee Hills of southern Illinois form an eastern outlier.

These highlands, located only a few hundred miles southeast of the center of the continental United States, excluding Alaska, are the most centrally situated upland of the country. They rise gradually (except for a short distance at the south end) from the Eastern Interior Low Plains on the west and north, and abruptly from the Mississippi West Gulf Plain on the east. Because of their greater relief, poorer soils, and forest vegetation, the Ozark-Ouachita Highlands have a culture and economy which differ considerably from that of the surrounding lowlands.

From north to south the province naturally divides into: (1) the Ozark Plateaus, including the Salem and Springfield Plateaus; (2) the Boston Mountains, separated from the Ozarks by the White River; (3) the Arkansas River Valley; and (4) the Ouachita Mountains (the Arbuckle and Wichita Mountains in south-central and southwestern Oklahoma are western outliers of the Ouachitas).

SURFACE FEATURES

The Ozark Subregion is a dissected plateau developed upon domed rocks, which are, for the most part, highly resistant to erosion. According to Sauer, "It (the subregion) has been uplifted very unevenly, and being composed of different rocks situated at exceedingly varying distances from vigorous drainage lines, its various portions have been modified in different ways and to different degrees by erosion."[1]

The western part of the Missouri Ozarks, although highest on the whole, is most remote from the major drainage lines. Therefore it has been eroded only slightly, whereas most of the eastern region is maturely dissected. Nearly flat remnants range in height from less than 1,000 feet at the edges to 1,700 feet near the center. In the northeastern part of the plateau, granitic rocks are exposed in some places. In

[1] Carl O. Sauer, *The Geography of the Ozark Highlands of Missouri*, Geogr. Soc. Chicago, Bulletin 7, 1920, p. 7.

this area of crystalline outcrops, known as the St. Francis Mountains, the topography is especially rough and rugged.

The Boston Mountains, 200 miles long and 35 miles wide, have been sculptured into truly mountainous forms by the Arkansas and White River systems. Elevations as high as 2,300 feet occur in this section, with an average crestline of about 1,800 feet. The subregion presents a bold, rugged, forested escarpment to the north and a general slope to the south.

The Arkansas Valley, located between the Boston and Ouachita Mountains, varies in width from 30 to 40 miles and extends in an east-west direction, providing easy access through the Highlands. It is a gently undulating plain, most of which lies between 300 and 600 feet above sea level.

South of the Arkansas Valley, the Ouachita Highlands consist of numerous ridges and narrow valleys which in general lie in an east-west direction. They were made by close folding, like the Appalachians of the Appalachian Valley Province, and at the same time. In the central part of Arkansas, near the city of Little Rock, the ridges are not well defined and have elevations of about 500 to 700 feet above sea level. They increase in altitude to the west, and mountains of more than 2,000 feet above sea level are common. Much of the land is too rugged for farming; a large part of this area is in the Ouachita National Forest.

CLIMATE

Two characteristic climatic features prevail throughout the province: humidity and pronounced temperature changes. The range in annual temperature is 55° to 60° F.; the annual precipitation averages from 42 to 50 inches; the length of the growing season varies from 170 to 210 days.

In general, the Ozark-Ouachita Highlands have a subtropical climate controlled by two air masses: (1) the dry, cold, continental air that moves from the west and northwest to the east across the northern part of the Highlands; and (2) the warm, moist air that comes in from the Gulf, affecting mainly the southern part. Since the Highlands stand out from the lower surrounding plain, they are subject to the prevailing winds. There is no nearby mountain range to act as a barrier against the fronts.

Figure 8-1. A virgin stand of hardwoods in the Ozark National Forest, Arkansas. Oak, hickory, and ash are the principal tree species. Shortleaf pine stands occur on the poorer soils and at higher elevations. (U.S. Forest Service)

NATURAL VEGETATION AND SOILS

With the exception of a few small areas of grassland, most of the region was forested when the first white settlers arrived.

The soils in the Ozark Highlands were formed by the weathering of limestone. In this process, the calcium and magnesium carbonates were leached out and residual materials were left to form soil with a high chert content, particularly on steep slopes. Chert interferes with tillage and mowing and reduces the water-holding capacity of the soils so that crops suffer sooner from lack of moisture. On the other hand, the cherty fragments on the surface protect the soils against the beating effect of raindrops and slow down the movement of water over the surface.

In the Ouachita Highlands the soils derived from the weathering of sandstone soils are rel-atively unproductive because of their coarse texture and deficiency of plant food. The residue from the shales and slates consists of fine clay particles that form heavy soils with poor drainage characteristics.

The alluvial soils in the flood plains of the Arkansas and White Rivers are the most fertile. Clearing the land of timber and providing adequate drainage and protection from periodic overflow have been the principal problems in utilizing these lands for farming purposes.

SETTLEMENT

Historically, the Ozark-Ouachita Region belonged alternately to the French, the Spanish, and the French again. The French have left their mark on names, as have the Indians. Many small streams are *bayous* (dead streams) in these mountains. Many towns bear the French suffix *ville*. Some are named for French explorers and some names have been changed so that their French origin scarcely is discernible.

The first white men to see the Ozarks were Spaniards under Hernando de Soto, who explored the area in 1541, but did not settle. More than a hundred years later (1673) two French Jesuit missionaries, Jacques Marquette and Louis Jolliet, appeared. In about 1682, Robert de La Salle lay claim, in the name of the king of France, to all the country watered by the Mississippi and its tributaries.

More Frenchmen came, but few stayed. The French were not efficient colonizers. Their pioneering groups were small, their numbers were not maintained by sufficient recruits from the homeland, and few of them sought to establish homes in the New World. They came to find wealth or adventure or to Christianize the natives, and then returned to their homeland.

The Ozarks were no exception to this general colonization pattern. Lead ore, salt springs, and, to some extent, furs were sought. Later the search for silver attracted settlers. Temporary visits in quest of these commodities soon led to permanent habitation. Organized mining began in 1720; the earliest land grant was recorded in 1723. Before 1763, however, there was very little population increase. Few grants of land were made and these were designed mainly to embrace mineral riches.

The Treaty of Paris (1763) ended French

colonial rule in the New World. Many of the French families left. The population remaining was soon diluted by the influx of American colonists following the Revolutionary War. After the Louisiana Purchase (1803), the influx of settlers from the East was greatly accelerated. The early immigrants were mostly of Southern stock, a majority coming from Tennessee and Kentucky.

From 1830 to 1850, the westward migration from the Southern States received a new impetus. The decline of prices of cotton and tobacco in the South, together with the exhaustion of the soil, sent many thousands of persons —including not only the poorer small farmers but also the more affluent planters caught by the general financial depression — northwest and southwest.

Most of those who migrated as far as Arkansas and Missouri did not settle in the Highlands, but sought the lowlands farther south. The more restless frontier type, leading a semi-nomadic life of hunting and farming, and moving to newer lands whenever the older region became fairly well settled, was attracted to the Highlands.

Watercourses were the highways. Families that settled along the rivers and streams were on the main thoroughfares. Passers-by were rare and neighbors few, but this was all the contact with others that the mountaineer desired.

The plateau and hill regions of the central Ozarks were settled last, in part because of their poverty, but principally because of their isolation. Only where river valleys established connection with the outside world and furnished good land were setlements made contemporaneously with those of the Ozark borders.

MODERNIZATION

Isolation has been the keynote to the backward economy of the Ozark-Ouachita Highlands. Dissected plateaus and mountainous terrain have always made transportation difficult. Much of the region is too rough for railroad building, except at great cost. Moreover, the uplands are too steep to be good farms, and because of their slope and low fertility they offer few freight possibilities.

With few exceptions highways follow the crest of the ridges. From the ridge roads private roads lead to the farms in the valleys. These latter often are impassable because of flooding. In such situations a subsistence economy has prevailed. Here the inhabitants are still independent; proud of their skill with fishing rod, shotgun, and rifle; apt at ballad singing and fiddling; and aloof from the outside world.

Because of larger resources and easier communication, the border areas, namely the Springfield Plateau of southwest Missouri and the Arkansas Valley, are exceptions to this isolation. The once-popular image of the Ozarks as a country of simple mountaineers leading a picturesque but stark life is no longer a true one in these two subregions.

THE SPRINGFIELD PLATEAU

A good place to see the new Ozarks is in southwest Missouri. Springfield, a growing trade and transportation center becoming increasingly industrial in complexion, is the area's metropolis. Farms spreading out from Springfield form one of the nation's larger milksheds and are also major suppliers of livestock and poultry. Smaller cities, scattered across the hills and prairies, contain manufacturing plants and bustling business districts. On the northern and southern borders are recreation and resort areas. Along U.S. 66 and other highways which tie the region together, hotels, restaurants, and other businesses serve a great flow of travelers.

In the first stage of southwest Missouri's development, from 1820 to about 1850, population growth was slow. Most of the early settlers, many of them from Tennessee and Kentucky, came in by the southerly route. Typifying the frontiersmen of history and legend, these pioneers did not take up the prairie land to any great extent, but located instead in wooded land along the rivers and creeks.

A self-sufficient economy emerged. Springfield, which had been established around 1822, became a natural trade center for the territory. Manufacturing of farm implements grew out of an early Springfield blacksmith shop and by 1850 the industry was known for 100 miles around. The farms were small, producing little more than was needed for support of the families living on them, but there was usually a little surplus that could be brought to town.

Corn, cotton, flax, and tobacco were grown in small patches to meet household needs. Water power sites were developed for gristmills and sawmills. Trade with the rest of the country was based primarily upon the export of livestock. Cattle and mules could walk to market over the crude roads of the day; salt pork was valuable enough to justify a long wagon haul and durable enough to survive it.

With the railroads established, the 1880's saw the breakdown of the area's isolation. Commercial farming began in earnest, with a greater emphasis on raising of grain. From the 1920's on, the building of highways knit southwest Missouri even more firmly into the national economy. As the growing metropolitan areas of St. Louis, Kansas City, and Springfield itself became more accessible, farmers of southwest Missouri turned to dairying to meet the needs of urban populations. Over the new roads came the advance guard of an army of tourists. And, at long last, manufacturing plants began to produce for national markets such diversified items as machinery, paper products, furniture, clothing, processed foods, fertilizer, feed, and building materials.

The postwar years have seen a general increase in mechanization on farms—milking machines, grain combines, hay balers, and tractors — to help keep in production the land vacated by people who shifted from farming.

THE ARKANSAS VALLEY

Agriculture in this subregion is quite varied and is best described as mixed farming. Although raising livestock, mainly beef and dairy cattle, is the leading farm enterprise, local areas are notable for the production of peaches, strawberries, green beans, tomatoes, peanuts, cucumbers, and watermelons.

Nearly 35 per cent of all land in farms is in woodland, and an even greater percentage is in pasture. Principal changes in agriculture in recent years have been a general increase in beef cattle production, in milk cows, and in the sale of fluid milk rather than cream. Broiler production has grown rapidly in the central part of the subregion.

The typical farm includes both bottom land and upland. The bottom land is used for intensive cropping; the upland, largely for pasture.

A significant trend has been the decline of cotton production. Soybeans and small grains, mainly wheat and oats, which can be handled with machinery and by less labor than required for vegetable production, are becoming more important.

FRUIT

Northwest Arkansas and southwest Missouri are the center of a region once rich in apple orchards and still rich in vineyards. As early as 1885, the Shannon apple was taking prizes in world expositions. In 1887, the first carload shipments were made from Benton County, Arkansas. Orchardists set out millions of trees during the next 20 years. A crop of 7 million bushels was picked and over 4,500 carloads were shipped in 1919. Two years later, drought and parasites damaged the orchards heavily and the 1919 peak has never been regained. Transparent, Jonathan, and Delicious are the most common apple varieties being marketed from this area today.

The concentration of grape growing was inspired in part by Italian and German settlers prior to World War I. Much of the nation's grape juice supply comes from this area. Strawberries and peaches have been grown commercially here since 1900. Arkansas ranks fifth in the nation in strawberry production.

FORESTS

Still retaining a primeval quality, the Ozark-Ouachita Highlands are thickly wooded. Their vegetation is more nearly akin to the oak-hickory forests of the Eastern and Central States. Varying conditions of soil and exposure account for many differences among the species covering the slopes. The only pine native to the area, the loblolly or shortleaf, is not nearly as frequent in the Ozarks as in the Ouachitas and on the flats farther south.

Forests cover almost two-thirds of Arkansas. The state leads the nation in the production of red gum, oak, and hickory lumber. Yellow pine is an important source of pulpwood.

Practical Federal interest in the conservation of the region's timber was first demonstrated in 1907, when President Theodore Roosevelt defined the boundaries of the Arkansas National Forest, later renamed the Ouachita. Since 1907, the original tract has been greatly expanded until it now includes more than 1.3 million acres extending into Oklahoma from about 20 miles west of Little Rock. The Ozark National Forest, 300,000 acres in Oklahoma and west Arkansas, was created in 1908.

Arkansas ranks ninth in the nation in lumber production. Primary forest industries range from sawmills and cooperage mills to plants engaged in the manufacture of pulp for paper, paperboard, and other wood cellulose products.

MINING

The principal minerals of economic importance in the Ozark-Ouachita Highlands are zinc near the Missouri-Oklahoma-Kansas border; coal in western Missouri and west-central Arkansas; lead, north of the St. Francis Mountains in Missouri; and iron ore at Iron Mountain and Pilot Knob in southern Missouri. Limestone, clay, gravel, and sand are widely distributed. The region has an important share of the nation's production of bauxite, manganese, barite, and fluorspar.

THE LEAD DISTRICT

Southeast Missouri has yielded lead ore since prehistoric times, when Indians mined small quantities. Lead has been mined there for the last two and a half centuries and the region has been a major producer of lead in the United States for the past 50 years.

The French developed lead mining early. The entire output up to 1800, however, was only about 18,000 tons. Lead ores found near the surface were mined by the simplest methods. A pickax and shovel were the only tools used to remove the earth; a drill, rammer, and priming rod were added when it was necessary to blast. Manual labor supplied the power. At times the shallow open pits filled with water and miners were exposed to both heat and cold. In dry weather there was insufficient water for separating waste materials from the ores. For these and other reasons the mines were worked six months or less per year. Furthermore, the first crude furnaces, made of logs, yielded only a little over half the lead in the ore.

Throughout this early period of development, heavy loads were moved by wagon over

Figure 8-2. *A typical stand of loblolly shortleaf pine in the Ouachita Mountains, Arkansas. These trees are about 80 years old. (U.S. Forest Service)*

crude roads that were often not much better than trails. Extension of railroads into the region in the 1850's, and the use of the diamond drill (1869) for shaft mining paved the way for large-scale operations.

Today, lead mining tunnels extend hundreds of miles underground and are served by more than 350 miles of railroad track. Electric engines hauling up to 200 tons of ore at one time have replaced the mules formerly used. Power shovels that load at the rate of 25 tons an hour have replaced the pick and shovel.

Figure 8-3. A typical lead mining operation in the Ozark-Ouachita Highlands Region. The region now produces about 30 per cent of the lead mined nationally. The total value of output amounts to more than $32 million. (Massie, Missouri Resources Commission)

Figure 8-4. Loading lead ore onto rail cars deep inside the mine at the St. Joseph Lead Company, Missouri. (Massie, Missouri Resources Commission)

A major advance in the separation of lead from ores was the selective flotation process, first adopted in the Lead Belt in 1911. Other improvements followed. Because of better techniques, ores are currently being mined that yield only two per cent lead, and old waste piles are being reworked. The milling process at one new mine is so efficient that it requires only 13 men, compared with 30 to 40 men for a similar operation at older mills.

The St. Joseph Lead Company, with 3,200 employees, operates the largest lead mine in the United States and the third largest in the world; it is surpassed only by the great Sullivan Mine in British Columbia and the Broken Hill Mines in Australia. It turns out about 25,000 tons of ore per day. In addition, chat,[2] which formerly was waste, is now being milled at about 4,700 tons per day.

TRI-STATE ZINC DISTRICT

Zinc has been mined in this subregion since 1871, when the first deposits were extracted near Granby, Missouri. The district covers an area of some 2,000 square miles in southwestern Missouri, northeastern Oklahoma, and southeastern Kansas. To date, more than 11 million tons of metal ore have been recovered from the region, which was the world's leading zinc mining district from 1885 until 1950. Since then, depletion of high grade ores and declining metal prices have resulted in a steady decline. About 14 per cent of the nation's zinc supply is now mined here. Leadership has passed to the Western States, which account for about 58 per cent of domestic output; the states east of the Mississippi River produce about 28 per cent.

Both zinc and lead ores are mined in the Tri-State District. The principal primary ore minerals are sphalerite (zinc sulfide) and, with galena (lead sulfide), associated with pyrite and marcasite. The gangue, or earthy material, consists of chert and calcite.

Zinc and lead ores occur either in broad tabular bodies, in flat runs from ten to 1,000 feet wide and from ten to 30 feet high, or as narrow vertical bodies or vertical runs that are from ten to 1,000 feet wide and ten to 30 feet high. The deposits occur in limestones and cherts at

[2] *Chat* is the mining term which signifies rejected waste material from lead and zinc ore concentrates.

depths of 100 to 400 feet below the surface. Reserves are estimated to be 68 million tons. Since 1918, Oklahoma has produced 65 per cent of the district's total concentrates. Kansas normally ranks second; Missouri, third.

IRON ORE

The discovery of a hill believed to be solid iron ore at Iron Mountain and a similar deposit at Pilot Knob, Missouri, inaugurated the opening of iron ore mines in the area in the 1830's. A railroad was built to St. Louis in hopes that the new deposits would make the region the iron mining center of the United States. But these ambitions were short lived. Richer deposits were discovered in the Great Lakes area and the Missouri ore bodies proved to be much less extensive than supposed.

Recently, however, the virtual exhaustion of the best ores of Minnesota's Mesabi Range, coupled with the growth of the steel industry and the development of better upgrading methods, has roused new interest in Missouri ores, for now it is profitable to recover low grade ores. The mine at Iron Mountain has operated steadily since World War II, with a present output of over 200 million tons annually. Moreover, higher grade magnetite ores (over 60 per cent iron content) have been found near Sullivan, about 50 miles southwest of St. Louis. This ore is more than a thousand feet below the surface. Present plans call for an eventual output of some two million tons of ore annually.

Additional minerals of the Ozark-Ouachita Highlands include: (1) barite, a heavy white mineral used in oil drilling, in chemicals, glass, paint, and rubber; and (2) cobalt, a by-product of lead mining at Frederickstown, Missouri.

POWER

Because of the rugged terrain, considerable head for hydroelectric power is provided by the Arkansas and White Rivers. Their development was authorized by Congress in the Flood Control Act of 1950. The authorized plan for the Arkansas River consists of an integrated system of projects to improve navigation, to develop hydroelectric power, and to provide for flood control. An installed capacity of 577,-000 kilowatts eventually will serve the urban

Figure 8-5. Bagnell Dam, a hydroelectric power dam on the Osage River, forms Lake of the Ozarks, Missouri's largest lake and one of the most extensively developed resort areas in the United States. Its coves, peninsulas, and rocky outcrops form a shoreline of 1,372 miles. Over 300 resorts and hotels dot its shores. (Massie, Missouri Resources Commission)

centers on the plains border and central lowland of Kansas and Oklahoma.

The White River and its tributaries drain an area of about 27,765 square miles. The northern and western parts of the basin, comprising approximately three-fourths of the area, are in the Ozark Plateaus. Future development of hydroelectric power calls for construction of 14 authorized multipurpose dams, an estimate based upon an ultimate installed capacity of 1,386,000 kilowatts.

RECREATION AND TOURISM

The Ozark-Ouachita Highlands are the only major hill areas between the Appalachians and the Rocky Mountains. Consequently they offer an attraction to the surrounding population centers. Residents of such cities as St. Louis, Kansas City, Tulsa, Oklahoma City, Little Rock, and Shreveport are within a 300-mile radius of resort facilities within the region.

Tourists are not new to the area. Indeed, the isolation which originally retarded its development has long been one of its main attractions to hunters and fishermen. Eldorado Springs was one of the several southwest Missouri cities that attracted health seekers by the hundreds before the turn of the century. Lake Taneycomo was formed by the building of Powersite Dam during World War I; it has been a tourist attraction ever since. Lake of the Ozarks was created in the 1920's.

Recreational advantages are heightened by the location of two national forests: (1) the Ouachita, oldest in the United States; and (2) the Ozark, a series of high ridges punctuated by deep valleys. Within the two forests are several government-built recreation areas.

Hot Springs, Arkansas, created as a national reservation in 1832, is the oldest national park in America. The apparently endless flow of mineral waters from 47 springs attracts thousands of people from all over the world.

OUTLOOK

Geographically, the Ozark-Ouachita Highlands are not as favored for receational develment as many other regions of Anglo-America. Elevations are not high enough to modify the heat and dampness of the humid continental summer. Milder winters and lower elevations result in a light snow cover that limits winter sports.

Despite these handicaps, the tourist business continues to expand. Since World War II, the rise in national income, the almost universal institution of paid vacations, and the increase in the number of people owning automobiles, have directed an ever-increasing flood of tourists into the Ozark-Ouachita Highlands.

Part III | CENTRAL PLAINS OF ANGLO-AMERICA

The Central Plains encompass one of the largest sections of Anglo-America—extending from the St. Lawrence Lowland and the Gulf of St. Lawrence in the east to the Rocky Mountains in the west and from west-central Texas in the south to northern Alberta in Canada. Their division into Eastern Interior Low Plains and Western Interior High Plains is based on elevation; the 1,500-foot contour forms the eastern edge of the High Plains. It also closely parallels the 20-inch rainfall line, a transition from subhumid to semiarid landscape. Westward, the economy changes rapidly from tilled agriculture (except where irrigation water is available) to grazing. Eastward, the greater population density and smaller farm units are a response to a more dependable rainfall that enables a wider variety of agricultural crops to be grown.

Because of the vast size of the Central Plains their economy is extremely varied. Portions are lands of teeming cities and industries, such as the urban belt on the borders of the Great Lakes; others are primarily devoted to the growing of grains or to dairying; still others are mining or grazing areas. Regardless of their economic pattern, however, they are basically lands of moderate to high relief, with a high percentage of near-level land.

9 | Eastern Interior Low Plains

THE Eastern Interior Low Plains make up one of the largest regions of Anglo-America. This area extends southward from the Canadian Shield to the Mississippi-West Gulf Plain, and westward from the Hills of the Ohio and Tennessee Basin to the Great Plains. It includes the St. Lawrence and Mohawk River Valleys and the narrow lowland bordering Lake Erie and Lake Ontario on the east. Sixteen states lie wholly or partly within the province. Of these, Illinois, Iowa, Michigan, Minnesota, and Wisconsin are included entirely. Other sections are the eastern thirds of North and South Dakota and Nebraska, the eastern half of Kansas, the middle portion of Oklahoma, northeastern Texas, the northern three-fifths of Missouri and a narrow strip in the southeast bordering the Mississippi River, the northern four-fifths of Indiana, almost all of western Ohio except the southwest corner along the Ohio River, eastern Ohio bordering Lake Erie, and the lake plain in central, western, and northern New York.

SURFACE FEATURES

With but few exceptions the surface of the Eastern Interior Low Plains is level to gently rolling. The term "low plains" is justified by comparison with the Hills of the Ohio and Tennessee Basin, the Western Interior High Plains, and the Ozark-Ouachita Highlands. In absolute elevation this province ranges from 1,500 or even 1,800 feet on its western border to 450 feet in southern Illinois and to less than 300 feet on the shores of Lake Ontario. The average elevation is perhaps a thousand feet.

The rocks are almost horizontal, a characteristic that accounts for the monotonous landscape in large portions of the region. They are largely of limestone and shale deposited in the interior sea before the Appalachian revolution.[1] The northern part was covered by glacial drift from a few feet to 800 feet thick, which is composed mainly of till, but also much water-laid drift.

The Eastern Interior Low Plains Province was subject to erosion during the entire time the older and younger peneplains were being made in the East. The whole has reached base

level[2] at least once. Most of it now stands above local base level, having been raised and eroded not long before the glacial epoch. The continental ice advanced over the region several times, each advance making a glacial stage. Three major subregions make up the Eastern Interior Low Plains.

THE UPPER GREAT LAKES SUBREGION

The Upper Great Lakes Subregion is a peneplain characterized by many lakes, swamps, piles of gravel, stretches of sand, sandy loam, and clay. Originally a land of high mountains, the subregion was eroded to an almost level plain, then it was submerged under the sea, uplifted again, partially eroded again, and finally scraped by the continental glacier. This evolution has caused enough physical differences within the area to justify a further subdivision into the following:

The Superior Upland. This section lies to the west, south, and north of Lake Superior in southern Ontario, eastern Minnesota, northern Wisconsin, the upper peninsula of Michigan, and the northern part of the lower peninsula of Michigan. It resembles the flatter parts of northern New England. The average altitude is 1,200 to 1,400 feet; Lake Superior is 602 feet above sea level. The rocks are very ancient; they are folded, faulted, peneplained, and covered by young glacial drift. Lakes and swamps are numerous and drainage is poor. The forests are in large part cut over. There is not much agriculture. The population is sparse, except around the mining centers.

The Western Lake Section. This section (Minnesota, northern Iowa, eastern North and South Dakota) has the same general features as the Lower Great Lakes Subregion but more till plain and fewer lakes and swamps, except in northern Minnesota. Much forest remains in the northeastern (humid) part. Prairie predominates in the south and west. The valley of the Red River is the best known lacustrine plain in Anglo-America (a result of glacial

---

[1] The period of folding and mountain building in North America at or near the close of the Paleozoic Period, some 200 million years ago.

[2] The lowest level to which a stream can wear its bed. The length of time taken for a bed to reach base level depends on the rate of erosion. Generally speaking, this will be less for a large stream than for a small one, and will be less over weak rock than over resistant rock. The permanent base level is the level of the sea. A lake provides a temporary base level, but the sediment deposited on it by the stream destroys its effect.

Lake Agassiz). It gives rise to the great wheat lands of North Dakota and Manitoba. All the drift is young and the drainage immature.

The Wisconsin Driftless Section. Southwestern Wisconsin was surrounded by ice but, except for a narrow margin of old and much-eroded drift, never covered. The southern part, containing considerable limestone, is a dissected plateau like western Kentucky and suggests the topography of the other sections before the ice epoch. The northern half is a lowland on weak sandstone and makes poor soil. It is partly covered by a deep sandy outwash, which is poorly drained and infertile.

The Dissected Till Plains. Northeastern, eastern, southern, and western Iowa and the northern half of Missouri are like the Till Plains, but were made in an earlier glacial epoch. Most of the area is covered by loess.[3] It is largely prairie or a gently undulating, almost flat, generally treeless, grassy plain.

The Till Plains and Dissected Till Plains comprise the great corn and livestock section of the American Middle West.

THE LOWER GREAT LAKES SUBREGION

The Lower Great Lakes Subregion has deep drift and numerous moraines, lakes, and swamps. Michigan and the southern shores of Lakes Huron, Erie, and Ontario have large areas of sandy outwash.[4] South and west of the Great Lakes are lacustrine plains[5] extending many miles. The drainage is everywhere young. The soil is good on the till plains and old lake bottoms. In the north considerable forest remains, along with great areas of cut-over land. All rocks dip toward the center of Michigan. The chief divides are on the outcropping edges of resistant strata.

Western Ohio and almost all of Indiana and Illinois south of the Great Lakes are mainly ground moraine[6] of faint relief, little eroded.

The drift is from a few feet to a few hundred feet thick. The preglacial topography is almost everywhere completely buried and obscured. Recessional moraines[7] are present, but are generally smooth swells, only here and there very prominent. There are few lakes and swamps, though much artificial drainage is needed because of flatness.

THE OSAGE SUBREGION

This section includes the eastern three-eighths of Kansas, the central third of Oklahoma, and northeastern Texas and lies south of the glacial limit. It slopes gently eastward over strata dipping faintly westward. Stronger strata cause east-facing scarps or hilly belts between which are fertile peneplains of small relief from ten to 50 miles wide. The thickest strong stratum causes the Flint Hills of Kansas, a ridge with maximum height of over 600 feet. Except for this upland, the highest and most ruggedly dissected escarpments[8] (several of them 300 feet or more) are found near the south end, where the larger streams are also sharply trenching the intervening belts of plain.

CLIMATE

The Eastern Interior Low Plains Province encompasses such a large land area (more than 1,400 miles from north to south and over 1,200 miles from east to west) that temperature, precipitation, and length of growing season, all of which affect greatly man's economic activities, vary greatly. There is a measure of uniformity throughout the province only in terms of seasonal distribution of precipitation and the influence of the continental land mass on temperatures.

The average annual temperature varies from 65° F. in the extreme southern portion of the region (northeastern Texas) to 35° in southern Ontario. The January average is 50° in the south, —5° in the north; July, 80° in the south, 65° in the north. Average annual minimum temperatures vary from 15° along the southern border to —40° north of Lake Supe-

---

[3] A deposit of fine soil, or loam, which is generally held to have been transported to its present position by the wind.

[4] The alluvial plain formed by the streams resulting from the melting ice of a glacier. The streams carry away some of the material of the moraine and deposit it over a considerable area. The coarser material is deposited near the ice, the finer mataral farther away.

[5] Former lake bottoms.

[6] Unsorted glacial debris deposited in sheets, sometimes over very large areas.

[7] Marginal moraines left by a retreating glacier or ice sheet at a halt in its retrogression. While it halted, material continued to collect at its front.

[8] An inland cliff or steep slope, formed by the erosion of inclined strata of hard rocks.

rior. A much narrower range occurs in summer, however; there is only a 10° differential in average annual maximum temperatures between the southern (105°) and the northern (95°) parts of the region.

The province as a whole is characterized by small variations in precipitation from year to year, frequent alternations of above and below normal, and comparative absence of prolonged drought periods. Precipitation increases from west to east (25 inches to 40 inches) and from north to south (25 inches to 50 inches). Winter is the driest period of the year; precipitation falls in the form of rain in the south and snow in the north. Cyclonic storms traverse the region and bring changeable weather on the average of every three to five days. The wettest period is from April to September, inclusive. Convectional rainfall throughout the province provides adequate moisture for crops without irrigation. Nowhere is less than 16 inches of moisture received, and over most parts a minimum of 20 inches is recorded during the six-month period. The frost-free season varies considerably—from less than four months in the extreme north to more than seven months in the extreme south.

UPPER GREAT LAKES SUBREGION

FORESTS AND FOREST INDUSTRIES

When the white man first came to the Upper Great Lakes Subregion, millions of acres of timber lay untouched before him. Within the United States portion of this forest were mixed broadleaf deciduous and coniferous trees. Farther north in Canada, conifers — white pine, Norway pine, hemlock, spruce, balsam, and others—formed the dominant species.

In this forest stood several hundred billion feet of white pine and as much more of other marketable timber. Among the pines were trees that scaled 5,000 board feet. There were townships from which 400 million feet of lumber were cut, and single acres from which 100,000 feet of white pine were taken.

The original forests were lumbered heavily toward the end of the 19th century. Three related geographic facts have been effective influences in the exploitation of these forests: (1) the plains-like character of the region made lumbering easy; (2) the radial flow of its rivers, their torrential character in spring, and their available water power facilitated logging; (3) the two important waterways on the borders of the area, the Great Lakes and the Mississippi River, aided in the marketing of lumber and lumber products.

To appreciate how geographical advantages in the Upper Great Lakes hastened the appreciation of its forest wealth, it is only necessary to note that its forests, though a thousand miles from the Atlantic Seaboard, were well-exploited before extensive lumbering operations were even begun in West Virginia. Around 1900, when the area's peak timber output was reached, these forests were the chief source of lumber. But the cutting as practiced proved shortsighted. The land was soon cleared of nearly all its original stands and left to regrow as it could. At least half of the cutover area subsequently was burned over, further reducing the quality and stocking of new growth.

Today, there remain about 53 million acres of commercial forest land in the three Upper Lakes states—Minnesota, Wisconsin, and Michigan — mostly in the form of second-growth forests.

Pulp and paper manufacturing. Pulp and paper manufacturing is an economic mainstay of the Upper Lakes Subregion. It is, for example, Wisconsin's leading industry both in employment and capital investment. In Minnesota, trees cut for pulpwood far outvalue those for other uses; nearly 6,500 persons find full-time employment in pulp and paper mills. Moreover, the economic activities generated by this industry are more widespread geographically than are those of copper and iron mining, other important industries in the Upper Lakes Subregion. Forests are found throughout the area, whereas the mines are concentrated in a few localities.

Pulp and paper plants were first established in the Upper Lakes Subregion to take advantage of ample raw materials. Dense forests that at one time covered nearly 100 million acres in Michigan, Minnesota, and Wisconsin held great volumes of spruce and fir. The fibers of these softwood trees were in prime demand for pulp making.

The present commercial forest area coincides rather closely with the original extent of softwood forests. Most pulp and paper mills in the

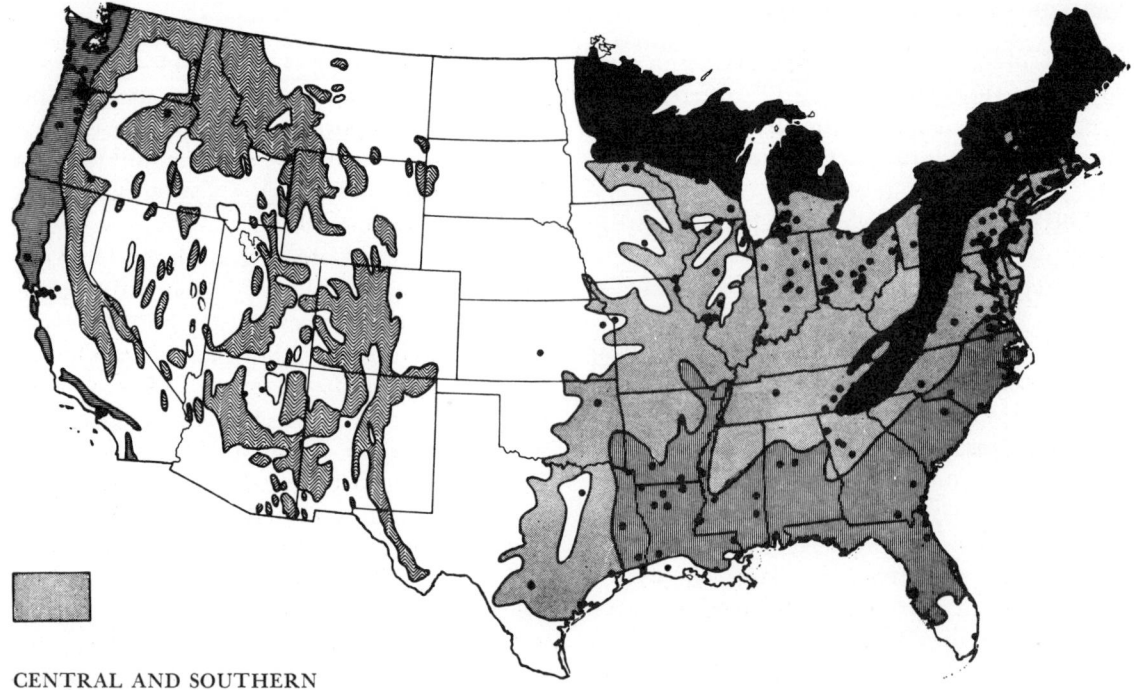

CENTRAL AND SOUTHERN HARDWOOD FORESTS

Northern portion: oaks; hickories; ashes; elms; maples; beech; black walnut; pitch, shortleaf, and Virginia pines; cottonwood; and others.

Southern portion: oaks, red and black gums, hickories, ashes, black walnut, Eastern red cedar, cottonwood, yellow poplar, beech, and others.

PULP OR PAPER MILLS

WEST COAST FORESTS

Douglas fir, Western hemlock, redwood, Western red cedar, Sitka spruce, sugar pine, lodgepole pine, incense cedar, white fir, Port Orford cedar, and others.

NORTHERN FORESTS

Red, black, and white spruces; balsam fir; white, red, jack, and pitch pines; Eastern hemlock; maples; oaks; beech; birches; and aspen.

SOUTHERN FORESTS

Longleaf, shortleaf, loblolly, and slash pines; Southern oaks; red gum; hickories; Southern cypress; Eastern and Southern red cedars; and others.

WESTERN FORESTS

Ponderosa pine, Idaho white pine, Western larch, Engelmann spruce, Douglas fir, lodgepole pine, sugar pine, Western red cedar, Western hemlock, white fir, and others.

Figure 9-1. Pulp and paper mills and forest regions of the United States. (American Forest Products Industries)

region are located in this area, or within an hour's trucking distance of its southern limits.

The pulp and paper industry of the American section of the Upper Lakes, with currently about ten per cent of the nation's pulp and paper making capacity, has shown a sizable growth in plant capacity over the past decade, but at a rate below the national average.

Ontario. Ontario has vast timber resources. There are enormous reserves of jack pine and poplar that now can be utilized for the pulp and paper industry with the development of two new processes—the semichemical and chemical groundwood pulping methods.

Based upon the forest resources of Ontario are an important lumber and wood using group of industries and a huge and growing pulp and paper industry. The total value of basic wood products manufactures in Ontario—lumber, veneers and plywood, laths, shingles, fuel wood, ties, poles, posts, mine timbers, and certain other minor products — exceeds $100 million a year. Chief among these basic wood items is lumber, with an annual value of more than $60 million from 800 million board feet of timber.

The volume of pulp approximates 2.4 million tons, nearly two and one-half times the production in the middle 1920's. The value of paper output has risen from about $86 million in 1945 to more than $272 million today. Output of manufactured paperboards, book and writing paper, wrapping paper, and tissue paper also has shown a steep rise since 1950.

Ontario's pulp and paper industry is primarily an export industry. The United States is Ontario's best customer and the most important export product of the pulp and paper industry is newsprint. Since 1950, however, overseas exports have shown a steady rise. Both newsprint and pulp have been allowed duty-free into the United States market since 1914, when the tariffs on these items were removed because of an acute domestic shortage.

FUR FARMING AND TRAPPING

Fur farming and trapping provide the raw materials for a small fur goods industry concentrated largely in the big cities. Ontario has approximately 600 fur farms, although numbers have been declining annually. Mink make up 90 per cent of the animals now on Ontario

fur farms; the remainder consists chiefly of chinchillas and foxes. Thirty years ago, mink were rare; foxes comprised about 90 per cent of all animals on fur farms. This change in emphasis has been the result of shifting fashions over the years.

The most important animals trapped in Ontario are beaver, muskrat, and mink. These contribute more than 90 per cent of the value of all peltries from trapped animals.

The cutover country of upper Michigan, northern Wisconsin, and northern Minnesota supports fur industries. The true trapper—the north woods type—still is found in portions of Wisconsin and Minnesota. Fox, mink, weasel, muskrat, and beaver are caught. Fur farming is also important. Wisconsin, Minnesota and Michigan account for more than 56 per cent of the nation's ranch mink peltries.

FISHING

Ontario leads Canada in the value of fish taken from inland waters. Approximately four-fifths of the fish are caught in the Great Lakes. The most common species are pickerel, whitefish, perch, lake trout, and bass.

In 1960, about 75 million pounds of fish worth $9.5 million were caught. This represented a decline of 17.3 per cent by weight and 5.4 per cent by value over the previous year. The greatest amount (29.6 million pounds) was gathered from Lake Erie. The second largest catch was from Lake Michigan (27.2 million pounds). American fisheries' production varies greatly from year to year, but the trend has been slightly downward.

One of the great problems of the Great Lakes fisheries is the sea lamprey, a snaky-looking, smooth-bodied marine creature somewhat resembling an eel, but not related. It is one of five species of lamprey known to Great Lakes waters. As its name implies, the sea lamprey is primarily a salt water denizen. It originally moved up the St. Lawrence into Lake Ontario in search of spawning grounds; there it remained. Not until 1921, following completion of the Welland Canal, were sea lampreys observed in Lake Erie. Progressively, since then, sea lampreys have been reported from the St. Clair River, Lake Huron, Georgian Bay, the North Channel, and finally, in 1947, from Lake Superior south of Thunder Cape. They also have invaded Lake Michigan. Lake trout, whitefish, carp, suckers, and yellow pickerel are among the fish most frequently attacked. Recent reports have indicated that the lamprey is now succumbing to poison and to weir controls.

MINING

Copper. Copper ores were first mined in the Keweenaw Peninsula of Michigan after 1845. Here copper occurs not as an ore but in its native state. Deposits in Michigan were once the chief source of United States supply. The rise of Butte, Montana, in 1880, followed by open pit mining at Bingham Canyon, Utah, and Globe, Miami, Bisbee, and Ajo, Arizona, lessened the importance of Michigan as a copper producer. Though dwarfed by the West's large-scale exploitations of low-grade ores, Michigan's shaft copper mines still yield on a small scale. Maximum production of 136,-846 tons was reached in 1916. Annual production is now about 24,000 tons. Total copper mined to date is nearly five million tons.

The earliest metal produced in Ontario was copper; it was mined by Indians several centuries ago. The first nonferrous metal mining in Ontario in modern times was done at the Montreal Mining Company's works at Bruce Mines, about 40 miles south and east of the Sault. In spite of inefficient methods, considerable copper was mined and shipped at great expense between 1847 and 1876. At first the metal ore was treated in Wales, which was then the world's great smelting and refining center for nonferrous metals, the skill of its workmen not yet having been made obsolete by science.

In 1848,. Sir William Logan, the first geologist of the old Province of Canada, reported that the north shore of Lake Huron was well supplied with copper minerals. Nearly thirty years passed before transportation improved sufficiently to make mining practical. These deposits in the Sudbury district were rediscovered in 1883 when the Canadian Pacific built its transcontinental rail line through the area.

The Sudbury district of Ontario has the largest known copper reserves in Canada. Copper occurs in huge, massive sulfide ore bodies in conjunction with nickel. Proven reserves total about 250 million tons of three per cent copper-nickel ore. Because of the general relative price levels of the two metals, copper is in effect a by-product whose production can be considred to cost less here than in operations producing copper alone. Sudbury, therefore, gives its copper producers a very great price advantage.

Certain other areas are also displaying highly promising copper potentialities. The most important of these regions is the Manitouwadge Lake area north of Lake Superior. Indeed, this is the region that may claim the greatest of the more recent base metal discoveries in Ontario. Not only have large deposits of copper been discovered there, but also deposits of lead, zinc, and silver. Other copper deposits in Ontario include one at Maimainse Point, north of Sault Ste. Marie, and another near Kashabowie, west of Fort William.

Nickel. The Sudbury district is the source of over 85 per cent of the free world's nickel output. The nickel industry in Ontario owes its start to the world's best supply of raw materials on the one hand, and to a demand for nickel to toughen armor plate on the other. One of the founders of the industry, S. J. Ritchie of Akron, Ohio, succeeded with his Canadian Copper Company against obstacles that ruined other companies. The company found itself in the nickel business by accident, for copper originally was believed to be the only metal in the Sudbury area. Among the company's problems were the difficulty of treating the nickel ore economically and the limited market for the new metal, caused partly by a trade prejudice in favor of New Caledonia nickel.

The International Nickel Company of Canada, Ltd., is the world's largest producer of nickel. It is partly a holding and partly an operating company. It owns approximately 100,000 acres in the Sudbury area and has options or claims on many other nickel deposits in Canada. Sudbury area operations consist of one open pit, five underground mines, and the crushing, concentrating, and smelting plants at Copper Cliff, Ontario. There are also an extensive railway and several hydroelectric plants. Sudbury yields almost one-half of Ontario's metal production in value, totaling 287.4 million pounds worth $160.4 million.

Asbestos. Asbestos is the name applied to several minerals, the commonest one in Canada being known to geologists as chrysotile and to chemists as hydrous magnesium silicate. The physical properties of asbestos — fiber length, tensile strength, flexibility, color, and the like—may vary considerably from deposit to deposit, along with the price. Although the largest known deposits are in Quebec, the mineral is also found in various parts of Ontario. In 1950, the Johns-Manville Company opened a mine at Matheson, in the Cochran district, which produces about 2.6 per cent of Canada's asbestos. Canada mines approximately two-thirds of the world's supply, most of which is sold in the United States.

Gypsum. Three-quarters of Canada's gypsum output, used in the making of cement and wall plaster, is shipped to the United States. Ontario is Canada's second largest producer. Production comes chiefly from a mine near Hagersville, Haldimand County, Ontario, in the Lake Erie region.

Nepheline syenite. This is a quartz-free rock chemically similar to feldspar but containing more aluminum. Like feldspar, it is used in ceramic industries, especially glass. There is only one mine in Canada producing this mineral. It is located near Petersborough, Ontario, where mining operations began in 1935. More than 100,000 tons are mined annually and marketed mostly in the United States, bringing a return of about $1.6 million.

Limestone. Limestone is the third important ingredient used in making pig iron; the other two are iron ore and coal. Michigan ranks second only to Pennsylvania as a producer of limestone. About 45 per cent of the limestone quarried is consumed as flux stone in the iron and steel industry. Other uses include alkali manufacture, cement making, concrete, road building, and burning for fertilizer.

Although the lime deposits are located some 300 miles from the blast furnaces, cheap water transportation via the Great Lakes makes possible easy movement to markets along the shores of the lakes from Duluth and Chicago to Buffalo. Large bulk freighters carry their own steel booms aboard for unloading the limestone. Coal is carried as return cargo. Furthermore, the lakeside location makes available cheap water for use in power generators and for washing stone.

Figure 9-2. International Nickel Company plant at Copper Cliff, Ontario. A recent $150 million expansion program permits the utilization of formerly uneconomical low-grade ores and a changeover from open pit mining and underground mining to underground mining almost exclusively. Nickel is crushed, concentrated, and smelted at the Copper Cliff plant. (Ontario Department of Travel)

In the years following 1900, large-scale industrialization caused a demand for limestone with special characteristics. Since most of the chemical uses of limestone require the stone to be as pure and as high in calcium content as possible, search was instituted for such deposits. It was discovered that Michigan was fortunate in having large, thinly covered deposits of very pure, high-calcium stone in the northern part of the state. Huron, Alpena, and Emmet Counties in the southern peninsula and Delta and Schoolcraft Counties in the northern peninsula offered large deposits at lakeside.

Highly mechanized quarry operations were begun, and today limestone shipments from Michigan are third in over-all Great Lakes tonnage. Michigan ports of origin are Calcite, Port Inland, Alpena, and Rockport.

Iron ore. Mining activities in the Upper Lakes Subregion began around 1845, when a Chippewa Indian chief, Marji Gesick, led interested white men to iron ore deposits unearthed by an uprooted tree near Negaunee,

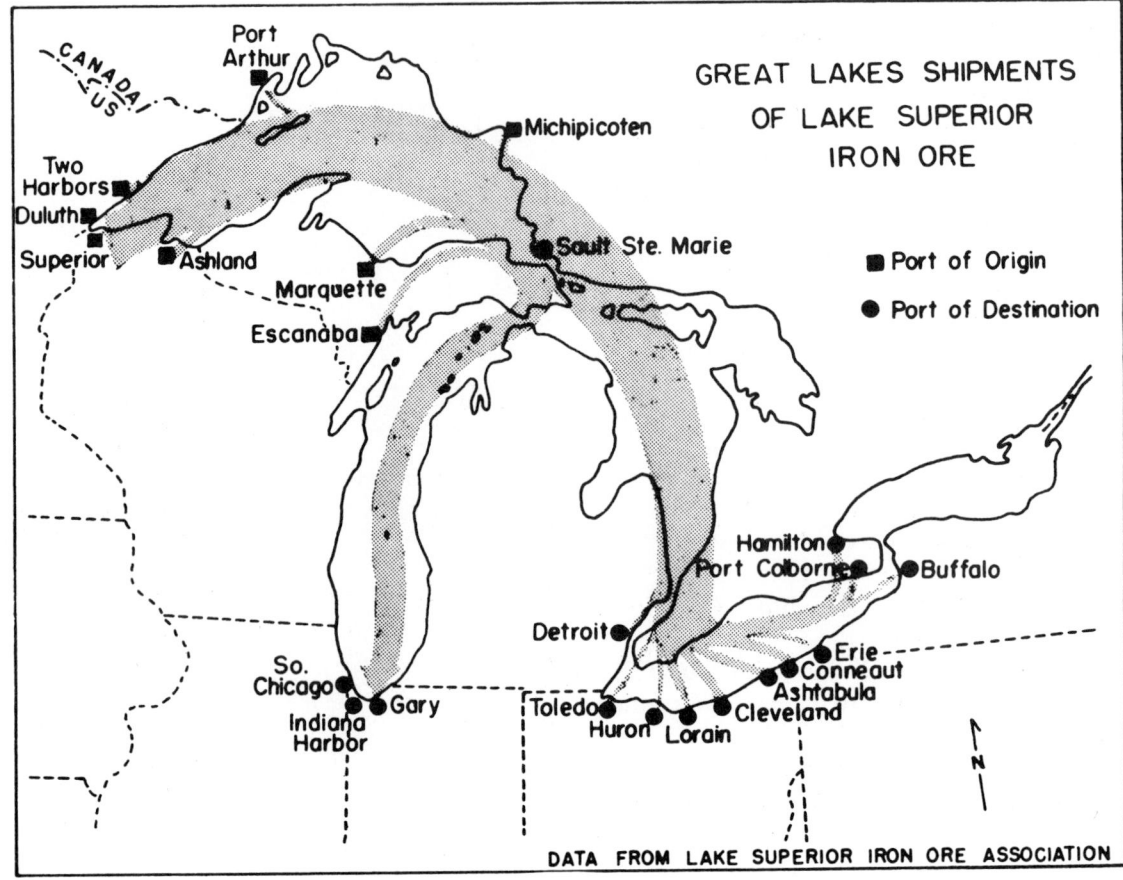

Figure 9-3. Great Lakes shipments of Lake Superior iron ore.

Michigan. Lake Superior district ore has been the backbone of United States industry ever since. In 1852, six barrels of ore were shipped out to New Castle, Pennsylvania. The following May a dock was built at Marquette and 152 tons of ore were shipped to Sharon, Pennsylvania. One thousand tons were shipped in 1854 —carried by wagons past the Sault Sainte Marie. After the "Soo" locks opened in 1855, shipments skyrocketed. Today a single ore boat will carry 12,000 to 20,000 tons from the area.

In Minnesota, the many ore deposits were once sediment on an ancient sea floor. Primitive forms of life living in the sea ate iron compounds dissolved in the water and carried them to the bottom. Later came sand, clay, volcanic deposits, earthquakes that tilted the whole terrain, and then glaciers that wore away the top earth in some places and covered the ore in others. Over millions of years, rains leached out the sand and minerals here and there, leav-

ing scattered deposits of ore rich enough to be ready for the blast furnace.

MESABI, IRON GIANT IN THE EARTH

"The biggest hole man ever dug." This is what guides tell you as you look into the fabulous Hull-Rust-Mahoning open pit mine at Hibbing, Minnesota, "the Iron Ore Capital of the World."

Minnesota's Mesabi iron was discovered on November 16, 1890, when a test pit was dug by J. A. Nichols, of Duluth, near a point where wagon wheels had sunk through pine needles into powdery reddish "dirt." The pit yielded hematite, in this case 64 per cent iron. When the Mesabi was officially opened in 1892, it contained 2.5 billion long tons of ore. Today nearly 60 per cent of this has been consumed.

Whether your car is a Ford, a Chevrolet, or a Plymouth; whether your food is packed in cans filled in the South or in the West; whether your building is made with steel frames, or of wood with steel nails; it is safe to guess that you are depending on Hibbing.

If the metals in these items did not come from this area, they probably were made with machines that once were Mesabi ore, for a third of the nation's iron ore has been dug from this pit.

Without Mesabi ore, and ore like it placed close to the surface elsewhere in Minnesota, Michigan, and Wisconsin; without water transportation to haul it inexpensively to the coal fields of Pennsylvania, Ohio, and Kentucky; without the great machines that can move this ore, coal, and stone; without the sweat of teams of men; America would still live in a world not too different from that of George Washington —a world where houses are heated with fireplaces, wooden wheels run on wooden bearings, and wooden plows crudely break the soil.

Four hundred feet down on the floor of the 13,000-acre pit at Mesabi are winding tracks, diesel locomotives, giant electric shovels, truck roads, and dynamite-hole drills. Trucks are used to haul ore to conveyor belts running day and night from the pit floor up to the surface. One truck—a hulking, 400-horsepower diesel— can haul 34 tons of ore to the dump. There, crushers break big chunks and drop them onto a rubber belt.

Some ore can be shipped straight to Superior, Wisconsin, or Two Harbors and Duluth, Minnesota, for a boat trip to the blast furnaces. Today, much of the ore must be beneficiated —washed to remove sand. Both magnetite and hematite ores come from the mines here.

Once ore is in a rail car, it appears to the layman that all the work is over. But such is not the case. The ore of each mine differs a little chemically from the ore of other mines. Blast furnace operators want a standard ore so they can predict how much limestone and coke must be added to make the best iron for their customers. Correct predicting can be accomplished only by sampling, sorting, and mixing—a procedure that begins at the pits.

In the five hours that it takes for huge steam locomotives to haul trainloads of ore down to the yards near the docks, this is what happens: Samples are (1) taken to a laboratory; (2) ground into powder; (3) weighed out into test pans; (4) tested for their content of iron, phos-

Figure 9-4. Loading an ore train by electric shovel at an open pit iron mine in the Mesabi Range, Minnesota, where a good percentage of the nation's iron ore is mined. (Bureau of Mines, U.S. Department of the Interior)

phorus, silicon, manganese, and moisture; and (5) all information recorded. From this, and from customer orders, advice is teletyped directing which rail cars are to be dumped into each ship so that the aggregate will make up a standard grade as ordered.

All this does not make the railroaders' job any easier. To sort 40 million tons of ore a year into 32 grades, to keep ore flowing to the docks fast enough to fill one boat every 15 or 20 minutes, to keep 7,000 rail cars moving 95 miles from the mines to the docks and back to the mines without bottlenecks that either would tie up a boat or shut down a mine—this takes a high order of skill.

The future of Mesabi. Since 1939, the Mesabi ore has been withdrawn over twice as fast as it was between 1920 and 1939. There is a divergence of opinion as to whether or not we shall continue making steel very long at the present rate, but if we are to achieve our national purpose of maintaining high production and employment we surely shall need steel in quantities very close to the present rate — at which rate we shall have used up the last of the Mesabi ores by 1964.

One striking effect of the depletion of the Mesabi Range will be that the steel industry no longer will be able to expand its output rapidly in response to unexpected needs, as, for example, the demands of war. Sixty per cent of the Mesabi ore lies so close to the surface that it is mined simply by removing the overburden of earth and attacking the ore with mechanical shovels. Open pit mining has made possible a rapid increase in the quantity produced. By contrast, the underground ores, some of which are thousands of feet below the surface, can be withdrawn in larger quantity only after shafts and tunnels have been built, which takes both money and time. Consequently every rapid increase in steel production has drawn heavily upon the open pit ores of the Mesabi. Open pit mining offered the United States a tremendous advantage in its belated and hasty rearmament program in the early years of World War II. From 1940 to 1945, the steel industry did not increase its use of the underground ores at all.

The ores will not, in fact, be exhausted by 1964, because our use of them will taper off. Some steel and mining companies have extensive holdings of Lake Superior ores. The United States Steel Corporation, for example, can draw from the reserves of its subsidiary in the Lake Superior region for another generation. But other companies are not as well provided. Within the next five or six years these companies will begin to encounter increasing difficulty in getting adequate supplies of Lake Superior ores to the steel plants along the lakes. Perhaps by 1980, the shipments of the present Mesabi ores will have dwindled to insignificance.

There is no single substitute for the Mesabi Range, even at higher costs. Where, then, will the industry turn to get the materials it needs? There are only two answers to the question: (1) the processing of taconite in northern Minnesota and (2) the development of reserves in Canada and abroad.

Other Lake Superior sources of iron ore in Minnesota include the Vermillion Range, first opened in 1865, and worked by underground mining methods. Minnesota's third iron range, the Cuyuna, was discovered in 1904. Marquette, in Michigan, and Menominee and Gogebic, in Michigan and Wisconsin, complete the list of Lake Superior iron ore ranges in the United States.

Taconite and jasper. In the recent search for iron ore, the Lake Superior region, which had supplied the country for many years, was not neglected. In fact, the biggest discovery was made by developing a way to process the billions of tons of low-grade taconite and jasper remaining in the area.

In the Mesabi Range, only about ten per cent of the accessible formation was high-grade open pit ore—"direct shipping ores." The balance was taconite — deposits of iron oxides mixed with sand, rock material, and other minerals and containing about one-third iron.

A handful of plants, either under construction or already in operation, use magnetic taconite, which proves to be almost as good for the furnace as direct shipping ores, although somewhat more expensive to process.

All this activity opens up vast new tonnages of Mesabi ore that should easily last for decades—certainly until methods can be devised to process economically the enormous quantities of nonmagnetic taconite remaining.

To quarry, grind, pulverize, and bake taconite balls takes mammoth machines that cost fortunes. One company spent $160 million to build a plant with only 3,500,000 tons capacity a year. Other companies expect to triple their payrolls as well as spend millions on machinery. To date, half a billion dollars has been expended or committed to develop taconite mines and processing plants in the eastern end of the Mesabi Range. Entire new towns are being built near the ore fields and along Lake Superior, north of Duluth. Large-scale production has already begun at Silver Bay, Minnesota. An even larger project at Aurora, Minnesota, represents a $300 million expenditure by four companies.

Iron concentrates are also being recovered from the jasper deposits of the Marquette Range in northern Michigan. Jasper is similar to taconite but has a slightly higher iron content. The capacity of present processing mills is

Figure 9-5. Loading iron ore at a Duluth ore dock. The ore is dumped from railroad cars into dockside bins, from which it pours down chutes and into the ship's hold. Approximately 13,000 tons of ore is loaded in four hours. (Standard Oil Co. of New Jersey)

expandable to about 27 million tons a year. Tentative estimates of the potential supply of low-grade iron ores in the Mesabi and Marquette Ranges alone exceed five billion tons.

Millions of dollars are being invested abroad, too, because no company wants to be forced to put up the sums necessary for enough taconite plants to supply all its needs.

CANADIAN ORE

Along the Canadian border are two iron ore districts, Michipicoten and Moose Mountain, lying partly in Minnesota and partly in Ontario near Atikokan.

The development at Steep Rock, in Ontario, also deserves mention. Located in the Canadian wilds 140 miles north of Duluth, these iron ore deposits rest beneath Steep Rock Lake. Part of the lake was drained in 1943 when Steep Rock Iron Mines, Ltd., was organized.

The ore-bearing earth is 150 to 400 feet below the original water line of the lake. In one of the biggest and most hazardous dredging jobs on record, a Chicago company is removing both the lake and the lake bed to clear the way for full-scale mining operations. Ore reserves are estimated at more than 60 million tons. Steep Rock Iron Mines hopes its mining operations will yield 2.5 million tons of ore a year.

UPPER GREAT LAKES PORTS

DULUTH-SUPERIOR

The bulk of Lake Superior ore clears through the vast loading docks at Duluth and adjacent Superior. Most of the ore shipments are from Superior, where the Great Northern Railway has the world's largest group of ore docks, capable of loading 24 freighters in as many hours.

Duluth (population 106,884) has an iron and steel industry based on local iron ore and coal from Pennsylvania and West Virginia borne as return cargo following the unloading of ore at the eastern end of the Great Lakes. It is the shipping outlet for one of the greatest grain producing areas in the world, extending west almost to the Pacific. Duluth's elevators can store 46 million bushels, and the port annually clears around 100 million bushels of wheat and other cereals. In addition, it ships large quantities of balsam wood and other forest products, wool, flax, shingles, fabricated iron and steel, and various other items that make up the so-called "package freight" business, as distinguished from the bulk traffic—ore, coal, and grain. Waterborne commerce of Duluth-Superior is second only to New York.

FORT WILLIAM-PORT ARTHUR

A whole day by train from the twin ports of

Duluth and Superior on the American side are the Canadian twins, Fort William and Port Arthur, outlets for grain from the Canadian West and supply base for the vast territory of northwestern Ontario. Once among the greatest fur trading centers in North America, Fort William now claims the world's biggest fur ranch, with 15,000 mink and other animals. The city is also the headquarters of a timber region producing 750,000 cords of wood annually—two-thirds of which goes to the United States.

Wheat, however, is by far the major commodity, filling the 92-million-bushel elevators at the lake front and flowing eastward to the St. Lawrence at the rate of 200 to 300 million bushels per year, with a small quantity going west to Duluth for transshipment to various mills in the United States. In exchange, Fort William and Port Arthur take in supplies of every description for the vast hinterland—nails, binder twine, barbed wire, canned goods, clothing, mining and agricultural machinery, and other equipment.

COAL

The Eastern Interior Low Plains contain parts of three important bituminous coal fields. These are (1) the Eastern Interior field of southern Illinois and the adjacent part of Indiana; (2) the Western Interior field of northern Missouri, Iowa, southeastern Kansas, and east-central and northeastern Oklahoma; and (3) the Southwestern Interior field in north-central Texas.

Only southern Illinois produces good coking coal in sufficient quantity to supply the iron and steel industry. Gary, Indiana, and other Midwestern steel centers provide a market for coal from this field. Considerable tonnage is used for steam purposes as well. One major technological shift, the "dieselization" of the railroads, has resulted in a considerable decline in domestic demands. Illinois usually ranks fourth in soft coal output behind West Virginia, Pennsylvania, and Kentucky.

The Western Interior field, although extensive, is not only low grade, ranging from lignite to subbituminous, but also is rather remote from the major centers of population. Production is small. For example, Oklahoma mines only two million tons annually. The coal is utilized as industrial fuel throughout the Southwest and Midwest.

Coal is found in a considerable area in north-central Texas, ranging in quality from middle to inferior bituminous. During the last few years coal production has amounted only to about 50,000 tons annually. Petroleum and natural gas are cheaper and better fuels in this state.

Michigan's North Interior field is the least exploited of the coal areas within the Eastern Low Plains. Its coal is no longer mined, for it is more economical to import high-grade coal from the Appalachian Province via the lakes than to mine and market inferior coal from this field.

PETROLEUM

No sooner had Drake completed his well near Titusville, Pennsylvania, than a rush for oil regions started. The search for oil soon spread throughout the Midwest, first in Ohio, where a well was sunk by spring pole at a spot one and a half miles southeast of Macksburg during the winter of 1860. Drilling spread through the years to northwestern, northern, and central Ohio. Production was begun in some 45 counties, and since 1860, approximately 175,000 wells have been drilled for oil and gas in the state. Ohio has produced an estimated 615 million barrels of crude oil to date.

LIMA, OHIO, FIELD

The largest producing formation has been the Trenton in the Lima Grade field in northwestern Ohio, which for a short time was the greatest in the world. During 1896, Ohio's peak year, 23,941,000 barrels were produced, of which 21 million came from the Trenton fields.

For many years, Ohio's oil production has been generally on a steady decline. Lima Grade now accounts for but five per cent of the state total, or approximately three million barrels.

The Lima field continues northwestward into eastern Indiana and is thus located on the west side of the Cincinnati Anticline. Production in Indiana reached a peak in 1904, and has been declining steadily ever since. Although the oil is of a high-grade paraffin base,

Figure 9-6. A pumping station in the Midcontinent oil field. There are more geologists, more drilling contractors, more oil companies, and more crude oil production in this area than in any other comparable section. The field now accounts for about one-third of the world's production and about two-thirds of the nation's. (Phillips Petroleum Co.)

it contains considerable sulphur, making it more difficult to refine.

THE MICHIGAN FIELD

This field came into production around 1925, and experienced a phenomenal rise from 4,000 barrels in that year, to a peak of 23 million barrels in 1939. Since then, production has dropped to about 13 million barrels annually. The Michigan field is located in the central part of the southern peninsula to the west of Saginaw Bay. New fields are being developed elsewhere in the state.

SOUTHEASTERN ILLINOIS

Southern Illinois is the center of an oil field that continues eastward into the adjacent portions of Indiana and Kentucky. Production began in 1889, and output was small for a number of years until, in 1910, more than 33 million barrels were taken from the ground. The field then experienced a rapid fall to less than five million barrels. Deeper drilling caused a second peak to be reached in 1940, when some 147 million barrels were produced. Like most highly-productive oil areas, the field again declined rapidly to its present output of 58 million barrels.

MIDCONTINENT FIELD

Only a part of this largest of all oil fields, namely north-central Texas, Oklahoma, and eastern Kansas, lies within the Eastern Interior Low Plains. The Midcontinent field includes northern and western Texas, part of New Mexico, and all of Oklahoma and Kansas. Thus defined, this is the most productive of all the oil regions of the world.

The first oil output of consequence occurred at Corsicana, Texas, where oil was discovered in 1894, while drillers were seeking water. This find, however, was merely a prelude to the development of the region's resources. It was the tremendous gusher at Spindletop, near Beaumont in the Mississippi-West Gulf Plain Province, on January 10, 1901, that opened up oil exploration. This well, flowing at an initial rate of 75,000 to 100,000 barrels per day—about one-half the total of all other wells in the nation—stirred world-wide interest and made people aware of the great oil potentialities in Texas.

For several years after the Spindletop discovery, exploration tended to be concentrated on the Gulf Coast, but the discovery of the huge Glenn Pool near Tulsa in 1905, shifted attention from the Gulf Coast to Oklahoma.

Figure 9-7. Oil wells are located even on the grounds of the State Capitol in Oklahoma City, Oklahoma. Oil is being pumped from a pool beneath the building itself. (Oklahoma City Chamber of Commerce)

Many important discoveries were made in Oklahoma in subsequent years, and this state led the Midcontinent field in oil production from 1906 to 1928. After the Cushing field began production in 1915, yielding 305,000 barrels daily, oil and gas became Oklahoma's greatest income producers. The Seminole field, opened in 1928, was one of the biggest. Today, oil derricks stand in front of the state capitol, amid corn fields, and in back yards.

Oil brought a great industry to the state, giving Oklahoma City and Tulsa metropolitan status. Petroleum in Oklahoma is valued at more than $567 million. The state ranks fourth nationally in oil production and in oil reserves (behind Texas, California, and Louisiana). Total yearly output has exceeded 100 million barrels for several decades. Peak production was reached in 1927, with 216.5 million barrels. Since then it has fluctuated from a low of 123 million barrels in 1923, to a high of 187 million barrels in 1951.

Since 1928, Texas has maintained its position as the leading petroleum state. In the past ten years, crude oil production has almost doubled, reaching more than one billion barrels in 1956. This increase has been caused by a combination of factors: (1) the sustained growth in the nation's demand for petroleum products, (2) the relative success of the industry in locating rich oil pools accessible to markets, and (3) an economic climate that has induced investment in oil exploration and production activities.

TRANSPORTATION OF OIL

Transportation influences oil development in a particular region in several ways. It constitutes a major factor determining which markets can be reached profitably by oil produced in a specific area. All other things being equal, a market is secured by the oil that offers the lowest transportation cost to that market.

In moving oil, almost all the principal media of transportation in this country are utilized—pipelines, tankers, barges, trucks, and railroads. Of these, pipelines are the most important. Nearly 43 per cent of the region's crude oil is moved this way; water carriers account for 30 per cent; trucks, 22 per cent; and railroads, five per cent.

PETROLEUM REFINING

More than half the crude petroleum in the United States in the last 30 years has come from oil fields located in the Midcontinent field, which, in turn, possesses only about ten per cent of total refining capacity. The location of refineries is obviously not determined solely by the geographic occurrence of crude petroleum; it is also influenced by the location of consuming markets and by differences in transportation costs.

Locational determinants. Transportation costs constitute an important part of the market value of refined petroleum products. In order to minimize these costs, it has been logical to locate refining activities at the source of crude oil; at marketing centers in the consuming areas; and at intermediate transshipment points between crude oil supplies and markets, where for any reason the journey is broken. The cost of refining petroleum generally has constituted only a minor portion of the final value of refined products, so that geographic differences in the cost of refinery operations have not been of great importance in determining refinery locations.

The ton-mile cost of moving petroleum and

petroleum products by pipeline is less than half the cost of shipment by railroad tank car. Movement by tank ship or barge is, in turn, substantially less expensive on a ton-mile basis than by pipeline. It follows that tank car shipments are proportionally small and that water transportation is used wherever available, except in cases where ice prevents winter transport for several months during the year and large storage costs are involved.

Primary refining centers. Of the total capacity of large refineries (those with a crude oil input capacity of 10,000 barrels per day or more), 34 per cent are located at transshipment points along the Gulf Coast, from which locations refined products can be shipped by tanker or barge to the East Coast markets and to markets along the Mississippi waterway. Large refineries located chiefly in or near marketing centers in the Great Lakes-Midwest territory from Buffalo to Kansas City comprise another 22 per cent of the total. East Coast marketing centers possess 16 per cent of the capacity of large refineries, and tidewater marketing centers and transshipment points in California account for a similar proportion. Large refineries located in or near the producing fields in the Midcontinent field constitute only about nine per cent of the total.

The chief refining centers in the Great Lakes-Midwest area are, in order of importance, the Chicago, St. Louis, Toledo, and Kansas City metropolitan centers. Taken together the refineries in these four districts constitute approximately 14 per cent of the crude oil handling capacity of the country. Refineries are located in marketing centers and transshipment points on the Great Lakes at Chicago, Toledo, Detroit, Cleveland, and Buffalo. St. Louis refineries have access to a fairly large marketing territory by barge up and down the Mississippi River and its connecting waterways. Kansas City is an important distribution center for petroleum products; it also lies astride crude oil and oil products pipeline routes from the producing fields to the consuming areas. Refining capacity in the Kansas City area is 96,200 barrels per day, 1.4 per cent of the national total. Other large refineries are located near the Illinois-southwestern Indiana and Lima-Indiana producing fields.

Refining capacity in the Midcontinent field is widely scattered. Tulsa is perhaps the focal point, with a capacity of 137,500 barrels per day within a 40-mile radius, of which Tulsa's own capacity is 82,000 barrels per day. Ponca City, Oklahoma, has facilities for handling 67,500 barrels of crude oil per day.

Small refineries. In contrast with the prevailing market orientation evident in the location of large refineries, many small refineries tend to cluster in the producing fields. Small refiners generally lack pipeline and tanker facilities for the efficient transportation of petroleum and must, therefore, locate their plants in the proximity of the oil fields to obtain continuing supplies of crude petroleum for processing. Large numbers of small refineries have sprung up in the past during the early stages of production in the newly-opened oil fields when the price of crude oil was depressed and when oil transportation and refining facilities were inadequate. But many of these small refineries operated only a few years before they were shut down and dismantled.

Information on the average size of refineries arranged by areas clearly indicates the presence of small- and medium-sized refineries in the producing fields and that of large refineries in the centers of high population and at transshipment points. For example, nine refineries in the Chicago area have an average daily capacity of 52,500 barrels per day, whereas the 38 refineries located in Kansas and Oklahoma (except Kansas City) each have an average daily capacity of 12,500 barrels.

Regional growth of refining capacity. The development of petroleum refining activities in the Eastern Interior Low Plains has taken place in response to the locational advantages of marketing centers for the industry. The growth in large refining capacity in the region has increased more than 1,200 per cent during the last 30 years and now exceeds that of any other area except the Gulf Coast. The marketing territory served by these refineries has consistently consumed more than one-third of all motor fuel used in the country; motor fuel is the most important of the refined products. Large refineries in the region constituted only eight per cent of the total of such capacity in the entire United States in 1922. By 1960, capacity in the area had increased to 22 per cent of the national total. The overwhelming predominance of market locations in the region makes it evident that what has occurred has been a shift of the location of the refining industry in conformity with the locational requirements for cost reduction.

An important factor contributing to the continued feasibility and the expansion of refining here has been the development of products pipeline facilities. Products lines now carry Midcontinent refined products cheaply to terminals in Kansas City, Omaha, Des Moines, Minneapolis, St. Louis, Chicago, Denver, and many other points. As a consequence, the Midcontinent has developed a large number of medium-sized refineries. Twenty of its 25 refineries capable of handling more than 10,000 barrels of crude oil per day range in size from 10,000 to 30,000 barrels per day; the largest refinery has a daily capacity of 56,000 barrels.

At the present time, the possibility of large crude oil reserves in the Williston Basin of Montana, the Dakotas, and southern Saskatchewan make probable the appearance of new refining centers, perhaps in the Minneapolis-St. Paul or Duluth-Superior areas.

DIVERSIFIED MANUFACTURING OF THE LOWER GREAT LAKES

By its very geography, the land that adjoins the shores of the lower Great Lakes is extremely suitable for the support of a large population—a population that brought with it a rigorous development in the manufacture of consumer goods. To this normal industrial activity have been added specialties that depend either upon nearness to natural resources or upon the trades generated by them, so that the Lower Great Lakes Subregion has become even more a source of producers' goods than of articles used directly by consumers.

Many factors account for the concentration and dominance of industry in the economy of the subregion. Chief of these are: (1) a large labor pool with diversified skills; (2) available and cheap fuel and power; (3) geographic location astride the Great Lakes close to the major population centers of the United States; (4) cheap and efficient forms of land, sea, and air transportation; and (5) plenty of room for expansion of existing industries and addition of new ones on flat land.

In terms of industry, commerce, and agriculture, the Lower Great Lakes Subregion is one of the best balanced areas on earth. Every important ingredient either is here or readily available: transportation, natural resources, location, labor, supplying industries, and markets. Nowhere is there such a meeting point of raw materials for processing into manufactured goods. Coal from the mines of Ohio, Pennsylvania, West Virginia, and Kentucky is abundant and comparatively cheap anywhere in the subregion as a fuel and as a chemical raw material. Gas and oil also are available, both from wells locally and by pipeline from other states. The Great Lakes ore fleet literally moves a small mountain of ore down the lakes each year from the Lake Superior district. Corn, wheat, soybeans, oats, and hay, together with dairy products and meat in the form of beef, pork, and poultry, pour into the area from the agricultural hinterland. Clay, shale, limestone, dolomite, sandstone for abrasive use, marl, peat, gypsum, and salt account in large measure for leadership in brick and tile, refractories, potteries, steel, and related industries.

The outstanding feature of the area's industry is its diversification. At the same time many of the industries are also large. This is illustrated by the fact that the area leads all other industrial districts in the nation in the fabrication of many items, including: steel, meat packing and packing house by-products, telephone equipment, radio and television sets, confectioneries, housewares, railroad equipment, automobile parts, machine tools, marine engines, rubber tires and tubes, metal wares, electrical and nonelectrical machinery, sporting and athletic goods, bolts and nuts, forgings, stamped and pressed metal products, framed pictures, mirrors, gloves, mittens, soaps, perfumes, cosmetics, window screens, shades and blinds, tin cans, and tinware.

POPULATION

With 148 persons per square mile as compared with 51 per square mile in the United States generally, the Lower Great Lakes Subregion is third in population density after the Middle Atlantic Region and the New England Lowlands. Its high population density and extensive industrialization also are reflected in the higher than average proportion of persons living in urban areas. Seventy per cent of the subregion's population lives in urban areas, compared with 64 per cent for the United States as a whole.

All of the states and the one Canadian province that have portions within the subregion—Illinois, Indiana, New York, Ohio, Pennsylvania, Wisconsin, and Ontario—border on one or more of the Great Lakes, and this feature of their location has had marked effects on their industrial and commercial development and on the population concentrations within them. Five of the subregion's major metropolitan centers—Chicago, Cleveland, Milwaukee, Buffalo and Toronto—are on one of the lakes, and Detroit is on a waterway connecting two of them. In all, there are 38 cities within the subregion with more than 50,000 population. The Chicago metropolitan area is by far the largest of these, and its employed population is second only to New York City in Anglo-America. Detroit, the automobile capital of the world, ranks fifth in employment among metropolitan areas within the United States. Other large metropolitan areas in the subregion, ranked in order of their employment, are Cleveland, Toronto, Milwaukee, and Buffalo.

MANUFACTURING INDUSTRIES

Manufacturing industries account for 35 per cent of all employment in the Lower Great Lakes Subregion. Although there is a broad range of industries with a sizable number of workers, metalworking activities predominate by far as a source of jobs—well over half the employed population. The emergence of the Lake Superior area as the country's main center of iron ore and the convenient access to it provided by Great Lakes waterways, together with the large coal deposits in the region and in nearby states, resulted in the location of a substantial proportion of the nation's basic steelmaking facilities in the subregion. Because of its role in steelmaking and because of its extensive water and land transportation facilities, the area took a leading role in the rapid growth of metal forming and fabricating industries that began shortly after the Civil War and which has continued to the present.

These factors helped the subregion become a center of industrial employment. Today, about 40 per cent of the national employment in

blast furnaces, steelworks, and the rolling mills industry is found here, considerably more than in any one other area. With this concentration of steelmaking facilities and with its central location among the industrial and household markets in the country, it was natural that the area should become the largest fabricator of metal goods. A striking example is the production of automobiles, in which the section accounts for the great bulk of the production and employment.

Nonelectrical machinery manufacture also is quite prominent, with the subregion having almost half the nation's employment in this category. Ohio's importance as a manufacturer of industrial machinery is shown by the fact that the workers employed in the manufacture of miscellaneous machinery, which includes machine tools, machine tool accessories, and a variety of machinery used in particular industries, account for almost a third of the subregion's total employment in this field. The area is also the main producer of agricultural machinery and tractors, possessing more than three-fifths of the industry's total employment, a large part of it concentrated in Illinois, but with Wisconsin also claiming a substantial number of employees. The almost 300,000 workers in the electrical machinery, equipment, and supplies industry partly reflect the substantial employment in radio, television, and electronics manufacturing concentrated in the Chicago metropolitan area.

The importance of the motor vehicles industry is emphasized by the fact that it accounts for about one-sixth of Lower Lakes manufacturing employment. Michigan is the major producer. Its workers make up over two-thirds of those employed in automobile manufacturing and assembly in the area, and over half of the national employment.

Outside of metalworking, food and kindred products make up the most important manufacturing industry, to account for about a quarter of the total national employment in the industry. Part of the Lower Great Lakes Subregion's importance as a food processor results from its strategic location with regard to transportation facilities and consuming markets. The meat products industry has the largest employment (over one-fifth) in the food and kindred products group.

Figure 9-8. An aerial view of the Soo Canal, Sault Ste. Marie, Michigan. Note ships traveling in both directions through the locks. (U.S. Army)

Agriculture, forest, and fisheries account for a somewhat smaller proportion of the subregion's employment, with 8.9 per cent, followed by professional and related services (eight per cent), and transportation, communication, and public utilities (seven per cent). Each of the other industry divisions employs five per cent or less.

IRON AND STEEL—THE BASIC INDUSTRY

The central steel region of the United States extends from Buffalo on the east along the shores of the Great Lakes to Chicago on the west. It produces more than one-third of the nation's steel. Pittsburgh, traditionally the nation's top steel producing center, yielded first place to Chicago in 1953. Across Lake Ontario, the lakefront city of Hamilton makes most of Canada's steel. The steel industry has concentrated in the Lower Great Lakes Subregion because it is here that its chief materials, iron ore and coal, can be brought together most conveniently.

The great markets for steel that have grown up around the steel producing centers are the automotive and machine industries, construction, and railroads. The metropolitan center of the machine industry and other steel consuming industries is roughly coextensive with the central steel region.

The Great Lakes ore fleet. A little over a hundred years ago the opening of the first locks at Sault Sainte Marie created a connecting link between Lake Superior and the rest of the Great Lakes and brought into being the greatest fresh water fleet in the world—more than 300 bulk freighters.

During the past hundred years, mines clustered around the head of Lake Superior have supplied the bulk of the iron ore consumed by the nation's steel mills. Nearly all the iron ore mined in the Mesabi and other Lake Superior ranges is carried at least part of the way to the steel mills by the Great Lakes ore fleet, moving from the head of the lakes through the Soo Canal to ports on Lake Michigan and Lake Erie.

Although the Lake Superior district's relative importance as an iron ore supplier is diminishing as imports of foreign ore mount at a rapid rate, reserves of iron ore will keep the ore fleet busy on the customary lake routes in the foreseeable future. Generally speaking, it takes about one and two-thirds tons of iron ore to make a ton of pig iron, and about one-half ton of pig iron plus an equal amount of steel scrap to make a ton of steel. Thus, feeding a steel industry capable of gobbling up more than 125 million net tons of iron ore in a year is no small task.

The size of the ore boats has grown steadily over the years, as bigger locks have been built at the Sault Falls on the St. Mary's River and as river channels have been deepened. The first locks at the Soo were only 350 feet long, 70 feet wide, and nine feet deep—more than adequate by pre-Civil War standards. In contrast, the Davis and Sabin Locks, opened in 1914 and 1919, respectively, each measured 1,350 feet in length, 80 feet in width, and 24.5 feet in depth. The MacArthur Lock, completed at the height of World War II, was not quite as long but had a depth of 30 feet.

Ore vessels launched since 1950 are, naturally, the biggest and fastest in the lake fleet. They can carry about twice as much ore as their 50-year-old prototypes, make the round trip to the head of the lakes and back in five days as against seven days, and accumulate about 45 trips a season instead of 30 trips. In short, one new ore boat can just about do the work of three old boats each shipping season.

The typical modern ore carrier is 647 feet long, 70 feet at the beam, and capable of carrying about 22,000 net tons of ore. The average vessel built between 1900 and 1909, on the other hand, measured 500 by 54 feet and carried close to 11,000 net tons each trip.

Boatloads of ore are distributed among ports on the lower lakes, with about one-third of the cargoes destined for Lake Michigan ports and two-thirds going to Lake Erie ports. At some Lower Great Lakes ports, the ore is transshipped to inland steel mills. At other ports, such as Cleveland and Lorain, part of the ore is unloaded directly into the stockpiles of local steel mills.

THE AUTOMOBILE INDUSTRY

Michigan is the center of the automobile industry, and Detroit the epicenter. The industry employs 475,000 workers in Michigan—almost half of the total labor force engaged in manufacturing. Detroit alone has almost 40 per cent of all auto workers in the United States and Flint has another six per cent.

Although there is a tendency towards some dispersal of automobile manufacturing, over 70 per cent is concentrateed in a triangular area extending from Flint and Detroit, Michigan, to Cleveland, Ohio, and South Bend, Indiana.

The triangle owes its importance in this industry largely as the result of an historical accident. Detroit, the automotive center, for example, is no better situated geographically for such production than are several other cities bordering the lower Great Lakes. Fortunately for Detroit, Henry Ford, the first successful automobile manufacturer, was born in Michigan and elected to locate his plant there.

Once the industry began, there were many favorable factors within the area to keep it there. The early models were little more than motored (horseless) carriages and the carriage trade was a well established local industry because of the presence of hardwood as a raw material. Marine engine building was also important, facilitating the adaptation of an engine suitable for use in automobiles. A skilled labor pool likewise was available. Fortunately, too, the flat terrain made it easier for these low-powered vehicles to win public acceptance. Presence of a hilly landscape possibly would have retarded development or discouraged the pioneer builders entirely. Finally, metal fabricating was well established and has expanded to keep pace with the growth of the automotive industry.

Other manufacturers followed in Ford's footsteps, and mass production of automobiles began on a large scale. Volume production combined with low prices put the automobile within reach of all classes. This feat was accomplished through division of labor, the use of interchangeable parts, and standardization. Actual production stages include: (1) the manufacturing of parts from raw materials, (2) primary assembly, and (3) final assembly. In 1951, the one-hundred-millionth American automobile was produced. Annual output has now topped the seven million mark.

Since 1900, more than 2,700 different makes of automobiles found their way to the market place. Between 1903 and 1926, over 183 different automotive companies were started. By 1927, there were only 44 companies left, and from 1930 on, the Big Three—General Motors, Ford, and Chrysler—have produced more than 90 per cent of all automobiles manufactured.

Rise of the independents. The postwar period gave rise to a group of independents—Studebaker-Packard Corporation, American Motors, and Kaiser Motors — manufacturing such familiar makes as Studebaker, Packard, Nash, Rambler, and Willys. Together their as-

Figure 9-9. Aerial view of the Buffalo River railroad yards and grain elevators. Buffalo has the largest concentration of grain storage facilities in the world. (Buffalo Chamber of Commerce)

sets total nearly $800 million. Since 1953 the independents' share of the market has fluctuated from a high of 18.5 per cent to below five per cent.

Social changes. Few inventions have had as revolutionary an impact on society as the automobile, which has destroyed and created industries. The automobile has given rise to traffic police; motor vehicle bureaus; garages; auto repair business; accessories; road building; finance companies; insurance concerns; drivers' schools; taxis; buses; trucking; and drive-in shopping centers, banks, and movies. It has caused many profound economic and social changes in American life, as epitomized by the rapid development of suburban communities; congestion and consequent decentralization of cities; heavy urban and rural traffic, and the subsequent rise in traffic deaths and accidents; new problems centering on driving-and-drinking; and many other problems that are direct and indirect results of the increased mobility that came with the development of the motorcar. It accounts either directly or indirectly for about one-seventh of the nation's payroll and has ranked first as a manufactured export item since 1929. The industry is the largest single consumer of gasoline, rubber, steel, lead, and

nickel; it also consumes large quantities of aluminum, copper, cotton, and zinc.

MEAT PACKING

Chicago, once the nation's leading meat packing center, has been replaced by Omaha. Both Swift and Armour have ceased their slaughtering operations in Chicago. Wilson dropped out ten years ago. Rehabilitation of existing facilities is deemed economically unsound.

Chicago still retains its position, however, as the world's largest competitive market for salable livestock. Several factors favor its importance in this industry: (1) geographical location on the shore of Lake Michigan, providing cheap water transportation via the Great Lakes; (2) all major railroads and highways crossing the nation focus on Chicago; (3) inland from Chicago in all directions is the livestock-grain area, where corn is grown primarily for feed for finishing animals for market; and (4) the metropolitan area, second only to New York City in size, provides a huge market for meat products.

FLOUR MILLING

Buffalo, New York, located on Lake Erie's eastern shore at the western terminus of the New York State Barge Canal, is one of the nation's leading flour milling centers. Buffalo is in a position to receive, at low transportation cost, and store or mill spring wheat from the Canadian Prairies and their counterpart in the Dakotas and western Montana. Both rail and lake shipments are used to transport the grain, some of which is received in bond for export. Cheap hydroelectric power from nearby Niagara, steam-generated power from Pennsylvania coal, and a large consuming market for flour within a few hundred miles combine to give this city a favored position in flour milling, although movement of grain on the St. Lawrence Seaway has caused much wheat to bypass Buffalo.

THE ST. LAWRENCE SEAWAY—AMERICA'S FOURTH SEACOAST

The St. Lawrence Seaway has opened the Great Lakes to the fleets of the high seas in a breakthrough that promises to reshape the economic future of Anglo-America. For the first time in history, ships can penetrate halfway across Anglo-America to Chicago and Duluth.

From the Gulf of St. Lawrence westward into the continent for more than 1,000 miles, the St. Lawrence River was able to carry ocean commerce to Montreal. From Chicago, at the southern tip of Lake Michigan, the chain of the Great Lakes provided a continuous passage of more than 1,100 miles eastward to Toronto and beyond. But, almost at the junction of these two magnificent watercourses, for 114 miles from the Thousand Islands downstream to Montreal, the rapids of the St. Lawrence blocked the path. Until April, 1959, when the Seaway was opened, the only way around the rapids was a series of canals. Barely 14 feet deep, these canals were cluttered by 22 locks, each too short for all but the smallest freighters, which carried only a trickle of overseas commerce into the lakes. In effect, the Great Lakes were landlocked. The Seaway cuts around this barricade with a new channel 27 feet deep, joined by a system of only seven locks.

This fourth seacoast, with 8,000 miles of shoreline, places Chicago and Cleveland, Duluth and Detroit, and Muskegon and Milwaukee on the doorstep of the world, for today ocean freighters of 8,000 to 10,000 tons and lake ships of 25,000 tons—80 per cent of the world's shipping—are able to steam up the network of canals, locks, and channels. Steamship lines engaged in this lakes-ocean commerce already serve the ports of continental Europe, the United Kingdom, South America, the Mediterranean, the Persian Gulf, the Red Sea, and the Caribbean.

Exchanging a great variety of goods, freighters now bring to the Great Lakes such items as steel, automobiles, coffee, spices, cement, wines, cork, and marble, and take out grain, all types of machinery, appliances, packing house products, pharmaceuticals, chemicals, and other cargo. Grain may be shipped from the Midwest breadbasket straight to Europe by sea. Iron ore can come from the new deposits in Labrador to feed the hungry blast furnaces of the Great Lakes area.

SEAWAY ROUTE DISADVANTAGES

The present Seaway is only a minor contender for the massive traffic of the North Atlantic. Its channel is outclassed by the 30- to 45-foot depths in Eastern ports; most of its locks can handle ships in only one direction at a time; and it faces a complete freeze-up for four months every winter.

The Welland Canal has proven to be a bottleneck both to vessel operators and to shippers of high value merchandise. Completed in 1932, it lifts and lowers vessels 327 feet between Lake Ontario and Lake Erie to circumvent Niagara Falls. The Canal has one guard lock and seven modern locks, three of which are twin installations that permit traffic to move in both directions simultaneously. The other four are single installations.

The closing of shipping on the Seaway for about four months each winter affects general cargo shipments more than it affects bulk shipments. Iron ore and coal may be stored cheaply at dock sites, and grain must be stored in any case because of the annual harvest. But manufactured products with high values must be moved by way of ocean ports. Unless shippers reap significant savings by the Seaway route, they may be reluctant to make the annual transfer.

Foreign trade involves highly complex relationships with such service industries as banks, insurance companies, freight forwarders, railroads or truck lines, and dock terminal facilities. The lack of freight forwarders and dock facilities along the Seaway route makes the transfer difficult.

Finally, the Eastern railroads serving Great Lakes ports east of Chicago also serve Atlantic and Gulf Coast ports. Because they reap more revenue on hauls to these ports than to lake ports, they favor them.

FUTURE

The Seaway is the first breakthrough toward an unobstructed avenue to the ocean that may be comparable, in the course of time, to the Mediterranean Sea. Industry is growing; its impact already is felt. With the promise of cheap, fast transport of Labrador iron, steel firms have committed hundreds of millions of dollars to Lower Lakes plant expansion. With power and a waterway next door, aluminum and automobile companies are pouring $125 million into factories on the St. Lawrence at Massena, New York. Yesterday, Massena was a sleepy spa. In 1960, 20,310,346 tons of cargo passed through the locks between the

Figure 9-10. Chicago is the center of one of the nation's richest markets. Within a 500-mile radius of the city are 35 per cent of the country's wholesale trade, 43 per cent of its farm population, 46 per cent of its manufacturing, and 38 per cent of its retail establishments.

Great Lakes and the St. Lawrence River at Massena.

In the first years there will be less of the exotic foreign cargo that the dreamers prophesied. But on the drawing boards of United States and Canadian inland cities are $335 million in port projects.

MAJOR MANUFACTURING DISTRICTS

SOUTHERN LAKE MICHIGAN

Chicago metropolitan area (6,794,461). The Chicago industrial area, embracing five coun-

ties (Cook, DuPage, Lake, Kane, and Will) in Illinois and one in Indiana (Lake County), has experienced a greater industrial, commercial, and financial expansion since World War II than that of any other metropolitan area in the nation.

Chicago stands at the nation's transportation crossroads — rail, highway, and airline. Just south of Chicago is the U.S. center of population. Chicago, therefore, is the nation's key city in any program for national distribution. This is why the nation's three largest mail order houses—Sears Roebuck, Montgomery Ward, and Spiegel, accounting for 93 per cent of the nation's total mail order business— are located here.

The outstanding feature of Chicago industry is diversification—about 94 per cent of all types of industry are found there. Steel production, the foundation upon which other industries rest, not only leads all other industries in the Chicago area but is, in turn, the largest in the nation, with an annual output of more than 24 million tons—almost as much as West Germany, Western Europe's leading producer. Chicago's prominence as an iron and steel center depends on the fact that iron ore, coal, and limestone can be brought to Chicago cheaply by water. The largest single producer in the metropolitan area is U.S. Steel Corporation's gigantic operation at Gary, Indiana, built in 1907. Fifty years ago this area was an inhospitable stretch of sand dunes and sloughs, scrub oak and brackish streams. Its only city was Hammond, population 12,000; East Chicago and Whiting were villages; Gary did not

exist. In 1906, Judge Elbert H. Gary, board chairman of the U.S. Steel Corporation, bought up thousands of acres of wasteland and started to build the world's largest steel plant. This plant has an annual steel ingot capacity of over 7,200,000 net tons.

With the building of Gary, the whole Calumet Valley roared to life. To Hammond came great printing plants, the huge Lever Brothers soap factory, and many more giants. East Chicago attracted Inland Steel and Youngstown Sheet & Tube. Even little Whiting had its inning, becoming the site of Standard Oil's biggest refinery, as well as the home of one of Carbide and Carbon Chemical's largest plants.

Today Gary and her sister cities of the Calumet, a heterogeneous complex of huge plants, represent one of the world's greatest concentrations of heavy industry. Six trunk line railroads and five arterial highways serve the area. Three big industrial harbors handle over 15 million tons of cargo annually, pouring close

Figure 9-11. Aerial view of Chicago, Illinois. The Chicago River is in the foreground. Lake Michigan can be seen in the background. (Chicago Association of Commerce and Industry)

Figure 9-12. Gary, Indiana, looking toward the main entrance of the Gary Steel Works of the United States Steel Corporation. (United States Steel Corp.)

Figure 9-13. Milwaukee, Wisconsin, with Lake Michigan in the background. Although only twelfth in population among United States cities, Milwaukee leads the world in the manufacture of diesel and gasoline engines, outboard motors, motorcycles, tractors, wheelbarrows, padlocks, and beer. (Milwaukee Association of Commerce)

to $450 million a year into the channels of retail trade.

Food products are the second largest category in the Chicago area, followed by nonelectrical machinery and electrical and electronic machinery and equipment. Other major categories of industrial production are fabricated metal industries (tin cans, stamped and structural shapes, and other products), petroleum, coal, chemicals, and transportation equipment.

Chicago is a leader in industrial research, with more than 1,200 laboratories in the metropolitan area. Moreover, the Chicago district continues to lead all other metropolitan centers in both number and value of contract awards for new manufacturing facilities.

Milwaukee, Wisconsin (741,324). Because of its size and maturity, as well as its capital goods specialization, Milwaukee differs in a number of important respects from most other Midwest industrial cities.

Milwaukee's largest industry is the manufacture of equipment for generating, transmitting, and distributing electric power. The 20 local firms in this industry produce items ranging in size from the smallest electric motor controls to 305,000-kilowatt steam turbine generator units capable of producing enough electricity to serve an industrial city of half a million people. The largest local producer is also the area's largest employer—the Allis-Chalmers Manufacturing Company, with close to 16,000 employees in the metropolitan area.

Ranking second and third in the industry are the Allen-Bradley Company and Cutler Hammer, Inc. Milwaukee producers account for close to a fifth of the nation's output of electrical control apparatus.

Milwaukee is the nation's beer capital, accounting for one-tenth of the country's production of beer and malt and housing four huge breweries, a number of small ones, and some major malt producers. The three largest—Schlitz, Miller, and Pabst—produce three of the only four brands having truly nationwide distribution. However, beer is hardly one of the area's bright spots, as far as growth is concerned, and for two reasons: the beer business nationwide is not growing, and brewing is decentralizing. Total beer sales have been stable for some time and have been declining per capita. The industry as a whole has the capacity to produce nearly half again as much as it now does.

LAKE SAINT CLAIR DISTRICT

Detroit, Michigan. Detroit was founded as the fur trading post of the strait (*de troit*) by the Frenchman, Cadillac, in 1701. From its population of 285,704 in 1900, it was raised by the motor car industry to be the fifth largest city in the United States, with a total population of 2,250,000 in its metropolitan district.

Detroit's position as motor car capital of the world has been discussed previously. The automobile industry creates a huge market for tools, dyes, gauges, and jigs and fixtures—all indispensable to the trade. Because of Detroit's concentration on automobile manufacturing, these supporting industries are also centered in that city. The same applies to manufacturers of paints, varnishes, upholstery, industrial chemicals, copper wire and brass, and iron and steel.

Windsor, Ontario. Located across the river from Detroit, Windsor shares with Oakville, Hamilton, and Oshawa the bulk of Canadian automobile manufacturing. These four cities account for 98 per cent of Canada's auto and auto parts industries.

The Canadian automobile industry started in 1904 when the Ford Motor Company of Canada, Ltd., began to manufacture automobiles for the Canadian market and for export. In that year, 17 employees were paid $12,000 to help assemble 117 cars. All parts were ferried across the river from Detroit. Today Ford of Canada employs about 25,000 workers.

The Chrysler Corporation of Canada began production in Windsor in 1924. This company recently doubled the size of its passenger car plant and now employs around 9,000 people.

Packard motor cars were built in Windsor from 1931 until the company joined Studebaker (1954) to become Studebaker-Packard, with the headquarters of its Canadian activities located at Hamilton.

Sarnia, Ontario. Ontario's important petrochemical industry is centered around Sarnia, the "Chemical Valley" of Ontario. Most of the province's $378 million chemical production comes from this area and in it are the province's major oil refineries. Among the chemicals of which Sarnia is the only Canadian manufacturer are carbon tetrachloride (an important industrial solvent) and glycol (used in making antifreeze, explosives, and cellophane). Imperial Oil, Dow Chemical, and the Polymer Corporation (manufacturer of synthetic materials) are the big three of Sarnia's industrial empire. Other companies—Cabot of Canada, Sun Oil, and Canadian Oil —recently have located new plants in the area.

Oil from the west is brought to Imperial Oil's refinery, largest in the British Commonwealth, at Sarnia by pipeline and lake tanker, and oil from the south by pipeline. It is broken down and its components rearranged with those from fresh water and salt, which is mined locally in large quantity. The resulting products range from wax to antifreeze; some shipped from Sarnia by rail, others by water, and still others by pipeline to all parts of Ontario.

LAKE ERIE'S SOUTH SHORE

Water and rail transportation, facilitating the movement of raw materials to fabricating centers along Lake Erie, and the ease of distribution of finished goods from this area have made it one of America's industrial centers.

Figure 9-14. The Ford Motor Company's River Rouge plant at Dearborn, Michigan, is one of the world's largest industrial manufacturing units. The production of automobiles is carried on from raw materials to the finished product. (Ford Motor Co.)

Toledo, Ohio (318,003). Toledo is the fourth largest city in Ohio. In total tonnage of Great Lakes shipping, it ranks first among Ohio's ports; shipments of iron ore, coal, lumber, and grain rank high. The city is an important rail and truck center, with terminals linking with port facilities. Toledo has made special efforts to accommodate new trade generated by the St. Lawrence Seaway.

Sandusky-Ashland, Ohio. This district lies west and south of the Cleveland, Lorain, and Akron metropolitan areas. The importance of manufacturing here is shown by the large number of manufacturing employees, 119 per 1,000 of population. The largest plants manufacture a variety of goods—ball bearings, auto parts, radio and television sets, washing machines, and paper products. Sandusky is important as a lake port, especially in coal shipments; boat building; commercial fishing; and the summer resort business. The city is also a center of the

Figure 9-15. The assembly line of the Ford of Canada plant, Windsor, Ontario, where engines are being assembled at the rate of 585 per day. (National Film Board)

wine industry. Ashland has a large plant for the manufacture of water pumps and sprays and several plants producing a score of rubber products.

Agricultural activity in the Sandusky-Ashland area reflects its proximity to Cleveland and several other metropolitan areas in northern Ohio. Dairying and raising of hogs, poultry, and beef cattle, together with other complementary enterprises, represent a balanced farming economy.

Cleveland, Ohio. Cleveland, with a population of 876,050, is the eighth city in size in the United States. As a metropolitan area it ranks twelfth nationally, with 1,673,000 inhabitants. Industrial activity of the Cleveland district is closely related to the city's historic importance as an industrial lake port. Located on the Lake Erie Plain at the mouth of the winding Cuyahoga River, Cleveland is a splendid site for industrial activity. Access to the upper Great Lakes iron ore deposits by way of water has made Cleveland an important steel center. The St. Lawrence Seaway opens the way to the rich deposits of iron in Labrador, which assure a continuous supply of high-grade raw materials to the steel mills of the area.

Approximately 20 million tons of freight move through the port of Cleveland annually. Of this total, iron ore and concentrates account for about three-fourths, and limestone for approximately one-tenth.

Unlike centers dominated by one major industry, Cleveland's industrial complex has grown as a collection of many small or medium-size plants, mainly under local ownership. Precision metalworking historically has been the strong point of Cleveland industry. Machinery manufacturing leads, both in employment and in value added by manufacture.

Transportation equipment, second in size, includes production of motor vehicles and parts, as well as aircraft, aircraft parts, and auxiliary equipment. Primary metals industries—smelting, rolling, casting, and forging of metals—also are significant. Located in the area are blast furnaces, steelworks, and rolling mills of several of the nation's largest steel producers, and also numerous foundries and forge shops, both ferrous and nonferrous, including an aluminum foundry and forging plant.

Other important industry groups that account for a substantial volume of employment include: chemicals, food processing, printing and publishing, and apparel.

Erie, Pennsylvania (138,440). Situated near the eastern end of the lake that bears its name, Erie's major industrial group is machinery, including electrical. Nearly 42 per cent of the area's total employment is engaged in this type of production. Metals and metal products account for another 20 per cent. Other large plants employing 1,000 or more workers manufacture such items as: locomotives, paper products, steel forgings and castings, electronic components, and cranes and power shovels.

Buffalo-Niagara district (1,306,957). The Buffalo-Niagara district lies at the junction of the Great Lakes and the New York State Barge Canal. It is within economical shipping distance of Lake Superior iron ore and Pennsylvania coal and enjoys convenient access to low-cost transportation, hydroelectric power generated at Niagara Falls, basic raw materials, and the great consumer markets of the Northeast, the Middle West, and Canada.

The district has a wide diversity of industry, led by the manufacture of iron and steel products, chemical and metallurgical supplies, and foods. Agricultural activity is substantial, with almost 70 per cent of the total acreage made up of farmlands.

Buffalo's iron and steel industry, which has a total blast furnace capacity in excess of three million tons, is one of the largest in the country. The giant Bethlehem Steel Company plant at Lackawanna, just south of Buffalo, has nearly four-fifths of New York State's basic steel and over half its pig iron capacity.

The chemical and metallurgical industries, utilizing the cheap power available from Niagara Falls, have huge factories making aniline dyes, aluminum, carborundum, drugs, soaps, and oil. Buffalo, an important transfer point for both American and Canadian wheat, is also one of the world's greatest milling centers.

Eleven major rail lines converge on Buffalo, which has 14 freight and five passenger terminals. Buffalo's waterborne freight averages 20 million tons annually. The area's communities are linked by some 3,300 miles of improved highways; the New York State Thruway con-

Figure 9-16. The Maumee River waterfront, Toledo, Ohio, at the southwest corner of Lake Erie. Manufacturing of automobile parts, motor vehicle assembly, glass making, and oil refining are Toledo's outstanding industries, but numerous other lines, especially of the hard goods variety, are significant. (Toledo Chamber of Commerce)

Figure 9-17. Cleveland, Ohio, on the south shore of Lake Erie. Cleveland's excellent inner and outer harbors constitute one of the finest ports on the Great Lakes. (Cleveland Chamber of Commerce)

Figure 9-18. Toronto, Ontario, with the harbor area in the foreground. Toronto's principal exports are woolens, bacon, grain, and farm machinery. It is the focal point of Anglo-America's two largest railway systems, the Canadian National and the Canadian Pacific. The city has 14 miles of frontage on Lake Ontario, and its harbor is one of the busiest on the Great Lakes. (National Film Board)

nects it with New York City via the Mohawk-Hudson depression. Five commercial airlines operating out of the Buffalo airport provide daily passenger and cargo flights to the nation's key cities. Buffalo is indeed the hub of a vast transportation network.

LOWLANDS OF ONTARIO AND QUEBEC

The lowlands of Ontario and Quebec lie south of the Canadian Shield where the surface is undulating to rolling. The southern or triangular part of Ontario, sandwiched between the lower lakes and the Ottawa River,

supports Canada's greatest concentration of population and is recognized as one of the world's major industrial areas. Almost 3,500,-000 people, 68 per cent of Ontario's population and 22 per cent of the population of Canada, live and work in the urban centers and rich farming areas south of a line running from near Oshawa, just east of Toronto on Lake Ontario, to Georgian Bay. Approximately one-third of these live in the metropolitan area of Toronto.

The province of Quebec lies on both sides of the St. Lawrence River, the great gateway of eastern Canada. The valley of the St. Lawrence, extending from Quebec City to the western extremity of the province, is a very fertile plain where the climate and soil, especially in the eastern townships, are well suited to general farming. In this valley are concentrated the province's great manufacturing industries and the bulk of its population. Montreal, the largest city and port of Canada, contains about one-third of the province's 4,520,000 people; another million live in the southwestern triangle below the St. Lawrence River and the remainder are located within 35 miles of the Ottawa, St. Lawrence, and Saguenay Rivers and Lake St. John. Quebec accounts for 30 per cent of Canada's manufactured goods, and its products are greatly diversified.

Ontario's Golden Horseshoe. The Golden Horseshoe, 50 miles wide and 150 miles long, is comprised of the area from Oshawa westward around Lake Ontario to Niagara Falls. It includes Toronto, the capital of Ontario and second largest city in Canada, with a metropolitan population of more than one million inhabitants. Toronto ranks among the business and financial centers of the world. Its Stock Exchange is second only to Wall Street's in transactions. More mining companies, banks, and investment companies have their head offices here than in any other city of Canada. Toronto, like Montreal, is an important distribution and transportation city for eastern Canada. It produces a wide diversity of manufactured articles—meat products, electrical appliances, metal products, machinery, clothing, processed food, and refined oil.

Forty miles to the west is the lakefront city of Hamilton, which makes most of Canada's steel. The Steel Company of Canada, Ltd., was formed in 1910 by the amalgamation of the Hamilton Iron and Steel Company with nearly all the important hardware producing firms in Canada. The new company thus covered the whole range of production from pig iron and steel ingots to finished consumer products. During its steady growth, it has absorbed over 50 companies and added equipment until it now has nearly half the pig iron capacity and more than half the capacity of steel ingots and castings in Ontario. By continuing to produce light goods and to supply steel to the manufacturers of light consumer goods, the company has been able to maintain a high degree of stability. Its Hamilton plants are situated midway between coal and iron resources; the 18 United States ore and coal companies in which it has an interest furnish a large part of its requirements, while limestone is obtained from a subsidiary 50 miles from Hamilton. Its largest markets are in the immediate vicinity. To the southeast is St. Catharines, which is introducing automation to Canada.

Dispersal of industry outside the metropolitan area of Toronto is arising, indicating a pattern for Ontario's industrial development in the years ahead. Up until 1950, the majority of new industries settled in the Greater Toronto district, an area extending from Oakville to Whitby and north to Aurora. Since then, decentralization of industry has increased in momentum.

London, Ontario, is a highly diversified manufacturing center specializing in radios, refrigerators, sheet metal products, knitted goods, machinery, and printing.

Other centers symbolizing the spread of manufacturing in Ontario are Thorold, a pulp and paper center, and Port Colborne, which is noted for nickel refining because of excellent transportation facilities and cheap hydroelectric power from Niagara Falls.

Ontario has been termed "the fabricator" of materials for the rest of Canada. Its plants manufacture steel, electrical goods, heavy machinery, and mechanical equipment needed for resource development. In addition, the province is an expanding source of iron ore, petroleum, essential minerals, and other basic materials.

United States manufacturers see great advantages not only on the basis of a Canadian market of 18 million people, but in Ontario's 2,362 miles of shoreline on the St. Lawrence Seaway and the Great Lakes. Branch plants may be located in Ontario within convenient distances from their parent plants in the major industrial areas of the United States, particularly in New York, Ohio, Michigan, Illinois, and Pennsylvania. Of the some 1,500 United States branch plants in Ontario, three-quarters originated from firms located in the Cleveland-St. Louis-Minneapolis triangle.

The Welland Ship Canal. This canal is a vital link in the flow of goods between American and Canadian industries and markets. It

Figure 9-19. Niagara Falls, New York. The Niagara Power Project, a $720 million enterprise built by the Power Authority of the State of New York through a treaty with Canada, is the biggest hydroelectric power plant in the Western Hemisphere. Its ultimate output of 2,190,000 kilowatts will surpass Grand Coulee's and will greatly increase the power resources of a region that has been running short. A prime consideration in the project has been preserving the beauty of Niagara Falls. To this end, the treaty states that during daylight hours only 50,000 cubic feet of water per second may be drawn from the Niagara River above the falls, but at night 75,000 cubic feet per second may be taken. The extra amount is stored for use the following day. (Chamber of Commerce, Niagara Falls, N. Y.)

crosses Niagara Peninsula about seven miles west of Niagara Falls to connect Lake Erie with Lake Ontario. The lift of the canal is 326.5 feet, distributed over seven locks.

The present canal, built between 1913 and 1931 to accommodate the large Great Lakes steamers, is the fourth Welland Ship Canal. The first was built between 1824 and 1829 by the Welland Canal Company as a private enterprise. Previously, all water freight was transported overland around Niagara Falls. The second and third canals were enlargements of the first. Today, the Welland Ship Canal connects Port Colborne on Lake Erie with Port Dalhousie on Lake Ontario. Port Colborne has a good harbor, docking facilities, and a sandy beach. It is the home of the International Nickel Company and its nickel refinery, one of the largest in the world.

ONTARIO LAKE PLAIN

Level to rolling land occurs south of Lakes Ontario and Oneida from Niagara Falls in the west to Utica on the east, a distance of approximately 190 miles. The plain merges with the Allegheny Plateau in the south and varies in width from 25 to 50 miles, reaching its broadest extent in the central portion at the Finger Lakes.

The Ontario Lake Plain is a highly urbanized area. Two of New York State's major cities, Buffalo and Rochester, are found there, along with several communities each with a population of more than 40,000. This urban concentration is a response to the area's gateway position between the Great Lakes on the west and through the Mohawk and the Hudson Valleys south to New York City on the east. This makes for convenient and rapid interchange of goods and services and provides a substantial market for even the most specialized item. The Hudson-Mohawk depression, leading inland to the Ontario Lake Plain, is the only major sea level break to the interior. A railroad network and the New York State Barge Canal early capitalized on this route. More recently, the New York

EASTERN INTERIOR LOW PLAINS

Thruway, a toll highway, further facilitates ease of travel and movement of goods. It was only natural, then, for cities to rise along this corridor and even more so on the plain at its western extremity. One can only foresee continued population growth and expansion of industries within this most favored area.

The Niagara Frontier. The extreme west of the Ontario Lake Plain has a wide diversity of industry. Iron and steel manufacturing leads, followed by chemical and metallurgical supplies, and foods.

The giant hydroelectric plants at Niagara Falls account for almost half the total rated water power capacity of New York State, which ranks fourth in the nation in water power resources.

Two-thirds of the manufacturing employees work in factories producing durable goods. The metals and machinery group leads, with primary metals representing the largest single industry. Next in order of rank are transportation equipment, chemicals, nonelectrical machinery, and foods.

The Niagara Frontier offers many attractions to the tourist, especially the world-famous Niagara Falls, which are visited by more than three million people annually. Viewed from either side, the falls are a magnificent spectacle. The brink of the cataract is divided by Goat Island, and the river plunges over the escarpment in two parts. The American Falls, 167 feet high, have a fairly straight alignment; they are about 1,300 feet wide with a normal depth of water of two to four feet. The Canadian Falls, 158 feet high, have a crest of more than 2,500 feet outlining the deep curve from which they get their name—Horseshoe Falls.

Below the falls the walls of the gorge rise perpendicularly 200 to 350 feet, and through this channel the river rushes in a series of rapids to the famous whirlpool.

The Genesee Valley. This is one of the leading industrial sections of New York State. Population, industry, trade, and commerce focus on Rochester, the valley's trade center and third largest city in the state. Early known as the Flour City, Rochester has added many industries, several of them as a result of the inventiveness of its citizens. The city leads the world in the manufacture of cameras and pho-

tographic supplies, optical goods, mail chutes, dental equipment, thermometers, and recording devices. It also produces radio and television equipment, men's quality clothing, shoes, gears, laundry and dry cleaning equipment, gauges, electric motors, and baby foods.

The famous photographic industry was established here by George Eastman in 1880. Another Rochester citizen, John Jacob Bausch, founded the city's optical industry in 1853.

Six major and three short-line railroads operate in the area, with five of the railroads converging on Rochester. Situated on Lake Ontario, the Genesee River, and the New York State Barge Canal, Rochester is also a port of entry for trade with Canada. The principal transportation routes of New York State traverse the area. Ample and dependable electric power is available throughout the section.

With Lake Ontario, the famous Finger Lakes, and the scenic Genesee Valley, Rochester is well provided with recreational facilities.

Syracuse, New York (216,038). Syracuse is advantageously situated at the intersection of the major traffic corridors of New York State. The city is favored with extensive rail, water, and highway transportation facilities; ready availability of raw materials; and a widely-diversified supply of factory and farm products. It is highly industrialized, with more than one out of every three workers engaged in manufacturing. Industrial products include: machinery and metal products, china, worsted fabrics, typewriters, air-conditioning equipment, pneumatic conveyors, washing machines, and laundry and dry cleaning equipment. Syracuse china has been noted for generations. The ceramic, brick, and pottery industry is one of the oldest in this community; it owes its origin to the large deposits of fine clay found in the locality. The Solvay Process Company, producing soda ash, caustic soda, potash, chlorine, and potassium, is west of the adjacent city of Solvay.

Within a radius of 35 miles of Syracuse are Auburn, the site of one of the leading manufacturers of diesel engines; Oswego, noted for paper and matches; and Oneida, known for its quality furniture.

Rome (51,646), *and Utica* (100,410), *New York.* These two cities are at the edge of the Ontario Plain and the Mohawk Valley, a region of sharp contrasts. The low valley of the

Figure 9-20. New York State's Barge Canal is a cross-state route from Albany to Buffalo, with sections connecting with Lake Ontario and Lake Champlain. (New York State Department of Commerce)

Mohawk affords a connection between the Hudson Valley and the Ontario Plain. This is the route of the Erie Canal (now New York State Barge Canal). The strip of land at the level of the canal and the New York Central Railroad is merely a flood plain, varying in width from zero to one or two miles. Steep slopes and bluffs rise sharply at most places from this flood plain.

The area's western edge is a densely populated industrial center, manufacturing a wide variety of products ranging from chewing gum to gas heaters and from carpets to copper wire.

Abundant water power, good transportation facilities, and westward migration account for the early growth of cities and villages there. The Mohawk River provided the chief means of travel for the migrants. With the construction of the Erie Canal, the Mohawk Turnpike, and the railroad, all paralleling the river, the valley became a manufacturing center and the major traffic corridor between the Atlantic Seaboard and the Middle West.

Utica is the hub of the region's transportation system and one of the largest redistribution centers in the United States for less-than-carload freight. Although textile production is the leading industry, there is considerable di-

versity of manufacturing. Mills in Utica and nearby communities produce a wide variety of textile products, including knit goods, underwear, sheets, and hosiery.

Rome is known as the "Copper City" and contains one of the largest copper rolling mills in the world. More than one-tenth of the copper goods manufactured in the United States comes from this city.

ST. LAWRENCE-CHAMPLAIN LOWLANDS

That portion of the St. Lawrence-Champlain Lowlands within the United States extends along the northern border of New York, with Lake Ontario and the St. Lawrence River on the west and northwest, Canada on the north, and Lake Champlain on the east.

The geographic features of the region have exerted a strong influence on its economic development. The Adirondack Mountains to the south provide the basis for many unique enterprises. Their forests supply the raw material for the chief industrial pursuits: logging and the manufacture of lumber and lumber products, pulp, paper, and paper products. The beauty of the forests and the lakes attracts many tourists, upon whom many of the communities depend. The Adirondack foothills contain valuable mineral deposits that support a sizable mining industry.

The St. Lawrence River provides an outlet to the Great Lakes and the Atlantic Ocean. Ogdensburg, a deep-water port, is the only American city on the river and an important port of entry for trade with Canada. Principal cargoes include pulpwood, paper, coal, and petroleum products. Water transportation is supplied to the eastern part of the area through Lake Champlain, which connects with the Hudson River by a branch of the New York State Barge Canal and with the St. Lawrence River via Richelieu-Plattsburgh.

Paper and paper products plants account for about 40 per cent of total manufacturing employment. These plants are located in a large number of communities in the area. The availability of water power and pulpwood account for the early development of paper production here, but today much of the pulpwood is imported.

Lumber and lumber products and machinery are also important manufacturing industries. Wood products include curtain rods, shade rollers, radio cabinets, doors, and millwork.

Watertown, the center of the machinery industry, manufactures air brakes, papermaking machinery, and other machine shop products. Presses and machinery are manufactured in Champlain. Other manufactured products include razor blades made in Plattsburgh, footwear in the Malone area, and aluminum ingots and other aluminum products at Massena.

The Canadian portion of the St. Lawrence-Champlain Lowlands is one of the most densely populated and heavily industrialized areas of Canada. Here are located the leading elements of heavy industry—railway shops, iron foundries, locomotive works, shipbuilding yards, steelworks, and the like. For it is here that raw materials, cheap power, and excellent transportation may be combined most advantageously.

For generations, industry and manufacturing have been located in the main centers of Montreal, Three Rivers, and Sherbrooke. The early 1900's saw an expansion to such points as Kingston, Brockville, Cornwall, Valleyfield, St. Hyacinthe, Shawinigan Falls, Sorel, Drummondville, and Hull.

Kingston, Brockville, and Cornwall are the most important Ontario cities along the St. Lawrence. Kingston was founded in 1673 as a fur trading post and strategic military stronghold. It is situated at the point where Lake Ontario empties into the St. Lawrence River, and at the head of the Thousand Islands. The city is an important lake port connected to Ottawa, capital of Canada, by the Rideau Canal. Kingston also is noted for its locomotive shops, shipyards, textile factories, and aluminum refining. Brockville, midway between Kingston and Cornwall, is another important link in the St. Lawrence corridor, turning out hats, hardware, abrasives, marine engines, and boats. Cornwall specializes in paper, chemicals, textiles, furniture, and clothing.

Montreal, Quebec. Situated on the island of Montreal at the confluence of the St. Lawrence and Ottawa Rivers, Montreal is the largest city in Canada, harboring in its metropolitan area nearly two million people.

Although it is a thousand miles from the sea, Montreal is the national seaport of Canada. Here, cargoes from the Great Lakes and from the Atlantic Ocean are transshipped. The harbor accommodates over 125 ocean-going vessels. Montreal handles more grain annually than any other port. It is also Anglo-America's second-ranking port for steamship passenger travel to Europe. Montreal and the other St. Lawrence ports—Sorel, Three Rivers, Quebec —and the Saguenay ports of Chicoutimi and Port Alfred are in direct communication with the rest of Canada and only a short run from the great railroad networks of the United States. With the advent of air transportation, Montreal has become one of Canada's outstanding air centers.

The city is the financial, commercial, and industrial metropolis of Canada. There are more than 4,500 industries, the most important of which produce locomotives, railway cars, structural iron and steel, tobacco products, textiles, chemicals, airplanes, and electrical appliances. The largest flour mill in the British Commonwealth is here, with a capacity of 6,000 barrels in 24 hours. The city is also the center of tremendous power resources.

Quebec City (170,703). One of the oldest and most historic cities in North America, Quebec is the only walled city on the continent north of Mexico.

After Montreal it is the greatest industrial

center of Quebec Province. Its leading industries are canneries, paper mills, breweries, foundries, fur processing, and the manufacture of shoes and other leather goods, candies and chocolate, drugs, clothing, and tobacco products.

The site of Quebec, the Indian town Stadacona, was visited by Cartier, discoverer of Canada, in 1535. In 1608, Champlain established a trading post there and gave the settlement its present name. It became the capital of New France and the center of French colonization in Canada. Almost impregnable, it was the last stronghold of the French in America, surrendering to the English under Wolfe in 1759. From 1760 to 1854, Quebec was the capital of Canada. More than any other city in Anglo-America, Quebec has retained its old French aspect and atmosphere.

Three Rivers, Quebec. This is one of the world's largest papermaking centers and a gateway to one of Canada's greatest sources of electrical energy.

In the South Shore region west of Montreal, Valleyfield and Beauharnois are the most important chemical cities. At Valleyfield, the Nichols Chemical Company, Ltd., operates a sulfuric acid plant and a plant producing aluminum sulfate.

The Ottawa Valley. The Ottawa Valley is also noted for chemicals. The Electric Reduction Company, Ltd., at Buckingham, was established during the 1890's and is one of the oldest chemical firms in Quebec Province. Originally, phosphorus (manufactured from crude phosphate rock mined locally) was the most important product, but now sodium chlorate, phosphoric acid, calcium, and sodium phosphates for the food and cleaning industries also are made here in large quantities. Not far from Buckingham, at Gatineau, is the modern ethyl alcohol factory of Commercial Alcohols, Ltd. This plant is of interest because it is one of a number of factories making use of waste sulfate liquor, an important by-product of the sulfate pulp industry.

Ottawa, Ontario, capital of Canada since 1858, dominates the trade and manufacturing of the Ottawa Valley. Founded by Champlain in 1613, it became important upon the completion of the Rideau Canal, which was built originally for military purposes.

Pulp, paper, and lumber industries supplied by power from Chaudiere Falls are the backbone of the city's diversified economy. There is a preponderance of printing, publishing, engraving, and bookbinding. Planing mills, metallic products, textiles, and chemicals are also important.

Ottawa is a city of 222,000 people. The splendor of its natural setting high above its namesake river and facing the rolling Gatineau Hills is enhanced by the beauty and dignity of its public buildings, its drives, and its parks, making it one of the more picturesque capitals of the world.

CENTRAL OHIO-INDIANA

Sometimes referred to as the "East-central Lowland," Central Ohio-Indiana is transitional between the highly urbanized manufacturing belt of the Lower Great Lakes on the north and the sparsely populated, rough, hilly land overlooking the Ohio River Valley on the south. The eastern boundary merges with the Appalachian Highlands, where differences in landforms cause a considerable change in the economy. Relatively flat land, rich soils, and a fairly long growing season in Central Ohio-Indiana favor livestock, grain, and general farming. A dense rail and highway network provides rapid transportation from one part of the area to the other. Although predominantly a farming area, the presence of large coal deposits, oil and gas pipelines, and ready markets favors industry, especially in such metropolitan centers as Columbus and Dayton, Ohio, and Indianapolis, Indiana.

Fort Wayne, Indiana. Unquestionably the most mature of the cities on the northern fringe of the Central Ohio-Indiana district, Fort Wayne is directly astride the country's main belt of population, transportation, and industry. With a metropolitan population approaching 200,000, it is a small-scale version of much larger cities. The casual visitor is apt to find it more like Chicago or Cleveland than other cities its own size.

Well over a third of the city's export earnings are derived from the production of insulated magnet wire for electric motors, transformers, coils, and electronics equipment. General Electric is by far the largest single employer in the area. Its major products consist of small (up to five H.P.) electric motors and transformers.

The city has been the country's magnet wire capital for a long time, turning out more than half of the nation's total production. Three major companies — Essex Wire Corporation, Rea Magnet Wire Company, and Inca Manufacturing Division of the Phelps-Dodge Corporation—have their headquarters here.

Fort Wayne is a truck rather than a passenger car center. The largest producer is International Harvester, which manufactures axles and transmissions and assembles large heavy-duty motor trucks in the city. The Fruehauf Trailer Company, the nation's leading trailer producer, makes tank trailers, stainless steel vans, auto haulers, and bulk products trailers.

Columbus, Ohio, metropolitan district (597,-000). Because of its position as a state capital and the location there of one of the nation's largest state universities, public employment in the Columbus area accounts for a sizable part of the labor force.

Leading manufactures are airplanes, appliances, and auto parts. Airplane manufacturing alone employs more than 15,000 workers. Foundry and machine shop products, packed meat, shoes, printing and publishing, railroad cars, and food products also rank high. One plant is the nation's largest producer of mining machinery; another leads the world in concrete-mixing machinery; another ships oil well derricks and structural metal to nearly every country in the world; another is the world's largest oil-cloth manufacturer, producing nearly 81 miles of oil-cloth per day; and still another is the foremost producer of photograph mountings.

Columbus is the shopping hub for an area 50 miles to its north and west and as far as 100 miles in southeastern Ohio.

Dayton, Ohio, metropolitan area (506,000). Dayton is a center for the production of office and store machines and devices. The 10,000 workers in this industry make up almost ten per cent of the national total for this group. Among nationally known firms located here are the National Cash Register Company, the Standard Register Company, the Dayton Rubber Manufacturing Company, the Airtemp Division of Chrysler Corporation, the Aeroproducts and Delco Products divisions of General Motors Corporation, and United Aircraft Products, Inc.

The Federal government employs an estimated 18 per cent of the total work force in the Dayton metropolitan area, most of it at the Wright-Patterson Air Force Base and other military installations.

Indianapolis, Indiana, metropolitan district (655,000). Indiana's boom town, during the last decade, has been Indianapolis. The city's economic renaissance has had various aspects. For example, not long ago Indianapolis was dominated by locally owned businesses. Today, the city consists predominantly of branch plants of national corporations—three-fifths of the area's "export" earnings from manufacturing originate in these branch plants. More and more firms find Indianapolis a good place to locate new or enlarged operations. Indianapolis has experienced more branch expansion and more merging of local firms into national ones than almost any other big city.

Like so many other American cities, Indianapolis was transformed when World War II brought into being many new enterprises and expanded old ones—for example, Allison Division of General Motors, Bridgeport Brass, and the Naval Ordnance Plant were all essentially war babies. Allison is synonymous with aircraft engines designed principally for the nation's defense. During World War II, Allison had upward of 20,000 people at work producing reciprocating aircraft engines for the military. Since then, the company has produced close to 30,000 gas turbine engines, after delivering its first turbo-prop engine in 1952. Allison continues in the front rank of American military aircraft engine producers and now is gaining new stature as the producer of the engines to power the Lockheed Electra, America's first turbo-prop commercial airliner.

ST. LOUIS, MISSOURI, METROPOLITAN DISTRICT (2,060,103)

St. Louis began as a fur trading post hacked out of the wilderness in 1764. It became the gateway to settlement of the West and was a major transportation center, first by river, then by rail. Transportation and furs are still important, but the city's stability and growth in the past half-century may be attributed to its broad industrial base.

Besides being the world's largest market for

Figure 9-21. Aerial view of St. Louis, Missouri, looking west across the Mississippi River from East St. Louis, Illinois. (Chamber of Commerce of Metropolitan St. Louis)

raw furs, St. Louis is the world's top producer of sugar mill machinery (because it is the largest industrial center with ready transportation to the cane sugar market of Louisiana). It is a leader in the manufacture of stoves and ranges, harvest hats, woodenware, and brick products. The city is the hub of the shoe industry, rising to national importance after 1900 when shoe manufacturers located there to be nearer the source of raw material—leather tanned from cattle hides, a by-product of the meat packing industry. Thirty-eight thousand workers are employed in shoe manufacturing plants in the area.

The city ranks sixth among the nation's chemical centers and is among the leaders in producing drugs. It is a big producer of aircraft, autos and parts, barbers' supplies, bolts and nuts, cans, coffins, electric fans, food products, bottles, hardware, iron and steel, lumber,

girls' apparel, millinery, motor and other electrical equipment, rail and street cars, mill machinery, and white lead.

St. Louis is among the top five farm markets in the nation. For the metropolitan area, the livestock and packing business volume is estimated at more than $400 million annually; grain, $200 million; produce, $100 million; poultry and eggs, $60 million; and dairies, $50 million.

St. Louis' eastern border is the Mississippi River. Surrounding her by land is St. Louis County. Legally the two are separate entities, but in culture and economy they are one. The county covers 497 square miles, from the Missouri River on the north to the Meramec River on the south. In this fast-growing area are 96 municipalities and 484,000 people.

There are eight bridges that link St. Louis to the eastern side of the Mississippi. They at-

tach four Illinois satellites to the core city—
East St. Louis, directly across the river from St.
Louis; Granite City, adjoining East St. Louis
on the north; Alton, to the northeast on a
bend of the Mississippi River; and Belleville,
which lies to the southeast of East St. Louis,
back from the Mississippi River. Together
these cities add another 184,000 people to the
metropolitan district.

East St. Louis, the largest satellite, is the center of aluminum refining; the city takes advantage of nearby coal and favorable location
along the Mississippi River to receive bauxite
shipments from Arkansas and from the Gui-
anas. The area between Alton and East St.
Louis is important for petroleum refining.
Crude oil from the Midcontinent field, transported by pipeline, crosses the Mississippi at
this point.

St. Louis, tenth largest city in the United
States, with a population of 750,000, is served
by three transcontinental highways and two

important north-south routes, by 22 bus lines,
by 18 trunk rail lines, and by seven airlines.

WESTERN SUBREGIONS—WIDELY SEPARATED CENTERS

DALLAS-FORT WORTH (TEXAS)

This subregion is part of the Eastern Interior Low Plains that extend into the state from
the north to constitute the North-central
Plains of Texas. It is part of the physiographic
province lying between the Blackland Prairies
on the east and the Cap Rock Escarpment that
bounds the Great Plains on the west. The land
between Dallas and Fort Worth is one of limestone soils, largely prairie, with elevations
varying from 500 to 1,000 feet, broken in some
portions and traversed in some parts by flat-
topped hills.

Dallas and Fort Worth are two of the fastest
growing cities in the United States. Already the

Figure 9-22. This view of General Dynamics Corporation's Convair Division plant in Fort Worth, Texas, shows the 4,000-foot-long assembly building and smaller buildings on the 607-acre reservation. (Convair)

Dallas district has reached the one million mark. Fort Worth lays claim to 575,000 within its urban confines. Currently about 85,000 people live on the Route 80 connection between the two cities. If Dallas and Fort Worth keep up their present pace, the metropolitan area may surpass the two million mark by 1970.

Dallas was founded a little more than a century ago as a settlement along the Trinity River. The railroads came in the 1870's, and Dallas, in what was once a farming area, has grown with celerity ever since. The city's nerve-center aspect is traced to top-level oil management, oil servicing, insurance, big banks, the 11th Federal Reserve Bank, wholesaling, transportation, and manufacturing of finished products. Wholesaling activity, reaching east to Mississippi, north to the Kansas line and into Arkansas, and westward to Arizona, has reached $1.9 billion.

World War II started the aircraft boom. Chance Vought, biggest Dallas employer with 12,000 workers, turns out bombers, carrier planes, and guided missiles. Nearby is Temco Aircraft, with 7,000 employees making subassemblies, modifying aircraft, and producing Temco's own planes. It has contracts for 13 different models and is a rather unpublicized but critical unit in the aircraft production field. To the west are the huge Bell helicopter and Convair plants, part of the Fort Worth scene.

The Ford Motor Company leads the local automotive industry, with the largest assembly unit outside its Detroit headquarters. General Motors has a plant at Arlington, closer to Fort Worth. Electronics plants are expanding, led by Collins Radio and Continental Electronics Manufacturing.

Dallas also has a collection of 15 planned industrial districts. The Trinity Industrial District, a $55 million project a decade old, has 650 tenants employing 10,000 workers; the list includes Ford, Sylvania, and Pittsburgh Plate Glass.

Fort Worth is a center of two modern industrial developments, aircraft and automobiles; a livestock marketing and processing headquarters; and a grain storage and milling focal point. The city is a mixture of heavy and light industry.

Fort Worth's stockyards, the largest south of Kansas City, move five million head a year, employ 10,000 persons, and have a $30 million payroll. The meat business began in 1902 when two plants were erected to process locally produced beef.

Other Fort Worth industries are foundry products, oilfield equipment, machine tools and dies, leather goods, and farm equipment. The city's railroads and highways radiate in all directions.

OKLAHOMA CITY-TULSA

Oklahoma, in common with the rest of the nation, has had a rapid increase in the number of cities. Oklahoma City (324,253) has always been the largest urban community in the state. Central location, importance as a political center, discovery of oil, and the development of manufacturing, wholesaling, and retailing have all contributed to this position of leadership. The metropolitan district now has more than 375,000 inhabitants.

Governmental employment constitutes a larger share of the total than any other form of enterprise because of important military installations, chiefly Tinker Field, in addition to the various state offices.

Other important industries in Oklahoma City include oil field equipment, meat packing, textile manufacturing, food processing, chemicals, furniture, and fabricated metals.

Tulsa (261,685), the "Oil Capital of the World,'" is headquarters for more than 300 oil companies and a center for the manufacture of oil field supplies. Although the relative importance of manufacturing is not high in Tulsa, manufacturing in combination with mining activities (oil and gas) accounts for about a third of total employment. Wholesale trade, along with industry, formed the basis of Tulsa's growth. The city is the trade center for the northeastern part of Oklahoma, and for the adjacent parts of Kansas, Arkansas, and Missouri.

Founded by the Creek Indians before the Civil War, Tulsa remained a small village until the discovery of oil in the Glenpool area. Its 1960 metropolitan population exceeded 300,000. The Turner Turnpike, a 99-mile toll highway, brings the two metropolitan centers of Tulsa and Oklahoma City within two hours traveling time by automobile.

KANSAS CITY-OMAHA

In manufacturing, as in transportation and trade, these two cities are part of a belt of industry extending from Omaha down the Missouri Valley to St. Joseph and Kansas City.

The history of the Kansas City district is linked with its geographic location at the confluence of the Kansas and the Missouri Rivers. Long before the prairie schooners were to wend their way over the grasslands, the pioneers followed the Missouri in its tortuous meanderings to the west. These early explorations were the prelude to the later land routes —the Santa Fe, California, and Oregon Trails —all of them fanning out from Independence and old Westport, settlements that were forerunners of modern Kansas City, Missouri.

Francis Choteau established a trading post called Westport Landing on the Missouri River in 1821. Later names were "Town of Kansas," "City of Kansas," and finally (1899), "Kansas City."

As the terminus for river transportation from the East, Kansas City was a logical outfitting point for westward migration. With the advent of railroad transportation, the city assured itself a place in the sun by building the first railroad bridge across the Missouri River in 1869.

The bridge, along with the city's position in the heart of America (85 miles from the then geographic center of the United States), contributed greatly to its prominence as a shipping and trading center. It was almost inevitable that development of the West and Southwest would come through the portals of Kansas City.

The area included in the Kansas City metropolitan district covers four counties and 1,643 square miles in Missouri and Kansas. The population of the metropolitan area now totals more than 900,000 people.

Both Kansas City, Kansas, and Kansas City, Missouri, are two-level cities. Their central business and commercial districts are built on the irregular surface of a rocky upland lying some 200 feet above the factories and railway yards spread over the valley bottoms. Near the mouth of the Kansas River, an intercity viaduct, built high enough above the valley floor to be out of reach of floods, connects the two cities.

The central business area of Kansas City, Missouri, occupies rocky terrain surrounded by bottom lands on which converge railway lines from the North, East, South, and West, to make the city one of the major railway centers in the country.

The industrial importance of the bottom land of the lower Kansas River is illustrated by the development of the Kansas City stockyards and the auxiliary packing plants along both banks of the Kansas River within two miles of its junction with the Missouri. A beginning of the livestock industry was made in 1868, when the Kansas-Pacific Railway built transfer and feeding pens for cattle on the site of the present yards. By 1871 a livestock market was organized; eventually the yards were expanded, and the packing plants grew in number, size, and facilities. By 1926, Kansas City had become second in the country as a slaughtering center, with nine packing plants.

Kansas City, Missouri (475,539). Kansas City is the natural capital of the tremendous agricultural region surrounding it. Crops produced are diverse in character, in keeping with the general economy of Missouri. Wheat, tobacco, corn, potatoes, fruit, soybeans, and livestock, together with oil, natural gas, coal, and other mineral resources, combine to furnish a stable economy for the area.

The meat packing industry is only one of the many big enterprises in the city. Food processing, flour milling, steel and steel products fabrication, petroleum refining, garment manufacturing, automobile and truck assembling, and aircraft and aircraft accessories production are among the leading industries.

Kansas City, Kansas (130,013). This is a major grain storage and milling, livestock, and meat packing center. It is also an important producer of soap and milled walnut lumber. The Turner Industrial District has the world's largest grain elevator and one of the largest railroad hump (freight classification) yards in the nation.

Omaha, Nebraska, metropolitan district. Situated on the west bank of the Missouri River, almost midway between the mouth and the source, Omaha occupies 42.82 square miles. The largest city in Nebraska, Omaha had a 1960 population of 301,598 people. The metropolitan district, including adjacent Council

Figure 9-23. The Mississippi River waterfront in Minneapolis, Minnesota. Flour mills are located along both sides of the river (center); the business district is in the background. (Minneapolis Chamber of Commerce)

Bluffs, Iowa (49,000), and suburban and community residents of Douglas, Saxpy, and Pottawattamie Counties, contains an estimated 400,-000 people.

Omaha is the agricultural capital of the United States and a leader in the marketing of grain and cattle. Because of its importance in agriculture the city is rapidly becoming a center of activity in the fields of chemurgy and chemistry. Furfural, used in about 50 industrial products including nylon, is produced from corn cobs at the rate of 10,000 gallons per day in the new Quaker Oats plant. Nitrogen and urea are manufactured by the Allied Chemical and Dye Corporation on its 1,100-acre site adjacent to Omaha. Insecticides, animal serums, and fertilizers are other local products in a growing list of items related to agriculture.

Metal fabricating is an important Omaha industry. Electronic furnaces produce steel castings for making tanks, structural steel of all types, electrical and hydraulic equipment, farm machinery components, instruments, railroad equipment, and many other items. The Continental Can Company has a $7,500,-000 plant employing 500 people in the manufacture of a wide variety of food containers.

Omaha's industrial plants produce a varied line of items that have earned national recognition. In addition to metal products, the area's factories turn out food products, batteries, and water softening equipment—all have wide distribution.

MINNEAPOLIS-ST. PAUL

The Twin Cities are located on the bend of the upper Mississippi River at the head of navigation. Founded as a fur trading post (Fort Schnelling), the early history of the area was associated with flour milling, which was powered by the Falls of St. Anthony. The combination of furs, water power, and strategic location with respect to east-west and north-south trade routes was sufficient stimulus for early and rapid growth.

Minneapolis (482,872) and St. Paul (313,-411) have a metropolitan population exceeding one million. Food processing leads among Minneapolis industries, followed by machinery, precision instruments, and printing and publishing. Still famous for flour production, it is third nationally, after Buffalo and Kansas City, Missouri. It is headquarters for General Mills, International, Pillsbury, Commander-Larrabee, and Russell-Miller. Its chemical industry processes Minnesota's large flax crop for linseed oil and oil cake. Meat packing is another important industry, along with the manufacturing of electrical machinery, heating equipment, agricultural machinery, and fertilizer.

Minneapolis has ten trunk railways, including the Burlington, the North Western and the Great Northern, making it a major transportation center. Water transportation by barge is also important; some 50,000 tons a year, about one-half gasoline, are imported by barge.

St. Paul, the capital, is among the larger transportation centers of the nation. The city is served by nine first-class railroads for ready access to markets throughout the country. Only New York and Chicago handle more freight in more trucks and deliver to more cities than the hundreds of vehicles constantly loading and unloading in St. Paul's Midway district. The Mississippi River provides excellent low-cost water transportation to all points on the Mississippi system of inland waterways.

More than 2.5 million tons of freight inbound and outbound via barge lines are handled in St. Paul annually. Manufactured items produced in St. Paul include adhesives, abrasives, paper products, beer, and motor vehicle assembly.

Generally speaking, the Twin Cities' trade territory is comprised of the same area as that served by the Ninth Federal Reserve District, which includes Minnesota, Montana, North Dakota, South Dakota, northern Wisconsin, and the upper peninsula of Michigan. This is not, however, the limit of the Twin Cities' trade territory. For many products, the northern half of Iowa, Nebraska, and the greater part of Wyoming are within competitive reach of the Minneapolis-St. Paul markets.

AGRICULTURE

The American Middle West, one of the world's most important agricultural regions, is favored by unusually rich, black soil and broad expanses of cropland with hot, humid growing seasons that are ideal for cultivation. Its fertile land, relatively level topography, ample precipitation, and favorable temperatures over a large area make an exceptional combination of natural resources.

Midwest farmers have adopted rapidly the improved practices and new technology developed at agricultural experiment stations and by industry and research-minded farmers.

The advance in technology has been accompanied by: (1) a growing investment in modern farm machinery, equipment, and buildings, as well as other improvements; (2) a rapid rise in annual cash outlay for fertilizer and feed; and (3) the use of a wide range of chemical and biological products designed to promote the growth and reproduction of plants and animals.

Output per hour of farm labor has been boosted phenomenally as a result of farmers' investments in new equipment and processes for putting advanced technology to work on their farms and by the improvement in managerial skill of the farmers themselves. The result has been a persistent increase in the flow of commodities from Midwest farms, although the number of farms and of people who work them has declined.

Possibly no measure of increased efficiency is as spectacular as that which traces the rise in output per man-hour. Since 1940, for example, the total production of corn and other feed grains has increased about one-fifth, the man-hours used to produce them have been reduced by more than one-half, and the output of feed grains per man-hour has increased nearly three-

Figure 9-24. Farm labor productivity. (U.S. Department of Agriculture)

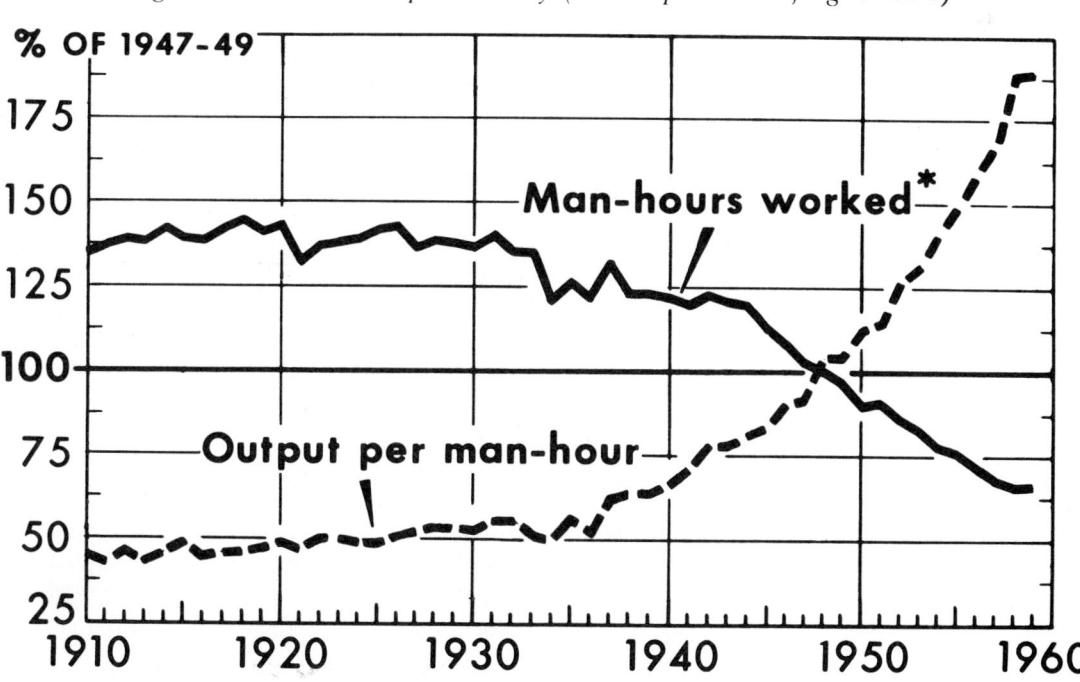

* IN TERMS OF TIME USED BY ADULT MALES

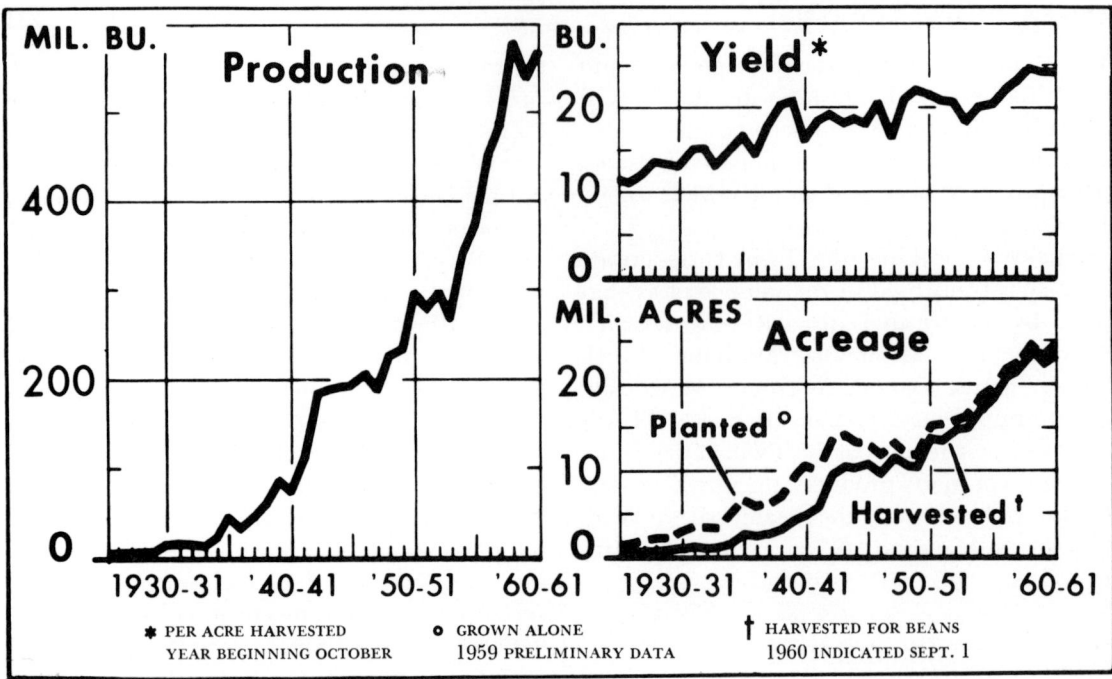

Production

400

200

0

1930-31 '40-41 '50-51 '60-61

BU.

Yield*

20

10

0

MIL. ACRES

Acreage

20

10

Planted °

Harvested †

0

1930-31 '40-41 '50-51 '60-61

* PER ACRE HARVESTED   ○ GROWN ALONE   † HARVESTED FOR BEANS
YEAR BEGINNING OCTOBER   1959 PRELIMINARY DATA   1960 INDICATED SEPT. 1

Figure 9-25. Soybean production has increased tremendously since 1931. Note the rise in yield per acre and the increase in acreage planted and harvested. (U.S. Department of Agriculture)

fold. Similar improvements have occurred in soybean cultivation and in the production of poultry, eggs, dairy products, and meat animals. Since farm labor is only one of the resources used to produce agricultural commodities, taken alone it does not provide an accurate measure of the change in efficiency of agriculture, but it is indicative of the substantial changes that an alert and progressive farm population is making in the Midwestern economy.

Although Midwestern agriculture has been spoken of as if it had a high degree of uniformity throughout, it is in fact many things, and may be divided conveniently into two broadly homogeneous areas—the Corn Subregion and the Dairy Subregion.

CORN SUBREGION

BOUNDARIES

The Corn Subregion is bounded on the east by the foothills of the Appalachians, on the south by the rough topography along the Ohio River and Ozark uplift in southern Missouri. Its western boundary is established by the dry weather of the Great Plains, and it is hemmed in on the north by the cool summer nights char-

acteristic of Minnesota, Wisconsin, and Michigan. These latter states include the Midwest section of the nation's dairy concentration.

SOILS

During the geologic age when Midwestern soils were developed, the topography of the "prairie soils" zone extending westward from Indiana through nearly half of Illinois, more than half of Iowa, and about one-sixth of Minnesota, was about as flat as it is today. There was comparatively little erosion, and the natural vegetation consisted of a luxuriant growth of tall grasses. Decomposition of this vegetation produced the abundant organic matter that characterizes these soils today. Formed predominantly from medium-textured parent material, either of glacial origin or of related windblown silts or loess material, the soils are generally permeable and quite favorable for tillage operations under a wide range of moisture conditions.

To the north, east, and the south of the prairie soils is an area of so-called "forest soils," whose organic matter derives from the decay of forest vegetation. These soils generally are light in color and low in organic matter, although areas of dark-colored, poorly drained soils are extensive. Developed from various types of glacial material, they differ considerably in texture. In northern Minnesota, Wisconsin, and Michigan, geologic and climatic conditions were such that a highly fertile soil could not develop. Over the remainder of the forest soils zone the development of a good topsoil was related primarily to topography. In areas where the land was reasonably flat—southern Wisconsin, southern Michigan, and northern Indiana—a relatively good soil was built up and the land today is quite fertile. To the south and east of the Corn Subregion the rougher topography prevented this favorable soil development; to the west the rainfall was too light and the vegetation too sparse for the development of a deep topsoil of high organic content. Three-fourths of the nation's excellent agricultural land is in the Corn Subregion; only one-sixth is in the Dairy Subregion.

CLIMATE

The Corn Subregion has a humid continental, long summer climate, with a five- to six-month growing season. Summers are hot and humid. Winters are bitterly cold. The average annual precipitation is quite uniform, varying from 20 inches along the western boundary of the Corn and Dairy Subregions to 40 inches along the Corn Subregion's southeastern edge. Summer convectional thundershower storms cause heavy downpours in a matter of hours, followed by hot, sunshiny weather. This seasonal distribution (between eight to 13 inches during June, July, and August) is ideal for optimum corn production. Moreover, the short, heavy showers reduce work stoppages in the fields to a minimum.

The Corn Subregion lies within the principal storm tracks that cross the country. As a consequence, the area experiences marked weather changes, especially in winter. In the northern part, the climate is most pronouncedly of the continental type, with warm summers and cold winters; in the central part, the summers are likewise warm and the winters moderately cold; and in the southern portion the summers are warm and the winters still less severe. A considerable part of winter precipitation is in the form of snow.

It is seldom that a summer passes without temperatures exceeding 100° F. Zero temperatures are experienced every winter. Relative humidity ranges between 64 and 68 per cent in the winter months and 72 to 75 per cent in the summer.

THE CROPS—CORN PARAMOUNT

The Corn Subregion's land and climate give it an advantage over other areas in the production of many crops, including several different grains, legumes, and grasses. If farmers in other regions grow these same crops, they do so at a distinct competitive disadvantage; they must choose, therefore, from among the "leftover" alternatives.

Although the Corn Subregion specializes in corn, several other crops are also grown, but in much smaller quantities. This wealth of alternatives tends to stabilize farm income from year to year. It also provides a readily available fund of technical know-how to facilitate shifts between crops whenever conditions warrant them.

The Corn Subregion is appropriately named, for the corn plant thrives on its deep, black, fertile soils. Furthermore, the high organic content of the prairie soils is associated with desirable characteristics of cultivability, aeration, water-holding capacity, and available nutrients; the relatively flat topography permits an intensive corn cropping program without excessive soil erosion; and the climate in the area is almost perfect for the crop.

Figure 9-26. Combining soybeans, Monmouth, Illinois. Commercial crops of soybeans are grown on farms in east-central Illinois and central Iowa. (International Harvester Co.)

Optimum corn yields are obtained under the following conditions: (1) ample moisture in early spring, followed by a warm dry spell in the first half of May so that the corn may be planted about that time; (2) a minimum of eight inches of rainfall during June, July, and August; (3) prolonged hot weather during the growing season (74° to 78° F. during the day and nights above 58°); (4) fairly dry weather before harvest; and (5) absence of killing frost through the month of September.

There probably has never been a perfect corn year, but the weather conditions delineated above are approximated in most years in the Corn Subregion, where about three-fourths of the nation's corn harvested for grain and about 40 per cent of the world's output of corn are produced.

For decades corn has ruled the Midwest, its patronage secure, its pre-eminence unchallenged. However, new crops and new varieties of old crops constantly threaten corn's position. Such changes affect the relative profitability of crops. For example, not too many years ago soybeans and soybean products were almost unknown in the United States. Today soybeans are one of the more profitable Corn Subregion crops; it is remotely possible that this plant eventually might become more profitable than corn. In that event the area simply would shift to more soybeans and less corn—and probably retain its advantage over other areas in the production of both.

It is even conceivable that grassland farming might eventually become superior to grain farming even within the Corn Subregion. Again, the area simply would shift its crop specialization into grasses and legumes—crops

in which it also has a production advantage over other regions. Essentially the same thing may be said for many other crops.

Regardless of its future, corn is today the most profitable major crop in the Corn Subregion, and the area has built its agricultural economy upon it. Obviously the relative profitability of a crop is influenced by demand and supply conditions. In order to appraise the present economic position of corn and its future prospects, the sources of its demand and the limitations to its supply must be examined.

Demand and supply. The demand for corn is derived largely from strong consumer preference for high-quality meats. This has resulted in relatively high values for grain-fed livestock. About 60 per cent of the corn crop normally is fed to animals produced primarily for their meat. Dairy cattle and laying hens, although not fed primarily for their meat, wind up at the meat counter eventually. If they are included with meat animals nearly 90 per cent of the demand for corn is accounted for. The importance of corn as a livestock feed is further emphasized by the fact that it accounts for more than half of all grain fed to livestock.

LIVESTOCK—CORN ON THE HOOF

Crops are the foundation of agriculture. This is true of the Corn Subregion as elsewhere, but in the Corn Subregion crops are only the foundation, since most of them are fed to livestock. Livestock, therefore, makes up the superstructure of the farm economy and accounts for almost three-fourths of that region's farm income.

The principal types of livestock—hogs, beef cattle, and farm flocks of chickens—require relatively small investment in specialized build-

Table   4
How Corn is Used

TYPE OF USE	TOTAL CONSUMPTION (PER CENT)
PROCESSED DIRECTLY INTO FOOD AND ALCOHOL	8
EXPORTS AND SEED	3
HOGS	48
BEEF CATTLE	10
MEAT POULTRY	3
DAIRY CATTLE	11
EGG POULTRY	10
OTHER NONMEAT ANIMALS	7

ings and equipment. Moreover, the production cycles for these kinds of livestock are relatively short. This permits farmers to adjust rather quickly to the changing economic conditions. Since the farmer has the choice of selling his corn or of feeding it either to cattle or hogs, and since he can change his decision effectively within a year or two, he is in a position to take advantage of unexpected changes in the crop and livestock markets.

Hogs. About half the corn fed to all livestock in the United States goes to hogs, and about two-thirds of the nation's hogs are raised and fed in the Corn Subregion. Their sale normally accounts for approximately 30 per cent of the cash receipts of the area's farmers. The area is densely populated with hogs, but the greatest concentration occurs in the eastern half of Iowa and the northwest quarter of Illinois.

By feeding corn to hogs, farmers do a larger volume of business with only a limited addition to their investment in fixed resources. Obviously, little additional land is needed and building and equipment requirements for this activity are not large. Hog feeding is a method of utilizing more fully the farm operator's labor and thereby boosting his annual income.

On the average, the feed equivalent of nine bushels of corn converts into about 100 pounds of live hog. Over the long run the price received by farmers for 100 pounds of hogs has averaged about 12 times the farm price of a bushel of corn. This is the famous "average hog-corn price ratio." So for his nonfeed costs and his labor, the hog feeder has received the value of about three bushels of corn for each 100 pounds of hogs he sells. Since this is a long-run average, it may be considered a "normal" return. The return in any particular year, of course, can diverge widely from the normal. A period of about 11 months elapses from the time the farmer decides on the size of his hog operation to the day the hogs are ready for market. During that period his business is exposed to the risk of price changes. The hog enterprises on Corn Subregion farms, however, can be reoriented completely within about a year's time.

Beef cattle. Between ten and 15 per cent of the corn fed to livestock in the United States is fed to beef cattle; about two-thirds of these "feedlot" cattle are fed in the Corn Subregion.

Figure 9-27. Corn fattened hogs on a McLean County, Illinois, farm. Because hogs convert concentrated feeds into meat most efficiently, they have first call on the corn grown. (U.S. Department of Agriculture)

Their sale usually accounts for approximately one-fourth of the cash receipts of farmers in the area. The feeding of beef cattle is rather common throughout the subregion, but this activity is concentrated most heavily in two areas —northwestern Illinois and northeastern Nebraska-northwestern Iowa.

The bulk of the cattle fattened in Corn Subregion feedlots are born on the Western ranges in the spring. Some of them are shipped to the Midwest as feeder calves in the fall. Others are wintered in their homeland and spend their second summer on the open range, after which they may have achieved a weight of 600 to 700 pounds. Then they are bought by corn farmers and shipped to the feedlots. The heaviest movement usually occurs in October. The feedlot diet is rich with corn, and cattle are fed to varying weights and degrees of fatness before being sold for slaughter. Many of the animals are marketed in the late spring and early summer, with the largest volume usually coming in June. The cattle feeding operation has a production and investment period that ranges typically between three and 12 months, six to eight months being the most common. The period within which substantial production adjustments can be made does not differ greatly from that for hogs.

Cattle feeding, like hog feeding, can be carried on with a relatively small investment in specialized buildings and equipment and, as with hogs, it involves a substantial investment in feed for a number of months. But cattle feeding, as it is carried on in the Corn Subregion, typically involves the outlay of a substantial amount of cash for the purchase of feeder stock; hogs, on the other hand, usually are bred and raised by the farmer who feeds them to market weight. Credit, therefore, plays a more important role in the cattle enterprise than it does in hog raising. Most of the credit is provided by commercial banks.

The substantial investment required to purchase animals causes cattle feeding to be somewhat more exposed to risk from price changes. Whereas the hog feeder must concern himself largely with two prices—hog and feed, the cattle

Figure 9-28. A field of hybrid seed corn in eastern Iowa. New corn hybrids now in commercial production yield about ten per cent more per acre than those grown less than ten years ago. (U.S. Department of Agriculture)

feeder must consider three: fat cattle, feeder cattle, and feed. A change in the price of fat cattle while animals are being fattened affects the selling price of the portion of the final weight that was purchased as feeder cattle, as well as the portion that was added in the feedlot. And since the weight of cattle purchased as feeders usually will be equal to 40 per cent or more of the weight at the end of the fattening period, price changes while cattle are being fattened may result in substantial cash losses or profits.

Southern Iowa, northwest Missouri and the adjacent counties in Illinois make up an area of rolling land in which considerable numbers of beef cattle are raised. Over one-third of the land in that area is kept in pasture utilized by maintaining herds of beef cows. However, the soil in the flatter parts is well adapted to corn, and enough corn is raised in the area so that the feeder cattle produced there can be fattened along with additional animals obtained from other areas. As far as investment, financing, and risk are concerned, this operation has essentially the same characteristics as the production of hogs, except that it is somewhat less flexible since the investment is relatively higher and the production period is longer.

Poultry. About 15 per cent of the corn fed to livestock in the United States is consumed by poultry. However, only one-fourth to one-third of the poultry is located in the Corn Subregion. Sale of poultry and products accounts for about one-tenth of the cash receipts of farmers in that area.

Corn Subregion poultry production is widely diffused; most farms have at least a few chickens. Only a small fixed investment in buildings and equipment is required for the average farm flock, and the poultry enterprise is thought to utilize some labor that otherwise would be wasted. The period of production is one year or less, and this livestock enterprise can be adjusted quite readily to changes in markets and market prospects.

In past decades, eggs were the primary output of the chicken house. The production of chicken meat was distinctly secondary and to some extent a by-product. For the Corn Subregion as a whole this pattern generally continues to exist. But within the past 20 years an important commercial broiler industry has developed, for the most part outside the corn area. It now far overshadows farm flocks as a source of chicken meat. Meanwhile, the consumption of poultry meat has been rising. In the last 15 years United States consumption has increased from 16 to 28 pounds per capita. Poultry now accounts for nearly one-sixth of all meat eaten by the American public—twice as much as calves, sheep, and lambs combined. However, beef and pork, the long time favorites at the meat counter, have been holding their own, based largely on a strong expansion in beef. Since World War II, consumption of beef and pork has risen from 125 to 140 pounds per capita.

CASH GRAIN FARMING

A rather sizable portion of the Corn Subregion specializes in "cash grain" farming, a program in which the bulk of the crops are sold in the commercial market and relatively little livestock feeding is done. Since less than ten per cent of the land in these areas is in permanent pasture and much of the clover is plowed under, the output can be marketed without much livestock feeding. Two areas of cash grain farming are outstanding: western Indiana and east-central Illinois.

LIMITS ON THE CORN SUPPLY

The fairly definite boundaries of the Corn Subregion restrict the corn supply and tend to maintain its relative value. Farmers within the area can profitably produce corn at a price and in a supply that make it relatively unprofitable in most other places. That is why three-quarters of the nation's crop is grown in this area.

It is possible that, in the future, technological advances will make those boundaries less definite. For example, the upper boundary of the Corn Subregion was moved perceptibly northward by the advent of hybrid corn adapted to a short growing season. Nevertheless, higher yields per acre within the Corn Subregion have been more than adequate to account for all the increase in corn supply in the last 30 years. In general, such new developments as hybrid corn and the greater use of commercial fertilizers have achieved their greatest results in the area that was most favored originally—the heart of the Corn Subregion.

Hybrid corn. The greatest progress in corn

Figure 9-29. *International mounted corn picker and towed "Ottawa" sheller harvesting male corn in a hybrid seed cornfield in Illinois. (U.S. Department of Agriculture)*

production has come within the last 30 years with the development and extensive use of hybrids. The production per acre has increased, stalks and roots are stronger, and all ears within a field mature more uniformly, facilitating rapid harvest methods with modern machinery.

Hybrid corn is produced by carefully controlled breeding, a procedure that results in uniform, hardy strains. A different strain is produced for different types of soil and climates.

Crop rotations. Only about 40 per cent of the Corn Subregion's cropland is planted to corn. In part this is because corn's requirement of plant nutrients is high; so high that it is frequently described as "an exhaustive crop." Also, corn is a row crop that requires heavy tilling between the rows; such cultivation leaves the soil surface exposed to erosion. It follows that if continuous raising of corn is feasible at all, it must be confined to fertile land with very little slope and must receive heavy applications of fertilizer.

At present almost all corn is grown in a crop rotation designed to maintain or improve the structure and productivity of the soil. On Midwestern cash grain farms, where corn is produced most intensively, one type of rotation consists of the growing of corn alternated

Figure 9-30. Strip cropping in Warren County, Iowa. Light patches show harvested small grains such as oats and wheat; dark areas include corn, pasture, and forage. Windbreaks of trees give protection from winter storms. (U.S. Department of Agriculture)

yearly with an oats-clover combination. The usual practice is to divide the cropland into two equal parts, plant corn on one part and the oats-clover combination on the other, and then rotate the crops year by year. This results in half the cropland being planted to corn each year.

It is possible that increased knowledge eventually will permit continuous cropping of corn through at least part of the Corn Subregion, but crop rotation undoubtedly will remain common in most areas for some years to come to retain an element of diversity in the crop output.

Oats. Primarily because of their usefulness in rotation, oats are a major crop in the Corn Subregion, occupying about 20 per cent of the cropland. Although the crop is not especially desirable from a profit standpoint, it contrib-

utes an element of diversity to the marketable output of the area.

Oats and clover are planted together. Oats mature quickly; clover is a slow starter. Taller than clover, oats may be harvested without much damage to the clover; after the oats are harvested clover develops a good growth of foliage. In the autumn, clover is plowed under as "green manure." In fact, the primary function of oats is to serve as a nurse crop to the clover, shading out weeds and providing some protection from wind and sun while young clover plants become established.

Clover. This is a legume—a type of plant with a very useful property. Legumes serve as hosts to a special type of bacteria that fixes on the roots of the plant nitrogen that the bacteria take from the inexhaustible supply in the air. Nitrogen is an important plant food, especially for corn, but plants do not have the ability to take this element directly from the air. Therefore, clover is grown and, when plowed under, supplies the soil with both plant nutrients and organic matter. Moreover, some types of clover are deep rooted plants; they help keep the subsoil porous and provide better drainage and aeration.

THE DAIRY SUBREGION

BOUNDARIES AND CLIMATE

To the north of the Corn Subregion lies the Midwestern section of the Hay, Forage, and Dairy Belt. These two belts shade into each other geographically. Milk is produced in the Corn Subregion, especially in the northern part. Corn is harvested for grain in the Dairy area, especially in the southern part. But, taken as a whole, the two belts differ substantially in soil and climate and consequently in their agricultural economies.

The boundaries, related primarily to temperature, generally follow the July 72° isotherm —the line that joins places where the average temperature in July is 72° F. In only two localities does the Dairy Subregion extend much south of the line—in southwestern Wisconsin, where the rough topography encourages dairy farming, and around Chicago, which provides a large market for fluid milk.

Elsewhere in the Midwest corn farming normally is the most profitable type of farming below the 72° isotherm. However, corn is harvested as grain from 13 per cent of the crop acreage in the Dairy Subregion, largely along its southern edge. This compares with 40 per cent in the corn area.

Roughage, the raw material. When corn was first gaining a foothold in the Midwest, it was preserved and exported from the area largely in barrels—some as fat salt pork from corn fed hogs and some, after fermentation and distillation, as whiskey. Today, much corn is preserved in giant barrel-like structures, but for another purpose. Harvested before it is fully matured, the entire plant may be chopped up and packed into silos where, after fermentation, it is "preserved in its own juice" and is available as livestock feed in the form of roughage. Although this type of feed, by itself, is not very

useful for putting a top-quality finish on meat animals such as hogs and beef cattle, it is entirely suitable for dairy cows. Moreover, because the cooler night temperatures within the subregion prevent corn from fully ripening, its adaptation for roughage is ideal.

For the Dairy Subregion as a whole, the land and climate are such that its advantage over other areas extends to the production of only a few widely grown crops. Much of its cropland may be used most effectively for the production of roughages—hay and ensilage, and in the remainder of the area the crop alternatives available are not much more profitable than hay. The yield of roughage is relatively high, although lower than in the Corn Subregion. For example, the average yield of corn ensilage in the Dairy Subregion is 8.2 tons per acre, compared with 8.8 tons in the Corn Subregion. For alfalfa hay the comparable yields are 1.9 and 2.1 tons.

Ensilage is bulky and heavy relative to its value, and deteriorates rapidly when removed from the silo. It cannot be transported economically for any significant distance and therefore has no commercial market. Usually it must be fed on the farm where it is produced and stored. Likewise, the commercial market for other types of roughage, such as hay, is predominantly local, and for the same reasons.

Thus, the value of roughage is determined by the value of livestock products that can be produced through its utilization as feed in the area where the roughage is grown. This is in sharp contrast with corn, which, although predominantly fed on farms where it is grown, has a sufficiently high value per pound to be shipped readily into areas where additional feed is needed. While the low value per pound of roughage insulates farmers from the competition of other areas, there is a well-developed nationwide market for the livestock products they produce. In this way the products from the Dairy Subregion come into competition with those from other areas. Hence the Dairy Subregion cannot escape the competitive effects of production advantages enjoyed by the Corn Subregion.

Oats. The climate of the Dairy Subregion is favorable to the growth of oats, a cool weather, early maturing crop. Consequently the subregion has a modest advantage over the Corn

Figure 9-31. Holstein cattle in an alfalfa-ladino improved pasture in Green County, Wisconsin. (U.S. Department of Agriculture)

Subregion in its production. The average yield of oats is 39 bushels per acre in the Dairy Subregion, whereas only 35 bushels per acre are produced in the Corn Subregion.

Oats are an acceptable feed for most types of livestock. But the digestible nutrients in 39 bushels of oats in the Dairy Subregion are less than half the amount contained in 45 bushels of corn, the average yield of that crop. And since other grains that can be grown in the Dairy Subregion also produce much less nutrients per acre than does corn in the Corn Subregion, the Dairy Subregion is at a disadvantage in the grain fattening of meat animals. However, oats are very useful as a supplement to the primarily roughage diet of dairy cattle, and in the Dairy Subregion about a quarter of the tillable land is planted to it.

HAY AND PASTURE

The cool climate of the Dairy Subregion is well suited to the growth of short-rooted grasses. For the deep-rooted legumes, however,

the fertility of the Corn Subregion soils more than offsets the disadvantage of that area's hot summer temperatures. Despite this disadvantage in the production of legumes, the Dairy Subregion plants as many acres to alfalfa as does the Corn Subregion, even though the latter region has almost three times as much cropland.

The grasses that supply much of the roughage in the Dairy Subregion grow on nontillable land, in permanent pastures and meadows. In addition, both grasses and legumes are planted on cropland and harvested and preserved as hay or ensilage. In terms of acreage, hay is the leading crop in the Dairy Subregion.

Primarily because of the rougher topography and poorer soils in the Dairy Subregion, only 60 per cent of the land area is in farms, with a smaller proportion of the land in farms tillable. The proportion of the land in permanent pasture, woodland, and waste is considerably larger than is the case for the Corn Subregion. The land not in farms has little agricultural

Table 5
Land Uses in Corn and Dairy Subregions (Per Cent)

	CROPLAND	WOODLAND AND WASTE	PERMANENT PASTURE
CORN SUBREGION	75	18	7
DAIRY SUBREGION	62	23	15

value and is utilized largely as a recreational area and for the production of wood products.

The adaptability of permanent pasture and hay land is restricted severely. Pasture can be utilized effectively by only a few types of farm animals, dairy cattle included. Thus the rougher topography of the Dairy Subregion is a factor contributing to the specialization of that region in milk production. Nowhere is this better illustrated than in southwest Wisconsin. Climatically that area should be part of the Corn Subregion. Nevertheless, southwest Wisconsin is predominantly a dairy area, primarily because of its rough topography. The average farm here has about twice as much permanent pasture as farms in adjacent areas to the east, south, and west.

The Corn Subregion could provide much more milk per acre of land than the Dairy Subregion because of the former's advantage in the production of feeds suitable for dairy cows. However, grains and meat animals are more profitable in the Corn Subregion than a roughage and milk economy would be. Milk production, a rejected alternative of the Corn Subregion, becomes the most attractive alternative for the roughage producing Dairy Subregion.

DAIRY COWS, THE ROUGHAGE CONVERTERS

Since roughages form the foundation of the farm economy in the Dairy Subregion, the livestock superstructure is made up of roughage-consuming animals. Cattle, sheep, goats, and horses are the possible alternatives. Goats never have been too important in American agriculture, and the horse virtually has disappeared. Practical alternatives are few indeed: milk cows, feeder cattle, and sheep. The Dairy Subregion specializes in milk production because price relationships historically have made milk cows more profitable than the other two types of roughage-consuming livestock, which are produced largely on cheaper lands further re-

Figure 9-32. Distribution of dairy cows in the United States. Note the heavy concentration of cows in Wisconsin and Minnesota. (U.S. Department of Agriculture)

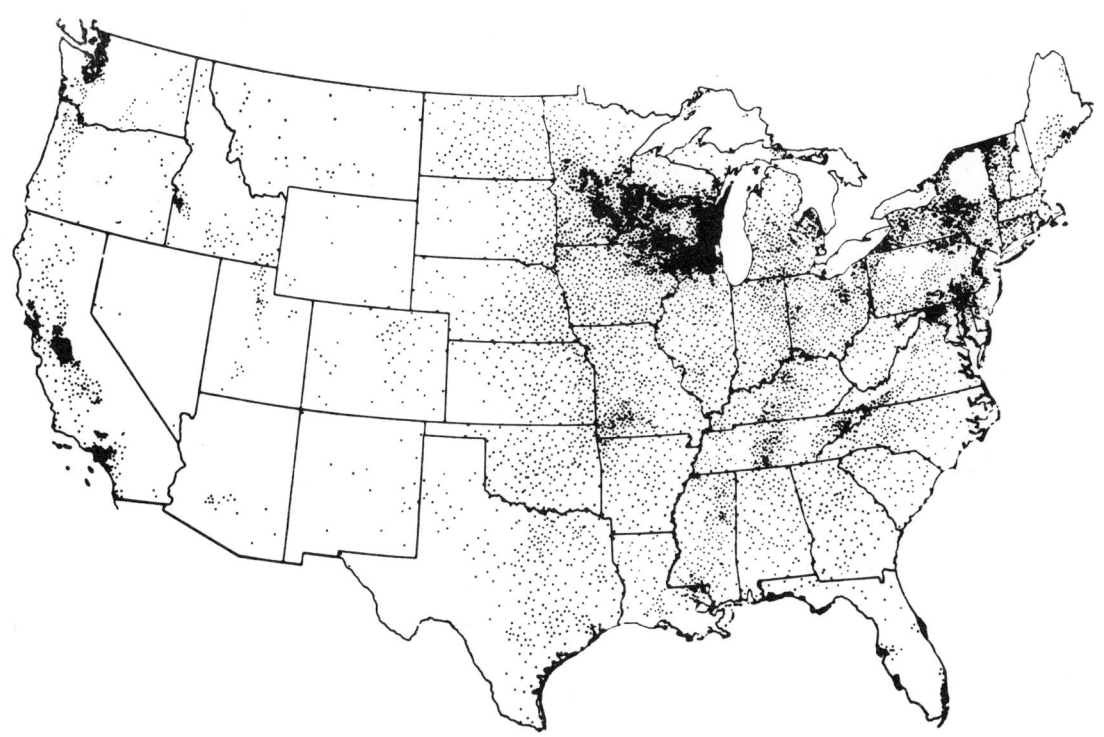

1 DOT = 2,500 COWS (county unit basis)

UNITED STATES TOTAL: 20,182,800

moved from markets and under climatic conditions less favorable to the growth of feed for dairy cows.

In recent years, technological developments have made it possible to replace dairy products with low-cost substitutes consisting largely of milk fat, and this has made milk production relatively less profitable than it was formerly. However, the Dairy Subregion has not shifted away from its specialization in milk, because this alternative still remains most profitable for the area.

Beef cattle could be raised in the Dairy Subregion and sold as feeders for shipment in the Corn Subregion to be fattened on grain. But with the present small size of farms (the average size is 144 acres: 111 in Michigan, 137.8 in Wisconsin, and 183.6 in Minnesota) and present price relationships, such a procedure would result in a rather drastic cut in farm income.

Along the southern boundary of the Dairy Subregion—for example, in southwest Wisconsin—enough corn is harvested for grain so that grain fattening of cattle is practical. Consequently, in the future the hillside pastures in that area may well provide a setting for more Herefords and Angus and fewer Holsteins and Guernseys. But there are not many parts of the Dairy Subregion that qualify climatically as a part of the Corn Subregion.

Sheep are an even less profitable livestock alternative than the raising of beef cattle. So the Dairy Subregion as a whole—especially its northern portion—is likely to continue to specialize in the production of milk and milk products, even though demand and supply have made milk production less profitable than it was previously.

Dairy breeds. Although nearly all the European dairy breeds are represented in the Dairy Subregion, Holstein cows are the most numerous. This is not surprising since they are large animals and heavy milk producers. However, they tend to give milk averaging somewhat lower in butterfat content than the milk of some other breeds. Guernsey cattle rank next to Holsteins in importance. Guernseys average smaller in size but usually give a relatively greater amount of butterfat in the milk; they therefore are most popular in the butter area of Minnesota and the cheese manufacturing

portion of Wisconsin. Sometimes it is the practice to include some Guernseys in Holstein herds to increase the average fat test.

Smaller numbers of Jersey cattle and Brown Swiss are scattered throughout the area. Minor breeds, such as Dutch Belted and Ayrshire, also are found, along with some dual-purpose breeds. Wisconsin now leads all states in dairying.

Demand for milk. As is the case with meats, the demand for milk originates in consumer preferences and incomes. Consumers like the flavor and texture of dairy products. They seem to be less inclined to shift their demand for dairy products in response to income or price changes than in the case of meat, *i.e.,* the demand for dairy products is less elastic. Furthermore, the demand for dairy products appears to be more vulnerable to technological change. For example, the flavor and texture of milk fat can be duplicated quite readily by the processing of vegetable oils; but it is difficult to conceive of a good vegetable substitute for a steak or a rasher of bacon. Because of the nature of consumer preferences and the competition from other commodities, the demand for milk probably will grow at a somewhat slower rate than the demand for meats as our national economy develops and per capita income rises.

However, just as an increase in per capita income leads to a greater expansion in the demand for meat than for dairy products, so also does a fall in consumer income lead to a greater comparable contraction in the demand for meat. That is why, in the past, the price and the profitability of producing milk have been more stable than have the price and the profitability of producing meat animals.

DAIRY PRODUCTS

Milk may be used fresh or it may be manufactured into a number of other dairy products. As the following table shows, these two sources of the demand for milk are of approximately equal importance.

Wisconsin manufactures a large amount of all types of dairy products but specializes in cheese and evaporated milk. Michigan is the leader in ice cream production, while Minnesota specializes in butter. The largest share of Minnesota's milk is manufactured. In Wiscon-

Table 6

Milk Utilization in the United States

TYPE OF USE	PER CENT OF TOTAL
FLUID CONSUMPTION	46.6
FED TO CALVES ON FARMS	2.7
MANUFACTURED DAIRY PRODUCTS	
BUTTER	26.9
CHEESE	10.7
FROZEN DAIRY PRODUCTS	6.5
EVAPORATED AND CONDENSED MILK	5.2
DRY WHOLE MILK	.7
OTHER MANUFACTURED DAIRY PRODUCTS	.7
	50.7

sin and Michigan the proportion of manufactured milk is smaller because those states supply fresh fluid milk for the large Chicago and Detroit markets.

Cheese. In Wisconsin more milk is used in making cheese than for any other purpose. Over 40 per cent of the milk supply goes into cheese production and the bulk of this is made into American cheese, which comprises some 76 per cent of all the cheese manufactured in the state. Output of American cheese has averaged well over a half-billion pounds annually since 1950. Swiss cheese is a very important product in some Wisconsin counties. The record Swiss cheese output was in 1950, when production reached over 52 million pounds. Italian type

Figure 9-33. Brining and salting Swiss cheese, Wisconsin. (Monroe Chamber of Commerce)

cheeses fluctuate in the amount manufactured from year to year, varying anywhere from 20 to 25 million pounds annually. Brick, Munster, and Limburger are minor cheeses produced in the area.

More than 1,100 cheese factories are distributed throughout Wisconsin. The largest concentration is in the southwestern district where nearly 300 factories are located. The eastern district, including Sheboygan and Manitowoc, is second, followed by the southern district. Each of these sections has over 200 cheese producing plants.

WIDELY SEPARATED AGRICULTURAL AREAS

ONTARIO PROVINCE

The vast area of Ontario gives rise to wide variations in climate and landforms, and therefore in types of agriculture. Most of the agricultural area is confined to the southern part of the province, where the climate is moderated by the proximity of the Great Lakes and where the soil is generally fertile.

Southern and eastern Ontario are by far the most important agricultural sections of the province. In terms of estimated net income per farm, the Lake Erie, Upper Thames, Upper Grand River, Metropolitan, and Border sections are the top five, in that order. There are several large, sandy tracts there now being extensively used for tobacco growing. The soils of part of the lake plains and St. Clair River areas have a high organic content and are well suited to the growing of cash crops. The whole of the Upper Thames area, particularly Oxford County, is effective for dairying. Fruit and vegetable growing are concentrated in the narrow strip of land surrounding the western end of Lake Ontario.

Another important agricultural area includes parts of the Quinte, Upper St. Lawrence, and Ottawa Valley sections. Handicapped by drainage problems in the growing of field crops, these regions emphasize dairy farming and cattle raising. These sections are the three leading producers of cheddar cheese in Ontario; the Ottawa Valley and Quinte areas also rank third in butter production, after the Blue Water and Upper Grand River sections. In the Ottawa Valley and sections of the Upper St.

Lawrence area away from the river, the emphasis has shifted to beef cattle raising, both for slaughter and as breeding stock for the United States market.

LAKE ERIE'S SOUTH SHORE

The land in most of the lake plain is well suited to the growing of grain crops such as corn, wheat, oats, and soybeans. Even though corn and wheat together comprise only one-fourth of all cash income, more farm land is planted in these crops than in any other. Much of the grain is used as feed for dairy cows, hogs, poultry, and beef cattle; in large measure the grain shows up indirectly as cash income from the marketing of livestock products. Agriculture in the area is marked by the prevalence of crop rotation and the use of other up-to-date farming techniques, including a heavy investment in machinery.

A basic crop in the western portion of this area is soybeans. This crop accounts for over 15 per cent of the income from agricultural products. All six of the leading soybean counties of Ohio are located in the Lake Erie South Shore district.

Agricultural activity in the central and eastern portions of the lake plain reflects its proximity to the Cleveland and Buffalo metropolitan areas. Dairying and raising of hogs, poultry, and beef cattle, together with complementary enterprises, represent balanced farming.

ONTARIO LAKE PLAIN

Fruit, vegetable, and dairy farms occupy about three-fourths of the acreage on the plain south of Lake Ontario. Sales of dairy products, principally milk, provide the largest source of agricultural income; they account for more than half of all farm products sold. Other livestock products, including poultry, represent the second most important source of farmers' cash income. The area's truck farms yield fresh beans, sweet corn, cabbage, tomatoes, spinach, beets, and onions. A large proportion of this produce is delivered to local canneries. The Ontario fruit belt abounds with orchards of apples, pears, cherries, peaches, and plums. With large dairy herds to feed, the area also has an extensive acreage of forage crops. Alfalfa production ranks high nationally.

ST. LAWRENCE-CHAMPLAIN LOWLANDS

The portion of the St. Lawrence Lowlands lying in the states of New York and Vermont is primarily a dairy land. Poor soils, short growing seasons, and considerable distance from markets, combined with little available flat land, preclude most other agricultural enterprises. St. Lawrence is the leading dairy county in New York State, ranking first in the number of cows milked and in milk and hay produced. It is fourth nationally in the number of cows milked, fifth in milk production and value of dairy products sold, and third in hay production.

Most of the milk from this area is shipped into the New York City market in fluid form. The surplus is processed locally into cheese, ice cream, and other dairy products. Other notable farm products include McIntosh apples from the Lake Champlain Valley, seed potatoes grown in New York's three northernmost counties—St. Lawrence, Franklin, and Clinton—and maple syrup and sugar from St. Lawrence County.

QUEBEC PROVINCE

Until 1870, nearly 80 per cent of the population of Quebec lived in rural areas; since the great industrial development of the last 50 years that proportion has been reduced to 35 per cent. Yet, the fast-growing markets provided by numerous industrial towns have created excellent conditions for the sale of farm products.

The average Quebec farm measures 112 acres, of which 67 acres are under cultivation, but the occupied farms vary greatly in size— from a few acres near urban centers to more than 600 acres in the more remote areas.

Mixed farming combined with dairy farming is widely practiced, because this system is best adapted to climatic and economic conditions. The improved quality of livestock, particularly of dairy cattle and bacon hogs, is the dominant feature of animal husbandry today. During the past two decades other important changes in the farm animal population have taken place. Horses were displaced by tractors and trucks and the number of sheep declined rapidly because of competition.

Dairy products rank high in the economy. Quebec has nearly 950 butter and cheese factories, over 50 plants for processing milk, and many city dairies. Altogether these industries employ more than 5,000 people, and the gross value of their annual output exceeds $100 million. Quebec is Canada's leading butter producer and ranks second to Ontario in cheese manufacturing.

Next in value are cereal products with an annual worth estimated at $70 million. Besides large mills (supplied by Western grain), Quebec has many small mills for preparing feeds.

Meat products, too, are important. Packing plants in Montreal and Quebec turn out products grossing around $90 million each year. Mention also should be made of the more than 140 hatcheries and numerous candling stations serving the poultry interests.

During the past 40 years, great advances have occurred in vegetable culture, a response to urban growth and needs resulting from industrialization. In 1920, only 7,457 acres were cultivated on a commercial basis, as compared with about 50,000 acres today. Canning factories, almost unknown in 1920, produce goods now valued at over $27 million.

Fruit growing, too, has been developed appreciably. Quebec apples and strawberries are famed for their quality and flavor. The apple crop is sizable—two million bushels a year on the average. The strawberry harvest yields about six million quarts. Other fruit crops include raspberries, currants, and cranberries.

SPECIALIZED FRUIT BELTS

The outstanding area of fruit and vegetable production in the Eastern Interior Low Plains Region is located along the eastern shore of Lake Michigan where the influence of the lake moderates temperature variations to produce a favorable climate. Smaller areas are scattered throughout Wisconsin, Minnesota, and the lower peninsula of Michigan. However, the production of commercial fruits and vegetables in the region is limited by two factors: (1) the climatic conditions favorable to some of these crops are quite localized, and (2) the market for these crops is not extensive enough for the region as a whole to specialize profitably in their production. Consequently these crops are only occasionally an attractive alternative to the present economy, although they provide some element of diversity in the salable output of the area.

MICHIGAN

Michigan ranks as one of the country's leading fruit producing states. The "fruit belt" extending along much of the west shore of the state is evidence of modified climatic conditions near Lake Michigan.

Apples. Michigan has ranked fifth among the states in apple production in recent years. More than four million trees yield an annual average of seven million bushels, with Jonathan, Delicious, McIntosh, and Northern Spy the leading varieties. Apple production is concentrated in a strip ten to 15 miles wide along Lake Michigan northward from Oceana County to Charlevoix.

Peaches. Five southwestern and western counties produce the bulk of Michigan's annual peach crop. In these areas, and elsewhere in the southern counties of the lower peninsula where peaches are grown, production is favored by relative freedom from temperatures that result in winter and spring frost injury, length of growing season, and nearness to markets. Michigan is among the four leading states in peach production. Although the number of trees, both of bearing and nonbearing age, has declined in the postwar years, production has remained fairly constant.

Cherries. Production of both sweet and red-tart cherries is concentrated in select areas along the Lake Michigan shore. Michigan is the leading state in the production of red-tart cherries and fourth in sweet cherry production. Tree numbers have increased in the past 15 years to a record 4,560,000 trees. About 4.2 million of these are red-tart, concentrated in the Grand Traverse area.

Fruits, nuts, and berries normally account for about 17 per cent of the state's crop sales, which generally total more than $30 million. Pears, plums, grapes, and strawberries are important adjuncts within the fruit belt. Raspberries, blueberries, blackberries, and dewberries round out production in southwestern Michigan.

NIAGARA PENINSULA OF ONTARIO

The narrow strip of land surrounding the western end of Lake Ontario, protected by the Niagara escarpment and favorably influenced by the large body of water, enjoys a long growing season and is largely devoted to fruit and vegetable growing. The Niagara and Burlington sections comprising this area rank first and third in value of tree fruits produced and account for 43 per cent of the value (over $20 million annually) of all fruit grown in Canada. Grapes, cherries, peaches, pears, and plums are the most widely grown fruits. St. Catharines and Welland are centers of the Niagara fruit belt and of the wine making industry.

LAKE ERIE'S SOUTH SHORE

The southeast shore of Lake Erie in Ohio, Pennsylvania, and New York is the center of a very important fruit belt. The climate near the lake retards the early blossoming of fruit trees until the danger of frost is past. Rolling-to-hilly land permits the drainage of cold air from the cherry orchards, peach orchards, and grape vineyards on the beach ridges.

A wide variety of deciduous fruits is grown in Ohio, where sales of fruit from orchards total more than $12 million annually. Over one-half of this sum comes from apples, followed by peaches, strawberries, and grapes. The leading orchard counties are Ottawa, with over 300,000 peach and 35,000 pear trees, and Sandusky and Lake Counties, which have large cherry orchards. There are over seven million grapevines near the lake and on the islands within the state of Ohio. Grapes are sold for fresh table use and for wine making. Well over 500,000 gallons of wine are pressed annually from local grapes; Ohio ranks sixth in the nation in grape production.

Apple orchards have been established chiefly near the metropolitan centers, where apples are sold largely as fresh fruit. Many sales are made directly to the consumer who visits the farm to buy.

North East, the northernmost community in Pennsylvania, is situated in the heart of the Concord grape belt and a large fruit orchard area. Ninety-three per cent of the grapes grown in the state are produced here and 41 million pounds of grapes are processed annually.

Figure 9-34. Northernaire, Three Lakes, Wisconsin, is typical of the resort development in northern Wisconsin.

Westfield, New York, is situated in the Chautauqua grape belt. Although this county has only a few hundred square miles of its land in vineyards, the productivity is so high that Chautauqua ranks among the seven leading grape growing counties in the nation. Many grape juice producing plants are located within this region. The home office and largest factory of the grape juice industry leader, Welch's, is in Westfield.

ONTARIO LAKE PLAIN

New York's largest fruit region is just south of Lake Ontario. Although cherries account for 15 per cent of the total value of fruit in this Lake Ontario region, apples are by far the most important single fruit enterprise.

A climate free from sudden changes in temperature, which results in a relatively long growing season, and accompanying soils with a good internal drainage favor the production of fruit. The Ontario Lake Plain area, although it lies in the northern half of New York, has more frost-free days than any other region in the state, excluding metropolitan New York and Long Island. The tempering effects of Lake Erie, Lake Ontario, and the Finger Lakes have a strong influence on fruit production there. Grape vineyards and orchards of apples, pears, cherries, peaches, and plums extend along Lake Ontario's shore.

RECREATIONAL RESOURCES

A region as large and diverse as the Eastern Interior Low Plains offers countless opportunities for tourism and recreational development. A network of modern highways opens an ever-changing panorama of attractions, and the range of selection is wide. There are vast for-

ests, natural and man-made lakes, and sparkling fishing streams. State, provincial, and national forests offer the enchantment of vast,
unspoiled playgrounds; summer and winter
health resorts; and camping, boating, swimming, hiking, picnicking, skiing, and sledding
facilities throughout many parts of the region.
Many of these facilities, however, are sandwiched between industrial towns and cities.
To reach them often involves a long drive and
heavy traffic. The parks are crowded with thousands of other human beings with the same
purpose in mind, relaxation.

Only in the northern portion of the Eastern
Interior Low Plains is there sufficient land
area relatively undeveloped or unspoiled by
cities that might be termed a true vacation
land. Upper Minnesota, Michigan, and Wisconsin are excellent vacation lands. There are
several thousand square miles of virgin forest
and some 50,000 square miles of lakes, rivers,
and streams—the natural haunt of a wide variety of fish and wild game—interspersed with
many fine towns and villages. Summer and
winter health resorts are ideally located in
beautiful natural settings.

Michigan is one of the great resort states of
the Middle West, with a resort income of $400
million a year. Wisconsin's 10,000 miles of
trout streams and 8,500 lakes make it a fisherman's paradise. There are nearly 300,000 acres
of recreational areas, including 29 state parks
and seven state forests, in Wisconsin. Minnesota is known as the "Land of 10,000 Lakes."
Its multiplicity of waterways make vacationing
an important industry. Approximately 18 million visitors spend about $225 million a year
enjoying the wonders of Ontario.

This northern fringe of the Eastern Interior
Low Plain clearly should continue to develop
its recreational resources. Few areas, if any, offering such a wide variety of recreational outlets are as advantageously located near the
population centers of Anglo-America. Some 70
million people living in areas with great density of thriving municipalities and intense industrial development are but a day or two from
the refreshing outdoors. Many city dwellers
find the cooler summers of the "North Woods"
and the lake country a welcome change from
the sweltering heat of the coastal cities or the
hot climate of the Middle West.

10 | *Western Interior High Plains*

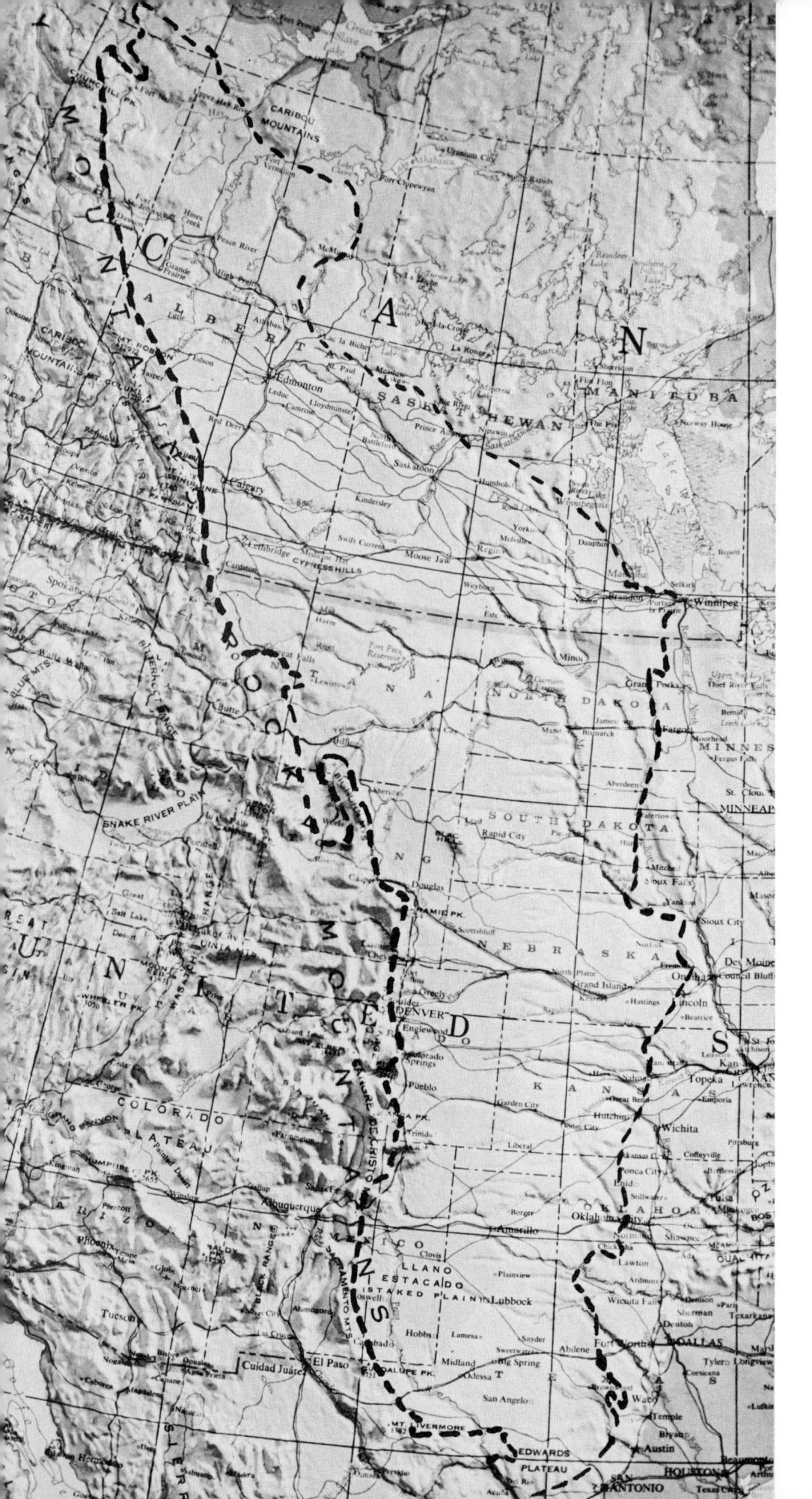

*(Relief map copyright
Aero Service Corp.)*

THE Western Interior High Plains Region, extending in a continuous belt from Mexico into Canada, comprises the largest uninterrupted area in Anglo-America with a semiarid climate. It includes the greater part of Alberta, the southern half of Saskatchewan, and the southwest corner of Manitoba in Canada; and the eastern two-thirds of Montana; the eastern thirds of Wyoming, Colorado, and New Mexico; the western thirds of Texas and Oklahoma; the western half of Kansas; most of Nebraska; and the western three-fourths of North and South Dakota in the United States.

SURFACE FEATURES

The area is a region of nearly horizontal rocks and a topography, varying from young through mature to old, that stretches 400 to 500 miles across and slopes eastward eight to ten feet per mile. It is 4,000 to 6,000 feet high where it abuts the Rocky Mountains on the west. Its eastern edge is 1,500 to 2,000 feet high, generally passing into the Eastern Interior Low Plains by a steeper slope. In some places there is a 300- to 400-foot escarpment that is dissected in other places into a belt of hills. The sections are distinguished mainly by the stages reached in the erosion cycle.

The High Plains from Nebraska to Texas are essentially flat except where crossed by streams (not numerous) or blown into sand dunes (western Nebraska). The largest flat is the Llano Estacado (Staked Plain) in western Texas, a surface made by alluviation[1] by overloaded streams pouring from the mountains. This flat once occupied the entire width of the province. When erosion succeeded the deposition, the eastern margin was first dissected. The Eastern Interior Low Plains and the marginal hilly belt are expanding westward at the expense of the High Plains. South of central Kansas this marginal hilly belt is narrow; to the north, it widens and is represented by the Smoky Hill section.

At the same time a more arid strip near the mountains in eastern Colorado and New Mexico was eroded because vegetation was insufficient to protect it. Only in west Texas, where the grass forms a tight sod, was the flat surface

preserved. Farther west in the Colorado piedmont are bunch grass and an eroded surface. The Raton section (northeastern New Mexico) has been raised a little higher and its streams run in canyons, some of them 1,000 feet deep. It has prominent volcanic features: great lava-capped mesas,[2] many volcanic "necks,"[3] and a few very young volcanoes. Part of the Pecos section (east-central and southeastern New Mexico) is reduced to a new peneplain 500 to 700 feet below the High Plains on the east and more than 1,000 feet below the Raton section on the north. Much of its northern part is quite rugged.

At the south end of the Llano Estacado the alluvial cover gives out. The Edwards Plateau is a limestone plateau with dissected edges that overlooks the Eastern Interior Low Plains and the Mississippi-West Gulf Plain. There is little left of the plateau surface in central Texas. Much of this section is eroded enough to be rugged (mature or past mature) and considerable areas are approaching old age.

The Pine Ridge Escarpment overlooks the Missouri Plateau. The plateau on the north, subject to long erosion, is much lower than the High Plains to the south (1,000 feet lower on the Wyoming-Nebraska boundary), and is expanding southward. It is not a perfect peneplain because the erosion cycle has been interrupted by occasional periods of uplift. Fragments of peneplain are found at different levels. There are also extensive areas of old river terraces developed at different stages of uplift. Recently revived erosion has made gigantic badlands[4] east and south of the Black Hills and along certain streams, especially the Little Mis-

[1] Depositing of soil, sand, gravel, or similar detrital material by running water.

[2] A flat, table-like mountain that falls away steeply on at least three sides and is formed from a plateau in an arid region. The word in Spanish means "table." The flat surface is due to the fact that the harder top layers of rock have resisted denudation and, being nearly horizontal, have maintained a uniform surface parallel to the stratification.

[3] A rocky crag consisting of solidified lava that formerly filled the central opening of a volcano and has been left isolated when the remainder of the cone has been worn away by weathering.

[4] An elevated, arid region that is seamed and lined with innumerable deep gullies by the occasional torrential rain, the normal precipitation being insufficient to support an adequate protective covering of grass or other vegetation. The unequal resistance of the rocks often causes tall columns and platforms to stand out above the surrounding land. So completely are the badlands gullied or bared by rain that they are almost valueless for agriculture or for pasture land.

Figure 10-1. A scene in northern Nebraska. The Western Interior High Plains Region in general has little relief except near streams. (Bureau of Reclamation, U.S. Department of the Interior)

souri River. There are several isolated mountain uplifts; the Black Hills uplift is the largest and farthest east.

The northern and eastern margins of the Missouri Plateau were glaciated. The course of the Missouri River was determined by the edge of the ice, which blocked former drainage toward the east. The river has since cut out a trough much like that of the Ohio River. The strip of the Missouri Plateau between the Missouri and the Eastern Interior Low Plains (James River Valley) is surmounted by strong terminal moraines called the "Couteau of the Missouri." There are numerous ponds, swamps, and stony hummocks; this is a grazing country bordering farm lands on the east.

The Black Hills are a dome-like mountain range 3,000 to 4,000 feet above the plain and 7,000 feet above the sea. Granite is exposed in the center where the overlying sedimentary rocks are eroded away, leaving the former monoclinal[5] ridges and valleys. The larger local rainfall causes forests and feeds streams used for irrigation on the nearby plains.

CLIMATE AND SOILS

The 20-inch isohyet is not far from the east-

[5] A fold in which the bend is in only one direction; the rock stratum changes its dip by increasing its steepness of inclination, and then levels out again or resumes its gentle dip.

ern limit of the province. In Kansas and Nebraska the region extends east to the 25-inch rainfall line. Farther north along the boundary there is less rainfall, but it is almost equivalent to 25 inches in Kansas because of reduced evaporation. The maximum rainfall comes in the growing season, so that the eastern margin of the province is farmed without irrigation. Westward, rainfall decreases to ten to 12 inches. In general the wind velocity, evaporation, and percentage of sunshine are high.

Nearly all the region's rainfall is caused by the interaction of great masses of air originating over the vast arctic tundra of northern Canada and over the Gulf of Mexico and the Atlantic between Bermuda and the Bahamas. In the northern region the air becomes cold, dry, and heavy and is called polar continental; in the southern, it becomes warm, very moist, and light and is called tropical maritime. At irregular intervals the polar continental air masses advance southward and eastward, spreading across the area east of the Rockies, where they generally encounter along their route maritime air advancing northward from the Gulf or the Atlantic. Because it is lighter and moister, the maritime air is forced to ascend, is cooled, and yields a portion of its water vapor as precipitation.

The path followed by the tropical maritime

air characteristically curves across the Gulf of Mexico, up the Mississippi Valley, and then eastward to the Atlantic; it tends to avoid the Western Interior High Plains altogether. The tropical air masses that flow northward across the plains come generally from the dry plateau of Mexico and are warm but contain little water vapor. When this air comes in contact with the cold, heavy air from the north, it, too, is forced up, but little precipitation results from the consequent cooling.

The moist air from the Gulf of Mexico, however, does not always avoid the Western Interior High Plains. Most of the plains' precipitation is caused by the incursions of tropical maritime air. The farther the tropical air has traveled from its sources of moisture, the drier it becomes and the lighter the precipitation that results from its cooling. The result is a gradual decrease in average annual precipitation from approximately 25 inches in south Texas to less than 12 inches in the northern part of the region.

Maximum summer temperatures in excess of 110° F. have been experienced nearly everywhere in the Western Interior High Plains, and records of 117° have been reported from both Texas and Montana. Below-zero temperatures have occurred throughout the region, but the minimum drops lower with increase in latitude, to reach a record of −68° at Havre, in northern Montana.

The hazards of hail, frost, and hot winds are all particularly severe in the High Plains and are caused by alternate inundations of the region by various types of air masses and their interactions. A vigorous upward displacement of warm air along the advancing front of a cold polar air mass is responsible for most of the hailstorms, which are common during the summer. In spring and autumn an advance of polar air may cause killing frost, accompanied by great damage to crops. Equally serious is the hazard presented by the hot, dry winds of summer that are at times experienced in all parts of the High Plains.

Broad zones of soils correspond to broad differences in climate and vegetation. The chernozem, chestnut, and brown soil zones are aligned in a generally north-south direction corresponding to climatic belts. The cherno-

zem soils, largely devoted to crops, occupy the most humid part. They have thick, black horizons and a large amount of organic matter. The brown soils occur in the driest parts and are devoted primarily to grazing. The chestnut soils, between the chernozem and brown soils and intermediate in their features, have thin black or dark-brown surface horizons and moderate organic matter.

The most extensive irrigation, in the valleys of the Yellowstone, South Platte, Arkansas, and Pecos Rivers, is mainly on stream terraces that occupy only a small fraction of the total area but yield very abundant crops. The high plains between the valleys cannot be watered, but they are ideal for grazing. Wells 50 to 200 feet deep furnish adequate water for domestic use and for stock, but little for irrigation.

The climate of the Western Interior High Plains, varying from subhumid in its eastern margin to semiarid in the central and western portions, naturally divides the province into three major land-use patterns: (1) cash grain farming, (2) grazing, and (3) irrigated farming.

CASH GRAIN FARMING IN THE WINTER WHEAT SUBREGION

HISTORY AND DEVELOPMENT

For some time after the geography of the West was fairly well known, much of Kansas (the center of winter wheat production) and the Great Plains was believed to be unfit as a habitat for the white man. Even after settlement of the eastern part of the area had begun, it was thought that the western portion never could become an agricultural country. Most maps of the 1830's and 1840's showed an area called the "Great American Desert," which frequently was compared with the Sahara. The location was rather indefinite, with the earliest maps including all the area between Missouri and the Rocky Mountains, and later ones giving the eastern boundary as approximately the center of Kansas.

If the facts had been known, the geographers would have put the desert districts west of the Rocky Mountains, where they still may be found. The two great divisions of the plains, as applied to natural production, are well de-

Figure 10-2. Desert conditions and improper use of the land took their toll of livestock in the late 1800's and early 1900's in the Western Interior High Plains Region. Scenes like this were not uncommon. (U.S. Department of Agriculture)

fined. They are separate, one from the other, and entirely unlike in physical aspect. They are the Prairies and the Great Plains. The Prairies extend from the Missouri border to an irregular line passing through Council Grove, Kansas, in Morris County—something less than one-third the distance to the western boundary of the state. It is rolling country with streams fringed with trees. For some thousands of years, at least, the Prairies have been grass clad, well watered, and fertile. In historic times they never possessed any of the characteristics of desert.

The Western Interior High (or Great) Plains extend from the western border of the Prairies near Council Grove to the Rocky Mountains. This is a country of disappearing streams. There was little or no timber originally. Stretches of drifting sand were to be found, but these were not deserts in the true sense. The country was covered almost entirely with buffalo grass. The Great Plains were the pastures, par excellence, of the buffalo. The antelope, too, was native to the Great Plains, along with deer, wolves, coyotes, rabbits, and numerous birds.

The history of agriculture in this area begins at the close of the Civil War, in the summer of 1865. Cheap land, the return of soldiers from the Civil War, rapid railroad development, improvements in farm machinery, and increasing immigration were important factors in the rapid westward expansion of population. Opposing these features were unfavorable weather conditions, grasshoppers, unadapted crops, and the fact that most of the settlers had come from humid regions and knew little of farming in the low rainfall areas (15 to 20 inches) of central and western Kansas. In addition, few of the newcomers had sufficient resources to survive a poor crop year, especially for the first year or two after their arrival. Yet, by 1875, settlements had been made in most counties in the eastern two-thirds of the state.

Corn was the most important crop, with wheat—both spring and soft winter varieties—in second place. Yet, as early as 1875, agricultural leaders were pointing out that winter wheat was better adapted to local conditions than spring wheat. One of the most important events in wheat production was the introduction of hard winter wheat. This generally is credited to the Mennonites who came from southern Russia to settle in Kansas in 1874.

By 1890 a vanguard of settlers had pushed beyond Kansas and Nebraska into eastern Colorado. The majority had come from the humid Northeastern States, and previous experience had in no way prepared them for the climatic hazards they now encountered. The initial settlement occurred during one of the more rainy periods, and the settlers were predisposed to believe that the climate was becoming permanently more humid—a delusion that was destroyed by the drought of the 1890's. The drought not only stopped further immigration but also caused a considerable emigration of earlier settlers. In some of the western Kansas counties, two-thirds of the farm population was forced to leave because of the drought. Many entire towns were abandoned completely.

One almost immediate reaction to the drought was a phenomenal increase in dry farming throughout the Great Plains. Dry farming was hailed as the solution to all agricultural problems within the region, and settlers again began pouring into the area.

All dry farming practices focused upon the single aim of conserving the scant moisture supply by reducing or eliminating run-off and evaporation and by increasing to a maximum the absorption and retention of moisture by the soil. It was thought that this could be accomplished by summer fallowing and by maintaining a dust mulch through cultivation after every summer rain. The mechanical treatment considered necessary for moisture conservation resulted in rapid deterioration of the soil structure and destruction of humus; its consequence introduced wind erosion as a menace to permanent settlement.[6] Before the beginning of World War I the enthusiasm for dry farming had waned and it was recognized that climatic risks still existed in the Great Plains.

The skyrocketing of agricultural prices during the 1914-1918 period tended to expand cattle production rather than crop production in the Great Plains; but, with the crash of the cattle market during the depression of 1920-1922, many ranchers were ruined financially. In the years following World War I rapid progress was made in agricultural mechanization. Various machines designed for use on the level land, including a manageable tractor, a disk plow, a disk drill, and a small combine harvester, made it possible to plant and harvest

wheat in the Great Plains at less than half the cost incurred on the smaller, rougher farms in the East.

The economic distress of the rancher, the development of power machinery for planting and harvesting wheat, the maintenance of high prices for wheat, and a series of wetter-than-average years resulted in renewed land speculation. At a time when land values the country over were falling toward prewar levels, land in the Great Plains, purchased from the ranchmen at $2 to $4 an acre, was resold for $30 to $40 to investors and speculators from as far east as Iowa and Illinois who were ignorant of the physical deficiencies of the area. Despite the speculative nature of much land purchase and the fact that a great deal of the crop production was by "suitcase farmers" who did not live on the farms and frequently stayed in the region only long enough to harvest one crop and sow the next, the population throughout the Great Plains continued to increase until 1931.

In 1931, a disastrous drought was experienced in the northern and central Great Plains, with desert climate prevailing in western Kansas. From then on, in every year until the end of the decade, some part of the area was affected by serious drought; in 1934 and 1936, the region was scourged with drought from end to end.

The depression, coming simultaneously with the onset of the drought, carried prices of agricultural products down to the lowest levels on record. Great Plains farmers, burdened with expensive farm machinery and land that had been overcapitalized, were bankrupted almost immediately. Federal relief in many forms had to be poured into the region. Despite the fact that the administration of relief tended to discourage movement of population, there was a tremendous emigration from the Great Plains between 1930 and 1940.

Man has learned to farm the eastern, more subhumid portion of the plains, however, and through use of adaptable crops and dry farming techniques, he has been able to establish a rather stable form of agriculture. Prairie farming, however, is not entirely a bonanza. Nature is not always smiling. In summer, drought and hot winds too often wither the flourishing crops, and insect pests too often take a heavy

---

[6] E. C. Chilcott, "Some Misconceptions Concerning Dry Farming," *United States Department of Agriculture Yearbook 1911.* Washington: Government Printing Office, pp. 247-256.

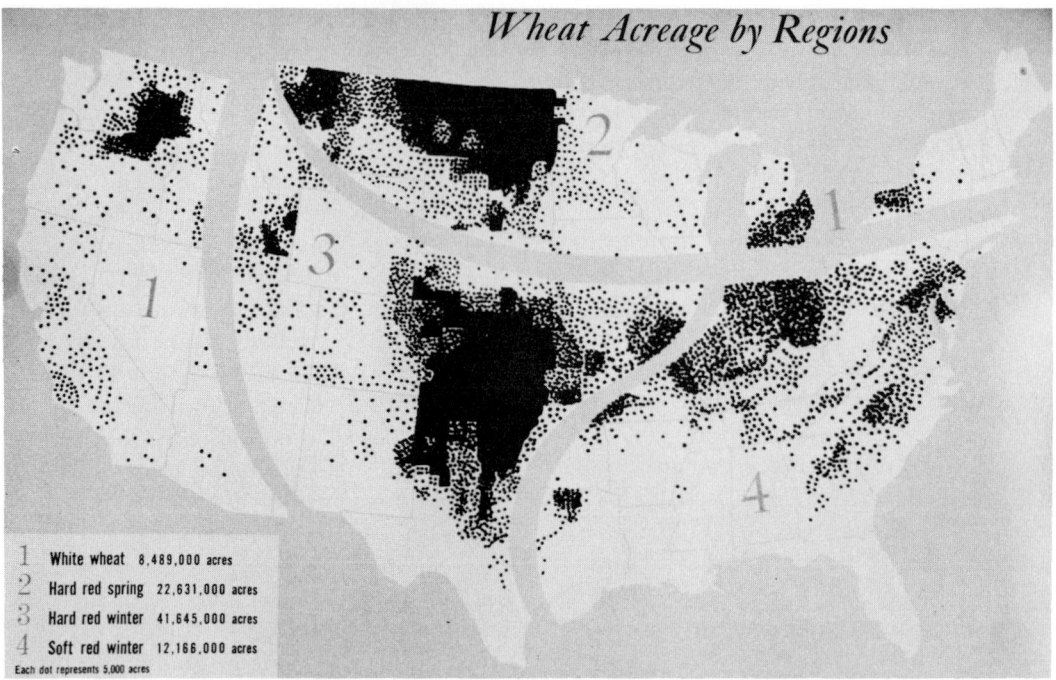

Figure 10-3. Wheat acreage in the United States, by regions. (U.S. Department of Agriculture)

toll. In late summer and autumn, disastrous prairie fires may sweep the grasslands, destroying crops, fences, and sometimes farmsteads as well. In winter, blizzards often take huge tolls among animal herds. Despite these handicaps the Winter Wheat Subregion (the eastern edge of the subhumid Great Plains) is one of the world's superior farming areas.

BOUNDARIES

Although wheat is grown in localities in the United States having widely different climates, it is a cool weather crop and produces the largest yield of best quality where cool, moderately wet weather prevails during the growing season, and dry, sunny weather during the ripening period. Wheat generally is not a safe crop where the mean annual precipitation is less than 15 inches. In the districts of densest production (Kansas) the annual precipitation ranges from 18 to 20 inches. Where the rainfall exceeds 45 inches a year wheat does not thrive, principally because rust and fungus diseases are more prevalent there than in less humid districts.

The distribution of the rainfall is as important as the total amount. For instance, even if the rainfall is normal in a given year, crop yields can fall to almost nothing if the spring growing months of April and May receive little rainfall.

The Winter Wheat Subregion lies in Kansas, Nebraska, central Oklahoma, and the panhandles of Oklahoma and Texas. On the east, wheat gives way to corn as more humid conditions and higher temperatures, especially at night, favor corn growing. On the south, the increasing heat and humidity and the longer growing season make cotton more profitable. The southern boundary of winter wheat production is limited by an average temperature of 68° F. from about April 15 to June 15, or for two months preceding harvest, and coincides rather closely with the northern boundary of cotton growth. The northern winter wheat boundary coincides in a general way with the mean winter temperature line of 20°, and corresponds rather closely to the southern boundary of spring wheat production, or the winter killing of fall sown grain. The western limit is set by frequency of failure of wheat crops caused by low precipitation and a high evaporation rate. The annual precipitation within the subregion varies from about 17 to

20 inches in western Texas to 30 or 35 inches in eastern Kansas and Oklahoma. Winters are moderately cold, especially along the northern border, and generally dry with little or at best uncertain snow cover.

GROWING WINTER WHEAT

Winter wheat will grow on a wide range of soil types, but well-drained medium and fine textured soils generally are considered best adapted for wheat production.

The usual time for seeding is September 15 to October 15; the optimum is about October 1, since the water requirement of wheat is very high, and wheat yields are influenced materially by the amount of moisture in the soil at seeding time in the fall. The wheat crop attains much of its growth in late fall and early spring when there is usually very little rainfall. During this period, except in seasons when rainfall is plentiful and well distributed during the growing period, growth must depend largely upon the moisture stored in the soil before seeding time. The close correlation between the yield of wheat and the depth of soil moisture at seeding time is shown in extensive studies by the Kansas Experiment Station.

Growing wheat and handling it are special major industries all across the country from New England to the Northwest and down into the Deep South. Two-thirds of the total output, however, is produced on the plains between the Mississippi River and the Rockies. Of this, about 47 per cent, or approximately 30 million

Figure 10-4. Combining wheat in a wheat field near Hayes, Kansas. Wheat is an entirely mechanized crop. Seeding is done by tractor-drawn, drill-type seeders, some of which also fertilize the ground at the same time. Harvesting is performed by combines, the combination reaping and threshing machines that cut the heads from the wheat stalks, shake out the grains of wheat, and discharge the chaff and straw back onto the fields. Most of the combines in use are tractor drawn and require a two-man crew, but this equipment is being replaced by the new self-propelled combines that may be handled by a single operator. (U.S. Department of Agriculture)

acres, is planted to hard red winter wheat in the central and southern Great Plains. Harvesting begins in central Texas in May just as the hard winter wheat that was planted the previous autumn becomes mature. Up in the Dakotas and Montana, at about the same time, spring wheats that will mature in the late summer are being planted. Seventeen bushels of wheat, on the average, are taken from every acre. Some rich fields produce 40 or 50 bushels per acre or more.

One man on a self-propelled combine and one man in a truck to pick up the wheat and haul it to storage comprise a harvest crew that handles as many acres as 12 to 15 men could handle in the 1920's. Two or three man-hours of labor per acre of wheat, from tillage to market, are all that are required today and the result is that one farmer often can handle his own fields, amounting to 500 or more acres, all by himself. Operators who farm two or three times that acreage require only small amounts of help.

Harvest time is the final critical period in making a crop, and each owner of grain land wants his wheat safely under cover the moment it is ripe enough to thresh. The Great Plains, in particular, have a tricky climate—a few days delay may bring a high wind or a rainstorm or hailstorm that shatters the heads and knocks the stalks down on the ground, decimating the crop.

Because of this danger, harvesting is always a rush operation and the crews work all day long and far into the night, every day of the harvest season. The emergency exists until the last acres are reaped.

Meanwhile the storage elevators and the railroads fight their annual battles to get the precious grain under a roof or on its way to the big central storage houses and the mills. New concrete elevators have been built every ten miles or so alongside the railroads that cross the wheat country; yet even their capacities are taxed by bumper crops. Some farmers have had to store their wheat temporarily on the ground. At some of the elevators, huge wooden cribs have been built alongside the bins to take care of the overflow.

The railroads are in a similar fix at harvest time. There are never enough cars to meet the demand, even though plans are made six months ahead of time to divert every available boxcar to the prairies. Extra locomotives are brought in from as far away as the Pacific Coast. Additional crews of engineers, firemen, conductors, brakemen, and switchmen are recruited from other divisions. The freight departments of the Santa Fe, Southern Pacific, Union Pacific, and other lines in the wheat territory reschedule many of their operations to give priority to the wheat specials.

Most of the grain that moves by rail goes to huge terminal elevators located in Kansas City, Chicago, Wichita, and other cities. Some of the elevators have a capacity of more than ten million bushels. Suction hoses sweep the cars clean of their loads; the cars then are made up into long strings of empties to go back for more wheat. Several of the largest elevators have automatic car dumps that can pick up an entire boxcar and tilt it so that all its grain is spilled out into a receiving hopper in only seven minutes.

Improved plant breeding has brought tremendous increases in yield—up to 50 per cent, in some cases, over the best varieties available in the past. Kansas harvests 30 million bushels more from the same acreage simply because of the success of the prolonged plant breeding

Table 7
*Effect of Depth of Moisture at Seeding Time on the Yield of Winter Wheat at Hays, Colby, and Garden City, Kansas, 1909-36, Inclusive**

DEPTH OF MOISTURE AT PLANTING TIME	PERCENTAGE OF YEARS THE CROP FAILED
DRY OR NEARLY DRY	71% (7 YEARS IN 10)
1 FOOT OF MOISTURE	34% (1 YEAR IN 3)
2 FEET OF MOISTURE	14% (1 YEAR IN 7)
3 FEET OF MOISTURE	10% (1 YEAR IN 10)

*Kansas Experiment Station Bulletin No. 273, *Soil Moisture and Winter Wheat Production.*

program. Over a period of 45 years the original hard red Turkey pioneer wheat of the Great Plains has been given built-in disease and insect resistance, has been refined to produce a higher yield, and has even been redesigned for machine handling. The newest Pawnee strain bears little resemblance to its Turkey ancestor; it almost guarantees a good crop in the particular region to which it is adapted.

Most hard red winter wheat is milled into flour for bread. Bakers want flour having certin characteristics of quality because bakeries must be able to produce a uniform product month after month.

SIZE AND TYPES OF FARMS

The average size of winter wheat farms has increased from 244 acres in 1910, to over 400 acres in 1960. Not only are farms in the western areas larger than in the eastern, but the increase in size during the 1910-1960 period has also been greater in the western section.

The cash grain farm is the most important, comprising 31.5 per cent of all farms in the subregion. Livestock farms other than dairy and poultry constitute 27.8 per cent of all farms. A small proportion of these specialize in hogs or sheep but the greater number are cattle farms. General farms (11.5 per cent of all farms) and dairy farms (6.5 per cent) are the other major types.

Wheat occupies 27.6 per cent of all the land in farms. This is more than five and one-half times the percentage of farm land in corn, the second most important crop. Sorghums rank third among the grains with 2.8 per cent; hay crops total 4.3 per cent. Oats and barley are minor crops, constituting only 1.7 per cent and 0.5 per cent, respectively.

CHANGES IN THE RELATIVE IMPORTANCE OF WHEAT AND CORN

There has been a drastic change in the relative importance of wheat and corn in the winter wheat area during the last 75 years. This change is best illustrated in Kansas where, except for 1894, when the acreage of corn fell slightly behind that of wheat, the acreage of corn was well above that of wheat until World War I. In 1914, wheat exceeded corn by 2.8 million acres and has remained the dominant crop since that time. In 1917, one of the poorer wheat years, less than four million of

Figure 10-5. This 1,320,000-bushel grain elevator in Garden City, Kansas, is the largest country grain elevator in the United States. Garden City is located in the middle of the Winter Wheat Subregion. (U.S. Department of Agriculture)

the 9.6 million acres seeded to wheat were harvested. Record acreages of wheat were harvested in 1931 and, following the low acreage in the drought years of the early 1930's, again in 1938. The acres harvested dropped sharply in 1939 and 1940, but have risen almost steadily since then. The average for the five-year period of 1945-1949, was 13.8 million acres, an increase of 31.4 per cent over the previous five-year period. In 1950, there were 14.5 million acres of wheat harvested compared to a corn harvest of only 2.6 million acres. During the 1950-1960 period this trend continued.

Many reasons might be given for the decreasing importance of corn in comparison to wheat. Probably the most important are: (1) the earlier and more complete mechanization of wheat growing; (2) the drought of the 1930's, which was even more unfavorable for corn than for wheat; (3) the development, for the western two-thirds of the region, of low growing, combine-type grain sorghums, more drought resistant than corn and suitable for growing and harvesting with the same machinery that is used for wheat; and (4) fading of the traditional preference for corn over wheat in the light of proven unfavorable environment.

THE FUTURE

An important problem confronting farmers, bankers, and other persons in the Great Plains is instability of income. Because of weather, insects, disease, and price hazards, farm income varies widely, particularly in those areas where highly specialized wheat farming prevails. These hazards may be minimized to a certain extent by properly conserving moisture, by the use of good production practices in growing wheat, and by efficient marketing. However, the problem of instability of income cannot be solved by following a system of highly specialized wheat production.

Farmers realize the advantages of diversification but in the western Great Plains region profitable alternatives to the wheat enterprise are limited. Livestock activities cannot be incorporated profitably into the farm business unless provision is made for providing feed at a cost that is comparable to feed costs in other areas of efficient livestock production. If satisfactory provision can be made for such feed supplies, livestock may be produced successfully in this area. Proper combination of livestock and wheat enterprises in the farm organization would enable farmers to utilize available labor more effectively and to increase the amount and stability of income that could be acquired from a given area of land. In periods when labor is expensive and difficult to obtain, planning for better distribution in the use of labor throughout the year is desirable. Furthermore, the availability of livestock on the farm makes it possible to utilize roughage such as wheat pasture and sorghum stubble that otherwise does not have a satisfactory market. Diversification helps offset damage done by certain insects, weeds, and diseases. It also alleviates wide fluctuations in farm income because of failure of one crop or a relatively low price for a specific commodity.

These and other advantages of proper diversification were partially responsible for the intensive efforts that were made to develop a crop such as grain sorghums that would provide an adequate supply of economically efficient food for the western Great Plains area. Sorghum varieties and their production methods have been improved to such an extent that livestock may now be produced successfully on a major scale in much of the Great Plains area.

Grain sorghum also may be produced successfully in competition with wheat as a cash crop in many sectors of this region. In recent years, the production of grain sorghum as a cash crop has become relatively important, particularly in the southern Great Plains. This importance is emphasized by the fact that the Chicago Board of Trade established trading in grain sorghum futures in 1951.

CASH GRAIN FARMING IN THE SPRING WHEAT SUBREGION

The eastern section of the northern Great Plains is characterized by the dominance of spring wheat. The yields per acre in this subhumid and semiarid region are lower than in the humid regions to the east, but along this marginal belt wheat can compete more successfully with corn and other productive crops, partly because of its adaptation to dry and cool climates, partly because of the extensive use of machinery that the crop permits, and partly (especially with relation to corn) because of the better ability of wheat to stand the cost of transportation to market.

BOUNDARIES

The Spring Wheat Subregion stretches over 1,000 miles in length and from 200 to 500 miles in width. It extends from the spruce and aspen forests of northern Saskatchewan and Alberta in the Peace River district southward to central South Dakota, northwestern Nebraska, and southeastern Wyoming. The eastern boundary follows the Red River Valley from Winnipeg and includes a large part of North Dakota and western Minnesota. South and east, corn becomes the dominant crop. Nearly all the flax in the United States and Canada is grown in this region along with much of the rye and barley. Wild hay, too, is a very important crop.

The northern limits of spring wheat are largely determined by the length of the growing season (80 to 90 days) and the mean summer temperatures (57° July isotherm). The natural boundary on the east is a zone of transition that may be defined in terms of climate, soil, or natural vegetation. The 98th meridian represents the average of these changing characteristis. Precipitation there averages about 20 inches a year; westward, it is less. The western boundary is the base of the Rocky Mountains in Alberta. The southern boundary is the northern limit for fall sown grain. Here, winter temperatures are too low to permit the growth of other than spring sown crops.

CLIMATE

The climate is semiarid and has wide extremes. Rainfall is the greatest limitation on crop production. Moisture comes as slow rains, as cloudbursts sometimes accompanied by hail, as gentle snowfalls, or as blizzards of severe intensity. The average is 27 inches in the southwestern part and less than ten inches in some places in the northwestern. Much of the rain falls in the spring and early summer.

Temperatures vary widely from north to south and, in a given locality, from day to day. A range of more than 100° F. often occurs between maximum summer and minimum winter temperatures. For example, a summer temperature of 116° and winter temperature of −41° have been recorded at Valley City, North Dakota. Great variations in summer temperature are reflected in the lack of dependability of rainfall. High daytime heat is generally the accompaniment of drought. On the other hand, although the advent of cool waves may bring welcome rainfall they may also bring scattered frosts, especially in the northwestern part of the subregion. Only a limited portion of the Canadian southern prairies, for example, has an average continuously frost-free period of 100 days or more, while North Dakota has about 121 days without severe frosts—more in the southern part and fewer in the northern.

SOILS

Chernozem and chestnut soils play a role in wheat production similar to that of the Prairie soils in corn production. Production is less hazardous in the eastern chernozem portion of the Spring Wheat Subregion; rainfall is heavier and the soils are darker and deeper. Yet wheat is relatively a more important crop in the chestnut and reddish chestnut zones, largely because of its ability to produce grain of excellent quality (high protein content) under the semiarid conditions existing to the west of the chernozem soils.

Generally the land is a gently rolling plain but some areas are rough and broken. Soil types and structure vary widely. The surface features of lake beds, river valleys, plateaus, and buttes are the result of glacial action or erosion. Part of the area is deeply covered with glacial drift. There are heavily eroded localities along the Missouri River, which drains a considerable portion of the Spring Wheat Subregion within the United States.

The spring wheat land is one of tremendous vistas and enormous sky. Unbroken by high or deep natural formations, the land offers no obstruction to the winds that blow more steadily here, on the average, than they do across any settled part of the continent except the winter wheat lands farther south. In wet years the farmers always are conscious of the wind and the pressures; in dry years, they can see it, smell it, and taste it in the form of acrid and bitter dust.

SETTLEMENT

For nearly a century after the Lewis and Clark exploration across the plains this grassland empire was largely unpeopled. A few pioneers had established ranch headquarters along the streams before the close of the century, when buffalo still grazed plains forage. Then a tidal wave of land-hungry settlers arrived to plow under millions of acres of grassland.

From that time on, the land history in this subregion is similar to that in the Winter Wheat Subregion.

Today, this is a sparsely populated land. There are no large cities. Three out of five people live on farms or in towns of less than 2,500 population. The average density of population is approximately six persons to the square mile within the American portion, and less than two in the Canadian Prairies.

About 25 per cent of the land is under cultivation, but the cropland is not distributed evenly. In some areas more than 80 per cent of the land is under cultivation; in others, less than one per cent. The proportion of cropland decreases generally from east to west, but not in regular belts. Between cultivated areas are large expanses of native grassland that have not been plowed and should not be plowed. Production varies greatly from year to year and from locality to locality because of the limited and variable precipitation.

Opportunities for industrial developments

Figure 10-6. Flax stacked for harvest in North Dakota. Flaxseed from the flax is crushed to produce linseed oil, an important industrial oil used in the manufacture of paint and varnish. (U.S. Department of Agriculture)

are restricted by long distances to central markets, high transportation costs, and a sparse population. Long and severe winters, high winds, and early spring and late fall storms that frequently destroy promising crops and range livestock are part of the environment. But drought that strikes at unpredictable intervals has been the nemesis of thousands of farm and ranch ventures. The rural population continues to decline.

GROWING SPRING WHEAT

Hard red spring wheat is still the major crop in spite of the many hazards farmers must face during the growing and harvesting seasons. This variety, known for its high protein content and excellent bread-making characteristics, is used extensively for blends with softer wheats in many parts of the world.

The hard red spring wheat region also produces annually about 35 to 40 million bushels of durum wheat, a crop concentrated mostly in northeastern North Dakota and extending slightly into South Dakota and, in recent years, into Canada. Because of its greater resistance to stem rust, durum wheat has had until recently a yield advantage compared with the prevalent varieties of hard red spring wheat; but this advantage has largely disappeared with the introduction of rust-resistant varieties of spring wheat, notably Thatcher and, more recently, Rival and Regent.

North Dakota. Agriculture in North Dakota gives a fairly clear picture of farming in the Spring Wheat Subregion. The crop patterns and farming techniques developed in North Dakota are the result of climatic conditions and geography.

The best crops fitting the needs of dry farming in North Dakota are found among the several varieties of small grains. Field crop farms make up over 60 per cent of all farms. Livestock units rank second (15.6 per cent), general farms (crop and livestock combinations, 14.9 per cent) are third, and dairy and poultry farms are last (4.3 per cent). The state leads the nation in wheat production. Other crops in the order of their production importance are oats, barley, potatoes, and corn. Seed flax, planted, harvested, and handled in every respect like wheat, is an important crop in North Dakota and Minnesota. Rye and other miscellaneous small grains are also produced. Wheat regularly has been the cash crop; despite diversification in the Red River Valley, it remains the greatest single source of cash income to the North Dakota farmer. Recent years have seen the introduction of several row crops, mainly potatoes and sugar beets, to the Red River Valley; but small grain crops continue to form the backbone of the state's agricultural production.

Dry land farming techniques have led to the development of large-scale farm units. The flat terrain lends itself to the use of power machinery and the farming of immense plots of ground with a small amount of labor.

Dry land farming, as practiced in North Dakota, involves an element of risk far greater than that of most types of agricultural production. The lack of diversification, the large capital requirements, and the marginal growing conditions tend to make it an "all or nothing" enterprise, with a resultant wide variation of income and employment. Under favorable climatic conditions—with adequate rainfall, normal seasonal temperatures, and an absence of drying winds—yields may achieve very high levels and, with large acreage, very substantial

Table 8
Average Acreage Per Farm in Nine U. S. States

STATE	ACRES
SOUTH DAKOTA	674.0
NORTH DAKOTA	629.9
NEBRASKA	442.9
TEXAS	438.5
KANSAS	370.0
OKLAHOMA	253.1
MINNESOTA	183.6
IOWA	168.7
MISSOURI	152.7

income. With slight variation in any one or a combination of these factors, yields may be reduced to levels that will not return the value of the seed planted.

In addition to variation in yield, grain prices have demonstrated a range of variation of over 500 per cent in the past 20 years. The North Dakota farmer sells for external markets and a considerable part of his product is marketed outside the United States. He can exert little influence upon price, and price changes may have little association with local conditions of supply.

Unless some basic change in the crop pattern of North Dakota farmers is accomplished—one that will require smaller units and more labor —the farm population and farm labor requirements will continue to decline. It is reasonable to assume that as long as cash grain produced by dry farming methods remains the basic item of production in this state, any policy directed at a reduction in farm size or an increase in labor requirements will be unsuccessful.

Montana. Only Kansas and North Dakota grow more wheat than Montana. Although some wheat is grown in every Montana county, production is concentrated in two general areas: the spring wheat area in the east and northeast and the spring and winter wheat area of the north-central part of the state. Montana farmers plant more than twice as much spring wheat as winter wheat.

Since 1953, United States wheat acreage has been cut by 30 million acres. The long-range outlook suggests that even further shifts will be needed to bring production into balance with market demands. Much of the acreage reduction has gone into production of oil crops,

feed grains, and forage crops. Further emphasis on feed crops probably will be needed to meet prospective demand for livestock and livestock products as population increases.

Particularly in Montana does the dry land farmer face production adjustment problems. On much of the nonirrigated cropland the only feasible substitutes for wheat are feed grains, especially barley. But marketing problems exist with feed grains, forcing efforts to be made to get greater quotas for Montana's superior quality grains.

Barley ranks third as a crop in Montana; it is surpassed in importance only by wheat and hay. Barley's future importance may be even greater if farmers expand their livestock feeding to produce more meat for the West Coast market. The crop would figure either in a program to raise more hogs or in a program to put more finish on cattle or sheep before they leave the state.

Barley is a good crop substitute for wheat when wheat acreage is reduced. It grows on the same kinds of soil, under the same climatic conditions, and uses the equipment and machinery of wheat cultivation and harvest. Increases in barley production, however, require adjustments in marketing patterns, marketing facilities, and storage space. More feeding of barley is related to such questions as pricing arrangements, freight rates, and development of packing plants in Montana.

Oats are grown in almost every Montana county. Normally about one-third of the acreage is on irrigated and two-thirds on nonirrigated land. About half is cut for hay and about half is threshed or combined for grain.

Corn is grown only in the eastern half of the

state, with most of the crop either cut for silage or pastured off. Summers are too cool and too short in most of the western half of the state for corn to mature.

South Dakota. Farmers in South Dakota grow chiefly wheat, corn, and oats. Minor crops are barley, rye, and alfalfa. Large areas of land poorly suited for cultivation are used for native pasture and wild hay.

For a long time spring wheat has been the principal crop raised under dry land farming. Wheat is better adapted to the soils and climate than most other crops and no other crop can compete with it as a cash crop.

SPECIALIZED AGRICULTURE IN THE RED RIVER VALLEY

The Red River Valley includes an area varying in width from a few miles in the south to from 50 to 70 miles in the north; it includes both sides of the Red River of the North, which forms the boundary between Minnesota and North Dakota. As the area lies in the bed of glacial Lake Agassiz, its topography is remarkably level. This uniformity of topography is its outstanding characteristic.

The soils are reputed to be among the most fertile in the world. The surface soils contain sufficient humus to impart dark-gray to black colors to depths of eight to 15 inches or more except in some of the very sandy soils. Texturally the soils range from heavy clays overlying clay subsoils, to sand overlying sand subsoils and thin loams, and to gravelly loams overlying gravel subsoils.

The mean annual temperature for the area during June, July, and August is about 67° F. This summer temperature and the long hours of sunshine are favorable for sugar beet production. Precipitation averages about 20 inches, 75 per cent of which occurs from April to September, inclusive; about one-half of the total normally falls during May, June, and July. The normal rainfall is near the lower limits necessary for successful production of beets without irrigation.

Sugar beets. Commercial sugar beet production in the Red River Valley began with the opening of a sugar factory at East Grand Forks, Minnesota, in 1926. The growth of the industry since that time, particularly its rapid expansion following the opening of a second factory at Moorhead, Minnesota, in 1948, has made the valley one of the major sugar beet producing regions of the United States.

Sugar beet production in the valley tends to be a specialized industry and, in terms of the over-all agriculture pattern of the region, sugar beets are a minor crop. Only a small portion of the farmers grow beets, but those who do so continue to follow this practice year after year.

In comparison with other sugar beet producing regions of the United States, however, the Red River Valley is an area of large-scale production. Only in some sections of California is the average individual beet enterprise as large as it is here. Table 9 indicates the comparative size of sugar beet enterprises in various producing areas.

Table 9
Average Number of Acres of Sugar Beets Harvested Per Farm,
by States and Red River Valley
Typical Postwar Year

STATE OR AREA	AVERAGE ACRES HARVESTED PER FARM
UTAH	8.21
MICHIGAN	9.68
IDAHO	11.29
COLORADO	20.11
WASHINGTON	23.53
NEBRASKA	23.88
WYOMING	25.55
MONTANA	28.01
RED RIVER VALLEY	53.05
CALIFORNIA	84.19

Sugar beets have proved themselves to be adapted to the valley soils and climate, and have provided an intertilled crop that fits well into desirable crop rotations. Many growers emphasize the value of beets in their rotations. They point out that beets following a summer fallow are much more effective in controlling weeds than in summer fallow alone. The beneficial effects of the additional year of intertillage upon subsequent grain crops is stressed as a factor in increasing total farm income.

At present, the sugar beet industry in this area, as in other areas, is in the transition period between hand and mechanical harvesting. Although the use of mechanical harvesters is increasing constantly, with 36 per cent of the beet acreage now being harvested by mechanical methods, some growers are not convinced of the feasibility or profitableness of present machines. Substantial improvements are necessary before sugar beet operations are mechanized completely.

Normally, farmers' requests for sugar beet acreage in this area exceed the capacity of the processing plants. The future growth of the beet industry is dependent largely on national sugar policy and related legislation. Since sugar beet acreage in the Red River Valley is approximately equal to local plant capacities, and since the present sugar beet quota tends to restrict the construction of additional processing facilities, further increases in acreage are not likely in the near future.

Potatoes. The Red River Valley of the North has, since the 1920's, moved from sixth or seventh position to among the three leading potato areas in the nation in terms of acreage. Potato production in North Dakota has always been confined to the Red River Valley counties.

This has not been true of Minnesota. At one time commercial potato production was rather widespread throughout Minnesota. Even now there are commercial potato producing areas in Minnesota outside the Red River Valley. Walsh, Pembina, and Grand Forks Counties in North Dakota, and Polk and Clay Counties in Minnesota comprise about 85 per cent of the total potato acreage. This trend toward specialization, with its attendant increase in production efficiencies, has been accelerated under the potato price support program.

The number of farmers growing potatoes in the valley has declined from about 19,000 in 1929, to around 5,000 at present, but the average potato acreage per farm has increased from nine to 28 acres during that period. Except for years with very unfavorable climatic conditions, the trend in potato yields has been sharply upward. For instance, for the Red River Valley as a whole, average yields were 83 bushels per acre in 1939, and 186 bushels in 1960. Adoption of better varieties, use of insecticides, effective weed control, intensive fertilizer application, and other improvements in production techniques account for most of these yield increases.

Other crops. The Red River Valley has been known for many years as a wheat producing area and wheat is still its major crop. During and since World War II, acreages increased and less emphasis was given to livestock production. In fact, farms without any livestock are not uncommon. Wheat, barley, oats, and flax are the principal crops. Considerable corn is grown in the southern part of the area.

THE PRAIRIE PROVINCES OF CANADA

Manitoba, Saskatchewan, and Alberta, Canada's Prairie Provinces, extend westward about 900 miles from Ontario to the Rockies and cover 753,000 square miles—about 20 per cent of Canada's area.

The greater part of the three provinces consists of the Great Central Plain, covered with grass in the south and wooded in the north. The Pre-Cambrian Shield, a rocky expanse dotted with rivers, forests, and muskegs, covers much of northern Manitoba and part of Saskatchewan. Western Alberta lies in the foothills and ranges of the Rockies, the site of the well-known holiday resorts, Jasper and Banff National Parks.

Settlement. In the days of New France in the 18th century, fur traders and missionaries were the first to travel through this country. Large-scale settlement did not begin until the next century. The province of Manitoba was created in 1870 and enlarged to its present size in 1912. Saskatchewan and Alberta were carved out of the vast Northwest Territories and organized as provinces in 1905.

The population of the Prairie Provinces came mainly in the wave of settlement that swept into the West during the first two dec-

Figure 10-7. A large wheat farm near Mileston, Saskatchewan. A tractor with a swather attached is driven around the wheat field to cut the grain and lay it in neat swaths. (National Film Board)

ades of the present century. With a population of less than 200,000 in 1891, the area grew to nearly two million by 1921. Today the total population is about 3,092,000.

People of European origin other than French and British make up almost 20 per cent of Canada's population. Many of them have settled in the Prairie communities. Although they are quick to adopt Canadian customs, they also retain much of their distinctive native cultures.

Agriculture. In spite of the recent development of industry, agriculture remains the chief source of income in the Prairie. The Great Central Plain forms one of the most important wheat exporting areas of the world. Its large, highly mechanized grain farms often cover an area of more than one square mile per farm. The average annual wheat crop of the three Prairie Provinces during the past ten years was 340 million bushels, with Saskatchewan the leading producer. Oats, barley, hay, rye, and flax are other important field crops.

Hog raising and other farming to supplement grain production has been increasing in recent years. Large cattle ranches are operated in southwestern Alberta. Irrigation projects have been built in dry areas and improved methods of crop rotation are followed to protect the soil.

Saskatchewan. Wheat is Saskatchewan's most valuable crop. The province produces two-thirds of all the wheat in Canada and well over one-third of the country's oats and barley.

Agriculture in Saskatchewan has gone through a period of transition. Farm settlement progressed rapidly during the first quarter-century, but began to decrease in the depressed 1930's. Seventy thousand people left the province permanently during this period. The drift away from the farms continued during the prosperous war years, encouraged by a changeover to mechanized farming and by a trend to larger farm units. The number of individual farms dropped from 140,000 in the 1930's to 112,000 in the 1950's. Two results of this migration were reflected in urban growth and a greater demand for nonagricultural work.

The booming market for grain in the war years and after resulted in a concentration in the production of wheat in Saskatchewan. There was a decline in mixed farming, with a steady drop in livestock and poultry production. A succession of good crop years and ready markets tended to make many grain farmers ignore the fact that by relying solely on one crop they were adding to the risks of an industry that lived perpetually in the shadow of disaster.

The testing time came with a crop failure in 1954. Hard upon the heels of this setback came marketing problems. Fifteen years earlier these blows would have inflicted the most serious injury upon agriculture and would have had an adverse effect upon the whole economy. That it did not do this in 1954 and 1955 was proof of two things: (1) the farm industry, bigger and more productive than ever before in its history, had greater reserves of strength to weather periodic storms; and (2) nonagricultural development had become a very real force in the economy, mitigating the effects of farm slumps.

Saskatchewan's development of an agrarian economy had its influence on the manufacturing industries. It stimulated manufacturing operations based on supplying some of the needs of agriculture and the processing of agricultural products.

Almost half of Saskatchewan's 910,000 people live on farms, and another 20 per cent in rural nonfarm areas. The population is spread fairly evenly over an area stretching 300 miles from the United States boundary.

Manitoba. The southern portion of Manitoba forms part of the Great Plains of central Canada; it is this area that supports 90 per cent of the population of the province, half of them engaged in growing grain, raising cattle, and dairying.

Present knowledge of Manitoba's land resources indicates that farm lands might be increased by five million acres. The major change in the cropping pattern will show a continuing decline in wheat acreage, and gains in coarse grains, hay, and pasture. At present 2,326,000 acres are planted to wheat. Forecasts indicate a decline to 1,900,000 by 1980. This is a logical change for Manitoba. A population increase of about 50 per cent by 1980, and the higher incomes expected, both in Canada and in Manitoba, will increase the total demand for livestock products. This will cause more acreage to be used for feed and fodder production. Since a larger population in the Central Provinces will demand greater quantities of fluid milk, fresh fruits, and vegetables, more of the land here will move into this production, reducing the acreage of feed grains.

Wheat still constitutes the main crop of the province in acreage sown and has remained relatively constant over the past quarter of a century. Acreages sown to barley have increased in the same period. Because of the great diversity of agricultural and industrial activities, Manitoba probably comes nearer to having a balanced economy than any other province in Canada. The leading grain growing districts are Red River, Killarney, and Virden.

In addition to their grain production, certain areas in the province are becoming important vegetable growing districts. The Red River Valley, that portion of the province west of Winnipeg and adjacent to the Trans-Canada Highway, and the area known as the Pembina Triangle, are particularly well suited for the growing of peas, beans, corn, and root vegetables. Farmers in the area nearest to Winnipeg (in the Eastern Interior Low Plains) cater mostly to city demands for garden trade, potatoes, other vegetables, and poultry. The Pembina Triangle, located in the southeastern part of the province, is the most suitable location for the growing of vegetables for canning purposes. The Triangle covers nearly 200,000 acres of the finest loam in the province. Its location on the western slope of the Pembina Range gives the Triangle a more moderate climate and longer frost-free period than any other part of Manitoba. Temperate climate and rich black loam make the Triangle the "Corn and Apple Belt of the Prairies."

Commercial fruit growing is very limited. Strawberries, raspberries, crab apples, and plums—the principal fruits—are grown mainly near Carman, Miami, and Portage la Prairie.

Sunflower growing is a relatively new addition; Manitoba is the only province in Canada producing sunflower seeds in commercial quantity. Sunflowers are raised mainly in the southern portion of the Red River district near a ready market at Altona, where one of the most modern vegetable oil extraction plants in Canada is situated.

Sugar beet production is confined largely to an area within 60 miles of Winnipeg. More than 22,000 acres are planted to beets. There has been steady mechanization of the sugar beet industry to help it fit into the essentially mechanized agriculture followed in Manitoba.

The chief commercial potato raising districts are around Winnipeg, Portage la Prairie, Steinback, Carman, Winkler, and Sprague. Principal varieties grown are Pontiac, Columbia Russet, and Irish Cobbler. The bulk of the annual crop is sold locally, but some 300 carloads normally are shipped each year to outside markets. Yields average 159 bushels per acre.

Livestock and livestock products constitute nearly half the entire net income of Manitoba agriculture. The production, marketing, and processing of livestock is the province's largest agricultural industry. The highly-developed meat packing industry in Manitoba accounts for 17 per cent of the total slaughterings for Canada, and 48 per cent of the total for the Prairies.

The major portion of milk produced in Manitoba for dairy consumption is produced within a 40-mile radius of Winnipeg, which is the principal market for fluid milk in the province. Manitoba ranks fifth in Canada in dairy products manufactured and in the number of dairy cows on farms.

The poultry raised by about 75 per cent of Manitoba's farmers make an important income contribution to the farm family, both in ready cash and food for the table. Manitoba is second only to Ontario in total number of approved flocks. Egg sales are very significant, with 27 million dozen marketed annually. Recent years have witnessed special interest by poultry raisers, particularly those in the Winnipeg area, in the production of broilers and fryers.

Alberta. The prospects for wheat production in Alberta cannot be separated from the question of wheat marketing for Canada as a whole. It is pertinent to the study of the position of wheat in Alberta's future farm production program to note that total world requirements for wheat as a bread grain are large and relatively inelastic, while the supply, because of variations in yield, is highly elastic.

Wheat acreage has decreased from 7.9 million acres in 1931, to 5.6 million. The proportion of improved land seeded to wheat has fallen from 45 to 29 per cent.

The resistance to change from wheat growing in the prairie region is positive in character. In the first place, the area is pre-eminently suited to the production of wheat. Comparatively level land surfaces facilitate the development of mechanized operations in relation to wheat growing on a large scale, and the prai-

rie farmers' resources are invested almost entirely in the production of wheat. Involvement in heavy capital investments in a highly-specialized farming enterprise is a major deterrent to change.

GRAIN MOVEMENT AND STORAGE

The grain from the Prairie Provinces of Canada concentrates at Winnipeg and, except for a small amount to Duluth-Superior via Fort Francis, most of it moves over three railway lines to the terminal elevators in Fort William and Port Arthur in Ontario, where it is graded and held for shipment. The grade given the grain here is the one on which it is sold and delivered in both eastern Canadian and foreign markets. By holding the grain at the head of the Great Lakes, the shipper can market it through either Canadian or United States channels. Only Canadian grain is forwarded from Fort William-Port Arthur, whereas some Canadian and a large amount of United States grain moves from the spring wheat area to Montreal from Duluth-Superior. Only United States grain is shipped from Milwaukee and Chicago to Montreal.

The routes of grain shipment from the head of the Great Lakes include: (1) the water route, (2) the water and rail route, and (3) the rail route. These alternative methods serve to keep transportation costs at a minimum. Canada has a further advantage in shipment because of low wheat freight rates resulting from an agreement made by the Canadian Pacific Railway for handling Western wheat in exchange for a charter.

GRAZING

The Great Plains were originally the feeding grounds of vast herds of buffalo. During the last third of the 19th century the buffalo were replaced by cattle. Today, cattle raising remains the dominant agricultural enterprise in the semiarid and arid portions of the Plains. Sheep and goats are also grazed; they are more important than cattle in some sections.

BOUNDARIES

Climatic conditions, especially the supply of moisture, were significant in the determination of this system of land use. Here the product of the pasture becomes of greater value than

Figure 10-8. A grazing scene in Gallatin Valley, Montana. The cattle are being moved in from the range. Note the rolling land, the short grass, and the size and sleek condition of the herd. (U.S. Department of Agriculture)

the crops. The average annual precipitation increases on the eastern boundary southward from 15 inches in Canada and northeastern Montana to 17 inches in central South Dakota and western Nebraska, 18 inches in eastern Colorado, eastern New Mexico, and west-central Texas, and 25 inches in extreme southern Texas, where the rainfall is more irregular and often torrential.

Great variability in precipitation, both in quantity and form, is characteristic of this area. Rainfall varies by as much as 30 inches annually from year to year. Upon occasion, a single shower will provide one-third of the total annual rainfall within a day, and as much as one-fifth within an hour.

Other boundaries deserving notice are those delimiting the driest areas where almost no crops are grown without irrigation (except a little corn, kaffir or sorghum, and sweet clover

for forage), usually on land that receives flood water from higher lands or that possesses other favorable conditions. This almost purely pastoral agriculture is found also on lands of rough topography or on very sandy soils that preclude cultivation. The districts of arid climate, rough surface, or sandy soil do not form a continuous belt, but include in the aggregate a large area.

In Montana, these grazing lands are found in the warm, dry valleys of the Yellowstone, Missouri, Musselshell, and Marias Rivers, where the average annual precipitation is below 14 inches; they include also much of the valley of the Milk River. In North Dakota, the badlands of the Little Missouri River constitute the only large area given over exclusively to grazing. In South Dakota, the grazing lands include the badlands along the Cheyenne and White Rivers. Most of northeastern Wyoming belongs to this grazing type of land. In Nebraska, the Sand Hills constitute the principal area. In Colorado, much of the nonirrigated land in the South Platte Valley and most of that in the Arkansas Valley are suitable only for grazing, as is also most of the southeastern portion of the state, in which the average annual precipitation is less than 16 inches. In Kansas, only the Arkansas Valley west of the Hartland and the Sand Hills to the south are included; and in eastern New Mexico, the Pecos Valley and the drier portions of the upper Canadian Valley. In Texas, nearly all the nonirrigated area west of Midland, Sonora, Carizzo Springs, and Hebronville is suitable for grazing.

HISTORY

Largely because of its natural vegetation the Great Plains became the scene of a range cattle industry that far exceeded in scale and results any of its predecessors in American history. The vegetation of the Great Plains was strikingly different from that of the United States to the eastward. The level land from the 98th meridian westward was almost treeless. The characteristic natural vegetation was grass and desert shrub, ranged according to the rainfall in generally north-to-south belts. To the west, on the High Plains, the grass was short but the surface sodded. Farther west the grass grew in tufts or branches because the rainfall was too scanty to support continuous growth.

Mexican land grants in Texas initiated the ranching practice there prior to Texas' independence. Following admission to the Union, enormous ranches grew up, but cattle were priced so low just before the Civil War that many ranches were abandoned and the cattle ran wild. Then, as war caused prices to rise from four or five dollars a head to $15 to $18, the boom set in.

Following the Civil War, Texas ranchers began driving cattle northward in search of a market and soon there were hundreds of professional drovers moving their herds over the "long drive." At first relatively small herds were driven into southeastern Kansas and the adjacent areas of Missouri, but by 1867 the Kansas Pacific Railroad reached Abilene, which became the most famous of the "cow towns." More than 600,000 head were driven to western Kansas in 1871, the last year a cattle business was done in Abilene. Then Fort Harkness,

65 miles farther west, became the shipping point. In 1871, too, the Santa Fe Railroad reached Newton and became a competitor for part of the trade, since this route represented a somewhat shorter drive. In 1872, a branch of the Santa Fe reached Wichita and, soon thereafter, Dodge City. The latter town for the next several years became one of the most important shipping points for Texas cattle.

The growth of population in the East and the advance of the railroads into the Great Plains provided both a market and a means of shipping the cattle. This combination of circumstances enabled the range cattle industry to dominate the Great Plains from the late 1860's to the late 1880's.

From 1890 until 1930, the cattle raiser retreated before the crop farmer in all except the rougher and drier parts of the High Plains. Since that date there has been a re-establishment of beef cattle raising in many areas that at one time seemed permanently given over to crop growing. The retreat of the farmer from much marginal cropland was one reason for the change, but improved breeding and feeding, together with the rapid urbanization of the United States, was the principal cause. The High Plains farmer and cattleman have found ways to produce more and better meat for a better market.

SIZE AND SOCIAL ASPECTS OF
LAND HOLDINGS

The size of the ranch will vary, depending upon the location and carrying capacity of the range, from less than 3,000 to more than 500,-000 acres, and from as low as 22 cattle per section of 640 acres to more than double that number. Maintenance of an acceptable standard of living on the larger ranches necessitates access to telephone, automobile, and radio, and in many cases the possession of a home in the nearest town as well as upon the ranch. The telephone and automobile are invaluable aids in dissipating the monotony, solitude, and seclusion of life far from the nearest town and several miles from neighboring families.

Although conditions of ranch life vary greatly from one end of the High Plains to the other, the ranch livestock industry almost everywhere follows a similar pattern. Problems of water, the need for supplemental feed in the

Figure 10-9. A typical small ranch headquarters in Cascade County, Montana. Windmills are still major items of equipment on ranches of the Western Interior High Plains Region. (U.S. Department of Agriculture)

drier portions of the range, marketing, and so on, are fairly similar throughout the area. The farther north the ranch, the less open it is in the winter and the greater the need for shelter and winter feeding of animals. Cattlemen who can avoid or reduce to a minimum the need for supplemental feeding are more likely to realize a profit. The industry, then, is a precarious one, for there are many variable factors beyond a rancher's control. A severe winter can wipe out thousands of head through starvation. By the same token, a rancher who is able to get feed to livestock during blizzards stands a good chance of going broke paying for the feed to keep his cattle alive. Severe droughts, such as those Texas has experienced in the past few years, may ruin rangeland for years to come. If natural hazards do not decimate the industry there is always the possibility that market prices will. Again, in good years, cattlemen

reap huge profits. In the long run a careful entrepreneur can make a good living if he is willing to take the bad years along with the good ones. And the high per capita meat consumption of the American people insures a continued use for millions of acres of land with little, if any, alternative uses.

A TYPICAL LARGE RANCH COMMUNITY

The Sonora community in central Texas is a good example of the large ranch in the more semiarid portion of the Western Interior High Plains. It is located on the Edwards Plateau near the southernmost end of the Great Plains and is roughly coextensive with Sutton County. Rainfall averages 23 inches and temperatures vary from 48° F. in January to 81° in July, or an annual mean of 65°. The topography is gently rolling with shallow draws. There is little or no permanent surface water; an absence of permanent running streams necessitates the use of pumps to tap ground water sources. The vegetation cover, chiefly grass, is curly mesquite, with liberal amounts of buffalo grass and grama grass. Needle grass is plentiful in the early spring. Clumps of live oaks are found here and there along the intermittent streams. Mesquite trees produce crops of beans. Soils of limestone origin predominate, some black loam and others gray and red.

After 1877, the area was open range. Sheep came in first, and then cattle; range wars were the result, because cattle and sheep cannot share the same range. Sheep crop the grasses so close to the ground that cattle cannot get enough to eat. Also, sheep excrement is obnoxious to cattle. Following the invention of barbed wire came the first use of fences in Sutton County in 1889, to bring an end to the open range.

Today Sutton is a leading sheep raising county producing an average of two million pounds of wool annually. Cattle are second in importance, goats third. Some quarterhorses and thoroughbreds are also raised. Small acreage is cultivated for grain sorghums, forage, and small grains. The growing season is 240 days.

Sonora, the county seat, is a market for lambs, wool, cattle, and mohair. The Sonora ranch community is made up of a group of ranches whose people are interdependent in the development of their economic and social institutions and activities. Ranch owners and operators of ranches comprise the chief element. Merchants, lawyers, doctors, teachers, bankers, mechanics, and the like are also part of the community.

The whole Sonora community is divided into several smaller units commonly referred to as neighborhoods. The people of a neighborhood do many things co-operatively. Neighbors lend and borrow items freely, and exchange work as well. The Sonora community covers about one million acres of land. Ranch size varies considerably. Of 97 ranches studied only one was less than 640 acres. Fifteen of the ranches had from one to four sections; 44 ranches contained four to 12 sections; 18 had 12 to 20; and 19 were over 20 sections in size.

The population numbers 3,746 in an area of 1,493 square miles, or 2.5 people per square mile. Caucasian Southern stock predominates, with minorities of Germans, Scotch, and Canadians. In addition, there are a few Negroes and quite a few Mexicans, who form the chief labor supply.

Ranch management. Efficient operation of a ranch requires varied knowledge and considerable managerial skill. The successful rancher skillfully culls and improves his breeding stock; he maintains a delicate balance between the number of animals and the amount of forage on his range. He allocates the proportions of his pastures in the most advantageous way between the different classes of livestock; he strives to manage labor, purchase supplies, and sell ranch products profitably. Because his income varies directly with the amount and quality of surplus livestock produced, he maintains maximum productivity of herds by the skillful use of good breeding stock and the removal of relatively unprofitable animals. Earnings may be increased by grazing as many animals as the range will safely support at all times. This involves an increase in number of livestock grazed during times when forage is abundant, and a reduction in size of flocks and herds without sacrificial selling during periods of drought when forage is scanty. Ranchmen also study the vegetation of their land to determine the proportion of cattle, sheep, and goats that make most efficient use of the range. For example, goats are more numerous on ranches having much stony, rugged land and an abundance of shrub vegetation; they can subsist on little. Cattle graze in greatest numbers on relatively smooth, grassy, well-watered pastures. Sheep find optimum conditions on rolling land having an abundance of both "graze" and "browse" vegetation, but do well on either the typically goat or cattle ranges.

Ranch labor. The character of ranch labor has changed materially with increasing intensity of the ranching industry. In pioneer days ranchers employed cowboys who could ride skillfully; rope, brand, and herd animals; and ably defend the employer's interests against Indians, thieves, and rival ranchers. When the use of wire fences became widespread and law and order came to the range, the fighting ability of cowboys lost its usefulness, and increased emphasis was given to skill in managing live-

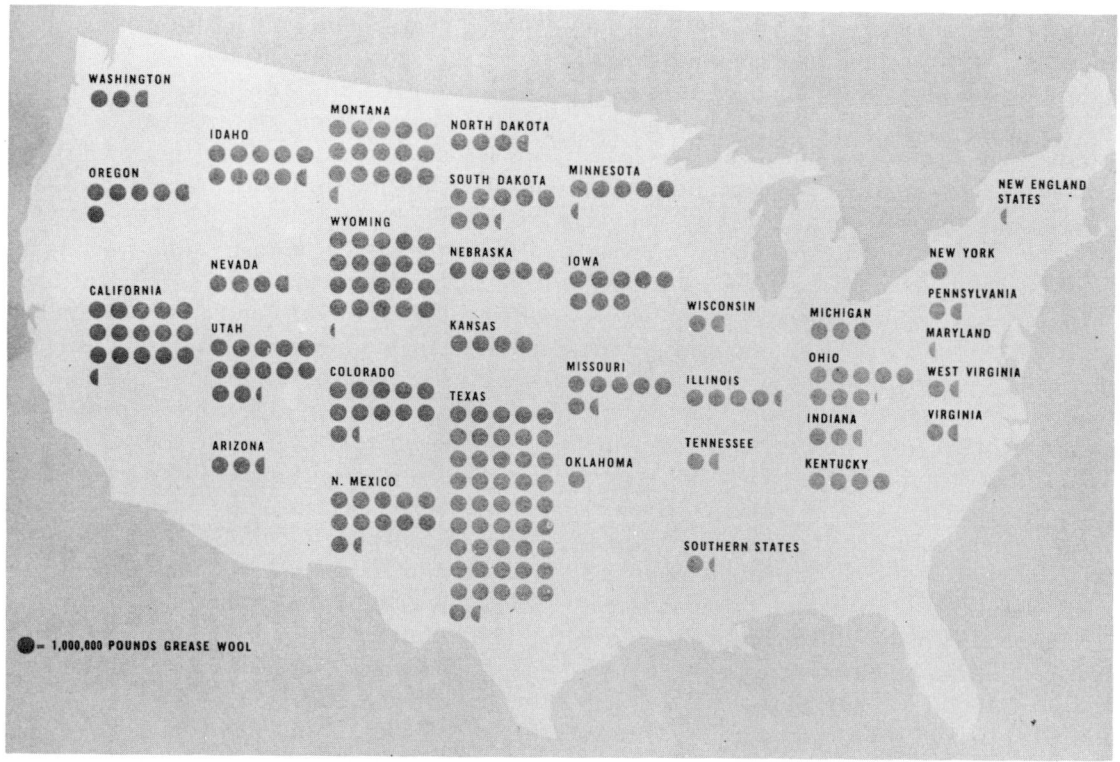

Figure 10-10. Grease wool production in the United States. (U.S. Department of Agriculture)

stock and range land under modern ranching conditions. The cowboy is still a good horseman, for much of his work must be done in the saddle. His primary business is to assist in caring for the needs of livestock and in the direction of their movements. He must possess an uncanny sense of where livestock might be feeding at any time, and be able to drive them to headquarters or another pasture as needed. He needs to be an expert with the lasso to cut out steers for market, to be able to use the branding iron quickly and efficiently, to be ready to assist in the dehorning of cattle and other chores, and to be a good team member during the roundup. So professional is the character of his work and, in his opinion, so superior is he to the farm hand, that he will often resign his position if asked to plow or do other agricultural labor.

SHEEP

Sheep are grazed in many parts of the Western Interior High Plains Region. Ranchers often run both sheep and cattle on their range; the cattle usually occupy the portions with better water and grass; sheep graze in the more arid sections, since they can subsist on less water and can graze on shorter grass. Three areas in particular specialize in the grazing of sheep: (1) the Edwards Plateau of Texas, (2) northern Colorado, and (3) eastern Montana.

Texas has long been known as cattle country. Yet, it is interesting to note that the sheep in Texas contribute a much greater proportion to the national total of sheep than is the case with cattle. Texas' cattle and calves contribute less than seven per cent of the value of all cattle in the United States, whereas sheep contribute more than 14 per cent to the value of all sheep. Although sheep are raised throughout the state, ownership is concentrated on the Edwards Plateau and in the eastern Trans-Pecos area. There, sheep production is a major undertaking, the primary or sole source of income to many ranchers.

No clearer illustration of a joint product and joint cost enterprise can be found than sheep raising. In the Western and Southwestern States initial interest of the ranchers who built great flocks was in wool. The animal had little value as meat but that value was always a significant one among those who ran small flocks. Indeed, it has been this difference in interest that has led to a general preference for "down" breeds of the medium wool class by those who run small flocks in the older and developed areas—breeds that furnish a good wool and, at the same time, a goodly poundage of meat either as lamb or mutton. Upon the open range, however, where in the past prime or sole interest has been in wool, the "down" breeds have gained slight acceptance; instead, interest has been almost wholly in the fine wool breeds, with one or another of the several Merino types widely favored.

Northern Colorado and eastern Montana sheep ranchers practice transhumance, a seasonal movement of flocks to high mountain grassland meadows during the spring and summer periods. During the winter, sheep are quartered in the protected valleys. Sheep have decreased almost steadily since 1942. Production also has been shifting from range to farm flocks and from the Western States eastward.

One of the causes of the decline in range sheep numbers is the increase in labor costs. To illustrate, the average family-operated sheep ranch in the northern Great Plains had a hired labor cost of $490 per year in the period from 1937 to 1941. In 1961 the hired labor cost was more than $3,000.

The United States is the world's greatest market for wool and woolen products, but, since it produces less wool than it consumes, it is dependent upon foreign supply for at least a part of its raw wool requirements. This fact stimulates wool growers in surplus producing countries to seek a market in the United States. As soon as the supply available for import into this country exceeds the margin between domestic production and consumption, the domestic producer must either restrict the inflow by selling his product, regardless of cost, at a price that will win the preference of the domestic mill owner, or he must look to government to check the inflow by tariff barriers, import quotas, or other such artificial restraints, which involve serious conflicts of economic interest between the wool grower, domestic woolen mills, and consumers of textiles.

ANGORA GOATS

For many years a major part of the nation's Angora goat population has been on Texas range. The great concentration of Angoras in Texas is on the Edwards Plateau and the upper Rio Grande Plain. In this area the vegetation is such as to make poor pasturage for cattle or sheep, but the shrubs and other growth are favorable for goats.

The Angora goat industry differs markedly from sheep raising in that it is only in small measure a joint product and a joint cost industry. The Angora is raised for its fleece; little income is derived from the sale of animals for meat, and at present there seems to be little likelihood that any demand comparable to that for lamb or mutton will develop for the kid as meat, let alone the mature animal. About the only consistent and considerable demand for kid or goat meat is among the Mexican population of the Southwest.

The industry's future is tied basically to the price of mohair, with no such alternative source of income available as that enjoyed by the sheep raiser in the sale of lamb. Mohair is a distinctive textile fiber that is the basic raw material for many types of fabrics. It is used in the manufacture of men's suits and overcoats. It adds to the coolness and wrinkle resistance of summer garments. In tweeds, it combats wrinkles and deepens color. Mohair is used in women's wear—in soft suits, dresses, and coatings—because it adds to color tones, to drape, and to wear. It is used also for other items of clothing, such as sportswear, robes, and sweaters. The chief use of mohair, however, is in the manufacture of upholstery for automobiles, buses, trains, planes, theaters, and the home.

IRRIGATED FARMING

In the arid sections of the West, irrigation has been used for over a century in agricultural production and undoubtedly will become more important with the passage of time. The Spanish settlers brought with them considerable knowledge and experience in instituting and practicing irrigation, which they adapted to conditions they found in the Southwest. Out of the combination of Spanish and Indian methods grew what is called the Spanish-American community acequia—a canal for irrigating land. Acequia groups were widely established in New Mexico. The Spaniards were likewise energetic in extending irrigation into Texas and Colorado.

The first Anglo-Americans to practice irrigation on an extensive scale in the United States were the Mormons, who, in about 1847, began the practice of utilizing water in crop production as a necessary means of livelihood. The Mormons extended their colonization activities into neighboring states, among them Colorado and New Mexico, and their irrigation institutions and practices went along with them.

As the opportunities for irrigation through easy and inexpensive methods of diversion of water gradually disappeared, there came a need for larger enterprises and higher per-acre expenditures to obtain water. The combination of a demand for developing the public lands of the United States and the need of Federal funds for the large undertakings led to the passage of the National Reclamation Act in 1902. The work done under this act has been extended to include reclamation of private as well as public lands.

SOURCES OF IRRIGATION WATER

Sources of irrigation water are grouped into two classifications: (1) surface water—lakes, rivers, streams, and flowing wells; and (2) ground water obtained from pumped wells. Ground water is used predominantly by single farm enterprises, while surface waters are used by most co-operative farm operations.

IRRIGATION AGRICULTURE PRACTICES

The general system of farming in the irrigated districts, like that along the northern margin of the corn area, is based on some intertilled crop, usually corn or sugar beets, followed by a small grain (usually wheat), and then by hay (commonly alfalfa), which may occupy the land for several years and be pastured incidentally. Commonly, both cattle and sheep are brought down off the plains into the irrigated districts during the winter and fed beet pulp or corn fodder, supplemented sometimes with grain.

IRRIGATION DISTRICTS

North Platte Valley. The North Platte Valley of western Nebraska and eastern Wyoming comprises a half-million acres of irrigated farm

Figure 10-11. Irrigation ditch taking water from the Platte River, Carbon County, Wyoming. Surface waters serve more than half the irrigation enterprises in the Western Interior High Plains Region, and better than 80 per cent of the irrigated acreage. The lakes and streams of the region constitute the most important single source of irrigation water. (U.S. Department of Agriculture)

land—the largest completely adjacent irrigated acreage in the United States. Pathfinder Reservoir, in the mountains of Wyoming, stores over a million acre-feet of water, and with the auxiliary storage of Guernsey Lake, Lake Alice, and Lake Miniature, assures the moisture to grow crops every year. Corn, small grains, tomatoes, peas, sugar beets, potatoes, beans, and many other crops of increasing importance make up a farm income of more than $65 million for the valley.

A highly favorable, mild, dry climate contributes to the success of livestock feeding in the area, as does the production of feed crops. Sugar beet tops from an average acre have a feed value equivalent to 60 bushels of corn. Beet pulp, a sugar factory by-product, is also an important livestock feed, and a tremendous tonnage is available. Corn, barley, and alfalfa are produced in great quantities.

Missouri River Basin. Agriculture in the Missouri River Basin is an important part of the national economy. The basin contains about 18 per cent of the land area of the coun-

Figure 10-12. An extensive sugar beet field near Fort Collins, Colorado. Irrigated sugar beets are one of the principal field crops of the Western States. Note the size of the root and leaves of this mature sugar beet. (Bureau of Reclamation, U.S. Department of the Interior)

try. Except for the Mississippi drainage area, of which it is a part, the Missouri Basin is the largest drainage area in the United States. Almost a fourth of the nation's farm land and slightly more than a fourth of the harvested cropland lie within it.

The Western Interior High Plains contain about half the land area of the basin. Except for irrigated areas the land is suitable for only limited cultivation. However, multipurpose uses—for grazing, timber, recreation, mining—and water yield make the land in this area a highly valued part of the basin's land resources.

More than 87 per cent of the land irrigated in the basin has a surface water supply. Most of this is served by gravity systems, but a small quantity of the surface water is pumped. About 11 per cent of the land is irrigated by pumping ground water from wells. A small acreage has both surface and ground water supplied.

IRRIGATED FIELD CROPS

Sugar beets. Grown in 22 Western and North-central States, sugar beets are not a major crop even in those states that are large producers. Less than eight per cent of the total

value of all crops was accounted for by beets in Colorado and Wyoming, according to the 1960 census. In Nebraska and Kansas, the proportions were about one per cent and 0.1 per cent, respectively. Beets have been an important factor, however, in the development of permanent agriculture in the irrigated areas of many Western States. In addition to providing a cash crop, they are suited to several rotation systems and thus complement diversified farming operations.

The overhead costs of irrigation on the Plains require a sizable acreage of crops having a high return per acre. Sugar beets have met this requirement. In a number of the irrigated areas, beets, beans, and potatoes represent important, high-value crops. They are grown in rotation with small grains, alfalfa, and corn. Livestock feeding operations are integrated into the farm program, with beef cattle and lambs being fattened, in part, on the feed crops, sugar beet tops, beet pulp, and molasses.

Cotton. The principal cash crop on the western Texas High Plains is cotton. Large areas of fertile, level land, a highly mechanized farming system, and irrigation have brought economic stability and prosperity to many cotton growers. Some land that formerly produced an income of a few cents per acre in brush is now yielding more than three bales of cotton with an annual gross income in excess of $500 per acre.

Because of the relatively high costs of irrigation, it is necessary to maintain a high output per acre to reduce unit costs. Consequently, farmers growing cotton under irrigation use heavy applications of fertilizer to boost yields and to offset the loss of plant nutrients leached out by irrigation water.

The lack of water, caused by the drought, has been a serious problem in western Texas during the past few years. Although cotton is a deep-rooted plant that can take much drought and heat, it cannot produce without adequate water when temperatures stay above 100° F. for many days. Therefore every effort must be made to utilize fully every drop of water that falls on western Texas.

Grain sorghum. With irrigation, the significance of sorghum to the economy of the Staked Plains of Texas cannot be overlooked. Wheat, long regarded as the major crop, has declined. With restrictions on wheat, sorghum has become even more important. Some farmers say that grain sorghum is so well established now that even if wheat were unrestricted they would still plant sorghum. Sorghum has about 90 per cent of the feed value of corn, does not compete with wheat for labor or machinery, and, with mechanization, is easy to harvest.

Alfalfa. Irrigated pastures make possible an expansion in dairy and farm-flock sheep and beef cattle production. In the High Plains, alfalfa is an important crop from Colorado north to Canada. It makes a good hay, pasture, and silage crop for almost all farm animals. It is an excellent soil improver; in combination with grasses it helps stop soil erosion. Alfalfa meal, dehydrated alfalfa, and other similar products are becoming increasingly important. Alfalfa's wide distribution shows a remarkable adaptability but the best yields are attained on deep loams with open, porous, well-drained subsoil.

Alfalfa may be cultivated and harvested with ordinary farm machinery for hay and seed crops, a characteristic that makes it ideal for rotation with wheat. An ordinary mower or rake is used in harvesting the hay crop; the combine harvests the seed.

Truck crops. With irrigation, truck farming, too, has become important on the Staked Plains. In the Hereford area of Texas there are about 300 potato growers, about 50 lettuce farmers, and about 100 farmers raising onions, carrots, cabbages, and melons. The main problem in truck farming is marketing.

EXTRACTIVE INDUSTRIES

A vast part of the more gently sloping portion of the Western Interior High Plains Region consists of sedimentary rock conducive to the formation of such nonmetallic minerals as coal, potash, petroleum, and natural gas. There are several isolated mountain uplifts, of which the Black Hills is the largest and farthest east. The Black Hills make up a dome-like mountain range rising 3,000 to 4,000 feet above the plain and 7,000 feet above the sea. Granite is exposed in the center where the overlying sedimentary rocks have eroded; intruded masses of igneous rock give rise to the formation of metallic minerals—gold, silver,

copper, lead, and zinc. Gold is by far the most important metal.

Gold from the Homestake Mine at Lead continues to be South Dakota's number one mining product. First opened in 1876, the Homestake is the largest gold producing mine in the United States. Uranium, feldspar, mica, bentonite, granite, gypsum, and limestone are other mineral products contributing to South Dakota's wealth.

Mineral fuels occur in considerable quantities and in many fields throughout the Western Interior High Plains Region. Petroleum and natural gas are found from Texas to northern Alberta, and some of the most spectacular discoveries in Anglo-America have taken place within this province. The major fields are: (1) the Canadian Prairie Provinces, (2) the Williston Basin, (3) the Powder River Basin, (4) the Denver-Julesburg Basin, (5) the Permian Basin, (6) the Texas Panhandle, and (7) the Hugoton field of Texas, Oklahoma, and Kansas.

CANADIAN PRAIRIE PROVINCES

Prior to 1947, the Prairie Provinces had only one major oil field, with an average daily crude oil production rate of less than 20,000 barrels. In February, 1947, Imperial Oil Ltd. brought in the discovery well at Leduc, Alberta—the beginning of a Canadian oil boom. Other companies rushed into the area, and within a year

Figure 10-13. Irrigating a field of grain sorghum south of Brownsfield, Texas, on the Llano Estacado. Almost all the grain and forage sorghum and some of the wheat are irrigated. Grain sorghum yields up to 5,000 pounds an acre and wheat 30 to 40 bushels an acre. (Texas Highway Department)

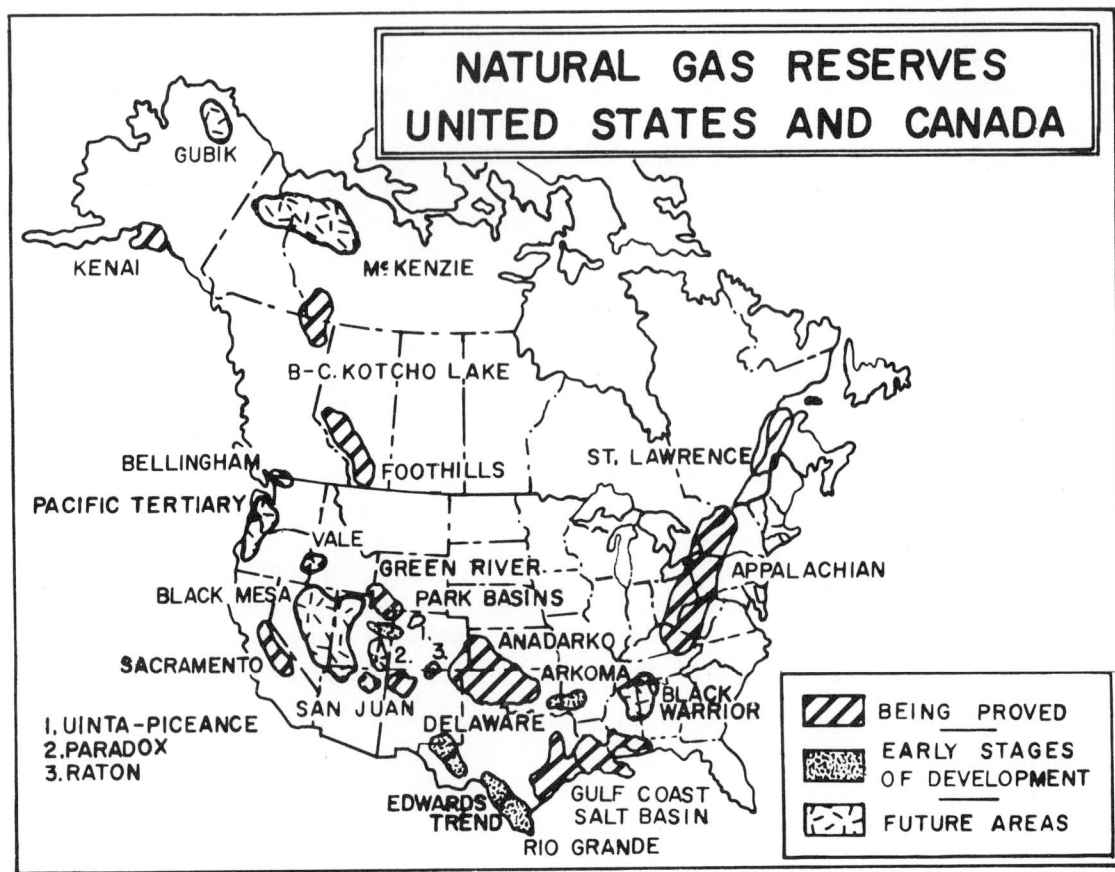

Figure 10-14. (The Oil and Gas Journal)

43 major producers had been drilled; the reserves for the field were some 250,000 barrels.

The Redwater field was discovered in 1948; its reserves are estimated at a half-billion barrels. This was followed by discoveries at Golden Spike, at Woodland, and in the Edmonton area. Rapid expansion soon spread through the length and breadth of Alberta, reaching the Peace River in 1949. Production soared with these new discoveries. The number of wells producing crude oil has grown from a few in 1950 to more than 500. Reserves of crude oil and condensate have increased to an estimated 1.9 million barrels. Daily output of crude oil now exceeds 250,000 barrels per day.

This expansion has produced certain marketing problems. The local Alberta refinery demand was soon saturated by available supplies and as a consequence new markets had to be developed. In order to meet this situation plans were made for the construction of a major pipeline outlet. In 1950, the Interpro-vincial Pipeline, Canada's largest, was completed. It connects Edmonton, Alberta, with Superior, Wisconsin, and Sarnia, Ontario, and has a capacity of 150,000 barrels per day.

The Trans-Mountain Pipeline, completed in 1953, is Canada's second largest; it extends from Edmonton to the West Coast. A $330 million gas pipeline, 1,300 miles long, is under construction; it will transport fuel from Alberta to California. Initial deliveries of 400 million cubic feet a day are expected in 1962.

In addition to these major pipelines there are many gathering systems serving the producing areas. Edmonton is the terminus of lines that bring in oil for refinery use and for shipment to points east and west.

Natural gas has been one of Alberta's major assets for many years. Today, local utility systems supply much of the urban population and also some markets outside the province on a limited scale. Proven gas reserves are estimated at 13.4 trillion cubic feet.

Saskatchewan. Less than ten years ago Saskatchewan produced only a trickle of heavy, black crude oil, valued at less than $18,000, from the small, old Lloydminster field on the Alberta border. Today, production exceeds $18 million and 12 million barrels annually.

The province is rapidly achieving stature as a major oil reserve region. Its southeastern corner has turned into the most lucrative oil and recovery area in the whole of western Canada outside of the Pembina field. Discovery performance has reached a point where two out of every three wells drilled has produced oil. Some 100 rigs are now concentrated in the southwest corner of the province.

Crude oil output is expected to exceed 20 million barrels annually. Already crude oil output has reached and passed a refinery capacity of 63,000 barrels a day. In the past seven years oil companies operating in the province have spent a total of $400 million on search and development.

Manitoba. Though drilling for oil in Manitoba occurred as early as 1887, interest was only sporadic until two wells drilled in the southwest corner of the province in 1949 revealed for the first time the presence of rocks containing oil. The first recoverable oil in significant quantity was obtained in January, 1951. This discovery led to increased interest in potential oil properties by a number of companies and to the development of the Daly field in southwestern Manitoba. Since that time progress has been rapid.

A number of economic considerations favor the development of Manitoba's oil industry: (1) The oil reservoirs are relatively shallow, resulting in relatively low drilling and production costs; (2) the oil fields are close to the Interprovincial Pipeline, making transportation readily available; and (3) both the consumer market and refinery capacity in Manitoba exceed local production, a situation that is likely to continue.

WILLISTON BASIN

The discovery of oil and gas in the Beaver Lodge Pool, 32 miles northeast of Williston, North Dakota, in April, 1951, caused a rush of major oil companies to the area. Geologists contend that it may be the greatest sedimentary oil deposit on the continent, with an estimated reserve of around three billion barrels. The Williston Basin extends into southern Alberta, southwestern Manitoba, the northern half of South Dakota, eastern Montana, and central North Dakota, an area of approximately 119,000 square miles. Already more than 1,600 wells are producing, refineries and pipelines have been built, and petrochemical industries loom large on the horizon.

Montana's eastern field, also a part of the Williston Basin, has been experiencing the most intensive oil exploration period in its history. Most recent developments are the addition of a fluid coking unit at the Carter Oil Company's Billings refinery, the establishment of a $1 million sulphur plant at Billings using refinery gases, and a $1 million catalytic cracking unit at the Phillips Petroleum Company's refinery in Great Falls.

Three refineries are proposed for North Dakota; one of these, already completed, has a capacity of 30,000 barrels a day.

The biggest difficulty confronting the industry is distance from large populated markets. Unless the area experiences a tremendous population growth, oil from the Williston Basin

Figure 10-15. An oil well in the Williston field near Williston, North Dakota. Wells are spaced quite far apart here. Note the uneven topography of this area adjacent to the Missouri River. In the background is the flat, undulating topography so characteristic of much of the Western Interior High Plains Region. (W. E. Shemorry, Williston Chamber of Commerce)

will meet serious competition from producing fields closer to consuming centers. At present, most oil shipped out of the region moves by tank car to the Minneapolis-St. Paul metropolitan district.

POWDER RIVER BASIN

This has been one of the leading oil and gas producing sections in the Western Interior High Plains for many years. Located in Wyoming, it has only recently been topped in production by Big Horn Basin, with its Elk Basin field.

Most oil discoveries have been made in the southern portion of the basin. The Salt Creek field, discovered in 1906, has been the most productive. In 1923 it attained a record output of 38 million barrels, the largest producer in the world at that time. It has leveled off in recent years at about four million barrels. Since 1948, a number of smaller fields have been discovered, several of them in the million-barrel class.

The Powder River Basin has produced a total of 374 million barrels of crude to date and it is estimated that there are 161 million barrels of oil remaining.

Gaseous formations have been found under about 9,000 acres of land. Best estimates place gas reserves at 370 billion cubic feet. Salt Creek also dominates here. Teapot Dome, at the south end of the Salt Creek anticline, could be a fairly heavy producer, but the wells have been shut in for a number of years. The gas produced in the Powder River Basin is high in quality and largely free from hydrogen sulfide.

DENVER-JULESBURG BASIN

The Denver-Julesburg Basin encompasses southeastern Wyoming, northeastern Colorado, and southwestern Nebraska. Oil was first discovered in the region in 1862, but the current boom dates from the Ohio Oil Company's 1949 discovery near Gurley, Nebraska. Within a few months, millions of acres were leased on the eastern flank of the basin and wildcat drilling boomed in the Nebraska and Colorado portions.

Although the proximity of the major trunk lines and the rapid development of a crude oil gathering system have done much to encourage activity in the region, a favorable land leasing situation and relatively fast and inexpensive drilling also have proved very attractive to operators. The Colorado portion has been the most productive, but the focal point of Denver-Julesburg exploration has shifted to western Nebraska.

THE PERMIAN BASIN

The Permian Basin is a producing field turning out one and a half million barrels of oil a day—one-tenth of the world supply. From western Texas it lies westward into New Mexico. Roughly it is bordered by Hobbs and Snyder on the north, Sweetwater on the east, San Angelo and El Dorado on the south, and Carlsbad on the west. The basin has an intricate interlacing of pipelines and railroads.

No small part of the present wealth of western Texas has been derived from oil, and oil has contributed generously to the transformation into cities of what must otherwise have been small towns. The farther westward toward the New Mexico border, the more do such marks of prosperity and wealth in evidence stand upon the cornerstone of oil.

Initial discovery of oil in western Texas was made in Palo Pinto County in 1902; latest of the counties to become a producer is Culberson in 1953. Within that span of years oil has been found and production is recorded for 35 out of 38 counties.

The most significant fact to note is the rapidly growing importance of reserves in western Texas. In 1940, these reserves constituted but 12.5 per cent of the national total; by 1945, the figure had increased to almost 15; in 1950, it stood at 20.2; and for 1960, the percentage of the nation's proven reserves to be found in western Texas alone stood at 20.6. In view of developments within recent years, it is probable that this percentage will remain relatively stable for a considerable period, and perhaps increase rather than diminish. There are no developments in other areas that now appear to threaten seriously the high rank of western Texas.

The most sensational discovery in recent years has been in Scurry and adjoining counties. The discovery well was brought in on November 21, 1948. From it developed one of the greatest booms in Texas oil history. In a year cumulative production was nearly two million barrels. The discovery in Scurry was followed by a revival of exploration in western Texas that, during 1950, brought more than 70 new fields, large and small, into production, in addition to important extensions of old fields. The western Texas area became the busiest in the oil world, with more than a third of the nation's rigs in operation there.

Almost all of New Mexico's production is derived from the Permian Basin fields. The first commercial development of oil resources in the state began in 1924 and production continues to rise. About one-fifth of the oil lands within the state's eastern portion are now leased.

The largest crude oil pipeline in Anglo-America, built to transport crude oil produced in the Permian Basin area of western Texas and New Mexico, was completed in May, 1953. This line stretches more than 466 miles across the state of Texas to Nederland, with a 112-mile spur branching off to Longview. Ten eight-inch lines would be necessary to move the 440,000 barrels daily that this giant tube can carry, a load equal to that of 20 trains of 100 tank cars each.

THE PANHANDLE AND HUGOTON FIELDS

The Texas Panhandle began producing oil in 1918. However, natural gas long has been more important than petroleum in this area. Drillers have found some of the largest and most important gas fields in the world there. The field extends northwest across six counties in the Texas Panhandle until it almost touches the Hugoton field. The Hugoton field underlies most of Sherman County and part of Hansford County in the Texas Panhandle and extends from there northward across Oklahoma into Kansas. The Panhandle and Hugoton gas fields together are more than 200 miles long and from five to 40 miles wide.

The real magnitude of the Texas Panhandle field was not realized until 1925. From that time on, the natural gas business in Texas began to develop rapidly. As time passed, additional supplies of natural gas were discovered in the search for oil, and the price of natural gas fell very low because of the much larger available supply in relation to the current demand. This caused great losses and waste.

The extension of long-distance transmission lines from the Panhandle in 1932 by the Eastern Pipe Line Company brought Texas gas to many consuming markets in all parts of the country. In that year, gas from the Panhandle and Hugoton fields was carried to Detroit. Since then natural gas has continued to flow to 33 other states, the District of Columbia, Mexico, and Canada.

HELIUM

The Great Plains have a virtual world monopoly on the production of helium, most of which comes from the Texas Panhandle gas field. Helium, in any appreciable amount, is a rare constituent of natural gas. A few fields have been discovered that contain sufficient amounts to permit extraction with a helium content generally about one or two per cent, but ranging as high as eight per cent in one field in New Mexico. Helium is isolated by reduction to a temperature at which the natural gas (methane) liquefies, leaving the helium in a gaseous state. Its present price is less than one cent a cubic foot, but prior to World War I it was a laboratory curiosity obtained from radioactive minerals at a cost of approximately $2,500 per cubic foot.

The world's sole producer of helium is the United States Department of the Interior. For many years its only plant was at the Cliffside gas field near Amarillo, Texas, but to meet the increased demand for helium during World War II three other plants were built by the government in Kansas and New Mexico. After the war, demand for helium declined sharply, but in recent years many uses have been found. The gas is used in the welding of magnesium, aluminum, and stainless steel. It also has come into considerable use in hospitals, where it is employed as an oxygen carrier in the treatment of respiratory cases and for admixture with anesthetic gases to minimize explosion hazards in operating rooms. Helium is a nonflammable gas only a little heavier than hydrogen, and it was employed at first to fill dirigibles, blimps, and other lighter-than-air craft.

Since helium is chemically inert, its presence in natural gas used for fuel is not objectionable. The low percentage of helium results in only a slight reduction of the heating value of gas. Helium need not be removed from gas to

Figure 10-16. The coal mining town of Blair-more, with the Frank Slide in the background and the town of Frank, Alberta, in the fore-ground. Alberta's reserves of mineable coal have been estimated at 48 billion net tons, approximately 48 per cent of Canada's total coal reserve. (National Film Board)

condition it for pipeline distribution, so the extraction is important only as a source of the helium itself.

COAL

The Canadian Prairie Provinces and the northern Great Plains contain enormous reserves of unmined coal, varying from lignite to high-grade bituminous. Competition from petroleum and natural gas, however, has kept its exploitation to a minimum. Where mining does occur, the coal is used chiefly to serve railways, for smelters, and as a domestic heating fuel. Sparse population within the area seems to preclude any large-scale production.

Prairie Provinces. Alberta is particularly rich in coal deposits that range from semianthracite to lignite. For a distance of over 700 miles from the international boundary northward, the Rocky Mountains and their foothills are studded with deposits of coal.

Coal-bearing formations underlie most of the southern half of Alberta. They occur in the plains, foothills, and mountains. Production of coal between 1905 and 1960, amounted to

approximately 300 million net tons, valued at over a billion dollars. This production is less than seven-tenths of one per cent of the estimated mineable reserves. During the last few years production has dropped rapidly, mainly because of changes in the railways' policy on fuels and equipment, and to a lesser extent because of competition from oil and natural gas in industrial and domestic heating and for power generation.

Lignite is found in Saskatchewan and Manitoba. In Manitoba, small deposits occur in the vicinity of Turtle Mountain, and the whole southern portion of Saskatchewan from Manitoba to the Alberta boundary is underlain with lignite. Reserves in Manitoba are estimated at 160 million tons, and in Saskatchewan at 60 billion tons. The principal deposits occur in the Sauris Valley in southeastern Saskatchewan; it is from this area that about 90 per cent of the present production is derived.

Lignite is a cheap fuel and, although of low grade, has been found of value to settlers in sparsely settled districts at some distance from railways. Since it occurs near the surface, the ease of mining has increased its usefulness in this respect. In the Prairie Provinces it is used largely for domestic heating purposes. As a commercial fuel its value has not yet been fully realized because of the readiness with which better grade steam coals are obtainable from Alberta.

Northern Great Plains. This northern portion of the High Plains includes the greater part of North Dakota and the eastern halves of Montana and Wyoming. North Dakota possesses extensive lignite coal. Completion of a $750,000 Federal lignite research laboratory at the University of North Dakota in 1950, was a big step forward in the development of almost unlimited supplies of this low-grade coal.

Lignite deposits of varying thickness underlie about 32,000 square miles of surface in the state. Nearly 634 billion out of a United States total of 966 billion tons of lignite deposits are in North Dakota; about 500 billion can be mined. Beds vary in thickness from a fraction of an inch to 35 feet; while six- to eight-foot veins are common. In places they are so close to the surface that the overlying soil is stripped and the coal mined in open cuts; other places the room-and-pillar method is used.

The lignite beds of North Dakota extend into eastern Montana, where they underlie more than 35 per cent of the state's surface. Much of it is mined easily, for it lies in thick seams free from waste materials. Recent developments include the construction of Montana's first steam electric generating plant using lignite by Montana-Dakota Utilities at Sidney.

The Powder River Basin of Wyoming is one of the most important areas of subbituminous coal in that state. Known mineable reserves total 96 billion tons. The coal beds are thick and continuous over relatively large areas. However, only a small amount is mined, primarily because the coal is younger and of lower rank than coals in other areas of the state.

POTASH

Potash, used mainly as fertilizer, has been in active demand for a long time. From the time of the Revolutionary War until the 1860's, domestic needs in the United States were met and a considerable quantity of potash produced for export; at that time the source of the mineral was wood ashes. In 1843, however, potash was discovered in the brine of a salt well; by the late 1850's potash in soluble form had been found to be helpful in stimulating plant growth; and by the early 1860's, so rapid had been progress in the separation of potash from its salts, that potash was being produced in large quantity. With the rise of German potash production, however, output in the United States declined rapidly. In 1872, mineral potash from Germany was first utilized by American agriculture; for the next 40 years agriculture in this country was dependent entirely upon such importation.

Overproduction of potash in Germany during the early years of the present century led to ruinous competition for markets and, in due course, to governmental control. High prices resulted in sharp protests from American users and immediate activity on the part of governmental and private interests to discover and develop domestic sources of supply. This activity, begun in 1910, continued over a wide area until the discovery and development of the rich deposits in the Carlsbad, New Mexico, area.

Since mineral potash in its various forms was found almost invariably in brines or in salt deposits, it was natural that attention should be directed early toward the Permian Salt Basin in Texas, New Mexico, Oklahoma, Kansas, and Colorado.

Mineral potash was first noted in the Permian Salt Basin in 1921, in the form of polyhalite, a compound of potassium sulfate, calcium sulfate, and magnesium sulfate. The deposit has not been developed, however, primarily because conventional methods of commercial potash production have been applied principally to sylvite and carnallite, which furnish most of Europe's commercial production. Possible development of Texas polyhalite also was discouraged by the subsequent discovery of a domestic supply of potash in sylvite and carnallite deposits at Carlsbad, New Mexico, now the center of commercial production of potash in the United States. Potash can be produced at a materially lower cost there than in any other area within the nation's boundaries.

Saskatchewan's potash resources, said to be the world's largest known reserves, are estimated at some 100 billion tons. Some 13 companies hold large acreages in the 340-mile-long potash belt that extends across central Saskatchewan. Represented among the companies in the field are major American potash firms and Canadian, British, and German interests. A $20 million concentrator has been built at the mine site of the Potash Company of America near Saskatoon.

MANUFACTURING

The Western Interior High Plains cannot in any sense be considered a prime industrial region. Industries that do exist are scattered widely; in no one place is there any great concentration. Distance from urban markets, a sparse population, and limited resources preclude any large-scale industrial expansion. Nevertheless, manufacturing establishments serving local markets are exceedingly important to the region's economy. Because of space limitation only the most important industries within the region are discussed here.

PETROCHEMICAL INDUSTRIES

Petroleum and natural gas have provided the basis for a limited industrial development in

Figure 10-17. Great Falls Refinery on the Missouri River in Montana. Great Falls is noted for copper smelting and refining and for coal, natural gas, silver, and lead deposits. (Anaconda Copper Co.)

the Western Interior High Plains Region, as is attested by existence of several carbon black plants, the many liquid petroleum gas plants, and a number of refineries varying widely in capacity. The Panhandle of Texas and the Canadian Prairie Provinces, in particular, are noteworthy for the development of new industries based on petroleum and natural gas.

Geographically, the heart of the American petrochemical industry is in the Gulf Coast, where an estimated 75 per cent of the total production is concentrated.

Like the American petrochemical industry, the Canadian counterpart has shown a very remarkable growth. The western portion, in Alberta, with energy supplies based on natural gas, has developed largely in the past five years. Since 1950, considerably more than 40 per cent

of the new Canadian petrochemical investment —about $120 million—has been in Alberta. Long distances from major markets and relatively high plant operation costs caused by severe climatic conditions and the lack of large industrial suppliers, however, will probably be instrumental in preventing any considerable percentage gain in Alberta's petrochemical industry.

FOOD PROCESSING INDUSTRIES

Food processing industries long have been important in the irrigated districts of the Great Plains, especially sugar beet factories. In northeastern Colorado, 12 factories are in operation, and the North Platte Valley accounts for five more. The largest refineries in terms of slicing capacity also are located in these two areas: at

Fort Collins, Longmont, and Loveland, and at Scottsbluff and Torrington.

Sugar beet factories in the Western Interior High Plains Region produce nearly a third of the nation's beet sugar. Refineries in Colorado produce about 21 per cent of the United States total; in Nebraska, seven per cent; in Wyoming, four per cent; and the single factory in Kansas, but five-tenths of one per cent. Sugar from the region is marketed principally in the Middle West, from the Rocky Mountains to the Mississippi River and Lake Michigan.

Meat packing. Edmonton is the meat packing center of the Canadian Prairies. Its plants account for a large proportion of the area's animal processing industry, a response to the excellent rail transportation network. Calgary is also an important meat packing center, ranking second to Edmonton.

Flour milling. Flour milling was one of Al-

berta's first manufacturing industries. Large flour mills are located at Calgary and Medicine Hat; smaller ones, which usually operate on a custom basis, are scattered throughout the province. The industry employs around 1,000 people and has a $40 million gross valuation of production.

SMELTING AND REFINING OF METALS

The smelting of copper, zinc, and manganese at Anaconda (in the American Rockies) and their refining at Great Falls; the refining of alumina into aluminum at Columbia Falls; and the manufacturing of aluminum products at Great Falls, are typical of a number of important and growing industries in Montana. It is apparent that great industrial diversity and consequent stability of the economy is being achieved through expansion of existing

Figure 10-18. Coke plant of the Colorado Fuel and Iron Corporation in Pueblo, Colorado. Steel from Pueblo is important in serving the needs of the region. Iron ore from Wyoming and Colorado and coal, limestone, and fluorspar from southern Colorado supply the raw materials at fairly low freight costs. (Colorado Fuel and Iron Corp.)

endeavors and the entry into new fields of manufacturing and processing for both national and local markets.

IRON AND STEEL MANUFACTURING

Pueblo, Colorado, often called "the Pittsburgh of the West," has been a producer of iron and steel products since 1882, when a Bessemer converter was established there to supply the Denver and Rio Grande Western Railway with steel. The enterprise, although insignificant as compared to the giant steel industries of the Great Lakes or Pittsburgh, occupies an important position in the local economy.

RECREATION

The Western Interior High Plains Region offers little to attract the tourist. The climate tends to extremes. Winter temperatures may fall far below zero over the northern two-thirds of the region; summer days are long and hot. The landscape, for the most part, is a fairly flat and monotonous expanse of semiarid and subhumid plain.

Because of its geographical position between the densely populated Midwest and East, on the one hand, and the Rocky Mountain Province, on the other, the High Plains are spanned by a number of major Federal highways running in an East-West direction. Transcontinental railways and airways also cross the region. This transportation pattern, then, does result in some tourist trade, with the majority of tourists staying only overnight on their way to attractions outside the region.

A few points of interest within the Western Interior High Plains Region, however, attract thousands of visitors each year. These include: Carlsbad Caverns National Park of southeastern New Mexico, the dude ranch country of the Edwards Plateau in southwestern Texas, the Black Hills and the Badlands of South Dakota, and, to a lesser extent, the lakes of the Canadian Prairie Provinces. Of these, Carlsbad Caverns, the Black Hills, and the Badlands merit more attention.

CARLSBAD CAVERNS

Carlsbad Caverns National Park is located in semidesert country in the rugged foothills of the Guadalupe Mountains. The cave for which the park is named is of unusual magnificence and size. Although many miles of passages have been explored, development has been limited to the 750-foot and 829-foot levels reached by trail from the natural entrance and by elevator.

When first established, the park surface area was only 700 acres. It since has been enlarged and now contains nearly 46,000 acres of Federal lands. Within its bounds are many caves of scenic or archeological interest.

Carlsbad Caverns are unique because of the vast size of the underground chambers and their high ceilings — features brought about partly by rock collapse. No rock has fallen within the cave for thousands of years.

The bat spectacle. The bat flight is one of the park's great attractions. Flying out through the cave entrance each summer evening, incredible numbers of bats spiral upward, stream southward over the rim, and later separate into flocks for night foraging. Bats return from their nocturnal feeding just before dawn. These bats are quite harmless to human beings, in fact, they are beneficial to man since they destroy harmful insects and also provide guano—a valuable fertilizer.

THE BLACK HILLS OF SOUTH DAKOTA

These are the oldest mountains on the continent and the highest east of the Rockies. Mile-high lakes, pine-clad peaks, verdant mountain valleys, and formations of towering granite often appear in one setting. The Black Hills cover an area of about 6,000 square miles. They rise on an average about 2,000 feet above their base. The mass has an elliptical shape; its long axis, which extends north-northwest to south-southwest, is about 120 miles long, and its shorter axis about 40 miles long. Carboniferous and older stratified beds still cover the western half of the hills, and the beds have been removed from the eastern half, exposing the granite.

Mt. Rushmore National Memorial is a major tourist attraction. With great detail, sculptor Gutzon Borglum carved the busts of four great Americans at the base of Mt. Rushmore

Figure 10-19. Mount Rushmore, South Dakota. More than a million tourists a year visit the site to marvel at the sculptured likenesses of George Washington, Thomas Jefferson, Theodore Roosevelt, and Abraham Lincoln. (South Dakota Department of Highways)

in the Black Hills. In depicting the prudence of Washington, the vision of Jefferson, the energy of Theodore Roosevelt, and the compassion of Lincoln, the sculptor told a story of America, taking a mountain as his medium. Under his direction thousands of tons of granite were blasted away with dynamite. It is tremendous in concept, sculptured to the scale of men 465 feet tall.

THE BADLANDS

Sixty miles east of the Black Hills is the Badlands National Monument, a startling contrast to the cool forests, sparkling streams, and lush valleys of the hills. Desolate, arid, eerie—almost devoid of vegetation, the Badlands seemingly are no part of the green prairies that surround

them. The jagged peaks, turrets, spires, and steep canyons of colored ocean sediments, unadorned by plant or bush, could well be the setting of Dante's *Inferno.*

Sixty million years ago, the Badlands were the floor of a great salt sea. As the waters receded, marshes, dank lagoons, and jungle-like forests emerged. Gigantic animals of strange shapes and habits roamed the land: the saber-toothed tiger, the titanothere (large, odd-toed ungulates related to the rhinoceros) , the brontosaurus (a huge herbivorous dinosaur) , and the eohippus (a small four-toed horse) . As the area became dry and barren, the animals disappeared, but their bones were preserved in the earth on which they once wandered. Today scientists and amateurs alike search for bones

Figure 10-20. The Badlands National Monument, South Dakota, is a 170-square-mile area of castellated spires, color-banded cliffs, and sharp ridges—a classic example of erosion by wind and water. (South Dakota Department of Highways)

Figure 10-21. Aerial view of Denver, Colorado, with the Front Range of the Rocky Mountains in the background. Denver's great freight distance from the nation's mass markets has resulted in a gradual selection of high value industries such as instruments, precision equipment, and publication services, which are not hampered by costs of transportation. (Denver Chamber of Commerce)

and skeletons of these prehistoric animals in the Badlands, one of the world's most noted fossil beds.

POPULATION

Only four widely separated cities—Denver, Edmonton, Calgary, and Amarillo—have a population exceeding 100,000. Distance, then, is a major factor in the development of institutional arrangements in the Western Interior High Plains Region.

Denver (493,887) is the regional capital of the Western Interior High Plains. Its location, at the base of the Rocky Mountains, makes it a geographic focus of Federal agencies and military installations and a center of national activity in the development of oil and minerals. It is also an oasis of health and recreation activity to which thousands of vacationers and retiring people are turning.

Edmonton (226,002) is the most important rail and air center in the Canadian Northwest. The distribution point of a rich farm country and coal mining area, it is also the hub of a large fur trade.

Calgary (206,831), as well as being the trading center of an extensive stock raising and wheat region, is the base of supplies for surrounding mining districts. It has large grist and flour mills, grain elevators, brick and cement works, lumber mills, oil refineries, and packing houses.

Amarillo (137,969) is the commercial and industrial center of the Texas Panhandle. It is the supply center for oil and helium gas. The city is noted for its zinc smelters, foundries, grain elevators, oil refineries, and meat packing establishments.

Part IV | ROCKY MOUNTAIN COMPLEX

The American Rockies and the Western Canadian and Alaskan Mountains are grouped together in Part IV because they are lands of high relief with a low percentage of near-level land. Their land use patterns and population density differ greatly from the other sections of Anglo-America. Rugged terrain, severe climatic conditions, and inaccessibility over the greater part of this mountain complex preclude any dense settlement. Economic activities, for the most part, either are of an extractive nature—hunting, trapping, mining, logging—or they are devoted to grazing or recreational industries.

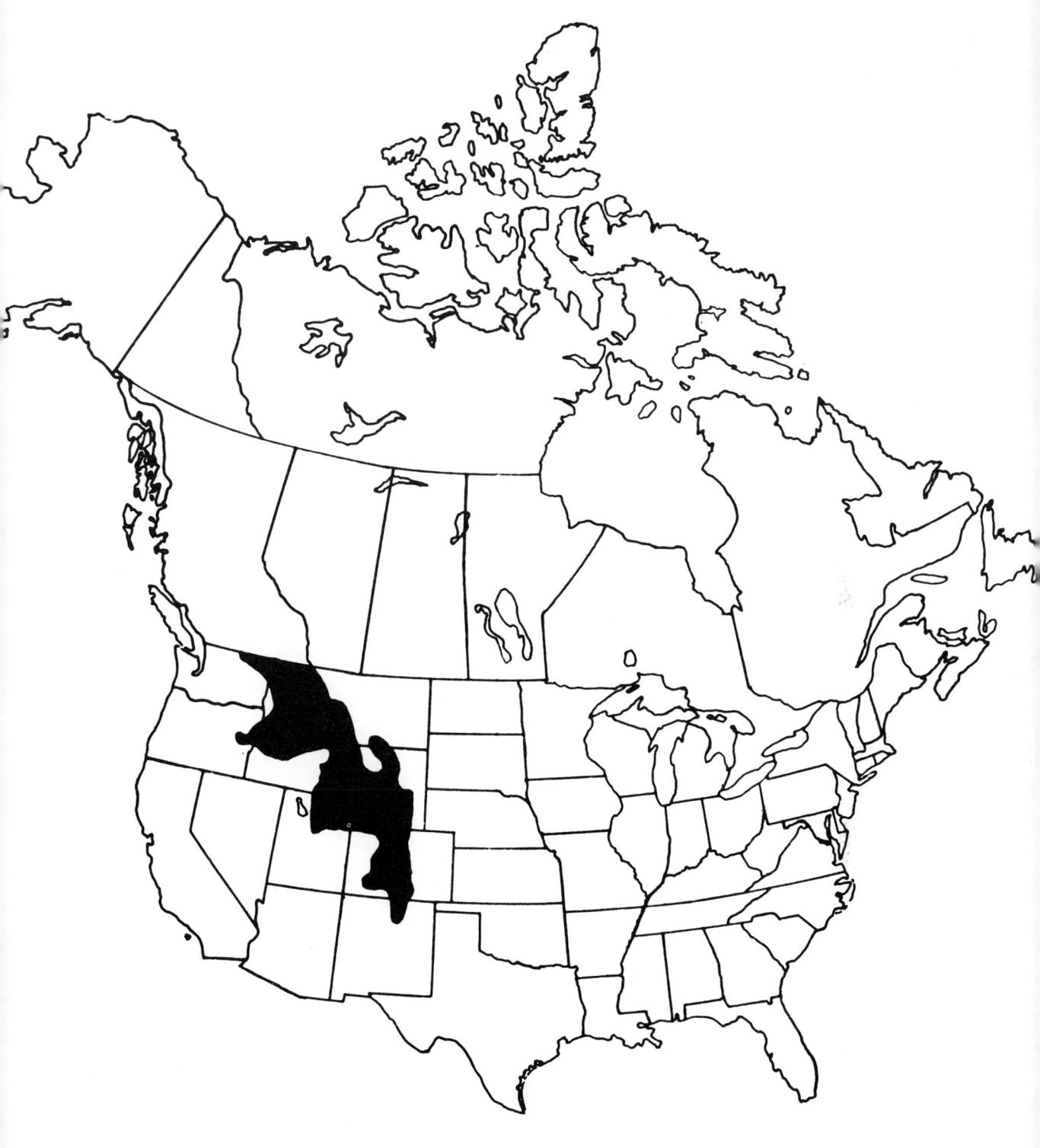

11 | *American Rockies*

(Relief map copyright Aero Service Corp.)

THE American Rockies Region includes: the western two-fifths of Montana, all of Idaho with the exception of the Snake River Plain and the Coeur d'Alene area, the western two-thirds of Wyoming, the northeastern corner of Utah, the central portion of Colorado, a small segment of north-central New Mexico, northeastern Washington, and a small portion of northeastern Oregon.

SURFACE FEATURES

The Rocky Mountain system within the United States may be divided into two parts: (1) the Southern Rockies, the north- and south-trending portion; and (2) the Northern Rockies, the northwest- and southeast-trending portion. Between these subdivisions of the system there is a marked orographic break in the form of high plains and tableland. North of this break are the Sweetwater Mountains and the much higher Wind River Mountains, which together form one of the culminating regions of the continent, since from them flow major tributaries of three of the great river systems of the country—the Missouri, the Columbia, and the Colorado.

SOUTHERN ROCKIES

The southern division of the Rocky Mountains, made up of a considerable number of quite distinctly marked portions, is about 600 miles in length from north to south and about half that in width. Its eastern edge is extremely well marked, with the ranges rising abruptly from a very gently sloping plateau.

Looking at this division in the most general way, one finds on its eastern edge a double range of mountains, well delineated in Colorado, where, between the parallels of 36° and 41° North, they enclose a system of high, basin-like valleys known as the North, Middle, and South Parks, and San Luis Valley. These valleys have elevations of from 6,000 to 10,000 feet above sea level; the enclosing ranges rise 3,000 to 4,000 feet higher. The first three "parks" are drained by the Platte, Arkansas, and Colorado Rivers, respectively, and in San Luis Valley—the largest of them all—the Rio Grande River originates. From here this river finds its way southward through New Mexico, having a well-defined lofty range on its eastern

side and less regular ranges on the west; these are the Front and Park Ranges of Colorado.

Front Range. The Front or Colorado Range proper begins in the north as a junction of the Medicine Bow Range and the Laramie Hills, which are low, inconspicuous ranges closing in the eastern and southeastern portions of the high plains and tableland separating the Northern and Southern Rockies. The Front Range south of 41° N. latitude is a broad, lofty mass, continuous as far south as Pike's Peak (about latitude 38° 45′ N.), where it runs out into the Great Plains.

The best-known summits in the Rocky Mountains are in this range—Long's and Pike's Peaks, both named in honor of early explorers of this region. Pike's Peak for some years gave its name to the whole region along the base of the Rocky Mountains now within the state of Colorado. During the early period of immigration to this region, it was known as "Pike's Peak country," and the immigrants were called "Pike's Peakers." Long's Peak (14,255 feet) and Pike's Peak (14,110 feet) are visible from the plains; they are conspicuous landmarks. Pike's Peak stands out especially, for it is more isolated than other Rocky Mountain peaks. Mount Elbert (14,431 feet) is the highest point in the Colorado Rockies but it lies too far from the eastern edge of the range to be visible from the plains.

The Continental Divide, which separates the waters flowing into the Atlantic from those emptying into the Pacific, follows the Front Range south as far as Gray's Peak. Then it is deflected westward for some 20 miles where it follows the Sawatch Range. In this deflection from the Front to the Sawatch Range, the divide passes between Middle and South Parks. The lowest pass in this part is the Tennessee, which leads from the head of the Arkansas River to the Grand River branch of the Colorado River. The pass is 10,418 feet above sea level.

Sawatch Range. The Sawatch Range is one of the highest and best-marked chains in the Rocky Mountains. It lies west of the head of the Arkansas; the dominating peaks along the whole range exceed 14,000 feet in elevation. In the Sawatch Range are such peaks as Princeton, 14,177 feet; Yale, 14,172 feet; and Harvard, 14,399 feet. A spectacular wonder is the

Figure 11-1. Pike's Peak (14,110 feet) as seen from the Black Forest near Colorado Springs, Colorado. The summit of Pike's Peak can be reached by automobile or cog train. (Colorado Springs Chamber of Commerce)

Mountain of the Holy Cross, the most northerly of the Sawatch peaks, named for the existence on its eastern flank of a large snow field lying in two ravines that intersect each other at right angles in the form of a cross conspicuous from a great distance in the summertime.

The Continental Divide follows the Sawatch Range to its southern end, at latitude 38° 20′ N., and then trends in a southwesterly direction for about 75 miles through a high region without any distinctly marked range. Here the divide turns and runs southeasterly to follow the crest of the San Juan Range, which has many points with an altitude of over 13,000 feet. This range forms the western border of the San Luis Valley, and from its northwestern end, going either north, northwest, or west, the explorer finds himself passing over a very elevated and exceedingly broken country, which finally merges in the plateau or mesa region of

western Colorado. Uncompahgre Peak (14,306 feet), a magnificent isolated summit of volcanic materials, is the culminating point of this region.

Elk Mountains. West of the Sawatch Range are the Elk Mountains, a volcanic mass of sharp pinnacles with its highest point, Castle Peak, reaching over 14,000 feet. Between the Elk Mountains and Uncompahgre Peak arise the various streams that unite to form the Gunnison Fork of the Grand River.

The Sangre de Cristo Range. This range, lying on the northeast side of the San Luis Valley, is almost a continuation of the Sawatch, having the same trend and similar rock formations. The two are separated by the broad depression known as Poncho Pass, about 9,000 feet above sea level.

Uinta Mountains. Directly west of North Park, and separated from it by the Park Range and by a broad belt of high mesa country, is the Uinta Range. The Uinta is unusual in that it has an east-west trend, and thus forms a sort of connecting link between the eastern edge of the Rocky Mountain system and its western border, of which the Wasatch Range is the most strongly marked division.

The Uinta Range starts from the eastern side of the Wasatch, heads eastward for a distance of 150 miles, and then dips and becomes lost in the mesas lying west of the Park Range. To the north is Bridger Basin, 6,000 to 7,000 feet above sea level, a continuation of the Laramie Plains.

The highest points in the Uinta Mountains are Kings Peak (13,498 feet) and Hayden Peak (12,473 feet) . The southern slope of this range is drained by the various affluents of the Green River, which unites with the Grand about 175 miles farther south to form the Colorado.

Wasatch Range. The Wasatch is one of the more conspicuous ranges of the Rocky Mountain system. Bordering the Nevada Plateau on its eastern side, it may properly be considered as forming the western limit of the Rocky Mountains. This range has a nearly north-south trend, rising with a bold escarpment to a height of over 12,000 feet in its southern portions, but falling off gradually toward the north. It is not recognizable as a distinct range beyond the Bear River. This stream starts on the northern slope of the Uinta Range in nearly the same latitude as Salt Lake City, and flows northward for more than 100 miles to 42° 40′ N. There it turns to follow an almost exactly opposite course, finds its way around the north end of the Wasatch Range, and empties into Great Salt Lake. In the loop thus made is a well-marked group of mountains called the Bear River Range, whose summits approach 10,000 feet in elevation.

The whole of the Wasatch area, which includes the range of that name and the parallel ranges and spurs on the east, is one of difficult and complicated topography. The Wasatch forms a connection between the northern and southern divisions of the Rocky Mountains and connects by spurs and irregular lines of elevation with the Wind River Range, the Tetons, and the Snake River Mountains.

NORTHERN ROCKIES

The northern division of the American

Rocky Mountains consists of a large number of ranges having a general northwest-southeast trend, although by no means regularly conforming to that direction. As a whole, the northern division of the Rocky Mountains is lower and less impressive in scenic terms than is the southern. As the traveler advances northwesterly, he finds less variety in the scenery, more uniformity in the elevation of the ranges, and almost no remarkable dominating peaks. Striking exceptions are the Wind River and Teton Ranges, the Yellowstone geyser region, and the peaks in Glacier Park.

The Montana and Idaho portions of the Rocky Mountains are more irregular in their development than the portions farther south. There is, however, a similar tendency in both areas to the formation of mountain-encircled

Figure 11-2. The Teton Range is one of the most striking mountain masses in Anglo-America. Grand Teton (below), highest peak in the range, is 13,766 feet above sea level. The southern portion of the range, including Grand Teton, is included in Grand Teton National Park. (Wyoming Travel Commission)

valleys locally called "parks" or "prairies." These parks are mostly destitute of timber, except for cottonwoods growing along the banks of streams. The mountains are partially covered with coniferous trees, not of great size but sufficiently large to be useful for ordinary building purposes. Some portions of the parks have a soil suitable for cultivation; others are covered with bunch grass and are well suited for grazing.

The Bitter Root is an important range that, in a portion of its course, forms the main divide between the headwaters of the Missouri and the Columbia Rivers and which, farther to the northwest, separates the waters tributary to the Snake River from those that help form the Clark Fork of the Yellowstone River.

The Clearwater Mountains lie to the west of the Bitter Root Range and unite the Rockies with the Blue Mountains. The latter are an important group of ranges that occupy a considerable part of the area lying west of the Snake River.

There are also various isolated groups of mountains lying to the east of the main range of the Northern Rockies, especially in Wyoming. Prominent among these are the Lewis Range in the extreme northeast and the Absaroka Range in the southeast. Still farther east of the Absaroka Range are the impressive Big Horn Mountains, separated from the Absaroka by Big Horn Basin, a broad structural depression that resembles a huge bowl.

CLIMATE

Because of the diversified topography within the American Rockies Region, there is a remarkable variety of climates, great differences often occurring within short distances. As far as temperatures and precipitation are concerned, altitude is, in general, a more potent factor of control than latitude. The entire region lies within the belt of prevailing westerly winds. Because of intervening north-south mountains to the west, especially the Cascade and Sierra Nevada Ranges, that rob the eastward-moving winds of much of their moisture, precipitation is light except at the higher elevations. There are alternating mountains and lower, comparatively flat intervening areas. These variations greatly affect the amount of precipitation, which varies from 40 inches in

the Bitter Root Mountains of Idaho to a low of eight inches in portions of southern Colorado.

At the lower levels of the western slope, wind movement is light and commonly of the mountain-and-valley type. At the summits of the mountains, the winds are generally from the west and are frequently very strong in winter and spring. High winds often interrupt traffic for considerable periods and their action in drifting and packing the snow is very important.

There is a tendency for a high pressure area to form in winter and to remain stationary for several days. When such a pressure distribution controls the weather, the sky is clear, the day temperatures are moderately high and uniform, and the nights are cold, though seldom excessively so except where the ground is covered with snow and where air drainage is poor. Night temperatures depend largely on the topography, with air drainage exerting a greater control than actual elevation. The lowest readings, from −40° to −54° F., are observed in the mountain valleys and parks, where the air tends to become stagnant. In such localities there is almost always an inversion of temperature during cold spells, when the greatest cold is generally confined to the lower strata of air whose upper limits do not always reach the higher altitudes. The mildest weather during the cold spells is found below, or near the mouths of, the larger canyons.

Because of the varied topography, the length of the growing season differs markedly from a minimum of 30 days in some parts to a maximum of 125 days in some of the more protected areas. At a number of stations at high altitudes in the interior, frosts or freezing temperatures are experienced in nearly every month of the year.

NATURAL VEGETATION

The Rocky Mountains are high, sharp, and rugged, their tops usually mantled with bare rocks. Timber line corresponds with air temperature zones. Tree species are controlled in their distribution almost wholly by the degree of insolation of the site, by the resultant temperatures, and by the closely related surface conditions of moisture. In Yellowstone Park,

Figure 11-3 Stanley Lake, Idaho, near the Salmon River. Note the dense pine stands along the lake and the timber line. (Ernie Day, Idaho Department of Commerce and Development)

for example, forests begin at 5,000 feet and disappear at 9,800 feet. On the Big Horn Mountains the limits of forest are 6,000 and 11,000 feet; in Colorado, 7,000 to 11,000 feet. In the lowlands bordering the Rocky Mountains, greasewood, sagebrush, and cactus are signs of aridity. The foothills are semiarid and dwarfed cedars and piñons appear as scattered clumps or groves of trees. Above the foothills open stands of pine, aspen, and, a little higher, spruce and fir trees predominate. Still higher on the mountain slopes are belts of juniper and cedars and many low-flowering plants and shrubs. Beyond the tree line is the zone of grasses, mosses, and large areas of bare rock.

EARLY SETTLEMENT

Within 50 years after the discovery of the New World by Columbus, Spanish explorers seeking gold and fabled cities pushed north from Mexico to the borders of present-day Colorado. Francisco Coronado led the venture. There was gold in Colorado but the Spaniards failed to find it—and failed to occupy the land. They did, however, send several expeditions into the region in pursuit of Indians. These Spanish adventurers named many of the mountains and rivers of southern Colorado; the musical names remain as a permanent heritage from old Spain.

French fur traders, pushing westward in the early 18th century, reached the Colorado country. But their influence was slight and their stay brief.

Not until the beginning of the 19th century did Americans appear on the scene. Meriwether Lewis and William Clark crossed the Rockies in 1805. Captain Zebulon M. Pike made an unsuccessful attempt in late November, 1806, to reach the summit of the peak that now bears his name. He was followed by other government explorers, including Major Stephen C. Long, Lieutenant John C. Fremont, and Captain John W. Gunnison.

Trappers and hunters such as Jim Bridger, Kit Carson, and Louis Vasquez were the real trail blazers of the Rocky Mountain West. In search of beaver skins they followed the streams and penetrated the most secluded mountain valleys.

The fur trade brought the first white men in numbers, for there was a ready market in England for beaver peltries for making hats. The traders and trappers, assisted by French rivermen, came up the Missouri. A few of them established fur trading posts, set out traps, and traded with the Indians. Others journeyed overland across the wide plains (along a route soon to be known as the Oregon Trail), crossed the Continental Divide, and went down to the Green River, where beaver abounded. Still others followed the older route to Santa Fe.

The era of the trapper lasted only about 30 years. By 1842, less than four decades after Lewis and Clark trekked to the Columbia River, the trail blazing period of the American Rockies was at an end.

MINING

SOUTHERN ROCKIES

Mining development accounts for the first extensive settlement of the Rocky Mountain West. A pioneer prospecting party from Georgia under Russell found placer gold during the summer of 1858 in the vicinity of what now is Denver, Colorado. Exaggerated accounts of the discoveries, when carried eastward, resulted in the Pike's Peak gold rush of 1859. Thousands of gold seekers hurried across the plains on foot, on horseback, in wagons, and even with handcarts and wheelbarrows. On reaching Cherry Creek and finding that the sands were not yellow with gold, many of the disillusioned adventurers started back for home. But on May 6, 1859, John H. Gregory discovered the Gregory lode, a vein of gold-bearing quartz near present-day Central City, Colorado. This discovery was followed by others in rapid succession. Mines were quickly devel-

oped on the branches of Clear Creek, in South Park, and across the Continental Divide on the branches of the Blue River.

During the decade following the Pike's Peak gold rush, development was slow. Refractory ore was encountered in the mines; the Civil War claimed citizens for soldiers; and an Indian uprising threatened the existence of the territory.

After surviving the ordeals of the early years, Colorado made rapid progress in her second decade of settlement. Railways were completed to the heart of the territory in 1870; towns were founded; new mines were opened in the San Juan area; and immigration increased greatly. These factors brought about the admission of Colorado to the Union on August 1, 1876.

During the 1880's, growth continued on a grand scale. Leadville, Aspen, Ouray, and other mining regions poured forth their wealth. Towns flourished as smelters for the reduction of ores were erected. Gold, silver, copper, lead, and zinc were the chief minerals produced.

Mining activities in Colorado have created over $2 billion in mineral wealth so far, and mining continues to be a leading industry. Today zinc is in first place as an income producer but lead still is mined from massive limestone replacements.

Climax, near Leadville, Colorado, produces 72 per cent of the world's molybdenum. The area has a reserve of over 450 million tons of ore, containing over two billion pounds of recoverable molybdenum; 50 million pounds of molybdenum were produced in 1960. Another molybdenum deposit has been opened about six miles from the town of Questa in the Red River mining district of Taos County in north-central New Mexico.

Colorado has immense deposits of coal that range from subbituminous to true anthracite. In the western part of the state vast shale deposits hold an estimated 300 billion barrels of oil.

Uranium. A new era for the uranium industry began in 1956, looking beyond the military market to the permanent, long-range, industrial atomic power market. The uranium industry has developed a pattern similar to that of most other metal industries. It runs a

Figure 11-4. Leadville, Colorado, was founded as a gold camp in 1860. Gold, silver, lead, zinc, copper, bismuth, manganese, and molybdenum are now recovered in this area. (F. L. Meredith, Meredith Studio, Leadville)

full gamut in size of operations, from the small independent mine or group of small mines, to moderate-size properties supporting a local custom mill, and to a large tonnage, integrated mining and milling operation.

Development of the Ambrosia Lake district, northwest of Grants, New Mexico, has made this the leading uranium source in the United States. The entire Grants area now represents nearly 70 per cent of estimated total United States reserves. Western Colorado is another of the nation's principal sources of uranium.

CENTRAL ROCKIES—WYOMING

Coal. A large part of the total land area in Wyoming is underlain by coal deposits, the extent of which is unknown. Coal-bearing strata underlie the Wind River, Green River, and Big Horn River Basins. Total production to date has amounted to 362.4 million tons.

Known reserves in the Big Horn Basin are in scattered, relatively small fields. There is both bituminous and subbituminous coal, but the major portion of the reserves is subbituminous. The known original mineable reserves are 581.64 million short tons. There have been about 12.6 million tons mined.

The Wind River Basin coal deposits, in central Wyoming, are not continuous and are lim-ited to small areas. The coal is subbituminous and the known mineable reserves are 875 million short tons.

The Green River area is a roughly triangular area within which are found coal deposits ranging from subbituminous to high-volatile bituminous. This section is one of the most important coal-bearing areas in the Rockies and has known reserves of 15,955 million short tons, over half of which is classified as bituminous.

No large-scale mining of coal has occurred to date within the American Rockies Province. By far the largest portion of coal production has been used by the railroads. Recently, however, diesel locomotives have put most of the coal-burners out of business. A much greater outlet appears certain with new industries and a greater population demanding coal for domestic heating, for the generation of electric power, and for use in processing for chemical derivatives.

Oil shale. Oil shale is a fine-grained sedimentary rock containing organic matter that yields oil when distilled. It is distinguished from certain coals by its content of more than 33 per cent ash.

In this sedimentary rock, formed in past ages like other underground deposits, a solid

Figure 11-5. Butte, the third largest city in Montana, is located over some of the largest mineral deposits in the United States. A maze of underground tunnels underlies the city proper. (Butte Chamber of Commerce)

substance called kerogen, or shale oil, is held. When shale oil is heated in a retort, it yields a liquid hydrocarbon resembling crude oil. Refining results in several valuable petroleum products—motor gasoline, jet fuel, and diesel fuel, for example. A ton of shale contains enough kerogen for five to 80 gallons of refined products.

The principal deposits of oil shale in the United States lie in Colorado, Utah, Nevada, and Wyoming. Some are in the Rocky Mountains, and some are in the plateaus to the west. The most important occurrences in the American Rockies Province are apparently limited to the central portion of the Green River Basin in Wyoming, where exploratory wells have indicated the presence, at depths ranging from 300 to 3,000 feet below the surface, of 35 to 262 feet of shale that will produce 15 gallons of oil per ton.

Both mining and treatment of shale require processes different from those used in handling petroleum. Oil from shale is not competitive at present with crude oil, despite some recent claims made by the industry. However, the vast oil shale deposits are now considered a part of the nation's liquid fuel supply. Estimated

reserves of recoverable petroleum from this source run as high as 300 billion barrels.

Petroleum. Wyoming has two major petroleum reserves within the American Rockies Region—the Elk Basin field, containing 104 million barrels of proven crude oil, and the Oregon Basin, with 56 million barrels. The Elk Basin field extends into southern Montana.

NORTHERN ROCKIES—MONTANA

Gold. The quest for gold brought a swarm of hardy prospectors into Montana after the discovery of rich placer deposits at Bannock in 1862. In the following years, the Alder Gulch strike, near the present site of Virginia City, attracted thousands more, who were rewarded during the next three years by more than $30 million in yellow treasure from the rich gravels. Last Chance Gulch (later to become Helena, the capital of Montana), Bear Gulch, Confederate Gulch, Blackfoot City, and other picturesque gold camps sprang up during the early 1860's.

Copper. The opening up of Butte, the richest hill on earth, in 1864, gave to Montana the title "Treasure State." The hill, first worked in 1864, made Butte a hell-raising camp, and then a city. Butte's workings yielded over $2.5 billion in 50 years. The city has 2,700 miles of tunnels, and is described as "a mile deep, a mile high."

Most important of recent developments in Montana's mineral industry is the Anaconda Company's current program to spend $140 million in expanding its Montana operations within a five-year period, in addition to its normal operating expenditures.

Illustrative of the implications of this program, as far as Anaconda's Butte operations are concerned, is the revelation that copper, long the principal metal taken from Butte mines, is now being extracted from ores of grades as low as one-half of one per cent. This brings into operation tremendous mineable ore reserves that previously were of too low grade for production under existing mining methods and market conditions.

Trial open pit runs in small bodies of ore have proved satisfactory and now, after approximately 30 miles of exploratory drilling, a large section of the Butte hill, containing over 100 million tons of ore, is marked out for open pit operations. This section is called the Berkeley Pit, after an old mine shaft. Mining began here in December, 1955; to date more than ten million tons of ore have been shipped to the smelter in Anaconda. Open pit operations will supplement underground mining, for as shafts go deeper, high-grade ores still are being found. The daily production from these sources is being increased as rapidly as possible along with that from surface mining.

Ore is concentrated and smelted at Anaconda, a city 25 miles northwest of Butte. Formerly, on arrival by rail at Anaconda the ore had to be pulled up a circuitous route to the top of a hill above the smelter, only 17 carloads at a time. The process was expensive and time consuming. To eliminate a nine-mile haul, a sectional conveyor belt 5,400 feet long has been installed to transport ore up the hill. A new plant was built for crushing the ore before it is conveyed to the concentrator bins located at the higher level.

Lead and silver. Lead ores have been produced on a small scale as a by-product of manganese and zinc mining in Butte and at a number of small properties outside of Butte. The lead ores are composed principally of galena and are smelted at the American Smelting and Refining Company plant at East Helena.

Silver was the most important metal in the second stage of the development of the Butte district, and Montana is still a leading producer of silver in the United States. At present the silver is recovered almost entirely as a by-product of copper, lead, and zinc ores from the Butte district.

Aluminum. The completion of the Anaconda Aluminum Company's 60,000-ton annual capacity aluminum plant in Columbia Falls in 1955, was another signal event in the expansion and diversification of Montana's economy. This Anaconda subsidiary is now producing aluminum, at capacity, for the manufacture of various aluminum products in many parts of the nation. Much of the aluminum made here goes to Anaconda's wire and cable plant at Great Falls, where other metal products also are produced. Raw material for the Columbia Falls plant is shipped by rail from Texas and Arkansas plants where bauxite from the Caribbean area is received for processing into alumina. Low-cost electric power is

directly responsible for the 450-man payroll at the Columbia Falls plant.

Phosphate rock. One of the largest mining projects in Montana is the Montana Phosphate Products Company's new development, between Garrison and Gold Creek, for mining phosphate rock. Reserves, as estimated by the United States Geological Survey, total 300 million tons and contain more than 70 per cent phosphate of lime, a boon to the fertilizer industry.

Significant also is the fact that phosphate rock contains fluorine and traces of vanadium, tin, boron, and uranium, and that some phosphatic shales contain oil. Future conditions may make it possible to recover many of these minerals.

Chromite. The American Chrome Company's operations at Nye in the Columbus-Red Lodge area account for 260,000 tons of ore annually. Fourteen thousand tons of concentrate are produced for the government stockpile. Further ore production possibilities are reported to exist in the Red Lodge area. Chromium is used in three industries—metallurgical, refractory, and chemical.

Tungsten. In the form of 60 per cent concentrate, tungsten has been shipped from Glen, Montana, to Salt Lake City for refining since 1953. The ore currently produced is low-grade sheelite, but a commercial deposit of richer tactite is reported to have been discovered recently at Wise River.

NORTHERN ROCKIES—IDAHO

Gold was first discovered in Idaho by Captain E. D. Pierce at Pierce City in 1860; this started gold rushes to Orofino, Pierce, Florence, Warren, and the Boise Basin. From the wealth prospectors found there, millions of dollars went to sustain the Union's needy treasury during the Civil War. Since Pierce's strike, Idaho has produced more than $1.5 billion in minerals, a large sum for a state with few more than a half-million inhabitants.

Two miners discovered the rich lead-silver lode that made Bunker Hill, near the Idaho-Montana border in the Kellogg-Wallace-Mullan area, a big name in mining. The famous Bunker Hill, Sullivan, Sunshine, and Morning mines have invested millions of dollars in present-day mining ventures.

Figure 11-6. The Bunker Hill-Sullivan zinc plant in the Coeur D'Alene area of northern Idaho, the focal point of the vast mining industry of Idaho. (Idaho Department of Commerce)

Until recently, 85 per cent of Idaho's minerals came from the region around Wallace. The Morning mine at Mullan led in zinc, and the Sunshine, largest silver mine in the United States, made Idaho first among the silver producing states.

The Coeur d'Alene district produces about 92 per cent of Idaho's silver, 87 per cent of the copper, 92 per cent of the lead, and 96 per cent of the zinc. The state, largely because of Coeur d'Alene's mineral wealth, is exceeded only by Missouri in lead production and by Montana in zinc output. Idaho is also an important producer of two metals that loom important in the national defense picture, cobalt and antimony.

AGRICULTURE

Physiography, as a direct and indirect agent, plays a dominant role in the agricultural development and utilization of the American Rockies Region. This is especially significant in the distribution of land used for crops, pasture, and forests. The temperature and the amount of moisture both are affected directly by the physical features, and the different soil groups are linked closely with the topography, temperature, and precipitation.

In general, the region's agricultural enterprises may be divided into two groups: (1) livestock, and (2) irrigated farming.

LIVESTOCK

The production of livestock is directly related to the condition of the range and therefore to the precipitation and general climatic conditions. Summer grazing takes place largely in the national forests. The park areas and some of the higher-altitude plateaus are also used during the season. Ranches usually are located within the mountain valleys or on the edge of the Great Plains. Sagebrush plains and grassy slopes at higher elevations favor summer grazing activity. Winter feeding from locally grown summer forage in the protected valleys is the common practice. A transhumance system is practiced widely throughout the region.

Grazing rights or permits are issued by the Forest Service on the basis of "commensurability," that is, on the basis of the amount of privately owned land available to the applicant.

The ranching economy has adjusted itself both in extent and practice to the possibilities of its physical setting. Although ranching is an important local enterprise throughout the province, it becomes increasingly more significant in the Northern Rockies Subregion and in the higher mountain valleys. The short growing season and susceptibility to frost during summer limit or rule out agriculture as such. Hence grazing represents the best adjustment to the environment.

Most ranchers keep both cattle and sheep. Cattle herds have increased considerably during the past decade, mainly because of market demand for beef and high selling prices. Normally, sheep outnumber cattle. According to ranchers, this is caused by the fact that sheep represent a "one-year crop;" that is, the lambs may be sold the year they are born, thus avoiding winter feeding. The mountain slopes are the summer ranges for the cattle and the higher Alpine meadows are especially suitable for sheep.

IRRIGATED FARMING

The irrigated lands are confined to a few watered valleys favored by local relief and protection from winds and frost. The parallel arrangement of mountain ranges in northern New Mexico continues across Colorado, giving rise to several high basins and valleys; in the Northern Rockies Subregion the ranges become numerous, with many intervening valleys.

Agriculture began during the mining period. Miners were forced to pay outrageous prices for food because, at first, the nearest agricultural-producing areas were as far away as 500 to 1,000 miles. The first settlers were literally forced to grow crops wherever water

and level land were available. In this way, a string of small farms developed, and hay, wheat, oats, potatoes, and other staple crops were cultivated. These enterprises were privately financed. Later, as the area became more densely populated, states within the region began to construct irrigation projects in an attempt to increase the acreage under cultivation. Finally the Bureau of Reclamation entered the picture. Under its supervision several large irrigation projects have made possible the reclamation of thousands of acres for intensive cultivation. One of the more recent developments is the Colorado-Big Thompson River Project. This diverts, by means of a 13-mile tunnel, 310,000 acre-feet of surplus water annually from the headwaters of the Colorado River on the western slope to northeastern Colorado on the eastern slope. Unlike most irrigation projects, the Colorado-Big Thompson is designed solely to provide additional or supplemental water for land already being irrigated.

San Luis Valley. The San Luis Valley in southern Colorado, a basin filled with alluvial fan deposits, is notable among the Rocky Mountain parks and valleys because of its size and importance in the local agricultural picture. Drained by the upper Rio Grande, it is about 100 miles long by 50 miles wide, and contains nearly 400,000 acres of cropland. Most of the crops grown are irrigated. The valley

Figure 11-7. Beef cattle in a corral on a ranch in Albany County, Wyoming. Saddles in the foreground testify to the fact that jeeps and pickup trucks have not entirely displaced the horse. (U.S. Department of Agriculture)

Figure 11-8. Hungry Horse Dam in western Montana. This dam, with a reservoir storage of 3,468,000 acre-feet of water, has irrigational, flood control, power, and navigational functions. (Bureau of Reclamation, U.S. Department of the Interior)

has over 3,000 artesian wells, but most of the irrigation water comes from streams, principally the Rio Grande. Because of the altitude, 7,500 feet in the center to 8,000 feet at the base of the mountains, only cool climate and frost-resistant crops are grown: hay (principally timothy, clover, alfalfa, and wild hay), potatoes, oats, wheat and barley, peas, and lettuce. Late lettuce (5,000 acres) is perhaps the most valuable crop in the valley, for it is worth more than $2 million a year.

The Upper Arkansas Valley. This valley, much smaller and a little higher than the San Luis, lies to the north of that area, over a low divide. It has about 25,000 acres in crops, mostly hay and small grains, all irrigated, in addition to 500 acres of lettuce.

Other valleys. Other notable irrigated basins in Colorado are South Park, Middle Park, and North Park. The land is used principally to supply winter feed (hay) for the cattle and sheep that graze in the national forests during the summer season.

In Wyoming, there are the Laramie and Carbon Basins, the Wind River and Bridger Basins, and the Big Horn Basin. Over half the irrigated land is in hay, principally timothy and native hay; over one-fourth in pasture; and the remainder in grain, mostly wheat, with a few hundred acres in potatoes.

In western Montana, there are a series of mountain valleys, some of which drain west into branches of the Columbia River and some east into the Missouri River and its branches. Of the total crop acreage in all these valleys, one-fifth is in wheat and over two-thirds in hay, mostly alfalfa. The hay is used to feed horses, cattle, swine, and chickens.

On the Pacific side of the divide most of the cropland is in a long trough that extends from the southern end of the Bitter Root Valley for 150 miles northward to Kalispell (for 25 miles its valley is occupied by Flathead Lake), and then northwestward 70 miles to the Canadian boundary, where it continues for 500 miles to near Fort George, British Columbia. The United States portion of the valley is drained by the Clark Fork River and the Canadian portion by the Kootenai, Columbia, and Fraser Rivers. This is one of the largest well-defined mountain valleys in the world. The width of the valley bottom between the steep mountain slopes seldom exceeds 20 miles, and does not average ten miles. In parts of this valley, particularly in Flathead County, Montana, crops may be grown without irrigation, but irrigation has been found desirable in most of the valley.

North of Flathead Lake there is little irrigation. In the Bitter Root Valley at the southern end of this trough nearly all the cropland and some of the pasture land is irrigated. The principal crops are hay and wheat. In addition, there is a considerable number of acres planted to oats and barley, and a few thousand acres are in potatoes and sugar beets. Most of the hay and grain (except the wheat) and the forage from millions of acres of range are consumed by dairy and beef cattle, sheep, swine, and chickens.

The Clark Fork of the Columbia River crosses this structural valley at Missoula, in a southeast-northwest direction. In this transverse valley along the Clark Fork are some 140,-000 acres of crops, mostly irrigated. Hay dominates, with the acreage of timothy and clover and wild hay exceeding that of alfalfa. In this narrower valley, with less crop acreage and more mountain range, beef cattle and sheep are important.

SUMMARY

Physical conditions will continue to limit the size and kinds of agriculture in the American Rockies Region. Distance from market and relative isolation tend to encourage production for local markets, since some staples may be produced in the area more economically than they can be shipped in from adjoining agricultural regions. One can anticipate, however, the use of additional range lands for cattle and sheep and the establishment of new irrigation systems as more industries are established to process the region's mineral wealth.

FORESTS

The Rocky Mountain forest is part of the Western pine region. Ponderosa, sugar, Idaho white, and lodgepole pines; Western larch; Engelmann spruce; white firs; and incense and red cedars are the most important species.

There are few forests in the Rocky Mountains at all that approach in density those of the Pacific Slope; nowhere in the Rockies are there individual trees as large as those on the slope. The trees of the Rockies usually grow most densely in the moist places at the foot of the ranges where the streams debouch, or in the ravines and gorges, or on the lower slopes. By far the most common deciduous tree throughout this region is the aspen, or quaking asp (often called cottonwood and, sometimes, poplar). This tree, almost worthless except for pulpwood, most commonly springs up to form dense thickets wherever the coniferous forest has been burned off. In various portions of the region there are scattered oaks, only here and there in sufficient quantity to be of importance. The black oak, the white oak, and a few other species dot the Southern Rockies Subregion. The most densely forested portion of the re-

gion, however, is the Northern Rockies Subregion.

The establishment of national forests within the American Rockies Region has withdrawn vast timberland tracts from commercial exploitation. Wilderness and wild areas in the national forests help preserve the natural beauty for all to enjoy. Timber stands also serve protective watersheds, preventing floods and providing water for large-scale irrigation projects. These factors, combined with a small local population, distance from large consuming centers, inaccessibility and poor quality of timber, and transportation costs have greatly limited the lumber industry. Exceptions occur in Montana and Idaho, where there are better stands of timber; they are consumed in large volume by the railroads and the mining industries.

MONTANA

One-fourth of Montana (over 22 million acres) is classified as forest land. Seventy per cent of the forest land is rated commercial; that is, suitable and available, now or prospectively, for timber production for industrial use. Estimated total volume in Montana's commercial forests is 56 billion board feet, or about 3.5 per cent of the national total. About one-half of this is Douglas fir and larch; other important species are Ponderosa pine, spruce, and lodgepole pine.

Large sawmills using lodgepole for lumber are in operation at Belgrade and Livingston; a new firm recently acquired 85 million board feet in the White Sulphur Springs area to supply a new mill; and the Forest Service is offering additional timber for a new operation in the areas of Butte and Deer Lodge.

Lumbering and wood products industries are beginning to play a dominant role in the economy on the eastern slope of the Continental Divide as they have for many years on the west, where forests occupy 81 per cent of the land area and furnish a large part of the local income.

Development other than lumbering, long sought after, is also being achieved. Most noteworthy is the construction of Montana's first pulp mill by the Waldorf Paper Products Company of St. Paul at a site near Missoula. Limited progress also has been made in other attempts toward more effective use of wood re-

Figure 11-9. Lower Falls in Yellowstone National Park, Wyoming. The park attracts over a million visitors a year. (Union Pacific Railroad)

sources. Plywood is produced in the Flathead area; prefabricated buildings of turned hollow logs are manufactured at Thompson Falls; and laminated building beams are constructed at Broadview. Toy stock, molding, and wood chips are made from scrap lumber produced at several sawmills in the state.

IDAHO

With one-third of its land area covered by forests, Idaho ranks fourth in the nation in volume of standing saw timber after Oregon, Washington, and California. Northern Idaho contains the nation's greatest remaining stand of white pine. Douglas and white fir, Alpine fir, Engelmann spruce, cedar, larch, and lodgepole pine stands also are important.

During the first half-century of lumbering in Idaho, the white pine and Ponderosa pine were the prime targets of the logger. The volume of mixed species cut was small in comparison to white pine and Ponderosa, because the cost of harvesting and marketing these woods was so much greater than their value as lumber. The demand for lumber increased to such an extent following World War II, however, that more and more of the so-called secondary trees are now utilized.

Like farmers and miners, the Idaho lumbermen are faced with the ever-present problem of high costs. Some of the contributing factors are distance from market, the constant menace of fire, and the inroads made upon the forests by destructive insects. Another cost problem is that involving stumpage. Ten years ago, prime standing timber ranged in price from five to ten dollars per thousand. Today, much of the prime stands are sold for from $30 to $40 per thousand.

RECREATION AND TOURISM

The tourist industry adds millions of dollars to the revenue of the states in the American Rockies Region. Colorado, Montana, and Wyoming list their tourist industries among the first three income producers. Thousands of visitors from many parts of the United States, and from other parts of the world as well, journey to the Rockies to camp, hike, hunt, fish, and prospect, or simply to enjoy its many scenic wonders. Fortunately the Federal government has set aside vast tracts for these purposes, administered by such agencies as the National Park Service, the Forest Service, the Bureau of Indian Affairs, the Bureau of Reclamation, and the Fish and Wildlife Service. Each of these government agencies performs valuable functions in maintaining and preserving the area's scenic beauty.

MAJOR TOURIST ATTRACTIONS

Rocky Mountain National Park, embracing 405 square miles of spectacular scenery, is easily accessible the year 'round over broad, paved roads. The park contains 14 massive peaks, including 14,255-foot Long's Peak. In the wildlife sanctuary are hundreds of species of flowers and animals, including elk and deer. The Hidden Valley Winter Use Area offers excellent skiing. The town of Estes Park, alongside

Lake Estes, at the park's eastern entrance, is a well-equipped, year-round resort area.

The Pike's Peak section, centering upon Colorado Springs and Manitou Springs, has long been an outstanding vacation area. Thrilling scenic drives include the Pike's Peak Highway and the Garden of the Gods to the north of Colorado Springs. The latter is an area where, because of folding and local faulting, red sandstone beds have been raised into a vertical position. Erosion has removed the weaker portions of sandstone, leaving the stronger portions to be weathered into fantastic forms.

Great Sand Dunes National Monument includes 46,034 acres of varicolored sand that lie in constantly shifting dunes and hills in the San Luis Valley, just west of the Sangre de Cristo Mountains.

Dinosaur National Monument, in northwestern Colorado and northeastern Utah, includes more than 250,000 acres of country untouched by civilization. Impressive formations have been fashioned by the Green and Yampa Rivers, which flow through deep, narrow canyons with precipitous, delicately tinted sandstone cliffs. These canyons are dark and forbidding, with sheer walls that reach a height of 3,000 feet. The western section of the area, soon scheduled to be a reservoir, contains great beds of dinosaur fossils.

Yellowstone National Park lies to the west of the Absaroka Range. Much of the park is a basin with a floor some 2,000 feet lower than the surrounding uplands. Yellowstone is world famous for spouting geysers, steaming pools, mountains, canyons, streams, lakes, forests, and waterfalls.

Yellowstone Park, the largest of the national parks, offers fishing, horseback riding, boating, and relaxation in the midst of magnificent scenery to over a million visitors a year.

Glacier National Park lies in the most rugged section of the Montana Rockies. It has more than 60 glaciers, 200 sparkling lakes, for-

Figure 11-10. Citadel and Fusilade Mountains in Glacier National Park, Montana. In the foreground is Upper St. Mary Lake; glaciers mantle the peaks in the background. (National Park Service)

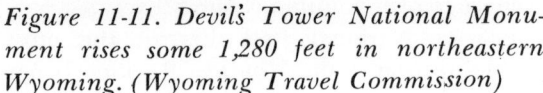

Figure 11-11. Devil's Tower National Monument rises some 1,280 feet in northeastern Wyoming. (Wyoming Travel Commission)

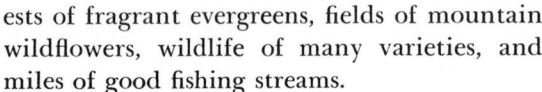

Figure 11-12. Sun Valley, Idaho, is rated one of the finest ski resorts in the world. (Sun Valley-Union Pacific)

ests of fragrant evergreens, fields of mountain wildflowers, wildlife of many varieties, and miles of good fishing streams.

Going-to-the-Sun Highway, a spectacular 50-mile drive running through the park, crosses the Continental Divide at Logan Pass. Lofty peaks, sheer cliffs, dense forests, distant glaciers, meadows of brilliant blossoms, shimmering lakes, inquisitive bears, and proud mountain goats make up its changing panorama.

Much of the park is accessible only by trail, and more than 1,000 miles of bridle paths and foot trails lead deep into the wilderness. The park, established in 1910, is the United States' section of Waterton-Glacier International Peace Park.

12 | Western Canadian and
Alaskan Mountains

ALEUTIAN ISLANDS

SCALE = 1:14,000,000
One Inch = 220 Miles
This Map is One-Half the Scale of the Main Map

(Relief map copyright Aero Service Corp.)

THE Western Canadian and Alaskan Mountains Region extends along the Pacific Coast in a belt about 400 miles wide from southwestern Alaska to southern British Columbia and western Alberta.

SURFACE FEATURES

The Canadian Rockies and the Mackenzie Mountains are its eastern ranges; to the west are the St. Elias Mountains and the Coast Mountains, in Alaska known as the Pacific Mountain Subregion, and including all of southern Alaska. Geologically, the Pacific Mountain Subregion is a continuation of the continental Pacific mountain system that can be traced through British Columbia into Alaska. At this point, the axis changes and sends two spurs in a southwesterly direction. One spur forms the Chugach and Kenai Mountains and reappears in Kodiak Island. The main spur forms the crescent of the Alaska Range and stretches over the Alaska Peninsula into the Aleutian Islands. The spaces between and within these parallel ranges are filled by the sea or form broad valleys and intermittent basins such as Matanuska Valley and the Copper River Basin.

The southeastern coastal portion of Alaska, consisting of many islands and a strip of narrow mainland, is sometimes called the Panhandle. It is separated from Canada by mountains that rise sharply from the water's edge to heights of over 9,000 feet. Among these mountains are found deep fiords—sea inlets with high mountain walls. This region has many glaciers and extensive spruce, hemlock, and cedar forests.

The south-central coastline resembles the southeast. North and parallel to the coast extends the 150-mile-wide Alaska Range, with numerous peaks exceeding 15,000 feet in elevation. One of these, Mt. McKinley, 20,300 feet, is the highest point in North America.

In the southwestern section for hundreds of miles along the narrow Alaska Peninsula and the chain of Aleutian Islands are volcanoes, glaciers, and slopes covered by moss, grass, and bush. Trees are nonexistent. The Aleutians are like stepping stones leading westward toward the Komandorskie Islands and the Kamchatka Peninsula of Siberia.

The main topographical features of British Columbia are the high parallel mountain ranges at each side of the province, the Rockies to the east and the Coast Mountains to the west, separated by a region of tablelands and low mountains that is 200 to 300 miles wide. Along the western base of the Rockies is the Rocky Mountain Trench, a pronounced feature of British Columbia topography, in which lie the headwaters of some of the province's greatest rivers—the Kootenai, Columbia, Fraser, and Peace. West of the great trench lie the Columbia mountain system in the south and the Cassiar and Omineca systems in the north.

The Yukon Territory is a region of hills and mountains separated by a network of large valleys. The main feature is a great basin-like area called the Yukon Plateau, which is drained by the Yukon River and walled by mountains on the north, east, and southwest. Two smaller basin-like areas drained by the Porcupine and Peel Rivers lie to the north (Central and Northern Alaskan Mountains and Valleys Region) ; a third, drained by the Liard River, lies to the southeast. Surrounding these basins are the St. Elias Mountains and the Coast Mountains in the southwest and the Mackenzie Mountains on the east. Ogilvie Range, a western spur of the Mackenzie Mountains, forms the watershed between the Yukon and the Peel and Porcupine Rivers. To the north the Porcupine Basin is separated from the Arctic Ocean by the Richardson and Buckland Ranges, which are northwest spurs of the Mackenzie Mountains (Central and Northern Alaskan Mountains and Valleys Region) .

On the northeast of the Yukon Plateau, the Mackenzie Mountains, one of the least known areas of Canada, form a barrier of ridges similar in structure to those of the Rocky Mountains from which they are separated by the broad embayment of the foothills and great plains along the valley of the Liard River. The loftiest sections are situated near the headwaters of the Snake River, a tributary of the Peel, and are reported to contain peaks more than 10,000 feet high and Alpine glaciers. Their westward spur, Ogilvie Range, has similar structure, but its peaks are not known to be more than 8,000 feet high and no glaciers have been found in it.

Figure 12-1. Surprise Glacier, Alaska. Knik Glacier is in the left foreground, Lake George in center background. (U.S. Department of Agriculture)

The plateau of the Yukon contains the best-known and most developed part of the territory. It is an area of rolling uplands whose summits show marked uniformity of elevation over broad expanses, although in many places this pattern is interrupted by isolated mountains and ranges, among which are the Dawson, Big Salmon, and Pelly Mountains. These mountains have few peaks more than 7,000 feet in elevation. A broad down-warped depression in the surface of the upland follows the central-northwest line of the plateau. A network of main valleys is deeply trenched from 1,000 to 2,000 feet below the upland surface. The valleys of the main rivers spread out in a great branching system connected by similar large valleys occupied by small streams. Several great valleys trend northwestward through the plateau, followed in different parts by different major streams. The greatest of these valleys extends through the territory from the Liard River Valley to the Yukon River Valley northwest to Dawson. It is occupied in part by the Liard, Pelly, Stewart, Klondike, and Yukon Rivers. Another great valley, the Shakwak, extends from Kusawa Lake northwest along Kluane Lake. To the northwest, the plateau continues on into Alaska. To the southwest,

it slopes upward and abuts against the Coast Mountains.

The Yukon River has played a vital part in the development of the Yukon, although the territory includes only the upper reaches of the river. The volume of the Yukon is less than that of many other rivers of the same length because of the semiarid climate of most of its drainage region. Its head streams, rising in mountains, gather volume quickly, but lose their gradient as they reach the plateau. This has resulted in the formation of an amazing branching system of navigable waterways. From Whitehorse, situated only 110 miles by rail from Skagway on the Alaskan coast, a river steamer more than 200 feet long, carrying several hundred tons of freight, can navigate to the Bering Sea without serious interruption by rapids. Smaller steamers have navigated over 1,400 miles of this river system, all within the Yukon Territory. A still greater mileage of smaller streams is navigable to suitable riverboats.

An area of some 30,000 square miles of the Northwest Territories, west of the Mackenzie River and between the Peel on the north and the Liard on the south, forms part of the great Cordilleran section of western Canada. The Mackenzie Mountains, which lie partly in this section and partly in the Yukon Territory, are made up of ranges trending in a northwest direction and ranging in elevation up to more than 8,000 feet, with a relief, where explored, of 3,000 to 4,500 feet. The drainage of the area is to the Mackenzie River; the chief streams are the Arctic Red River, the Carcajou, the Keele (formerly the Gravel), the Root, the North Nahanni, and the South Nahanni, the last of which empties into the Liard. All these streams have steep gradients. On the Keele River, where the belt is widest, the high mountains lie about 50 miles from the Mackenzie, and between them and the Mackenzie Lowland is a zone of foothills about 3,000 feet in height. Farther south at the "Great Bend" of the Mackenzie near its junction with the South Nahanni, the mountain front is an abrupt, unscalable escarpment, the top of which is 2,000 to 3,000 feet above the valley plain.

Many peaks in western Canada rise to over 11,000 feet. Mt. Logan (19,850 feet), in Yukon Territory, is the highest point in Canada.

CLIMATE

Any mountainous region is likely to have within its borders great differences in weather and climate. The Western Canadian and Alaskan Mountains Region is no exception, although in a broad sense one might consider the climate throughout to be of the temperate marine type, with the exception of the inland portion. From Puget Sound north to the Bering Sea, winds from the ocean moderate the coastal climate nearly all year, so that extremes in temperature are rare. Average January temperature readings tend to be only slightly below freezing along portions of the coastline exposed to seaborne breezes. Minimum temperatures below 0° F. are rare and summer days with readings above 90° are few.

Farther inland, however, the ameliorating effects of the sea are not as pronounced, and winters are much more severe than along the coast. Inland valleys separated from the ocean by steep mountains are likely to have weather typical of continental locales. Winters tend to be long and fairly dreary anywhere within the region; during winter one storm follows another, particularly near the coast.

Precipitation, too, varies markedly within the region. Exposure to the moisture-laden winds blowing off the Pacific is the number one prerequisite to heavy precipitation, which, at low elevations near the coast, usually is in the form of rain. Thus, a windward slope might receive 175 inches annually, while the leeward side of the same range might suffer from drought, with less than 20 inches. Even coastal points have large annual differences. Haines, for instance, averages 56 inches, while nearby Skagway has only 27 inches. Cordova, on the Pacific, has 145 inches, and protected Anchorage, 14 inches.

The climate of the Yukon Territory is characterized by extremes in temperature and very moderate precipitation. Continuous daylight prevails from the middle of May to the first week in August. Although winters are long and cold, low temperatures are borne with less discomfort than in other parts of the North because of the absence of high winds and the dryness of the atmosphere.

In the central and southern parts of the Yukon, the climate inclines to aridity. As a result, there is a variation of the flora on the northern and southern slopes of the hills. Whereas the flora on the southern slopes is limited to such species as brush and sage grass, the northern slopes are well wooded and support Alpine and Arctic flora.

The extreme variation in the annual range of temperature runs from 125 to 160 degrees —an average of 142 degrees. The maximum recorded at the Dawson Meteorological Station is 92° F. and the minimum, —68°. The average precipitation is 12.8 inches per year; the greatest precipitation on record is 17.9 inches, and the least, 9.3 inches.

AGRICULTURE

First-class agricultural land in the region is limited and its use varies from a subsistence level in the Yukon and northwest British Columbia to commercial fruit farming in the Okanogan Valley and vegetable farming in the Matanuska Valley. The three major agricultural areas are: (1) the Okanogan and Kootenai Valleys, (2) the Matanuska Valley, and (3) the Kenai Peninsula.

OKANOGAN AND KOOTENAI VALLEYS

These dry, hot, interior valleys are ideally suited to irrigation farming of tree fruits and vegetables. Fruit growing is a specialized enterprise and the prosperity of the area is dependent to a large extent upon the fruit output.

Apples are the most important of the commercial fruits in Canada; British Columbia normally produces about 45 per cent of this crop. Ten acres is the usual size for orchards in the Okanogan Valley and the western Kootenai. The first carload of apples was shipped from the Okanogan in 1898; beginning with that casual experiment, a business has developed that now absorbs an average of six million boxes annually. Penticton was the site of the first orchard. It is now the fruit center of the Okanogan Valley. Vernon, to the north of Penticton, is also important for the growing, packing, and shipping of fruit.

Pears and various berries and soft fruits are grown in commercial quantities. Canning and processing industries have developed in the fruit growing districts and, although the importance of the processing markets depends

Figure 12-2. Fruit farms in the Okanogan Valley, near Okanogan Falls, British Columbia. A large portion of Canada's apple crop is grown in this fertile region. (Canadian Government Travel Bureau)

upon the type of fruit, they provide a valuable outlet for substantial proportions of most Canadian fruit crops.

The northern Okanogan and the Salmon Arm districts are ideally suited for mixed farming. In the central interior a huge tract is devoted to cattle raising. These cattle ranches vary in size from whole sections of 640 acres to several sections, often with rented grazing land in addition.

YUKON

Although agriculture cannot be classed as one of the primary industries of the Yukon Territory, field crops, including cereals, fodder, and vegetables, are grown with considerable success. Since the principal industry of the territory is mining, agricultural development is determined by the volume of mining operations.

Wheat, oats, and barley are grown in a number of localities as far north as Dawson. Excellent hay crops—timothy, red top, and brome grass—are cultivated for the domestic market. Alfalfa, white Dutch clover, red clover, sweet clover, and fodder corn also are raised.

The Yukon excels in small gardens, and most of the vegetables normally consumed in the territory are home grown and of excel-

lent quality. Remarkable results have been achieved in growing potatoes, particularly in the vicinity of Dawson and Mayo.

Some cattle, hogs, and poultry are raised, and a few small dairy farms are operated successfully.

MATANUSKA VALLEY

Agricultural activity began on a subsistence level in the valley about 1900. During the late 1920's and early 1930's, the Alaska Railroad promoted additional settlement. A major impetus came with the 1935 colonization of the Matanuska Valley, which had its roots in the great depression of the 1930's. At that time, some 202 new families entered the valley. The colony was backed by nearly $5,400,000 worth of credit. This spurred land clearing and the building of houses, barns, and storages. Only a few of the original colonists stayed on their places, which generally were laid out as 40-acre subsistence farms. Their improvements and the transfer of credit privileges to their successors made the valley what it is today.

The important thing about the colony was its credit feature, for never before had credit been available for farming in Alaska; no other farm region in the state has enjoyed comparable assistance. Out of this colony arose a farm community large enough to support its own services. Crops were harvested in sufficient volume to permit fairly effective marketing.

This nucleus of productive farms emerged shortly before World War II. Following a great expansion of market opportunities created by the construction of huge defense installations in the vicinity of Anchorage, the Matanuska Valley burgeoned as the major food producing area of Alaska. Without this market development, the valley might have remained in a state of slow stagnation—a collection of low income, subsistence farms. And without the colony and its long-term credit, farming could not have grown, as it later did, in response to market demands. The colony provided a firm base for Alaska's present-day farm industry.

Farm ownership and occupancy in the Matanuska Valley is changing rapidly. The lure of high-paying jobs created by defense construction has attracted many talented people who might otherwise have made good farmers. A rapidly increasing population created temporary booms in land values that have encouraged land sales. Together with the extreme immaturity of the Matanuska Valley's agricultural industry, these factors make for a rapid turnover in occupancy. New farmers, rather than old farmers, are the rule in Alaska. Only a few farms have been retained through the second generation of a single family.

Farmers increased their average holdings from 184 acres in 1949 to 247 in 1954. By purchase, land clearing, and, most of all, field rental, they increased their cropland average from 47 to 82 acres.

The basic trend in the area is toward specialized dairy farming, with potatoes and vegetables growing as an income supplement. The greatest percentage of land is in hay, silage, and seeded pastures.

Anchorage farmers usually are included with Matanuska Valley farmers when agricultural regions of Alaska are discussed. Major differences in farming concern land values and distance from market. Land is more valuable near Anchorage as the result of a growing demand for house lots and industrial sites.

Anchorage farmers receive about eight per cent of Alaska's farm income. Over half of this is from potato and vegetable sales. Egg and poultry sales are second as sources of income. Several hog ranches are based on a garbage-feed program utilizing waste from nearby military mess halls.

THE KENAI PENINSULA

Persistent interest in farming is noted among people living south of Anchorage in Alaska's Kenai Peninsula. There are three major areas of agricultural activity: (1) between Homer and Ninilchek, where beef is raised; (2) around Kasilof, where part-time retirement farms are common; and (3) the Sadotna-Kenai neighborhood, comprised mostly of new homesteads taken up by veterans since World War II.

Most foods grown on the Kenai Peninsula are marketed locally or consumed on the farm. Seward is an important market. Some eggs and beef find an outlet in Anchorage. New defense construction near Kenai promises additional market opportunities.

OTHER AREAS

Scattered sites favored by grass cover and fair accessibility support beef cattle and sheep enterprises in the Aleutians and on Kodiak Island. Some 9,000 head of sheep and 2,500 head of cattle are reported in these areas. At several ranches, sheep and cattle are able to graze all year in the temperate climate made possible by the westerly winds blowing across the relatively warm North Pacific waters and the Japan Current. Most ranchers put up some wild hay or silage to carry their stock through

Figure 12-3. The Matanuska Valley south of Palmer, Alaska, with the Talkeetna Mountains in the background. (Alaska Agricultural Experimental Station)

occasional severe winters. Others buy corn or concentrated feeds to supplement grass or for emergency needs. Transportation is difficult; the majority of sites are serviced by nonscheduled air carriers or boats.

In southeastern Alaska most foodstuffs are grown near populated areas, especially north of Juneau. In order of importance these foodstuffs are: milk, eggs and poultry, beef, potatoes, and other vegetables. High rainfall and generally wet conditions favor cool season vegetables. The small amount of cropland is used mostly for potatoes, vegetables, pasture, and roughage. Native hay from tideflats is cut for dairy cattle feed. Some beef cattle feed on native grass almost entirely. Dairymen preserve available roughage as silage, and do not depend on local grains that mature and ripen very slowly. Many dairy farms lack cropland so that some roughage, as well as grain, has to be imported. Both Canadian milk and that from other American sources offer severe competition.

FISHING

Commercial fishing is an important industry along the coasts of British Columbia and Alaska, and canned salmon is easily the leading product. Halibut, herring, crab, and fresh and frozen salmon also bring in a considerable revenue each year. Other commercial catches include: tuna, cod, sole, clams, oysters, and whales. This area of the Pacific is one of the world's great fishing grounds.

BRITISH COLUMBIA

The coast of British Columbia is so deeply indented with long, sinuous inlets that actual measurement would reveal something like 7,000 miles of coastline. Between the coast and the sea are many islands, the peaks and plateaus of a submerged mountain chain that forms a breakwater against the direct onslaught of the Pacific. These islands offer thousands of miles of safe, sheltered waters—vast feeding grounds that harbor myriad salmon, halibut, and cod, and are visited regularly by great schools of herring.

With these advantages, it was only natural that commercial fishing would become a basic industry. Almost half of Canada's total fish-eries wealth is taken in the waters off British Columbia. Salmon are so high in food value and so admirably adapted to the process of canning that an enormous trade has been developed. For the most part, the fish are taken with lines and nets; normally 9,000 boats and 19,000 to 20,000 fishermen and shore workers are employed. Swift carriers attend the salmon fishing fleets and hurry the salmon to canneries while they are still fresh and in full flavor. The canneries are efficient and scrupulously clean. In large canneries, fish are handled exclusively by machines.

Herring fishing, although of comparatively recent growth, is now second in value to salmon. The fish are processed in reduction plants for conversion into oil and meal, the latter for use in feeding stock and poultry. Herring oil finds a market with manufacturers of soaps, paints, and food products.

British Columbia's fisheries are highly productive and splendidly organized, and some of the more important of the fisheries have been exploited to the point where further development is likely to be slow. The value of fisheries products in some years in British Columbia has reached $83 million. There are many other species of fish that have not been exploited to the same extent as salmon and herring, and in this direction lie the best opportunities for expansion.

ALASKA

The principal industry of Alaska is catching and processing fish; it forms the basis of the state's wealth. The total wholesale value of fisheries products prepared for market since Alaska was purchased by the United States in 1867 passed the $2 billion mark in 1950, a sizable figure when compared with the purchase price of $7.5 million paid for Alaska. The value of fishery products annually prepared for market averages in the neighborhood of $100 million, with a return estimated at $28 million to the fishermen. Of the various fish, salmon are the most valuable, accounting for about 90 per cent of the total catch. Other important commercial fish are halibut, herring, sablefish, crabs, shrimp, and cod. The industry employs approximately 30,000 workers.

One of Alaska's major problems has been the steady decline for many years of the salmon

Figure 12-4. A salmon purse seiner working near one of the many islands off the coast of Alaska. Fishermen must work long hours during the short summer season to balance out the slack winter season. Boats range from elaborate vessels with large crews, capable of cleaning and processing the catch, to small ships such as the one shown in the photograph. (E. P. Haddon, U.S. Fish and Wildlife Service)

catch, even though more men and equipment were concentrated in the salmon fishing areas. The decline has increased costs, lowered profits, and reduced the industry to a state where drastic measures are necessary if it is to survive. Research and regulation offer hope for gradual restoration of the earlier volume.

The first legislation to control Alaskan fisheries was enacted by Congress in 1906. The basic law was rewritten and enlarged in 1924 by the White Act, which forms the basis on which regulations are promulgated. Biological investigations were started about 1924, and continue to be carried on, in much greater scope, today. Because of the constant shifting of prevalent species, the regulations are revised extensively each year.

Alaska's fishery resources offer a number of other opportunities, both in new species of fish and in new treatment of species already caught commercially. For example, there has been very little use of bottom fish, which are found along the entire coast. Shellfish production has increased but can be developed still further. There is additional potential in the processing of fish waste.

Approximately 120 canneries operate in Alaska. A small number of them are floating and hand-packing canneries, but the great majority are modern land operated plants using automatic machinery. These plants require a large capital investment.

WILDLIFE

Among the important resources of the Yukon Territory is its mammalian wildlife, which includes such big game as mountain sheep, moose, caribou, and bear. The more widely known big game districts include a large area extending northward from Kluane Lake to the Upper White and Donjek Rivers; the section adjacent to Teslin Lake in the southern part of the territory; and areas near the Big Salmon, the Macmillan, the Ross, and the Stewart Rivers. Game is also found in the area between the Yukon, the Porcupine, and the Peel Rivers.

Mountain sheep are numerous in the Yukon. Among the species that occur is the Dall, or white mountain, sheep—one of the most prized trophies of hunters. Dall sheep are found principally in the southwestern and northern parts of the territory. Mountain sheep, ranging in color from gray to brown, are also found in various sections of the Yukon. They are closely related to, and intergrade with, the Dall sheep. Mountain goats occur in a few districts of the southern Yukon.

The Alaska moose, largest and darkest of the species, reaches superb dimensions in the Yukon. Moose range in the lowlands and are numerous in the White River area. Caribou include the Osborn and Stone varieties. The Osborn caribou intrudes from the Cassiar Mountain district of British Columbia and is found mainly in the southern Yukon. The Stone caribou, a large variety of the barren ground caribou, occurs in the Upper White River section and northward through the Peel River and Porcupine River areas to the Arctic.

Grizzly, black, and brown bears are fairly numerous. The polar bear is seen occasionally on the Arctic Coast, where the ringed seal, white whale, timber wolf, northern gray wolf, and tundra timber wolf also are found.

Fur bearers include beaver, ermine, Alaska mink, marten, wolverine, muskrat, lynx, and white Arctic fox. Red, silver, cross, and black varieties of fox also abound.

FORESTRY

Climate and soil conditions on the Pacific Coast are particularly suitable for tree growth, and the forests of this region display magnificent stands of Douglas fir, hemlock, spruce, and cedar.

BRITISH COLUMBIA

The forests of British Columbia produce an annual wealth of more than $500 million. In recent years, the industry has been capable of supporting well over 60,000 persons and the payroll tops $200 million a year.

Of British Columbia's 234,403,000 acres, approximately 90 million, or 38 per cent, are economically suitable solely for the growth of forests. Of the remainder, only a little over 6.5 million acres are classified as arable land. This leaves some 135 million acres composed of water, muskeg, swamp, and rock. Because of this, the forest industries have attained a dominant position in the provincial economy; they account for over 40 cents of every dollar earned. From 1949 to the present, the average annual cut has amounted to nearly five million board feet.

Only a world-wide market can furnish sufficient demand to keep this colossus running at anything like capacity. Since 1949, and in spite of monetary difficulties in Europe and Britain, British Columbia's lumber exports to foreign countries have averaged a healthy two million board feet per year.

Douglas fir, Western hemlock, spruce, and Western red cedar are the leading commercial species. Sawmills in British Columbia manufacture about 55 per cent of the lumber produced in Canada, and 65 per cent of national exports of planks and boards and 16 per cent of national exports of pulp and paper originate from this province.

British Columbia's forest survey program, jointly sponsored by the Dominion and provincial governments, indicates that, in general, the forests of British Columbia are not being overcut at present. However, this does not dispel the fear of overcutting, because almost 80 per cent of the annual cut is concentrated in the great rain forests of the coastal districts. Here, the forests—the best softwood forests in the Commonwealth—most assuredly are being overcut and, in instances, very seriously so. The imbalance of the industry is the main concern. Interior forests could not begin to support the huge coastal operations as presently conceived. The government has pursued an energetic program of artificial reforestation of the denuded coastal areas since 1933. A new forest nursery has been opened in the interior as well. Probably the most significant steps toward putting the forests on a sustained-yield basis are legislative: (1) the Forest Management Licenses, (2) the Public Working Circles, and (3) the Farm Woodlot Licenses. There are also amendments to the Taxation Act to encourage the growing of trees as a crop. All these instruments are based on the principle of cutting no more than is grown. Only by the growing of trees as a crop to ensure the perpetuation of British Columbia's greatest resource can her present high level of industrial activity and prosperity be expected to continue.

YUKON

The forests of the Yukon are in the Boreal forest region of Canada, in which not only the number of tree species is few, especially toward its northern border, but the area covered by forests and the rate of growth is relatively small. Although the Yukon Territory south of the Porcupine River may be classed as forested country, most of the forests occur in the valley of the Yukon River and its tributaries and on the upper courses of the Peel River. The Arctic tundra or treeless zone commences north of the Porcupine watershed.

This is a mountainous country with ranges and plateaus isolated by wide valleys and depressions in which occur forests with a generally open character. White spruce forms the bulk of the stands, mixed with aspen poplar, balsam poplar, and Alaska white birch. Black cottonwood is found in the southern river valleys. Lodgepole, or Western jack pine, occurs in small groves with a local distribution. Black spruce and tamarack are found in swamps and low places. Toward the tree line, which reaches the 4,000-foot elevation, Alpine fir becomes dominant.

For about 30 years after the gold rush of 1898, nearly all lumber used in the Yukon Territory was of local manufacture. A number of sawmills operating at Dawson and other points along the Yukon River supplied the lumber used in the construction and building of Dawson, as well as the large quantity required for the construction of flumes and sluice boxes necessary for the mining industry. These operations have almost exhausted the supply of timber suitable for sawn lumber in the area close to the Yukon River, and since 1930 the requirements of Dawson and Whitehorse have been met by shipments from British Columbia.

White spruce and birch are used extensively as fuel, and poplar is substituted where they are unavailable. In the southern part of the territory, jackpine is plentiful and forms an important fuel supply. Wood is used as fuel in all steamboats operating on the Yukon River and its tributaries; over a period of 60 years, a very large quantity has been consumed. The average consumption of an ordinary river steamboat for a round trip from Whitehorse to Dawson is 150 cords of wood.

Figure 12-5. A logging tug in Alaska. Tidewater location of forests makes logging easier in southeastern Alaska. (U.S. Department of Agriculture)

COASTAL ALASKA

Alaskan coastal forests offer the most immediate and important prospect for resource development. The state's two national forests comprise 20,883,400 acres along the coast from Portland Canal on the south to Cook Inlet on the north. The Tongass National Forest (16,073,200 acres, containing about 78 billion board feet of commercial timber) covers most of southeastern Alaska. The Chugach National Forest (4,810,200 acres with an estimated seven billion board feet) includes the coastal area surrounding Prince William Sound and the eastern half of the Kenai Peninsula. This timber is about 74 per cent hemlock and 20 per cent spruce, with small quantities of Western red cedar and Alaska cedar, all close to tidewater.

Figure 12-6. Juneau, Alaska, with the Tongass National Forest in the background. Extensive areas of softwood trees are one of Alaska's prime resources. (U.S. Department of Agriculture)

Outside capital is interested in southeastern Alaska's timber. American Viscose and Puget Sound Pulp and Paper formed the Ketchikan Pulp Company in 1954 and constructed a $52 million dissolving plant at Wards Cove, Alaska, six miles northwest of Ketchikan. The company has a 50-year cutting contract in the Tongass National Forest.

The Ketchikan mill is the opening wedge to a great industrial development of the area's resources. Other lumber companies with capital investment in Alaska's forests are: (1) Pacific Northern Timber of Portland, Oregon; (2) Alaska Pulp of Japan; and (3) Georgia Pacific Plywood.

MINING

During the 80 years following Captain James Cook's visit to the west coast of Vancouver Island in 1778, little attention was paid to the wealth of mineral resources in the Western Canadian and Alaskan Mountains Region.

The Hudson's Bay Company first recovered coal from the beach at Suquash near the northern end of Vancouver Island. In 1852 coal mining began at Nanaimo. In the same year, gold veins were discovered at Mitchell Harbor, Queen Charlotte Islands.

By the end of 1858, 8,000 gold miners crossed the border from Washington and Oregon, and another 23,000 came from California via Victoria. They pushed their way up the Fraser River, settling at Fort Langley, Hope, Yale, Lytton, and Boston Bar.

Rich placer ground was discovered in the Cariboo Mountains on the Quesnel River in 1861 and 1862. Gold was obtained so quickly by the thousands of individual miners working shallow gravels that the peak was reached in 1863.

Placer deposits have been worked in many

parts of British Columbia. As early as 1880 many of the shallow diggings had been worked out. Miners turned to underground mining, and to hydraulic methods for the recovery of lower grade ores.

The Tulameen River and its tributaries and streams in the Cariboo area have yielded placer platinum. Boulder Creek near Atlin has yielded placer concentrates of tungsten and tin.

Lode deposits—gold, silver, copper, lead, zinc, and tungsten—have been worked in many parts of British Columbia. Except for gold, iron, mercury, and tungsten, most of the deposits contain at least two metals; some deposits have as many as five.

PRESENT OPERATIONS IN BRITISH COLUMBIA

The largest operator in British Columbia is the Consolidated Mining and Smelting Company of Canada, Ltd. Its operation at Kimber-ley in the southern interior is the biggest nonferrous metal mine in the Commonwealth. Ammonium phosphate fertilizer is an important by-product.

The smelter at Trail, originally built to treat gold-copper ores from Rossland, is one of the leading lead and zinc smelters in the world. It treats concentrates and ores from mines in British Columbia, the Yukon Territory, and Quebec, and from many distant parts of the world.

Mining metallic and nonmetallic minerals is second only to forestry as an industry in British Columbia. The province produces about 18 per cent of Canada's metal ores and is the Dominion's prime source of lead, tungsten, tin, zinc, antimony, bismuth, and cadmium. It accounts for 33 per cent of Canada's silver. Coal, asbestos, and sulphur are the important nonmetallic minerals.

Mining has developed mostly in the southern 150 miles of the province. Opportunities

Figure 12-7. Metallurgical and chemical plants of the Consolidated Mining and Smelting Company at Trail, British Columbia, produce lead, zinc, silver, antimony, bismuth, cadmium, gold, and chemical fertilizers. (Consolidated Mining and Smelting Co.)

for greater expansion in all primary mineral fields depend upon further exploration and development in the central and northern regions. Increased copper and asbestos production may be anticipated from Stewart northward to the Alaska Highway. Completion of the pioneer road now under construction in that area will open up one of the province's most promising mining areas; it also may make possible a major smelting industry at Stewart and the utilization of major undeveloped water power potentials in that area.

DEVELOPMENT IN THE YUKON AND NORTHWEST TERRITORIES

Gold was reported in the Yukon by the Hudson's Bay Company in the 1850's; prospecting began in 1872. Fine gold was discovered on the bars of most of the main rivers. Hundreds of thousands of dollars in gold was recovered from Steamboat Bar on the Stewart River and from Cassiar Bar on the Lewes River. In the early 1890's, prospecting spread to the side streams, where coarse gold was disclosed. Klondike placer creeks were discovered in 1896; their amazing richness attracted miners from other parts of the Yukon. It was during this period that nearly all the known placer creeks in the Yukon were discovered, along with the deposits of the Whitehorse copper belt and the Mayo silver-lead district.

Placer mining. The climate and the nature and richness of the gold placers at first favored hand methods of mining, with the result that each claim soon became a productive mine in itself. Gold output rose rapidly, to reach a peak value of more than $22 million in 1900. By 1906 most of the rich, easily-mined ground was worked out, and in 1907 gold placer production declined to $3,174,510. Following a combination of interests and the introduction of dredging, placer production increased during the next few years until in 1913 it reached a value of around $6 million, an amount that has not been exceeded since.

No separate records have been kept of the placer gold output of the other districts. The Sixtymile Camp, which includes Miller, Glacier, and other creeks as well as the Sixtymile River, has been worked continuously for over 60 years. In the Mayo district, Highet and Haggart Creeks each have yielded gold to the value

of hundreds of thousands of dollars; several other smaller creeks have been worked since 1897. South of the Klondike district other creeks continue to be worked intermittently; their total production to date is large.

Lode mining. Lode mining in the Yukon has not yet attained the importance of placer mining, and most of the production has come from the Whitehorse and Mayo areas. The Whitehorse copper belt, discovered in 1897, is near the railway and therefore had advantages for early development. The first shipment of ore was made in 1900; from then until 1912 production was intermittent. Since then the area has been worked sporadically, as the price of copper fluctuated. The deposits are of the contact metamorphic type—exceptionally rich, but spotty and hard to follow.

The Mayo silver-lead veins were found by placer miners in 1906. Mining began in 1913 and, with the exceptions of 1919 and 1920, some ore has been shipped each year from the camp. The veins are exceedingly rich in silver; large tonnages of ore containing 200 to 300 ounces to the ton and many pockets containing 1,000 or more ounces to the ton have been mined.

Coal. Coal produced in the Yukon is used to meet local needs, which are small and uncertain. Coal comes from four localities: Rock Creek on the Klondike River, Coal Creek on the Yukon River, Carmacks, and the Whitehorse-Wheaton area. In the first two areas lignite, and in the other two areas good bituminous coal, have been found. Most of the output, however, has come from three mines near Carmacks, where production began in 1900. Tonnage is small, running less than 16,000 tons a year.

Petroleum and natural gas. Discovery, in 1959, of oil and gas in the Yukon about 200 miles northeast of Dawson, offers considerable hope for greater mineral exploitation. The discovery area is about 450 miles from Pacific tidewater. If found in commercial quantities, oil could be sent to the coast by pipeline for loading aboard tankers 12 months of the year.

Test drillings indicate that the oil is the type best suited for gasoline production. This is the first discovery of oil in the Yukon Territory and the first in the Far North since the Norman Wells oil field was discovered in the Northwest

Territories in 1920. The rate of flow has not been determined; gas flow up to 10,000 cubic feet a day has been recorded.

Summary. Yukon mineral production to date has been derived from a few rich deposits. No area has been thoroughly prospected and little mining has been done except for placers because of the remoteness of the territory and the severity of the winter climate. The variety and widespread distribution of the lode and placer prospects, however, suggest possibilities for expansion in mineral development.

The current mineral developments of the Yukon are centered on gold, silver, lead, and zinc. Gold production is valued at more than $2.7 million annually; silver at $3 million; lead at $2.95 million; and zinc at $1.9 million.

Many interesting deposits are being explored in the Yukon. One of the most promising is a nickel-copper discovery at Kluane Lake close to the Alaska Highway. In addition, a Canadian company is investigating the possibility of developing a large volume of hydroelectric power from the headwaters of the Yukon River and certain of its tributaries. If this development should materialize, it would bring a tremendous increase in economic activity to the Yukon and to northern British Columbia.

The most exciting new mineral discovery was made in the summer of 1959, 150 miles north of Watson Lake, just east of the Yukon-Northwest Territories boundary. More than a million tons of tungsten—not mined in Canada before—are already indicated, and production is expected to begin soon. The milled ore will be worth approximately $1,400 a ton.

ALASKA

Mining, for many years Alaska's second largest industry, virtually ceased during World War II. The industry has not regained its former status. Production thus far derived from Alaska's mines has been largely of high value and low volume—such metals as gold and platinum, which can be concentrated into marketable form under frontier conditions. The famous Kennecott copper mines on the Copper River are this type of deposit. As Alaska develops, more of its minerals will be produced for local processing and consumption and for shipment to markets outside the state. Gold probably will continue to be the leading mineral product, but an increased and diversified output of base metals, nonmetallic minerals, construction materials, and fuel also is expected.

Sand and gravel now rank on a par with gold. Production has been stimulated by Alaskan construction requirements. Gypsum, limestone, and marble are also available in quantity. Extensive iron deposits, some in combination with sulphur, are found in southeastern Alaska. Huge nickel ore reserves exist near tidewater.

The development of these resources depends in part on additional information. Much of Alaska still is geologically unexplored. But the major development questions are costs and markets. Alaskan minerals ordinarily will not be competitive in the rest of the United States, and the market in Alaska itself is very limited. Much of this wealth, however, is ready to be tapped now. The rest will increase in value as various materials become less plentiful in the other states.

HYDROELECTRIC RESOURCES

During the last 31 years the installed hydroelectric power in British Columbia jumped from 350,000 to 2,143,860 horsepower—about 1.7 horsepower per capita, compared with an average of 1.0 horsepower for all of Canada. Projects now under immediate development total almost a half-million horsepower, emphasizing the important part being played by water power in the economy of the province. Although a portion of this growth is a result of a rapid increase in population, the major portion of the power goes to supply the demands of the forestry, chemical, metallurgical, and other industries.

POWER FOR KITIMAT

One of the outstanding examples of power development for a special industry is the Aluminium Company of Canada (Alcan) project now under construction. The damming of the canyon of the eastward flowing Nechako River, which drains the vast uplands watershed of Tweedsmuir Plateau, has created a large inland lake of some 355 square miles. One of the ten-mile tunnels carrying waters

Figure 12-8. Alcan's Kitimat smelter and dock area at the head of the Douglas Channel, 70 miles inland from the Pacific Coast in British Columbia. The plant has a capacity of about 192,000 tons of aluminum a year. (Aluminium Ltd.)

westward through the Coast Range already has been completed. The ultimate installed capacity of more than two million horsepower will aid the production of 500,000 metric tons of aluminum annually at nearby Kitimat.

The most highly developed river within the province is the 25-mile stretch of the Kootenai River from Kootenai Lake downstream to its junction with the Columbia River. Power has been developed to a total installed capacity of 402,300 horsepower.

UNDEVELOPED POWER

Although British Columbia has about nine per cent of the population, it possesses 24 per cent of the water power resources of Canada.

The total known undeveloped water power resources are estimated at 11 million horsepower, not including the province's northern streams that have not yet been investigated.

The province's two greatest drainage basins are the Columbia and Fraser Rivers. The Columbia River, which is 1,200 miles in length, has a total fall of 2,650 feet, the upper half of which occurs in Canada. Its Canadian tributaries include the Pend d'Oreille, Kootenai, Kettle, Okanogan, and Similkameen Rivers.

Potential power sites exist on the Columbia River at Murphy Creek near Trail, and at Little Dalles and Downie Creeks just above Revelstoke. Storage at the outlet of Lower Arrow Lake and at Mica Creek (recently approved for construction) make it possible to create an installed capacity of about 2.5 million kilowatts.

The Fraser River system drains an area south of the 54th parallel that includes part of the western slope of the Rocky Mountains (or Continental Divide), the eastern slopes of the Coast Range, and the great intervening tablelands that lie between these mountain ranges.

YUKON

No comprehensive examination of the water power possibilities of the Yukon Territory has been undertaken, but superficial investigations carried out some years ago by the Dominion Water and Power Bureau of the Department of Mines and Resources indicated resources of quite substantial magnitude in the Whitehorse and Mayo districts. For the most part, the great rivers of the territory and many of their tributaries are of uniform gradient and are navigable except in their upper reaches. Water power possibilities, therefore, are to be found chiefly on these upper reaches. The climate and topography are such as to cause great variations in the seasonal flow of the rivers, with high flows in the open season and greatly diminished flows during the winter months. Power possibilities, in turn, are affected by the seasonal flows.

Development of water power in the Yukon Territory has taken place wholly in connection with placer gold mining operations. The Yukon Consolidated Gold Corporation owns and operates a hydroelectric plant on the Klondike River about 26 miles above Dawson. Power is transmitted principally for the operation of gold dredges, for pumps in stripping and thawing operations, and for the company's machine shops in the Dawson area.

ALASKA

Hydroelectric power is one of the three bulwarks of Alaska's industrial future. Like the other two—forestry and mining—its potential is not yet fully measured. The Bureau of Reclamation, in a preliminary survey of over two-thirds of the area, has located 200 sites with a potential capacity well over eight million kilowatts. This equals one-tenth of the present capacity in the rest of the United States from all types of power plants, or 40 per cent of the hydroelectric power. It exceeds by more than half the present capacity of the power-rich Pacific Northwest States and equals one-fourth of their ultimate potential.

Low-cost hydroelectric power is important to serve a growing population, but it is even more important as a base for industry. The most conspicuous opportunity in this line is the Taiya Project, a proposal by the Aluminum Company of America for development of 800,000 kilowatts of power and a huge new aluminum plant near Skagway. In this case the water rights are Canadian and the plans are held up by international complications. Another prime site, on the Copper River, is being investigated by the Harvey Aluminum Company. A third site of major proportions—actually the largest single site, but isolated—is located on the Yukon River near Rampart. Finally, and perhaps more important than any of these because of its location near the Anchorage population center, is the potential of the Susitna River, which has at least three major sites for hydroelectric power. About 25 per cent of the hydroelectric power potential is located in the southeastern panhandle and 39 per cent in the south-central region.

INDUSTRY

The Western Canadian Mountain area, with ample hydroelectric resources, ranks high in Canadian manufacturing. Major industries include pulp and paper, slaughtering and meat packing, petroleum products, and aluminum refining. The Aluminium Company of Canada's new plant at Kitimat makes British Columbia an important producer of primary aluminum. Production, now 192,000 tons annually, ultimately will reach 500,000 tons.

Alaska's economic history prior to World War II was written by the successive development of three natural resources—furs, gold, and fish.

During the ten-year period from 1950 to 1959, the value of Alaska fishery products was $832 million; minerals, $231 million; furs, $59 million; and forest products, $182 million. By way of comparison, defense expenditures in Alaska for the same period totaled around 1,160 million. The possible curtailment of military construction and the continued decline of the salmon industry are twin problems of no small import to the state's future. On the other hand, the rapid population growth of recent years, combined with improved transportation and the gradual exhaustion of certain resources in the United States, has brought conditions that make possible a new phase of development. The most promising fields are: (1) forest products, particularly the establishment of pulp mills in the southeastern region; (2) minerals, including iron, nickel, sulphur, nonferrous metals, coal, petroleum, and industrial minerals; and (3) hydroelectric power, the basis for aluminum and other industries.

Alaska's economic base has been described as narrow and precarious; but her opportunities — given capital, intelligent management, and enterprise—are far greater than anything in her past.

RECREATION

The Western Canadian and Alaskan Mountains Province has so many scenic attractions that even a native son could not begin to describe them all.

The Canadian Rockies rival the Alps in beauty and grandeur. There are seven national parks in the Canadian Rockies: Jasper in northern Alberta, with an area of 4,400 square miles; Waterton Lakes in southern Alberta (120 square miles) adjoining the United States' Glacier National Park at the international boundary; four parks along the main line of the Canadian Pacific Railway through the Central Rockies and Selkirks—Banff, Yoho, Glacier, and Mount Revelstoke; and Kootenai Highway Park along the Vermillion-Columbia section of the transmontane motor road.

BANFF NATIONAL PARK

Banff was the first Canadian national park to be established and was originally named Rocky Mountains Park. It has an area of 2,585 square miles of high mountain territory on the eastern side of the Rocky Mountains, comprising the whole northerly watershed of the Saskatchewan River.

One of the special attractions of the park is the town of Banff, with its famous mineral hot springs; its two excellent bathhouses at the Cave and Basin and the Upper Hot Springs, respec-

Figure 12-9. Lake Louise and Victoria Glacier, Banff National Park, Alberta. (National Film Board)

tively; its outstanding hotels, museum, and zoological garden; its golf course; and its many scenic drives. Here also are the headquarters of the Alpine Club of Canada, where many Alpine climbers of international fame have stayed on their way to fresh climbing victories.

Of the scenic attractions in this great park, Lake Louise is probably the best known. Another tourist attraction is the Columbia Ice Field, which lies to the north of Banff.

YOHO NATIONAL PARK

At the Great Divide, the summit of Kickinghorse Pass, the traveler passes from Alberta to British Columbia and from Banff to Yoho Park. Seen from Kickinghorse Pass, Yoho is only a narrow cleft between heavily wooded mountain walls stretching north to the gleaming whiteness of Yoho Glacier. Yet that narrow opening is a valley 14 miles long and more than a mile deep, walled in by almost perpendicular mountains hung with primeval forest and crowned by enormous snowfields that creep down from the peaks in slow-moving rivers of ice or fall in tremendous cataracts.

JASPER NATIONAL PARK

Jasper Park is on the main line of the Canadian National Railway, about 240 miles west of Edmonton. It embraces a rich variety of river, lake, forest, and mountain scenery. Largest of the Canadian national parks, it contains the headwaters of the Athabaska River system that flows into the Arctic Ocean. The park, an Alpine resort of great interest, offers golfing, tennis, boating, swimming, hiking, and riding.

THE YUKON

The Yukon offers many attractions to the visitor. It is a land of contrasts—even extremes —in climate, physical characteristics, wildlife, and population. Its snow-capped mountains, beautiful lakes, and majestic rivers flowing smoothly to the sea provide an ever-changing panorama.

ALASKA

Alaska is one of the world's great potential tourist areas. The establishment of airlines has brought the area within the time limits of the

Figure 12-10. Yoho National Park, British Columbia. Coniferous vegetation mantles the lower slopes; bare rock and steep cliffs are found at higher elevations. (Canadian Government Travel Bureau)

ordinary vacation traveler. Air service, along with transportation by steamer from Seattle or Vancouver and by automobile on the all-season Alaska Highway, may well make Alaska a year-round sports center.

Hunting and fishing in one of the world's great game regions are made possible by the airplane, which opens untouched areas and adds hours and days to actual hunting time. The total number of big and small game animals, game birds, and sport fish in Alaska is large, but they are spread over a vast region. The result is a much smaller density per square mile there than in the United States. It is almost as necessary to seek remote and inaccessible areas and streams for good hunting and fishing as it is in the Western States.

TRANSPORTATION

WATER

Shipping lines connect British Columbia with the major ports of the world, and coastal shipping is also a very important segment of the transportation picture. British Columbia has an integrated fleet of coastal steamships operated by the Canadian Pacific and the Canadian National Railroads, the Union Steamship, the Gulf Line, and others. These vessels give regular freight and passenger service to all coastal points.

Steamship service, primarily out of Seattle, still is the workhorse of transportation to Alaska. By far the largest share of freight travels by water, despite the handicaps of limited volume at many Alaskan ports and a spotty and expensive history of labor disputes on the Seattle waterfront. Steamships face a growing competition from barge lines, both in Seattle and Port Rupert. The latter, British Columbia's most northerly rail terminus, is only 108 miles south of Ketchikan, 641 miles closer than Seattle.

During the navigation season (May 15 to October 15) the White Pass and Yukon Route operates steamboats on the Yukon River between Whitehorse and Dawson. In normal times a biweekly service is provided. Steamer service also is provided at intervals between Dawson and lower river points, including Eagle, Fort Yukon, and Tanana, Alaska. Steamers connecting with the main Yukon River route operate on the Stewart River and provide a service to Mayo Landing.

RAIL

British Columbia is crossed from east to west by two transcontinental railways, the Canadian Pacific and the Canadian National. Both have terminals at Vancouver; the Canadian National also serves Prince Rupert. In addition, there is the provincially-owned Pacific Great Eastern, which joins Squamish, a short distance from Vancouver, with Prince George in the heart of the province.

For more than 30 years the Alaska Railroad has played an essential role in developing Anchorage, the Matanuska Valley, and the interior. Currently it carries over a million tons of freight each year and provides streamlined passenger service from Seward to Fairbanks.

The White Pass and Yukon Route connects Skagway with Whitehorse, 110 miles distant. In normal times, a daily service is provided between Skagway and Whitehorse during the summer season, and a biweekly service exists during the remainder of the year.

HIGHWAY

Construction of the Canadian-Alaskan Military Highway through the southern Yukon opened to motorists regions previously inaccessible to all but the most intrepid explorer or prospector. The highway connects Dawson Creek, British Columbia, with Whitehorse, Yukon Territory, and Fairbanks, Alaska, and links up with an existing route at Dawson Creek to Edmonton, Alberta. From Dawson Creek, it traverses the northeastern corner of British Columbia before entering Yukon Territory in the vicinity of Watson Lake. Crossing the 60th parallel, the northern boundary of British Columbia, the highway follows the wide, open valley of the Liard and Yukon Rivers.

Descending the western slope of the divide, the route touches Teslin Lake, then bridges the Teslin and Lewes Rivers, reaching Whitehorse. Westward from Whitehorse it heads through Champagne to Kluane Lake. From there it continues northwesterly to cross the international boundary into Alaska, following the Tanana River to Fairbanks.

AIR

Several airlines offer services to and within Alaska. Northwest Airlines operates air coach and deluxe services between Seattle and Anchorage and between Minneapolis and Anchorage. Pan American World Airways provides service from Seattle to Ketchikan and Juneau, to Fairbanks, and to Nome. Daily flights are conducted from Juneau to Anchorage by Pacific Northern Airlines. Several other lines also provide services within the state.

In the Yukon Territory, transportation by air is a necessity, for other means of transportation are limited. Extension and improvement of commercial air transportation services have brought the Yukon within a few hours' flying time of populated centers in western Canada and the northwestern United States. Passenger

Figure 12-11. A typical section of the Alcan Highway. Although unpaved over large portions, the 1,523-mile highway is an important link in surface transport between Alaska and the rest of the United States. (U.S. Bureau of Public Roads)

services are operated by Canadian Pacific Air Lines from Vancouver to Whitehorse, via Fort St. John, British Columbia. These services connect with Trans-Canada Air Lines and other services at Edmonton and Vancouver. A service is also maintained by Canadian Pacific Air Lines from Whitehorse to Dawson twice a week in summer, and weekly in winter.

POPULATION

Because of its rugged nature and degree of isolation, the Western Canadian and Alaskan Mountains Region is sparsely populated. Most of the cities and towns are located along the coast. What population the interior does possess is clustered in a number of small towns and hamlets that act as centers for the local economy.

PRINCIPAL CITIES AND TOWNS

Whitehorse (3,000). This Yukon Territory city is a transportation center. The railroad from Skagway meets the Alaska Highway here. The city has a first-class airport served by airlines from Seattle, Vancouver, and Edmonton. Whitehorse is an important outfitting center for big game hunting parties.

Dawson (1,000). The administrative center of the Yukon Territory, Dawson is situated on the east bank of the Yukon River north of the mouth of the Klondike River. It is a base of supply and distributing point for the Klondike gold fields.

Anchorage (45,000). Alaska's largest and fastest growing city, Anchorage is the business, transportation, and sports center of Pacific Alaska. There are 100,000 people, including military personnel, within a ten-mile radius. Population has doubled within the last five years. Leading industries are fishing, food processing, mining, and construction. The economy of the area is highly dependent upon government and military activities.

Juneau (6,800). In Juneau, the capital of Alaska, and the Gastineau Channel area live the workers who play the major role in the operation of the state and Federal governments. Juneau is about 900 miles northwest of Seattle and approximately 75 miles from the open Pacific Ocean. It is sheltered by Douglas, Admiralty, and Chichagof Islands to the west. The approach to Juneau through the inland channels is surrounded by mountains; those of the mainland are the highest. Mt. Juneau and Mt. Roberts, on whose slopes the town is built, rise precipitously to over 3,500 feet. Under these peaks are the workings of the Alaska-

Figure 12-12. Whitehorse, Yukon Territory, is a major center for the territory. (National Defense Photo)

Juneau mine, long one of America's largest gold producers. Behind them, the Coast Range peaks attain heights of up to 7,500 feet and more. To the east, a large icefield and high peaks extend across the border into British Columbia.

Access to the town is by boat or plane only; at this time no highway connects it to the United States or Canada, although a ferry operating in the summer carries cars and passengers between Juneau and Haines, where connecting highways to Fairbanks and Anchorage start.

OTHER CITIES AND TOWNS

Ketchikan, Alaska (6,500, trading area population—9,850), is the first port of call for northbound steamers and the self-styled salmon capital of the world, where the annual King Salmon derby is held.

Seward (1,891), the "Gateway City," located on beautiful Resurrection Bay, is the unofficial capital of Alaska's Kenai Peninsula, a mecca for sportsmen.

Sitka (3,237) is unique in having been the last Russian capital and the first American capital of Alaska. Items of historic interest are displayed in the old Greek Orthodox church.

Valdez (700) is the coastal terminus for the Richardson Highway and is an important year-round ice-free port of the Alaska mainland. The principal businesses are fishing and transportation.

Prince Rupert (12,500) was thought to be destined to be the Pacific Coast's major port to link the continent with Asia, for it is the westernmost terminus of the Canadian National Railroad and is closer to the Far East than any other port served by a major railway. Although it never achieved the greatness many thought it should attain, Prince Rupert is the largest coastal British Columbian community north of Vancouver. There is some trade with the Orient, but coastwise movements dominate. Fish canning is an important local industry and there are several nearby pulp and paper mills.

Part V | INTERMOUNTAIN WEST

The Intermountain West comprises a vast semiarid to arid territory, bordered on the east by the Rocky Mountains and on the west by the Cascade-Sierra Nevada Province. It is an area of varied topography. There are partially dissected tablelands—lands of moderate to high relief, but with a high percentage of nearly level land that lies relatively high—in the Colorado Plateau. Plains with widely spaced hills and mountains—lands of moderate to high relief, but with a high percentage of nearly level land, most of which lies relatively low—are the dominant landforms in Nevada, northeastern and southeastern California, and central and southeastern Oregon. In eastern Washington, southwestern Idaho, and north-central and southeastern Oregon, lava plateaus, drained by the Columbia River system, predominate.

Land uses differ greatly from one part of the section to another depending upon local weather, terrain, mineral deposits, and geographical position. In general, the more arid areas support a grazing economy. Irrigation farming prevails in those favored valleys where water is available. Mining, health resorts, and recreational activities are found in areas suited to these enterprises.

13 | *Southwestern Interior Plateaus,*

Plains, and Mountains

(Relief map copyright Aero Service Corp.)

THE Southwestern Interior Plateaus, Plains, and Mountains Region includes the western third of Colorado, all of Utah south of the Uinta Mountains and east of the Wasatch Mountains, the extreme southeastern tip of Nevada, the western two-thirds of New Mexico, the extreme southwestern corner of Texas, all of Arizona, and the southeastern desert, mountains and valleys of California.

SURFACE FEATURES

Physically, the province is characterized by horizontal rocks, great elevations, deep canyons, and enclosed basins. Not much of its area is less than 5,000 feet high; it has some plateaus of over 10,000 feet. There are hundreds of canyons, with the deepest at 6,000 feet. Gigantic faults and monoclines affect the topography, and there are also a few eroded domes similar to, but smaller than, the Black Hills.

The High Plateaus of Utah, on the west side of the state, are nine plateaus 9,000 to 11,000 feet high, separated by great faults or erosion valleys or both; they are eroded and partly forested. Escarpments that face out all around rise 3,000 to 6,000 feet. These plateaus are capped in part by lavas resting on Tertiary strata that make up the Pink Cliffs. The underlying Mesozoic rocks form enormous rock terraces on the south, descending by the White Cliffs, Vermilion Cliffs, and so on, 6,000 feet to the platform of carboniferous rocks in which Arizona's Grand Canyon is cut.

The Uinta Basin consists of Tertiary rocks dipping, as the surface slopes, gently northward toward the mountains to form a basin, the whole of which is higher than the section on the south. The southern edge of the Tertiary rocks is an escarpment 2,000 to 3,000 feet high called Roan Cliffs and Book Cliffs. The Uinta Basin is mainly a dissected plateau. The higher sections are forested; grasslands and some badlands occur at lower elevations.

The Canyon Lands of southern and eastern Utah are a plateau 6,000 to 7,000 feet high with several eroded domes and laccoliths—the Henry Mountains, for example. Intricate systems of deep canyons branch out from the Green, Muddy, Colorado, and San Juan Rivers, cutting the plateau into isolated tablelands. They are very difficult to cross and are largely desert.

The Navajo section in northeastern Arizona and northwestern New Mexico is less dissected than the Canyon Lands because it has few streams flowing through it to cut the main valleys. The strata of the San Juan Basin are turned up around its margin, exposing coal seams which are mined at Gallup, New Mexico, and Durango, Colorado. A similar synclinal basin in northeastern Arizona is underlain by Mesozoic beds. Red Triassic sandstones and shales come up in a monocline on the southwest side. Their outcropping edges comprise the Painted Desert. The Painted Desert is bounded by the Little Colorado River, which flows in a strike valley.

The Datil section, which lies to the south and east of the Little Colorado River, is an almost level plateau at an altitude of about 7,000 feet. A feature of special interest is the Petrified Forest, near Adamana, Arizona. Here thousands of silicified tree trunks have been exposed by the weathering of the red Triassic sandstones. Logs were washed into this area during Triassic times and buried under conditions that made their preservation possible. This involved burial below the level of the ground water, where dissolved silica soon filled the cell cavities and pores in the wood, thus making a cast of the interior wood. Later, the wood itself was replaced by a second infiltration of silica.

In the Zuni Mountains of western New Mexico, an elliptical dome known as the Zuni Uplift rises 2,000 feet above the surrounding country. It is about 70 miles long and 35 miles wide. To the east of the Zuni Uplift rises Mt. Taylor, a young volcano 11,389 feet high surrounded by several lesser cones. Numerous lava flows cover a large portion of this eastern area.

The Grand Canyon section, averaging 5,000 to 7,000 feet high, is on carboniferous rocks, largely limestone. There is a large patch of overlying lava, much of it very recent. San Francisco Mountain, a volcano, is 12,700 feet high. On the north and east the carboniferous rock goes down by monoclines under younger formations, 6,000 feet of which have been stripped off from this section.

All of the area south of the Colorado River and west of the Datil section comprises the San Francisco Plateau. It has a rolling surface with open forest on the higher parts. North of the

Grand Canyon, faults running north and south cut the plateau into four parts. The parts rise step-like toward the east. The easternmost part, Kaibab Plateau, is 10,400 feet high and well forested. West of this are many volcanoes and lava flows, some of them very recent.

The Colorado River is in a canyon for over 500 miles, but the specific name "Grand Canyon" is applied to a 200-mile stretch below the mouth of the Little Colorado. The maximum depth is 6,000 feet; the minimum width at the top of the canyon is about 4¾ miles. The width at the most impressive points is 10 to 15 miles. The Grand Canyon was eroded through nearly horizontal sedimentary rocks of unequal resistance; hence there are many cliffs, benches, and platforms of varied colors. Locally, the lower part is cut in granite. This river carries a tremendous load of silt. With an average fall of 7½ feet per mile, it has great cutting power.

The Sonoran Desert, which takes its name from the state of Sonora in Mexico, lies to the south of the Great Basin and extends southeastward to near Tucson, Arizona. Its western portion is the Mojave Desert, a region of interior drainage; the eastern portion is drained by the Gila River.

The Sonoran Desert is lower than the Great Basin. Its height varies from 2,000 to 4,000 feet on the north and east to 500 feet on the lower Colorado River. Its mountain ranges are small, occupying about one-sixth of the area and trending northwest-southeast. In the California portion are many bolsons (enclosed basins) with central alkali marshes (soda lakes, borax lakes, etc.). Death Valley is an example. Death Valley is the result of the down-faulting of a block whose floor is 282 feet below sea level. This valley, 135 miles long and from three to ten miles wide, was once filled by a lake fed by streams from the Panamint Mountains on the west and the Spring and Amargosa Mountains on the east. The lake had no outlet. When its water evaporated, valuable salts were deposited—to a depth of several feet in places. All the bolsons are very hot and arid. Official maps list 323 places supplying water, often very bad, in 10,000 square miles. Such springs or wells are often 40 to 50 miles apart. Needles, on the Colorado River, receives only 2.47 inches of rain per year. The bolsons in the Arizona portion are better connected, in many cases giving continuous slopes to the sea. There are, however, no through streams south of the Williams River for 500 miles except the Gila. Many of the bolsons are rock platforms with little or no cover of detritus.

The Salton Trough is separated from the Sonoran Desert by the low Eagle and Chocolate Mountains. It is a great bolson, 2,000 square miles in extent, sloping toward Salton Sink, which is 241 feet below sea level. It was formerly an extension of the Gulf of California and was cut off by the growth of the delta of the Colorado River. It is emptied by evaporation when the river discharges into the Gulf of California on the south side of its delta. Occasionally, as in 1905-1907, the river flows down the north side of its delta and makes the Salton Sea.

The Mexican Highland lies to the east of the Colorado River and south of the Colorado Plateau. It is a northward extension of a great area of similar country in Mexico. It is not unlike the Great Basin, except that many of its drainage basins are connected, giving continuous slopes to the sea. It is so arid, however, that water flows down some of these slopes only at very long intervals. Some tributaries of the Gila River are dissecting old alluvial slopes into badlands. The Rio Grande flows through a series of bolsons, cutting 300 feet into their floors of detritus. It derives its water from an area north of central New Mexico. South of that for 600 miles it has no perennial tributaries. Irrigation in New Mexico uses most of the Rio Grande's water. About half the total area of this section is occupied by mountain ranges like those of the Great Basin; altitudes of 7,000 to 8,000 feet are common.

The Sacramento section, between the Rio Grande Valley on the west and the Pecos Valley on the east, is a highland region comprising scarcely more than faulted plateaus tilted east, some of them 10,000 feet high. The plateaus are made rugged by mature dissection on the higher side but they decline eastward and merge into the Pecos Valley.

CLIMATE

In climatic characteristics this region shows great variety. Except in the high mountains, precipitation is light. More than 75 per cent of the total annual precipitation occurs during the winter or wet season. The mean annual precipitation varies from 25 inches or more in the higher mountains to two or three inches or less in the Mojave Desert and in Death Valley. At several places in the Imperial Valley and in Death Valley there have been periods of a year in which less than an inch of precipitation was recorded. In the mountains, on the other hand, very heavy rains have been recorded within short intervals of time.

In general, the area is characterized by an abundance of sunshine, very little cloudy weather, wide variations in the length of the growing season in different parts of the region, considerable range of temperatures within a 24-hour period at any given point, low relative humidity, scant annual precipitation, and very rapid evaporation of moisture from the surface of the ground. The prevailing winds are generally from the southwest and west.

In the desert region the daily, monthly, and annual temperature ranges are wide. In the Imperial Valley the summers are dry and hot; the winters are dry and moderately cold, with occasional light rain. In Death Valley the air is relatively dry throughout the year, the winters are moderately cold, and the summers are the hottest in the United States.

Throughout the lower sections, mainly in southwestern Arizona, including the valleys of the lower Salt, Gila, and Colorado Rivers, where elevations are less than 3,000 feet above sea level, readings above 100° F. in the shade occur frequently during the long summer, which lasts from April to November. However, because of the dry atmosphere, temperatures in the high 90's in these desert regions are more comfortable than those of 80° in the Atlantic and Gulf Coast States, where the principal cause of discomfort during periods of hot weather is excessive humidity rather than high temperature.

The southern section of Arizona has a delightful winter season, located as it is in the belt of maximum sunshine and minimum relative humidity for the entire United States. This part of the state has become a mecca for winter tourists and health seekers. The scenic and recreational areas in the mountain sections of the north and east have a pleasant summer climate, with cool, bracing nights and frequent showers.

In the higher areas, above 7,000 feet, temperatures average as low as they do in southern Minnesota, whereas in the lower elevations of the western and southern parts of the region, conditions are semitropical.

SOILS

The Southwestern Interior Plateaus, Plains, and Mountains Region has a wide variation in soil conditions and soil types. This is caused chiefly by a relatively large variety of parent rock from which the soils were derived, by variations in the climatic conditions that prevailed during the soil forming periods, by the manner in which the soils were formed, and by variations in the age or maturity of the respective soil types.

The mountain and foothill soils cover the foothill lands, most of which are wooded; the isolated, sharp mountain ridges; other high mountainous areas generally covered with brush; the grasslands occupying some of the mountain valleys and parks; and the smoother, undulating, untimbered high ridges. The soils of this group are mostly loams and sandy loams, which are shallow and more or less stony. The mountain valley grassland soils are usually deeper, darker, and more productive than the soils of the rough, timbered areas of the region.

Soils mantling the mesas, plateaus, and high plains within the province vary in texture from coarse gravel and sand, at one extreme, to clay loams, clay, and adobe, at the other. It is on this group of soils that nearly all of the dry farming is done. The silt loams and clay loams are best adapted to the production of small grains. Over much of this area the surface soils are shallow, because they are underlain by caliche. The caliche varies in thickness from a few inches to many feet. In some places, where the topsoil has been eroded away, the caliche comes to the surface.

Soils that occupy the slopes, alluvial fans, and escarpments, form more or less continuous long areas unsymmetrical in relief and broken here and there by erosion channels that continue the erratic deposition of colluvial material when flash floods occur. The surface soils of this group are quite variable. They are usually gravelly and in places stony. Their mois-

Figure 13-1. Giant saguaro cacti in Saguaro National Monument in southern Arizona. The saguaro cactus is typical of desert forms of vegetation. Through such features as large and extensive root systems, water storage facilities, and hard waxy exteriors, these plants are able to adjust to their harsh environment. (National Park Service)

ture-holding capacity is generally low because of the porous gravelly material in the subsoil. Most of the lands occupied by these soils are poorly adapted to crop production and for this reason have not been brought under cultivation.

The Sonoran Desert is a region of red desert soils because of its low rainfall, very hot summers, and mild winters. Organic matter and nitrogen are low. Agriculture is dependent upon irrigation.

NATURAL VEGETATION

A great diversity of vegetative types is to be found within the borders of the province because of differences in elevation, precipitation, temperature, length of growing season, and soil. Desert plant life—desert sage, scrub trees,

cacti, salt tolerating shrubs, bunch grasses, and, at widely spaced intervals that follow the spring rains, sudden bright bursts of desert wild flowers—is characteristic of the lowlands. Junipers and piñon pines grow on the flanks of some of the higher mountain ranges with which the Mojave Desert is dotted and in the no man's land northeast of the Salton Trough. Open stands of forest are found at the higher elevations in Arizona, New Mexico, Colorado, and Utah. Beginning at 7,500 feet, Ponderosa pine is the common timber specie; at 9,000 feet, they give way to the Douglas fir, white fir, and quaking aspen that grow up to about the 10,500-foot line.

SETTLEMENT

Folsom man lived in the American Southwest 20,000 years ago. Traces of their early agriculture are found in the region. High, almost inaccessible cliff dwellings still stand in evidence to another, much later prehistoric race.

Written history began when the Spaniards sent exploration parties northward from Mexico. The first traveler was a Franciscan priest named Marcos de Niza, who entered the territory in 1539. Later, others made their way into this land. The most famous of the explorers was Francisco Vasquez Coronado (1540-1542). Spanish priests followed to establish missions to bring Christianity to the Indians. The Spaniards introduced the use of metal tools, utensils, and weapons, and the wooden plow; they introduced most of the domestic animals found in the area today. They also introduced small grains, vegetables, tree fruits, and grapes.

From the date of the first colonization venture (1598) until Mexico gained her independence (1822), the region had virtually no outlet for her products and no source for obtaining supplies except through Chihuahua City and Vera Cruz. During that period of more than 200 years, development was very slow; exports consisted mostly of sheep, wool, dressed deerskins, buffalo robes, furs, salt, and copper vessels. As a rule, the balance of trade was overwhelmingly against the province. The policy pursued was intended to keep the colonists short of funds and to prevent them from having outside commercial intercourse. However, as soon as Mexico obtained her independence, the commercial policies were changed; traffic over the Santa Fe Trail increased materially and a thriving commerce between the Missouri River points and Santa Fe soon developed. This continued from about 1825 to 1845.

The admission of Texas to the Union in

Figure 13-2. These Indian cliff dwellings in Mesa Verde National Park in southwestern Colorado were built around A.D. 800 and were occupied until A.D. 1200. The origins and fate of the peoples who built the cliff dwellings of the Southwest are unknown. (Colorado Department of Public Relations)

Figure 13-3. Monument Valley, a sandy plain with monumental buttes in northeastern Arizona and southeastern Utah, is the home of the Navajo Indians. The contrast of old and new cultures is evident in the manufactured shirt and buckboard and the homemade earrings, blanket, and whip of the aged Navajo in the photograph. (Hal Rumel Studios)

1845, the extension of the authority of the United States over the territory acquired as a result of the war with Mexico, and the discovery of gold in California in 1848, resulted in a great westward migration. This westward movement was prolonged by the discovery of gold in Colorado some ten years later. The Southwest absorbed many of these immigrants, and it was during this period that the value of the "American Desert" for grazing purposes was discovered. It was during this period, also, that the range cattle and sheep industries got under way. Although seriously hampered by Indian hostility, the Civil War, and the lack of market outlets, cattle increased to such an ex-

tent that ranchmen, in 1865 and 1866, began moving their herds to the north and northeast in order to make connection with the new railroads building westward through Kansas. This system continued until the 1890's, when railroad transportation became available in the eastern part of the region.

Law and order were slow to catch up with the sudden growth of the frontier. Bitter gun battles broke out between the cattlemen and sheepmen, each wanting the grazing land and water rights. Under the leadership of the pioneers themselves a peaceful community was established, where crops, cattle, sheep, and mining as well, all became important economic activities.

MINING

It was the lure of gold and silver that prompted Coronado's famous expedition in search of the Seven Cities of Cibola. Mining continues to play a dominant role in the economy of the Southwest. The value of precious metals, however, has been exceeded many times by that of industrial minerals.

PRECIOUS METALS

Gold. Gold is now produced largely as a recoverable metal from copper ores. Gold mining received a severe setback with the "gold-closing order" in 1942. Many gold mines have not reopened. Despite the $35 per ounce price, rising costs prohibit economic mining of all but high-grade ore or ore containing some valued by-product.

Gold has been mined in the region for more than a century. Pichacho, Largo Muchacho, and the Chocolate Mountains in California, and Oatman, Arizona, at one time supported rich mines, but these have been drastically curtailed.

Silver. The history of silver, if written in detail, would automatically contain much of the early history of the Western States. Silver, like gold, is tied up closely with government, a factor that overshadows all others. However, silver enjoys a much broader use than gold in industry. Today, silver is obtained mainly as a by-product of copper, lead, and zinc mining and varies with the production of those metals. Bisbee, Arizona, is the region's leading producer. Between four and five million ounces are being mined annually.

INDUSTRIAL METALS

Copper. This metal may well be said to be mankind's oldest friend. It is easily worked and is beautiful as well as useful. The electrical industry is almost completely dependent upon copper. No other metal, except silver, can do its electrical job as well. The light metal industry could hardly maintain itself without copper as a hardening agent. Copper tubing finds greatly increased use in the building trades.

Arizona leads the nation in copper production. The state accounts for more than 40 per cent of the national and more than 14 per cent of the world output. The most important mines are the Phelps-Dodge Corporation's Lavender Pit, one of the world's largest open pit copper operations, at Bisbee; the Clay Pit (also Phelps-Dodge) at Morenci; Castle Dome in the Globe-Miami district; New Cornelia (Phelps-Dodge) at Ajo; Magma at Superior; Inspiration in the Globe-Miami district; and San Manuel, the nation's largest reserve, estimated to contain 500 million tons of ore.

Arizona's copper in late years has been won from ores of decreasing copper content, much of it containing less than one per cent metallic copper. Only large-scale mining operations are feasible under such conditions.

Iron ore. Although iron ore deposits had been known to exist in several of the Western States for decades, they were of little significance until the beginning of World War II. At that time the need arose for iron and steel production in the West to supply Pacific Coast shipyards and factories with steel. Two integrated mills constructed at Fontana, California, and Geneva, Utah, began to process local iron ore deposits.

The Kaiser Steel Corporation at Fontana operates Eagle Mountain, a source of iron ore 50 miles from Indio north of Highways 60 and 70. Since 1948, the mines at Eagle Mountain

Figure 13-4. This open pit copper mine at Morenci, Arizona, measures approximately one mile by 1.4 miles. Workings such as this have enabled the United States to lead the world in copper production. (Bureau of Mines, U.S. Department of the Interior)

Figure 13-5. The Kaiser Steel Corporation's Eagle Mountain iron ore mine is located appproximately 163 miles southeast of Fontana, California, the site of the Kaiser steel mill. (Frasher, Inc.)

have shipped a steady stream of iron ore to the mills in Fontana in sufficient bulk to produce steel for 100 cars per day.

Large iron ore deposits are being mined west of Cedar City, Utah, at Iron Mountain and at Desert Mound. Average iron content runs approximately 54 per cent. Iron ore is shipped to the Geneva steel plant near Provo, Utah; the Colorado Fuel and Iron plant in Pueblo, Colorado; and the Kaiser Steel mill at Fontana. Potential reserves are estimated at 500 million gross tons.

Lead and zinc. These metals are found in association with copper-bearing ores. Their production varies widely, depending upon national demand, stockpiling policies, and the like. Bisbee, Arizona, is the major area of recovery.

Manganese. Low-grade manganese ore occurs in Arizona. Reserves are estimated at 200 million tons, with about four per cent manganese. A buying station for the convenience of Arizona shippers established at Wenden, Arizona, has resulted in a substantial production of this mineral.

Uranium. The Southwestern Interior Plateaus, Plains, and Mountains Region is a major source of the nation's uranium. Moab, situated in southeastern Utah along the Colorado River, became nationally famous in 1952, when Charles A. Steen, miner and prospector, discovered a high-grade uranium-vanoxite ore about 40 miles southeast of the town in what is known as the Big Indian Wash district. Many mining and milling companies are operating in this area. Such names as Hidden Splendor, Hecla, Continental, Standard, National Lead, Utex, Ureco, and others are well known in uranium circles. The Uranium Reduction Company's $11 million mill in Moab processes an average of 1,500 tons of uranium ore daily. In the country surrounding the mill work 1,000 miners.

A hundred miles south, on the Navajo Reservation near Mexican Hat, tribesmen are employed at Industrial Uranium mines adjacent to Monument Valley and in the Texas-Zinc Minerals Corporation mill. At Grants, New Mexico, five mills are working at near-capacity concentrating ore from what is the nation's richest uranium district. The companies here are Anaconda, Homestake, Phillips Petroleum, and Kermac. Across the state line in Colorado, Union Carbide, Climax Uranium, and the Vanadium Corporation of America process ores mined near Rifle, Uravan, and Durango for some of the earliest uranium mines opened in the nation.

Ten years after initial major uranium ore finds on the Colorado Plateau, 82,500,000 tons of uranium ore reserves have been staked out. The need for multimillion dollar mills, costly equipment, and skilled operators has meant a major change in the industry's fiscal picture.

NONMETALLIC MINERALS

Clays, gypsum, feldspar, asbestos, barite, mica, pumice, and perlite are produced on a minor scale within the region. Since these minerals occur in great abundance in many parts of the nation and are relatively low in price, the Southwest has been handicapped by adverse freight rates and its distance from industrial centers.

Coal, natural gas, petroleum, and oil shale play an important role in the economy of the Southwest. They supply most of the region's energy and constitute a high percentage of the wealth derived from natural resources.

Petroleum. The Four Corners field, so named because it extends into the corners of four states—southwestern Colorado, southeastern Utah, northeastern Arizona, and northwestern New Mexico—holds great promise as an oil producing field. Many oil men expect this area to become one of the nation's richest sources of oil. The Four Corners Pipeline from the Aneth field to refineries in Los Angeles and the Texas-New Mexico Pipeline from the Aneth field to Jal, New Mexico, provide the necessary outlets for crude oil from the highly productive Paradox Basin in the Four Corners

field. Daily capacity of the two pipelines is 170,000 barrels.

Oil from shale. Shales containing 15 gallons of oil or more per ton occur in the 16,500-square-mile Green River area in Colorado, Wyoming, and Utah. The shale deposits, with an estimated oil content of over a trillion barrels, were laid down about 50 million years ago when the Green River area was covered by fresh water lakes surrounded by hills. Over a period of millions of years, sediment containing organic matter from plants and possibly from aquatic animals eroded from the hills and settled into the lakes to a depth of 3,000 feet. Eventually this hardened into marlstone, or oil shale. Movements of the earth's crust later raised portions of these shale beds to about 9,000 feet above sea level. Rivers then cut deeply into the formation, producing almost vertical cliffs and exposed cross sections.

Natural gas. The natural gas industry is expanding rapidly in the Southwest as Pacific Coast and national markets continue to demand more and more of this cheap, clean fuel. The San Juan field is particularly promising. Connections to wells in the Paradox Basin were completed in 1956 by the El Paso Natural Gas Company. The gas is processed at the company plant in Farmington, New Mexico, and

Figure 13-6. Uranium reduction mill at Moab, Utah—one of three such mills in the state, 25 in the nation. In 1960, production of uranium ore in the United States was 6.9 million tons. The 25 mills produced a total of 16,390 tons of concentrate. (Moab Chamber of Commerce)

Figure 13-7. Branding cattle in an Arizona corral. The cattle are roped and tied, branded, and dehorned in one operation. Well-trained horses are a vital part of the process. (U.S. Forest Service)

the residual gas is marketed to consumers through pipelines.

Coal. Utah ranks tenth among the states in coal production and first among the states west of the Mississippi. Its total output exceeds that of the other ten Western States. The bulk of Utah's coal (98.3 per cent) is produced in the Southwestern Interior Plateaus, Plains, and Mountains Region. Reserves are estimated at 93 billion tons. The coal is relatively hard, does not slack, and is blocky in structure. Most of it is highly volatile and noncoking, although there are several deposits of coking coal.

Approximately one-half the mined coal is marketed for commercial and residential heating in the Western States; the other half is mined for coking by U.S. Steel and Kaiser Steel for blast furnaces at Geneva, Utah, and Fontana, California. The chief mining centers are Price and Sunnyside, Utah.

RANCHING

Range livestock ranching utilizes by far the major part of the land area of the Southwest. Ranch operations are built around the use of grazing land—mostly publicly owned and ad-

ministered. However, many of the ranches, particularly the cattle ranches, have some cropland from which forage and feed crops are harvested to feed the animals through the winter. Some cattle and many sheep graze all year, a system that necessitates moving herds considerable distances from summer to winter grazing grounds. Since feeds suitable for fattening cattle or sheep are relatively scarce, most cattle and lambs are marketed out of the region as feeder animals. Exceptions to this practice may be found in the Phoenix area and in the Imperial Valley, where many feedlots have been established since World War II to meet the needs of a rapidly expanding population.

Vegetation varies greatly, depending mostly on precipitation and elevation. The western areas have semidesert grass and shrubs interspersed with woodlands at higher elevations. Important grasses are blue and black grama, curly mesquite, tobosa, and mesquite grass. Important shrubs are mesquite, shinnery oak, yucca, and mountain mahogany.

Precipitation ranges from an average of 8.5 inches in the extreme south-central and western portions of the area to more than 20 inches at the higher elevations.

The beef cattle industry is by far the most important of the ranch enterprises. Grazing is planned to take advantage of the seasonal growth of grasses and weeds. Breeding is carried on throughout the year, which results in calves being born the year 'round. As a result of the climatic conditions and ranch practices, the average weight of cows, the percentage of calf crop, and the weight of calves when weaned and sold are comparatively low.

Sheep ranching is on the decline in the Southwest, as it is in the rest of the nation. Competition with more intensive forms of agriculture, higher labor costs, and a scarcity of competent shepherds have plagued the industry.

The feeding capacity of much of the grazing land has been materially reduced by years of overstocking that has resulted in: (1) a weakening or deterioration of the vegetative cover; (2) an increase in both wind and water erosion; and (3) a decrease, where the overstocking is excessive, in both the quality and total pounds of livestock produced.

IRRIGATED AGRICULTURE

With the building of strategically situated dams along the region's major streams that began at the turn of the century, the miner and the cowboy have had to make way for the less glamorous but economically more sound farmer. Several million acres of desert land have blossomed into one of the world's richest farm areas, bearing alfalfa, cotton, citrus fruit, melons, dates, and all kinds of vegetables. The chief irrigated districts are: (1) the Mesilla and Estancia Valleys in New Mexico; (2) the Salt, Gila, and Yuma River Valleys in Arizona; and (3) the Palo Verde, Coachella, Imperial, Borego, and Antelope Valleys in California.

THE MESILLA VALLEY

This is an irrigated area of the Rio Grande Valley in south-central New Mexico. It extends north from the southern boundary of the state to the vicinity of Radium Springs. Irrigation water is impounded in the Elephant Butte Dam, a Federal reclamation project located on the Rio Grande near Truth or Consequences, New Mexico.

The two principal crops produced in the valley are cotton and alfalfa. On most farms, cotton is the main crop and alfalfa is a leguminous rotation crop furnishing farm feed and cash income.

Livestock is not of major importance in the valley, but there is some dairying and livestock feeding. In recent years farmers have increased acreage of permanent irrigated pastures. This use of land offers opportunities for cheaper production of beef cattle and dairy products.

THE ESTANCIA VALLEY

Located south and east of Albuquerque in Torrance County, New Mexico, this area specializes in the production of pinto beans and furnishes a good example of a situation in which physical conditions have reduced the alternatives available to farmers to a point where a single cash crop type of farming strongly predominates.

SALT RIVER VALLEY

Water stored in eight reservoirs on the Salt, Verde, and Agua Fria Rivers supplies 465,000 irrigated acres in Maricopa County, making it one of the nation's wealthiest agricultural districts. Irrigation in the Salt River Valley dates to 1867, although a prehistoric tribe of Indians, the Hohokams, farmed by irrigation centuries before white men came to the valley. In 1911, Roosevelt Dam on the Salt River was completed, giving the valley its first dependable supply of irrigation water.

Cotton leads all other crops in acreage and value (132,000 acres), followed by alfalfa, barley, grain sorghums, vegetables (winter lettuce, carrots, early potatoes, onions, cabbage, celery, cauliflower, and broccoli), and wheat.

Cattle feeding continues to increase. Several feedlots are located in the Salt River Valley in response to the growing demand in the Phoenix metropolitan area.

THE YUMA PROJECT

The Yuma Project, a Federal irrigation development authorized in 1904, is located in California and Arizona, along both sides of the Colorado River. The Reservation Division, the California portion of the project, is made up of the Bard and the Indian sectors, which previously were served by a canal from Laguna Dam and now are supplied by the All-American Canal. In addition to lands in Arizona the project covers a gross area of about 25,000 acres in California. The present irrigated area (about 11,000 acres) lies partly within the Bard Irrigation District, which was organized in 1927. Field crops of barley, oats, wheat, soybeans, corn, sorghums, and cotton, and major truck crops such as melons, lettuce, and tomatoes are grown here.

THE PALO VERDE VALLEY

The Palo Verde Valley lies along the Colorado River in eastern Riverside County, California, and resembles the Imperial Valley in climate and agricultural pattern. The district embraces an area of 104,500 acres bordering and extending along the river for nearly 30 miles and 17,500 acres of adjoining lands on the Palo Verde Mesa. Substantially two-thirds of the land in the district is now under irrigation, and the irrigated area continues to expand. Alfalfa hay and seed, melons, lettuce, cotton, grain, field corn, and sorghums are the principal crops.

Figure 13-8. Cultivating young lettuce in the Imperial Valley of California. The operation is dependent upon migrant laborers, many of whom are "braceros" from Sonora and Sinaloa, Mexico. (Bureau of Reclamation)

THE IMPERIAL VALLEY

The largest irrigation development in the desert area of southern California is that of the Imperial Valley.

The water storage capacity of the Hoover Dam safeguards the Imperial Valley against the danger of destructive spring floods and of summer water shortages alike. When the All-American Canal was completed in 1940 bringing Colorado River water to the valley entirely over American land, increased irrigated acreage and augmented hydroelectric power were made possible. Eighty miles long, 232 feet wide, and 21.6 feet deep, the canal feeds 1,700 miles of distribution canals that fan out from it.

The economy of the Imperial Valley is based squarely on agriculture; its industries are related almost entirely to the processing and packaging of food products. The valley specializes in the raising of winter vegetables and other crops that mature here earlier than in almost any other part of the United States. A very wide range of truck and field crops can be grown. Since only a minor area of the acreage is put in permanent crops, farming is rotated and flexible. Double cropping is common, about ten per cent of the total acreage being farmed in this way.

Farming is characterized by highly commercialized large-scale operations that utilize a considerable amount of machinery even by California's agricultural standards. Machines are used to prepare the fields, to plant them, to cultivate them, and to harvest many of the crops. The area has nearly 5,000 farms, averaging about 100 acres each, whose total crop value amounts to $150 million a year. Labor consists mainly of Mexicans, Orientals, and Negroes.

Imperial Valley products are shipped to all parts of the United States, chiefly by rail. They also find important local markets in the Los Angeles and San Diego metropolitan districts, for fine paved highways connect El Centro to Los Angeles, 210 miles away, and to San Diego, 118 miles.

Field crops are of the greatest importance in the area, if judged by value and acreage. They take up nearly 350,000 acres, or about 80 per cent of the cultivated land.

Alfalfa ordinarily covers about 40 per cent of the cultivated area each year, and it is used as a soil builder in almost every system of crop rotation. After two to four years of truck crops, flax, or grain, the land must be planted to alfalfa for the same number of years to restore its productivity. Since it is less profitable than flax or vegetables, alfalfa is generally maintained only to complete the rotation cycle. With climatic conditions of the valley favorable to its growth, alfalfa can be cut five to seven times a year.

Even though acreage controls reduced the amount of land planted to cotton from a peak of 112,895 acres in 1953 to the present figure of 43,955 acres, cotton still has a value of over $120 million annually, with an additional $4 million from cottonseed and cottonseed by-products. It therefore remains the most important local crop. Furthermore, reduction of acreage resulted in an intensification of yield of from 1.54 to more than two bales per acre. Though cotton grows well in any part of the valley, it is concentrated chiefly in the north, where the Acala strains produce both the short- and long-staple varieties. A long growing season encourages the high yield per acre. Culture and harvest are both mechanized.

Sugar beets thrive on the local climate, yielding 50 per cent more per acre here than the national average. Harvested when southern California's sugar refineries would otherwise be idle, the sugar beet provides a good cash crop that fits well into the rotation farming of the region. Moreover, sugar beets can be grown successfully for at least two years on the same land. The accepted rotation practice of the region is as follows: vegetables or flax for two or three years, sugar beets for one or two, and alfalfa for three. Since sugar beets may be planted from June to October and harvested from early February through June, they make it possible to employ the same labor on a yearly basis. Sugar beets rank second to cotton as a valuable field crop.

Barley is sown throughout the valley and is the most important of the cereal crops. It can be grown alone and harvested as barley hay or can be combined with alfalfa to form winter pasture; it also can be cut in spring with the alfalfa to become mixed hay. The extremely hot weather, however, limits plantings to not later than the first of February. Commercial fields yield an average of 2,000 pounds per acre, and sometimes as much as 4,000. Crop values vary with market prices and in recent years have fluctuated between $3.5 million and $4 million.

Flax has been a major crop since its introduction in 1932; it now grows throughout the valley, which produces more flax per acre than any other region of similar size in the state or in the nation. Yield per acre exceeds the national average three or four times.

The oil derived from flaxseed, linseed oil, constitutes the principal drying oil used in paints, varnishes, linoleum, and other products. It accounts for about 70 per cent of the cash value of the flax crop. Linseed meal, the part of the flaxseed left after the oil has been extracted, is a high-protein feed for livestock. The manufacture of cigarette paper provides a market for flax straw.

Minor field crops include various types of beans, corn, wheat, oats, clovers, safflower, vetches, and sorghums.

Truck crops, such as lettuce, carrots, cantaloupes, peas, tomatoes, and watermelons, grown in the fall, winter, and spring, prove highly profitable, for they can be shipped at times when they are not available in other regions. Some 40 to 50 per cent of the cultivated land is devoted to vegetables in any one rotation period.

The Imperial Valley is probably most famous for its winter lettuce. From December through March about 90 per cent of the lettuce retailed in California comes from the valley. On a year-round basis the lettuce grown in the valley makes up about one-fourth of all the lettuce produced by the state, but it is marketed at a time when the other lettuce growing areas offer little competition. Aside from the uncertain Florida iceberg lettuce, only lettuce produced by the Yuma and Salt River districts can be harvested in the winter.

For the last decade close to 25,000 acres have been planted to lettuce annually. In a recent year nearly 17,000 carloads brought in a return of slightly more than $16 million.

Also a winter crop and one of some commercial importance, carrots rank second to lettuce in value but account for only about one-third as much revenue. The Imperial Valley ships over 5,000 carloads of carrots annually, to all parts of the United States.

The raising of muskmelons, which include cantaloupes, Honey Ball, Honey Dew, Persian, Casaba, and Crenshaw melons, is concentrated in the Central Valley as a summer crop and in the Imperial Valley as a spring crop.

At one time the Imperial Valley supported almost 75 per cent of the state acreage devoted to spring-maturing melons. Despite a recent decrease in production chiefly caused by the increase in mosaic diseases, the valley still remains the major center in the state, with over 9,000 acres planted during November, December, and January for harvest during late April, May, and early June. Cantaloupes bring the highest profit. Ninety per cent of the total acreage devoted to melons is set with cantaloupes to provide approximately 4,000 carloads in a normal year.

Well adapted to the region, watermelons are second to cantaloupes in value of crop and amount of acreage devoted to them. The Imperial Valley is the chief producer of watermelons in the state, with 4,000 acres annually bringing in $1 million.

Tomatoes have been grown successfully in the warmer parts of the valley for many years. Here again the production of varieties that come to fruit early has made tomatoes a desirable crop. The fall-planted tomato matures in November and December and harvesting continues into February or March. The winter-planted crop begins to mature in late April, reaching its peak production during mid-May to early June.

Grapefruit, although the valley's most important fruit crop, has a total local value of less than $500,000 a year. The plantings are widely scattered in those well-drained sandy loams that are reasonably free from alkali; they require special protection against wind, sunburn, and frost. This protection entails a high production cost disadvantageous to the valley farmers when they come into competition with grapefruit raised more cheaply elsewhere.

Dates are concentrated around El Centro and along the Colorado River in the Bard Valley. The relatively high temperature, low humidity, fertile soil, and abundant irrigation water of these regions furnish a natural environment for date culture. Date palms, although far less important here than in the Coachella Valley, yield approximately 3,000 pounds of dates annually.

The seed and cut flower industry is well established in the valley, which produces a good part of the important grain and vegetable seeds used in other parts of the state, the nation, and in Canada. The seed industry furnishes large quantities of flower, lettuce, onion, clover, barley, cotton, wheat, flax, and other seeds with a total value in excess of $3.3 million annually. This figure does not include alfalfa seed, produced mainly around El Centro.

The importance of the relation between livestock and agriculture in this desert area could scarcely be overemphasized, for the crop rotation essential to the maintenance of the fertility of irrigated desert land necessitates that one-third of the land always be planted in alfalfa, which assures an abundant supply of low-cost and high-quality feed. Into a situation of this kind livestock fit very naturally. Beef cattle are brought into the valley for fattening from all parts of the United States, but primarily from west of the Rocky Mountains. Until recently, this industry was limited entirely to autumn, winter, and spring fattening. Today, however, cattle feeding operates on a year-round basis.

Sheep are brought to the valley to be finished from their ranges. Some 350,000 sheep winter here every year and are marketed directly from the local green alfalfa or other pastures. Their total value amounts to $6.5 million annually, about one-half the value of beef cattle.

Southern California's dairying tends to locate near the centers of population. Some dairies in the valley, however, have installed the buildings and equipment essential to the production of Grade "A" milk and export the product. The long, hot summers decrease milk production, a factor that works a hardship on those breeders of purebred cattle who try to achieve a very high production from a limited number of selected cows. On the other hand, hay is cheaper in the valley than it is on the coast, and pastures are available on almost a year-round basis. Sorghum silage, available locally and very inexpensive, also cuts feed costs and makes the production of replacement stock economically profitable.

In a recent year the dairy cattle and dairy products of Imperial County reached a value of almost $5 million. As southern California's population continues to rise, the valley will become even more important as a dairy center.

With the exception of the period when grain

Figure 13-9. Date gardens and citrus groves (mostly grapefruit) in the Coachella Valley, near Indio, California. The Coachella branch of the All-American Canal crosses from right to left in the background. (Bureau of Reclamation)

prices rose sharply immediately after World War II, swine raising has been an important agricultural activity in the valley. Over a period of time, the farmer who markets his feed grains effectively by using them to fatten swine profits more than the farmer who merely sells his grain.

Heat never seriously handicaps the raising of pigs as long as they have an abundance of water for drinking and for wallowing. With excellent metropolitan markets nearby, the swine raising industry turns a profit of about $250,-000 annually.

Apiculture and poultry products annually total slightly more than a million dollars in value. Brawley and El Centro produce eggs for local use. Bee keeping centers exist in alfalfa seed districts; from 40,000 to 50,000 colonies of bees cross-pollinate and feed on the flowers. At least two strong hives of domestic honeybees per acre are considered desirable in or around the alfalfa seed fields. The apiaries' chief product is honey.

Agricultural trends in the Imperial Valley follow and parallel those of most of rural California. Cultivated areas are decreasing in size; the result is a larger capitalization per area. Today the average farm consists of about 90.4 acres. A minimum capital of $250,000 is necessary in order to realize a six per cent return on the initial investment. The use of tile to line irrigation ditches is an important recent innovation, and land so equipped now sells for $750 an acre; it is valued as highly as the water supply itself.

THE COACHELLA VALLEY

The Coachella Valley occupies the northern part of the Salton Basin, and has, for the most part, been developed since 1900.

Figure 13-10. Looking across the Coachella branch of the All-American Canal. Note the character of the landscape. The vegetation typically is sparse and low, the soil sandy in nature. Water is the key to growth and production in the area. (Bureau of Reclamation)

The Coachella Valley County Water District was organized in 1918 to protect the existing water supply from artesian wells and to secure additional water from the Colorado River. The Coachella branch of the All-American Canal was begun by the United States Bureau of Reclamation in 1934 and completed in 1948. It crosses the Coachella Valley just north of Indio, turns south to supply the West Side, and now conveys Colorado River water along the eastern side of the Coachella Valley. An underground distribution system delivers water to most of the valley's 136,000 acres of developed land lying within the area serviced by the All-American Canal.

The principal crops of the Coachella are early table grapes, dates, citrus fruit, vegetables out of season in other areas, and field crops. They contribute more than $26 million to the valley's yearly income.

Grapes make up the Coachella Valley's most important crop. Only the early table varieties are raised, but these bring in an annual return of more than $7 million. The favorite and most extensively cultivated variety, the Thompson Seedless, covers about 8,000 acres.

About 90 per cent of the date acreage in the United States, or 4,430 acres, is in the Coachella Valley. The relatively high temperatures, the fertile soil, and an abundance of water, have made the valley a natural environment for dates.

Probably no activity in the Coachella Valley has experienced as rapid a growth as cattle feeding, which each year becomes a more important factor in the total economy. Cattle are brought here from Montana, Arizona, Texas, and New Mexico to be fed. There are always at least 40,000 head of cattle here each year, with 12,000 during the hot summer months. The local operation proves that cattle can be fattened all 12 months, and that scientifically designed shades, the use of cool water, and the feeding of balanced rations to obtain the greatest yield can stabilize the year-round aspect of the business.

MANUFACTURING

Growth of manufacturing in the Southwestern Interior Plateaus, Plains, and Mountains Region has, of necessity, been in those industrial enterprises whose products have low freight costs per unit to markets. Industries also have to turn out products that do not require in processing large amounts of water. Manufacturing must be relatively smoke-free. The electronics and aircraft components industries furnish the chief answers to these requirements. With products of this type, freight rates no longer are an overriding consideration and production is not necessarily market oriented. Along with these industries have come research laboratories, warehousing facilities, and growth in supporting industries. Food processing, an old established industry within the region, has grown considerably in recent years in response to the great increase in population.

Modern scientific and technological advances are responsible for the rapid growth in manufacturing in this region. Atomic and space research centers are located at Los Alamos, White Sands, Holloman, Kirtland, Sandia, and Albuquerque, New Mexico; Phoenix and Tucson, Arizona; and Palmdale and Lancaster in California's Antelope Valley. Los Alamos, a closed city high on a mesa, was the site of research for the first atomic bomb. At the giant Edwards Air Force Base dozens of civilian contractors work with the Air Force and the National Aeronautics and Space Administration on jet and rocket development. To the south, at Air Force Plant 42, other thousands are employed by five air frame manufacturers in a unique production and testing center for Air Force and Navy jet fighters and bombers. At Phoenix, Arizona, AiResearch Manufacturing Company, a division of the Garrett Corporation, employs over 3,000 workers in its electronics equipment factory. Motorola, Sperry-Rand, and General Electric also have electronics divisions here. Near Tucson, Arizona, not far from the Mexican border at Fort Huachuca, is the Army's electronics proving ground.

Many industries have been attracted to the mushrooming desert electronics areas. The rapid population growth in Phoenix since 1950 has created a home market for more than 35 new firms to supply building materials and equipment to local contractors. Their products include such items as aluminum thresholds, lighting fixtures, concrete blocks, and prefabricated steel buildings.

Just north of Lancaster, California, the U.S. Rubber Company maintains its tire testing facility for controlled road tests of auto, truck, tractor, and aircraft tires. Nearby is the Great Lakes Carbon Company's multimillion dollar installation for production of carbon and graphite products. The only plant of its type west of the Mississippi River, this is one of the four major producers in the nation; it is capable of supplying all carbon needs of the West.

The Mojave industrial area includes Helendale and Lenwood along the Mojave River; Hinkley in the Hinkley Valley; and Barstow, Daggett, Newberry, and Yerma in the Mojave Valley. Those industries related to mining, such as sand, rock, gravel, cement block, concrete mix, and asphalt plants, contribute more than a small part to the local economy.

RECREATION AND TOURISM

From a region to be shunned, the Southwest-

Figure 13-11. Zion Canyon in Zion National Park, southwestern Utah. This magnificent gorge has a depth of from 1,500 to 2,500 feet. (National Park Service)

Figure 13-12. Hoover (Boulder) Dam, the fourth highest concrete dam in the world, has a hydro-electric capacity of 1,344,000 kilowatts, which can supply the domestic needs of 7,500,000 people. It is the highest dam in the United States. (Bureau of Reclamation)

ern Interior Plateaus, Plains, and Mountains Region, in a few short years, has become the goal for a vast number of people seeking health, rest, and winter recreation.

The region displays many scenic wonders. The Grand Canyon, the Painted Desert, Bryce Canyon, and Zion National Park are perhaps the best known, but Canyon de Chelly, Navajo National Monument, Saguaro National Monument, and the Petrified Forest in Arizona, Arches National Monument in Utah, and such spectacular engineering feats as Hoover Dam lure visitors to this area from many parts of the United States and the rest of the world.

DESERT RESORTS

Modern transportation has transformed the lowlands of this region into one of the West's most fascinating playgrounds. The warm, sunny, and dry winter has created a tourist industry of major importance. The face of the land is dotted with new hotels and resorts—sometimes entire new communities.

One of the nation's famous desert resorts, Palm Springs, California, receives over a half-million visitors annually. Other resort cities of some note include Palm Desert, La Quinta, Cathedral City, North Palm Springs, and Desert Hot Springs, all in California's interior desert.

POPULATION

Except for metropolitan areas—Phoenix and Tucson, Arizona; El Paso, Texas; and Albuquerque, New Mexico—the population of the Southwest is characteristically sparse and widely scattered, with the cities and urban communities very small. Included in this latter category are cities such as Santa Fe, capital of New Mexico (34,676).

In the past ten years, Arizona has led the nation in the rate of growth of manufacturing employment. Companies making aircraft equipment and parts have provided 46 per cent of the industrial jobs created since 1950 in the Phoenix metropolitan area, which now has a population of 652,032 (1960). The city of Phoenix had 430,459 people within its corporate limits in 1960, a 303 per cent gain over 1950. Phoenix and its environs offer a strategic dispersal area for light, diversified, smokeless industries. This appeal to industrial capital comes from a city which less than a century ago was just a wide spot in a desert road. The history of Phoenix provides an arresting comment on what a healthy climate, controlled water, and human initiative can do for a community.

Tucson, Arizona (212,892), with a percentage increase of 368.4 in population in the past decade, is one of the nation's rapidly growing communities. It also is one of America's oldest cities, founded about A.D. 800 by a long-vanished Indian tribe. Spanish conquistadores, in their 16th-century search for the Seven Cities of Cibola, were the first white men to see the city. Modern Tucson is world famous as a winter health resort. It is a railroad junction and a distribution center. Like Phoenix, it has become an important center for electronics and guided missiles development.

Albuquerque, New Mexico (198,856), with a metropolitan area population of 260,318, is another of the West's fast-growing urban centers, having more than doubled its size in ten years. The largest city in New Mexico, Albuquerque is a commercial center for agricultural, lumbering, and mining activities, and for wool growing, canning, packing, and oil refining. It is also the home of Kirtland Air Force Base.

Figure 13-13. The Grand Canyon, part of Grand Canyon National Park in Arizona, is the world's most spectacular illustration of erosion. (National Park Service)

Figure 13-14. Tucson, Arizona, world famous as a year-round health resort, has had unparalleled growth during the past decade. (Manley Photography)

El Paso, Texas (272,239), has a metropolitan population of 310,690. It is the largest city on the United States-Mexico border and is a port of entry with a large international trade. El Paso is also an important junction point for East-West transcontinental and north-south axial rail lines and highways. Industries include smelters, oil refineries, cotton gins, oil mills, cement mills, railroad shops, clothing factories, brewing and soft drink plants, textile mills, food processing concerns, and a copper refinery.

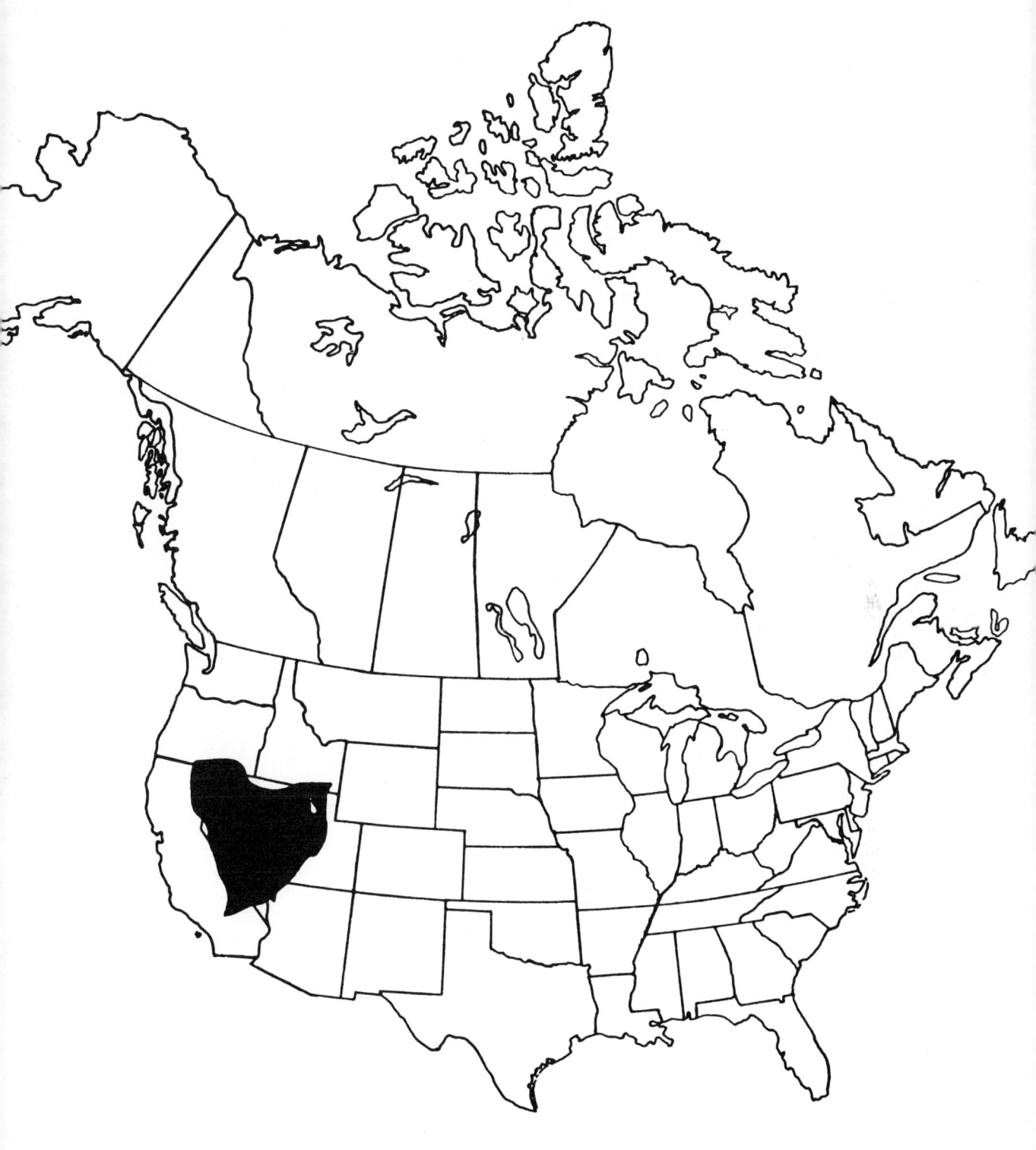

14 | *Basin and Range Province*

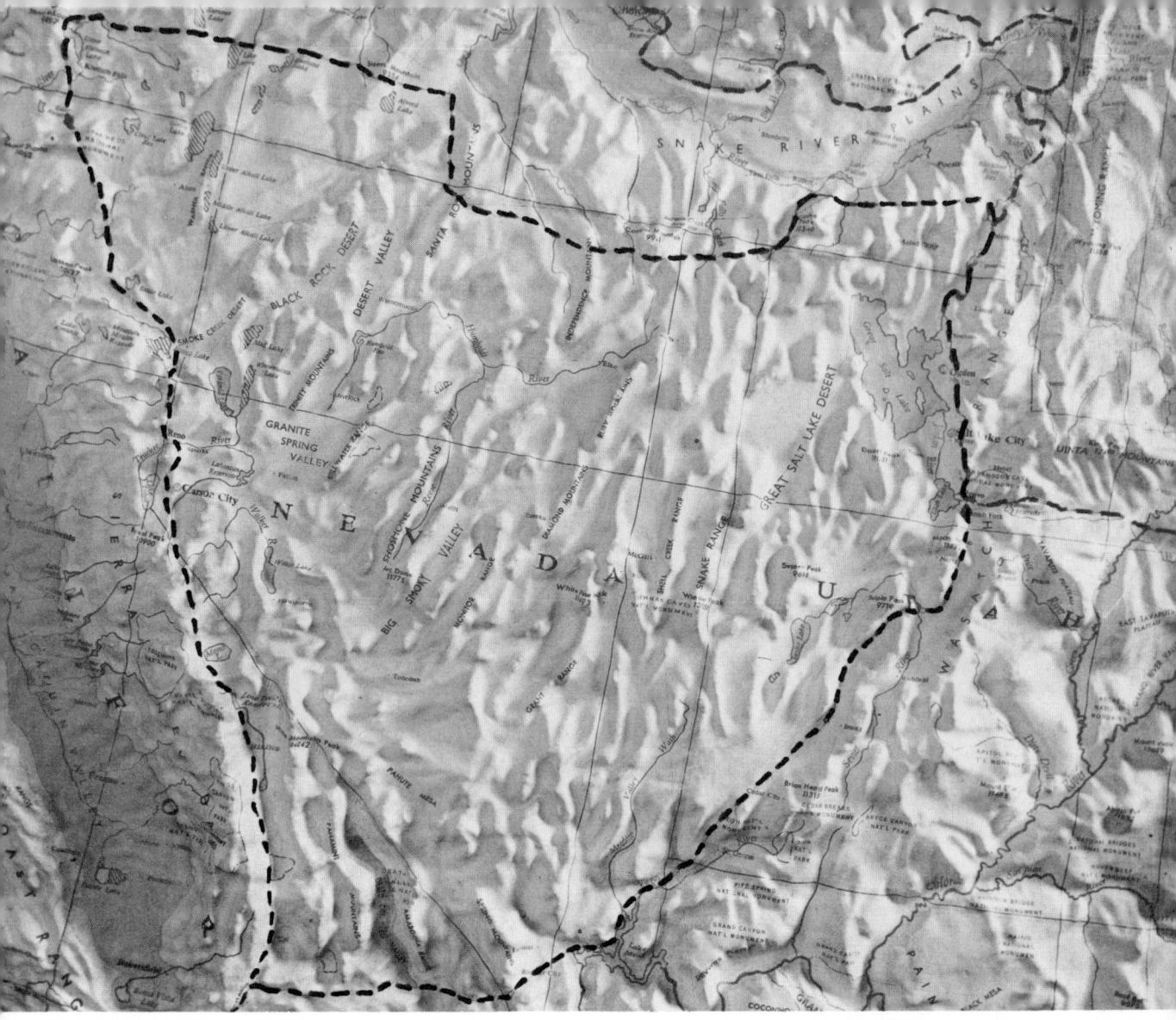

(Relief map copyright Aero Service Corp.)

THE Basin and Range Province encompasses nearly all of Nevada, most of Utah west of the Wasatch Range, southern Oregon east of the Cascades, northeastern California, and the Mono-Inyo area, which includes Death Valley, east of California's Sierra Nevada Range. It consists mainly of high (3,000 to 6,000 feet), smooth, desert basins, above which rise several hundred isolated, generally north-south trending mountain ranges 2,000 to 5,000 feet higher. The basins are floored with detritus from the mountains that the feeble drainage cannot carry to the sea. Most of the area has internal drainage.

Mountains on the west (Sierra Nevada and Cascades) mark the boundary clearly. Between mountains the basins merge with the Columbia Plateau on the north. The eastern boundary against the Wasatch Mountains and the escarpment of the Colorado Plateau is generally clear. On the south the region merges with the Southwestern Interior Plateaus, Plains, and Mountains Region.

SURFACE FEATURES

The Oregon lake section is like the adjacent Columbia Plateau but is faulted into young block mountains 1,000 to 2,000 feet high made of formerly horizontal lavas. Some of the intervening lakes overflow regularly; others overflow occasionally.

The Nevada and Utah portions differ from the Oregon lake section in having older and larger block mountains, for the most part eroded to maturity. Their 50 to 100 ranges occupy fully half the area. Many are complexly deformed sedimentary rocks. It is as though an old folded mountain region were nearly base leveled, covered in places by lava, broken by new north-south faults—the new fault blocks being tilted into mountains—and then maturely eroded in a climate so arid that the intervening troughs were filled with waste that in a humid climate would have gone to the sea. Trees occur only on the highest mountains (8,000 to 10,000 feet) or in occasional protected gorges. There is little soil on the mountains; bare rocks of bright colors are conspicuous.

Some of these ranges are so eroded that their forms no longer suggest fault blocks, especially when it is remembered that the strata were complexly folded before the faulting. Their opposite sides may have equal steepness.

There are about 100 enclosed basins, generally with sinks. Some have salt lakes; a few, fresh lakes; and others, playas or salinas. In some cases alluvial fans from opposite sides meet. The depth of filling is sometimes 2,000 feet. Some basins are absolute deserts; some have sagebrush and bunch grass like the mountains. Generally, where cattle can find water there is also some grass.

In the glacial epoch, Lake Bonneville, in the eastern part of the Basin and Range Province, rose 1,000 feet above Great Salt Lake and covered 20,000 square miles, overflowing to the Snake River. "Fossil" shorelines, cliffs, bars, deltas, and the like, are striking features of the present topography. Lake Lahontan, in the western part, covered 8,440 square miles; it left similar shorelines but did not overflow.

Great Salt Lake is the biggest and most famous lake west of the Mississippi. It is also the strangest. Five hundred miles inland, it is saltier than any sea. Although 1,750 square miles in area, it averages only 13 feet in depth. Many people travel over it daily, but by train, not by boat. Surrounded by arid desert, it should be an oasis of animal and vegetable life —yet little lives near it and nothing in it except algae and a tiny brine shrimp three-eighths of an inch long. The lake annually loses 40 inches of water by evaporation.

One hundred million years ago, before the North American continent had taken its present form, a huge ocean covered the western part of it from the Arctic to the Gulf of California. When the continent emerged, the sea disappeared, leaving behind it vast deposits of marine sediment, limestone, and sandstone, and a great, mountain-ribbed basin that stretched from central Utah to eastern California. Some 100,000 years ago a long period of rainfall sent torrential streams crashing down the mountainsides, carrying with them tons of the ancient marine sediments and salts. This gradually filled part of the basin with water and silt, creating an inland sea that, unlike ordinary lakes, has had no outlet to the ocean during most of its existence. Eventually the surface of this inland sea stabilized at what geologists now call the Bonneville level.

As eons passed and the Pleistocene streams reduced to relative trickles, Lake Bonneville began to shrink. Evaporation carried off its water but left the heavier salts, which are present in varying degrees in all lake waters. As a result, the proportionate salt content of the remaining waters was increased enormously. Today, one glass of lake water reveals an inch of salt after evaporation.

Geologists began predicting the ultimate death of Great Salt Lake by evaporation decades ago. But, though its level varies cyclically and it has lost 400 square miles in the last 80 years, it has refused to die.

The northeastern part of California is an extensive tableland broken by numerous mountain ranges. Surface configuration bears almost universal evidence of former volcanic activity. Lava flows are visible wherever streams have cut valleys sufficiently deep to produce rapid erosion. Such flows also are apt to be apparent on the sides of the larger valleys; and the Pit River, the principal stream of the area, has eroded spectacular canyons through them.

With the exception of a few high summits at the eastern margin, elevations above the local valleys are not great. Broad terraces of lava lie on the flanks of many of the ranges. The uplands between the mountains are wider than the terraces but only gently rolling, although deeply cut by the larger streams. These tablelands are not to be thought of as elevated plateaus falling away to steep cliffs on all sides. Instead, they were formed when liquid materials poured into prevolcanic depressions, leveled off, and solidified into lava.

Near the eastern edge are the Warner Mountains, a backbone of volcanic rocks upraised by a series of earth movements. The highest point in the range is Eagle Peak, which now stands almost 10,000 feet above sea level. Other peaks seldom rise above 7,000 feet. Flatlands in the area range from 3,300 to 5,100 feet in elevation.

The Mono-Inyo portion of eastern and southeastern California is a continuation of the Basin and Range Province. Its mountains and valleys have a definite north-northwest to south-southeast alignment. The major ground depression is the Owens Valley immediately to the east of the Sierra Nevada. Behind it the mountains are crowned by Alpine peaks, which are usually visible.

East of Owens Valley is the White-Inyo Range, as high as the Sierra Nevada but less glaciated. White Mountain Peak, with an elevation of 14,246 feet, is the third highest in California. Long, steep slopes lead downward on both sides so that the White Mountains differ markedly from the Sierra Nevada, which present a steep slope only to the east.

The Panamint Range, almost as massive as the White-Inyo Mountains, lies east of Panamint Valley. From Telescope Peak, at 11,045 feet, one may look directly into the depths of Death Valley, where Bad Water, the lowest point in the United States, lies at 282 feet below sea level.

Several smaller valleys and ranges of the same pattern exist. They stretch northward to the ancient volcanic cones and craters just south of Mono Lake where the Mono Craters—weird formations of volcanic glasses, unusual lava flows, and large, ash-covered craters—may be seen.

North of Mono Lake, drainage leads into Nevada by means of the East and West Walker Rivers. Here, too, the landforms lie primarily north-south.

CLIMATE

Nowhere in the United States has climate influenced the patterns of settlement and culture more definitively than in this arid region of the West. Together with topography and soils, it has determined rather rigidly the location of most settlement, whether in individual farms, rural communities, or larger population centers. It has restricted the number of people that the region as a whole can support within relatively narrow limits, and as a result many rural communities already are experiencing population pressures of severe intensity. It has been primarily responsible for the development of irrigation, a distinctive and highly specialized type of agriculture. Finally, it has given rise to certain basic problems inherent in an environment where man has had to utilize meager resources to the fullest possible extent and resort to specialized techniques and disciplines to make agricultural development possible and settlement a success.

Figure 14-1. Typical ranch scene in southwestern Nevada. Note the arid landscape and evidences of mechanical weathering. (Nevada State Highway Department)

The factor that significantly alters the general climate of the region is topography. The Sierra Nevada-Cascade Mountains crests, rising to a maximum elevation of about 14,000 feet, act as a barrier to storms moving eastward and are responsible for much of the relatively heavy precipitation on the western slopes and the aridity on the eastern side. Similarly each successive mountain range eastward acts in turn to increase precipitation on its western slopes and to make for greater aridity on the slopes and valleys to its east. It is not uncommon to find some valleys receiving only four to five inches of precipitation while mountain slopes less than 40 miles away receive in excess of 40 inches.

Topography also greatly modifies temperatures. Some valleys are not free of frost for a sufficiently long period to grow anything but the hardiest grains and forage while others in the same latitude but at lower elevations have summer growing seasons warm enough and long enough to permit the growing of such late maturing crops as sugar beets, fruits, and corn.

The great and abrupt differences in precipitation and temperature induced by topography form the important feature of the climate. They give rise to characteristic "humid islands" wherever mountain masses project to a substantial height above the floor of the desert valleys. Many of these islands receive enough precipitation to support dense stands of Ponderosa and lodgepole pine, quaking aspen, Engelmann spruce, Douglas fir, and Alpine fir, as well as a wide variety of lesser vegetation in the forests and in Alpine meadows, brush fields, and woodland areas.

Great variations sometimes occur within short distances. A small valley near the mountains may be covered with grasses and trees, while less than ten miles away the parched earth and scanty desert shrub vegetation give evidence of a drastically reduced rainfall. Salt Lake City, for example, is located in the semiarid zone at the base of the Wasatch Mountains at an elevation of 4,408 feet; it receives 15.79 inches of moisture annually. Forty miles west of the city the desert receives less than six inches of rainfall a year; 20 miles east of the city, Silver Lake, at an elevation of 8,700 feet in the Wasatch Range, has a mean annual precipitation of 40.82 inches.

The importance of this interrelationship between cool, humid mountain islands and warm, arid valleys cannot be emphasized too strongly. The islands, for the most part, are not habitable because of steep slopes, low temperatures, rocky soils, the short growing season, the deep snow mantle, their inaccessibility, and similar factors. They are, however, the gathering grounds for creeks and rivers that flow to the valleys. These creeks and rivers provide water for irrigation and give rise to population clusters.

Over most of the region the summers are hot and the winters are cold. The average maximum temperatures range from more than 100° F. on the floors of the desert basins to less than 50° at the higher elevations. Temperatures below zero occur quite generally in cold winters, though prolonged periods of severely low temperatures are not nearly as common as in the Middle West or the East. This is because the mountains ward off the intensely cold continental polar and arctic air masses that sometimes move down from Canada into the United States.

Because of the high altitude and extreme dryness and clearness of the air, there is rapid nocturnal radiation of heat, which results in wide daily ranges in temperature. In extreme instances the daily range may become as great as 50 to 60 degrees. Humidity is normally low, and the dryness of the air makes both the heat of summer and the cold of winter less disagreeable.

The most striking climatic features are the high percentage of sunshine, low rainfall in the valleys, and high evaporation rate.

Precipitation, in addition to being generally low, is also extremely variable, following a pattern of successive wet and dry periods rather than a heterogeneous occurrence of single wet and dry years. This variability in precipitation is illustrated and confirmed by 80 years of weather records and over much longer periods by studies of changes in the levels of interior lakes and of tree growth. The above- and below-average periods may be as short as two or three years, or as long as 20 years. The longer periods may be broken by single years of an opposite character.

Most of the precipitation occurs during the winter season; summer rainfall is very light. Storms with high winds rarely occur—and even more rarely do they cause appreciable damage. Thunderstorms are infrequent.

Over most of the region, frosts begin early in autumn and continue till late in spring. The shortest growing season is in the extreme northeast and the longest in the extreme south; the range is from less than 100 days at several stations in the northeast, to 140 in the west, and to over 225 in the extreme south.

SOILS

The soils of the croplands are almost as complex and variable as the landforms, climate, and other natural features of the region. Parent materials include limestone, lacustrine deposits, and a wide range of volcanics. These soils were deposited by wind and water on the bottoms of old lakes, on lake and stream terraces, on stream flood plains, and on alluvial fans. Very little of the soil on lands used for crop production was developed in place from original parent material.

Arid region soils are generally low in organic matter and nitrogen; the amounts reflect somewhat the climate and native vegetation. Shrubs and bunch grasses are the principal vegetation in places where rainfall is less than ten inches. The soils are light in color, alkaline in reaction, and often high in lime and mineral nutrients.

As rainfall increases, native vegetation changes to sagebrush and larger shrubs, then bunch grasses, and then short grasses. The content of organic matter in the soil increases accordingly, which permits wider varieties of farming and farm crops. In most of the unforested parts, precipitation has been inadequate for leaching, and the soils therefore are generally alkaline in reaction and rich in mineral nutrients. Zones of lime accumulation are typical. They are near the surface in the deserts and progressively deeper in the higher rainfall belts.

AGRICULTURE

HISTORICAL DEVELOPMENT

Since the Basin and Range Province is an arid region, the settlement and use of the land, the growth of communities, and the entire culture of the area were possible only through the development of irrigation.

Permanent settlement began with the arrival of the Mormon pioneers at what is now Salt Lake City in the summer of 1847. Modern irrigation in America dates from this period. Within two decades settlement spread to all parts of the region that could be irrigated easily. Expansion in numbers of farms and livestock and in the acreage of irrigated land continued until about 1900. Dry farming expanded considerably between 1900 and 1920. Since 1920, the total acreage of cropland has remained about the same.

Settlement in nearly all parts of Utah followed a village pattern. The village lot of one to three acres was the site of the family home, and the village was the center of farming activities. Croplands and grazing lands were outside the village — sometimes at considerable distances from the home. This resulted in a noncontiguous land ownership and use pattern. Partly because irrigation made it a necessity and partly because of the philosophy of the early settlers, farm holdings were small. Irrigation systems were developed by co-operative effort, usually without benefit of trained engineers and with the use of crude mechanical equipment. Time has modified the original agricultural pattern somewhat, but early characteristics still prevail strongly.

Agricultural development began in Nevada during the California gold rush. Stations were established at points along the westward route where native grasslands furnished pasture for horses and oxen. A permanent settlement was founded in Carson Valley in 1850. During the following decade very little land was enclosed or cultivated, however; farming was limited to harvesting a small amount of native hay and growing a few vegetables. Flour and other staples were imported from California.

Settlement expanded in Carson and adjacent valleys after discovery of the Comstock Lode. Wheat for flour, potatoes, and a rather wide variety of vegetables were produced for local markets.

Farming on the Truckee River resulted partly from the building and operation of the transcontinental railroad and partly from the Comstock Lode. The Walker River Valley was developed originally as cattle country, with markets first in the California mining camps and later in those of Nevada. The Humboldt River lowlands got their start as winter pastures for cattle. Smaller valleys in northern Nevada and southern Oregon were opened up later as the cattle industry expanded.

East-central and southern Nevada were settled largely by Mormons. Some cultivated crops; others produced milk and butter for the local mining camps. Range livestock, however, was almost the only commercial agricultural enterprise in this section until the railroad was built from Salt Lake City to Los Angeles in 1905.

The decline of mining and the change in cattle production methods from year-long grazing to winter feeding effected marked changes in Nevada agriculture. Crop farms were reorganized and consolidated into cattle ranches. The organization of many of these ranches later proved inadequate to meet drought conditions and economic change. Considerable adjustment is still in progress.

Diversified farming experienced a recovery in Nevada with the tide of reclamation that swept the West after the turn of the century. This development was financed by the government and by large-scale borrowing. The first effect of increased diversification was a surplus of alfalfa hay above the demands of the livestock industry. Dairy, poultry, livestock, and crop enterprises were then developed in alfalfa producing areas. This revival of general farming did not occur in the range areas but was limited to the west-central and southern Nevada valleys. Its development in these areas still is influenced by the varying local demands for range livestock feed.

THE PRESENT PICTURE

The type of agriculture in any area represents an adaptation to the physical and economic environment. In the Basin and Range Province there are three general types of agriculture: (1) general irrigated farming, (2) dry land farming, and (3) range livestock raising. Although most farms belong entirely in one of these three categories, some are a mixture of two or of all three types.

General irrigated farms make up about 70 per cent of the total farms, although acreage of irrigated lands is relatively small and in many cases the supply of irrigation water is so inadequate that maximum crop yields are not obtained and the acreage of the most profitable crops is seriously curtailed. Most of the farms contain some grazing land, the major part of which is not irrigated because of inadequacy of irrigation water. The grazing land is largely in pasture for dairy cattle and work animals.

Figure 14-2. Aerial view of the White Mountains from 30,000 feet over the Sierra Nevada. Owens Valley is in the center of the picture. The White Mountains, which lie in the rain shadow of the Sierra Nevada, are quite barren. (Robert Symons Flying Service, Bishop, California)

The tilled acreage produces a wide variety of crops with greatly differing degrees of intensity and profitableness. The larger part is planted to alfalfa hay and feed grains for winter feeding of farm livestock. Cash crops include grains where water for irrigation in summer is not available. Where water is available, potatoes, sugar beets, canning peas, beans, tomatoes, vegetables for fresh market, apples, peaches, pears, apricots, cherries, and berries are grown. More intensive crops generally are restricted to areas with better soils, longer growing season, and an adequate water supply — particularly late season water. Dairy cows and poultry, including turkeys, are the major livestock enterprises on irrigated farms.

Major irrigated areas. Streams draining into the Great Basin, principally from the Sierra Nevada-Cascade and Wasatch Mountains, form the chief water supply for irrigation. These are: (1) the Bear and Sevier Rivers and Weber River-Utah Lake in Utah; (2) the Truckee, Carson, Walker, and Humboldt Rivers in Nevada; and (3) the Long and Owens Rivers in California. Exceptions are the Pit River of northeastern California, which rises in the Warner Range and flows westward into the Sacramento River's drainage, and the Virgin River of southwestern Utah, which is part of the lower Colorado River complex. Other irrigated areas include a number of small basins in northeastern California and the Pahrump Valley of southwestern Nevada.

The Bear River Basin embraces an area of nearly five million acres. Water is diverted directly from the Bear River or its major tributaries, the Logan and Little Bear Rivers, to irrigate some 240,000 acres of land, which includes irrigated pasture. The total water used annually is 585,000 acre-feet, an amount about 80 per cent adequate for the needs of the area.

The Weber River-Utah Lake drainage basin is located in north-central Utah. Within it are found the three largest cities of the state, most of the industrial activities, and the major part of the production from irrigation agriculture. The major streams that drain the area are the Weber River and its tributaries that empty into Great Salt Lake and the Provo and the Spanish Fork Rivers that discharge into Utah Lake, which in turn empties into Great Salt Lake through the Jordan River. Except for the Jordan River, which rises in Utah Lake and flows northward into Great Salt Lake, these streams originate in the mountains east of the valley and flow westward.

Diversions from the natural flow of the streams provide some water for irrigation.

However, since the natural runoff peak is in May and June and the peak demands for water are in July and August, the areas that are dependent entirely upon natural stream flow usually have an inadequate supply in late summer. To equalize the supply during this low period, several storage reservoirs have been constructed. The more important ones are: the Pineview on the Ogden River, a tributary of the Weber; the Echo and East Canyon on the Weber; the Deer Creek on the Provo; and the Strawberry, whose water is conveyed through a tunnel from the Colorado River Basin to the Bonneville Basin. In turn, the Strawberry reservoir empties into the Spanish Fork River.

The land irrigated in this basin amounts to 369,800 acres. On this acreage, 1,100,000 acre-feet of water are normally used, which is about 86 per cent adequate. This shortage adversely affects 144,500 acres.

Since the major cities and the principal industrial activities are located in this area, the need for water for nonirrigation purposes also is large. The total population, mostly urban, is nearly 500,000. One of the major problems of some of the municipalities has been to obtain adequate domestic water supplies. In some cases the insufficient water supply has limited industrial expansion.

The Sevier River drainage basin includes most of the southwestern fourth of Utah and comprises an area of approximately 14 million acres. The river rises in the southeastern corner of the basin and flows northward. It breaks through the mountain range westward, circles back, and empties into Sevier Lake. The river and small streams, many of which either dry up completely or partially during the late season, are the main sources of irrigation water.

Some 254,000 acres of land are presently irrigated in the basin, of which only 36,000 acres are adequately irrigated. Of all the areas of Utah, the Sevier drainage basin has the least water in relation to the amount of arable land. Furthermore, because of low precipitation, only a limited amount of the land not irrigated may be dry farmed.

The requirements for water for municipal and industrial uses are not large. There are no cities of more than 5,000, and the total population of the basin is between 62,000 and 65,000.

The Truckee Meadows area includes Truckee Meadows, Washoe, Steamboat, Spanish Springs, and Pleasant Valleys, and lands along the Truckee River down to Pyramid Lake. Irrigation water comes from the Truckee River and its tributaries. The general quality of the land in this area is not good. Conditions have been unfavorable for the formation of deep, fertile soils in all but a few locations in the valley floor of Truckee Meadows and along the streams.

The urban influences of Reno and Sparks strongly affect the type of farming in this area. The suburban fringes of these cities cover a large part of the agricultural land. Production of fresh milk is the major commercial enterprise. Several hundred acres are devoted to the production of vegetables for the local market.

Included within the Carson Valley area are Carson Valley proper, Jack's Valley, the irrigated lands around Carson City and Stewart, and the lands along the Carson River from Carson Valley to Lahontan Reservoir. It derives its water supply from the Carson River and its tributaries. The quality of land under irrigation is fairly good, partly the result of favorable conditions for formation of deep and fertile soils and partly the effect of a short season water supply that has tended to limit the development of irrigation to the better soils. The poorer soils in use are mainly on the granitic fans along the west side of the area. Some shallow, poorly drained soils on the floor of Carson Valley are used for pasture and hay.

Carson Valley is free from urban influences and is held almost entirely in commercial farming enterprises. Stock ranching is the prevailing type of farming. The organization of most ranches includes the use of grazing lands in the national forest, on other Federal range lands, or in leased or owned mountain meadow pastures.

Dairying is quite well developed and appears in fairly large units. A creamery for the local market is located in Carson Valley. The Lake Tahoe area offers a good summer market for milk, and Reno is a year-round market.

Carson City, Minden, Gardnerville, and Dayton are distributing and marketing towns. They are well served by surfaced highways and by a railroad that runs from Reno to Minden.

The Smith and Mason Valleys are irrigated from the west and east forks of the Walker

River. Because of the topography, natural drainage is not well developed. This has resulted in the formation of considerable areas of alkali concentration and the need for extensive artificial drainage.

Livestock farming and ranching is by far the most important farming type. These farms and ranches make up nearly two-thirds the total value of products for the area. Dairy and poultry enterprises are well developed, with a local creamery and a poultry dressing plant. This is also Nevada's principal potato growing section.

The livestock farms and ranches of Smith and Mason Valleys use summer pastures in nearby Antelope and Bridgeport Valleys in California. They also have access to range lands in national forests and the Federal ranges.

The extensive area of irrigated lands along the Humboldt River includes Lovelock Valley, Paradise Valley, the middle river section from Winnemucca to Palisade, and the upper river area above Palisade.

There is a marked difference between the Lovelock Valley and the remainder of the Humboldt River area in climatic conditions, soils, topography, type of farming, and irrigation patches. The climate is milder at Lovelock than farther up the river. The soils are excellent for general farming in most respects, and the cultivated area lies in a compact body not subject to overflow. These conditions have resulted in agricultural developments quite different from those that have taken place elsewhere along the Humboldt River.

The lands in the Lovelock Valley are leveled to permit irrigation by flooding methods. The Rye Patch Dam provides water for 40,000 acres. Many of the farms in the valley are large and general farming methods are rather intensive. Alfalfa production and cattle feeding have long been the principal enterprises. Dairying has been developing slowly to meet the needs of a postwar population increase.

North of Winnemucca, in beautiful Paradise Valley, farming has been carried on since 1863. The Santa Rosa Mountains along the northwest side of the valley are the source of many small streams. Little Humboldt River drains an extensive area of hills and small sections of somewhat low mountains to the north and east.

The production of beef cattle is the major farm enterprise in Paradise Valley. Toiyabe National Forest, part of which is in the Santa Rosa Mountains, has supplied dependable summer range even through the drought years. Crop production is favored and winter losses of livestock are reduced by a rather moderate climate. A limited amount of grain, which thrives on most soils in the valley, serves as a catch crop in good water seasons. Some fruits and vegetables are grown for the local market.

The Middle River section includes lands irrigated from the Humboldt River and a few minor tributaries from below Winnemucca to Palisade Canyon. Alternate periods of flood and drought limit the vegetation to plants able to survive extreme conditions, and the crops are confined almost entirely to native meadows and pastures. Attempts have been made to develop other crops but there has been little progress to date. There is usually not enough time to get a crop started ahead of the spring floods and there is danger, also, of damaging the soil through the loss of the plowed layer during the flood season.

The Upper River section consists of an extensive area of bottomland along the main river from above Palisade Canyon. Irrigation water is obtained directly from the Ruby Mountains, the highest and most dependable watershed on the whole river.

Because of good soils, easily developed water supplies, a relatively favorable growing season, and a ready market in the early mining camps, this area first developed a diversified type of farming. Grain for feed and flour, vegetables, dairy products, and hay were the chief products. As railroad transportation became available and the mines were worked out, these early markets were largely lost and attention was turned to hay and cattle raising.

Agricultural development is confined on the Long and Owens Rivers drainage basin to the eastern base of the Sierra Nevada Range. First developed by settlers in the late 1860's, the Owens Valley had some 50,000 acres of fertile land under irrigation by 1910 and produced crops of alfalfa and deciduous fruits. The growth of Los Angeles, however, and the tapping of the Owens River as a metropolitan water source restricted irrigated acreage in the area. Now livestock and livestock products, which include beef, sheep, wool, and dairy

Figure 14-3. Death Valley National Monument in California. Ancient lake beds are surrounded by the Panamint and Amargosa Ranges. The highest temperature ever recorded in the United States, 134° F., was recorded here. Rainfall averages two inches a year. (National Park Service)

items, with hay as the only field crop of importance, are the mainstays of the local economy.

The irrigated valleys of northeastern California have less than three per cent of the land devoted to crops, although farm land of some importance is found at Shasta and Butte Valleys, the Tule Lake Basin, and at Warm Springs, Susan, Goose Lake, and Surprise Valleys.

The most important of these is the Tule Lake Basin. Veterans of World War II came here to farm and they tend to be more progressive than the older farmers in farming methods. Potatoes and barley are the most important crops. Farmers also are trying to introduce durum macaroni, which is in short national supply.

Pahrump Valley is Nevada's most productive agricultural area. Located on the westerly slope of Mount Charleston, one of the highest peaks (11,700 feet) in southern Nevada, it lies 62 miles west of Las Vegas. A new hard surface highway puts farmers within one hour's driving time of Las Vegas, the marketing center for many of the valley's products.

Pahrump Valley yields fine cotton, the only place in Nevada where this crop is produced. Some 2,000 acres are planted to cotton. Mechanical cotton pickers are used instead of hand pickers; one machine does the work of 90 men.

Gravity irrigation from pumped wells and artesian springs provides the necessary water for crops to reach maturity. The low rainfall, only four inches a year, prohibits any form of nonirrigated agriculture.

The long growing season, with the warm, dry summer and mild, dry winter, permits the growth of a wide range of crops. Many fruits are grown, especially peaches, apricots, plums, pears, pomegranates, figs, many kinds of berries, walnuts, and pecans. Successful crops of corn, milo, sorghum, alfalfa, and grains also are produced.

RANCHING

Range livestock ranching utilizes by far the major part of the land area in the Basin and Range Province, although this type of agricultural enterprise accounts for only about one-fourth of the total farms. Some of the farms are specialized cattle ranches, some are sheep ranches, and a few keep both cattle and sheep. These ranch operations are built around the use of grazing land, mostly publicly owned and administered. However, many farms, particularly the cattle ranches, have some cropland from which forage and feed crops are harvested to feed the animals through the winter. Some cattle and many sheep graze all year, a procedure that usually necessitates moving considerable distances from summer to winter grazing lands. Since feeds suitable for fattening cattle or sheep are relatively scarce, most livestock is marketed out of the region as feeder animals. Some are marketed as "grass fat" animals, and a small percentage is finished in local feed lots.

The low carrying capacity of the open ranges gives rise to large ranches. The bigger ones run from 6,000 to 100,000 acres. Privately owned lands comprise only a small part of the total. The cattle ranches are composed principally of meadows along streams, some winter range, and varied lands that ensure control of water. Nearly all the grazing area is public domain, with the United States Forest Service

Figure 14-4. The Basin and Range Province exhibits great variation in vegetation. Pictured are various forms of xerophytes, plants that have made an adjustment to high temperature regimes and the scarcity of water. (Nevada State Highway Department)

administering most of the higher lands where stock is summered. All grazing on public lands is carried on by individual permits specifying the number of head that may be taken into an area and the length of time the herds and bands may remain. The fees charged for use of the public lands are usually less than the tax assessments on adjoining private tracts. To a considerable extent, priority of land use belongs to the ranchers who can prove they have grazed on specific areas for a number of years.

Beef cattle. Two types of cattle operators are characteristic of the Basin and Range Province. One runs most of his stock on the open range in winter; the other keeps his herds on the home ranch in winter and feeds them hay. Some operators combine the two methods.

As many as 75 acres are required to support a beef animal on the open range in Nevada. Such a low carrying capacity forces ranchers to scatter their stock over a wide area, a situation which makes them reluctant to practice controlled breeding, for it is difficult to get the bulls properly distributed throughout the herd when they are not turned out with the rest of the cattle. It is estimated that 500 head of cattle form the smallest unit that may be operated economically.

Shorthorn, Hereford, and Angus are the main cattle breeds within the region. Shorthorns are well represented in areas where the stock is maintained under fence a good part of the year and wintered in feed lots. Elsewhere, the Hereford is especially popular, fattening better than other cattle on poor range and requiring less attention than the shorthorn. The Angus, hardiest of beef breeds, is not raised in considerable numbers, for it becomes so wild under range conditions that it is difficult to handle.

Most of the cattle coming off the ranges of the Intermountain West do not carry enough flesh to be sent directly to market as beef. These feeders are sold to speculators and packing companies who ship them to California or the Midwest. There they are fed a special fattening ration for from 90 to 120 days before being sent to the slaughterhouses.

Sheep. Sheep raising presents a different set of problems than cattle ranching. Sheep range most of the year on the public domain or in the national forests and sheepmen need

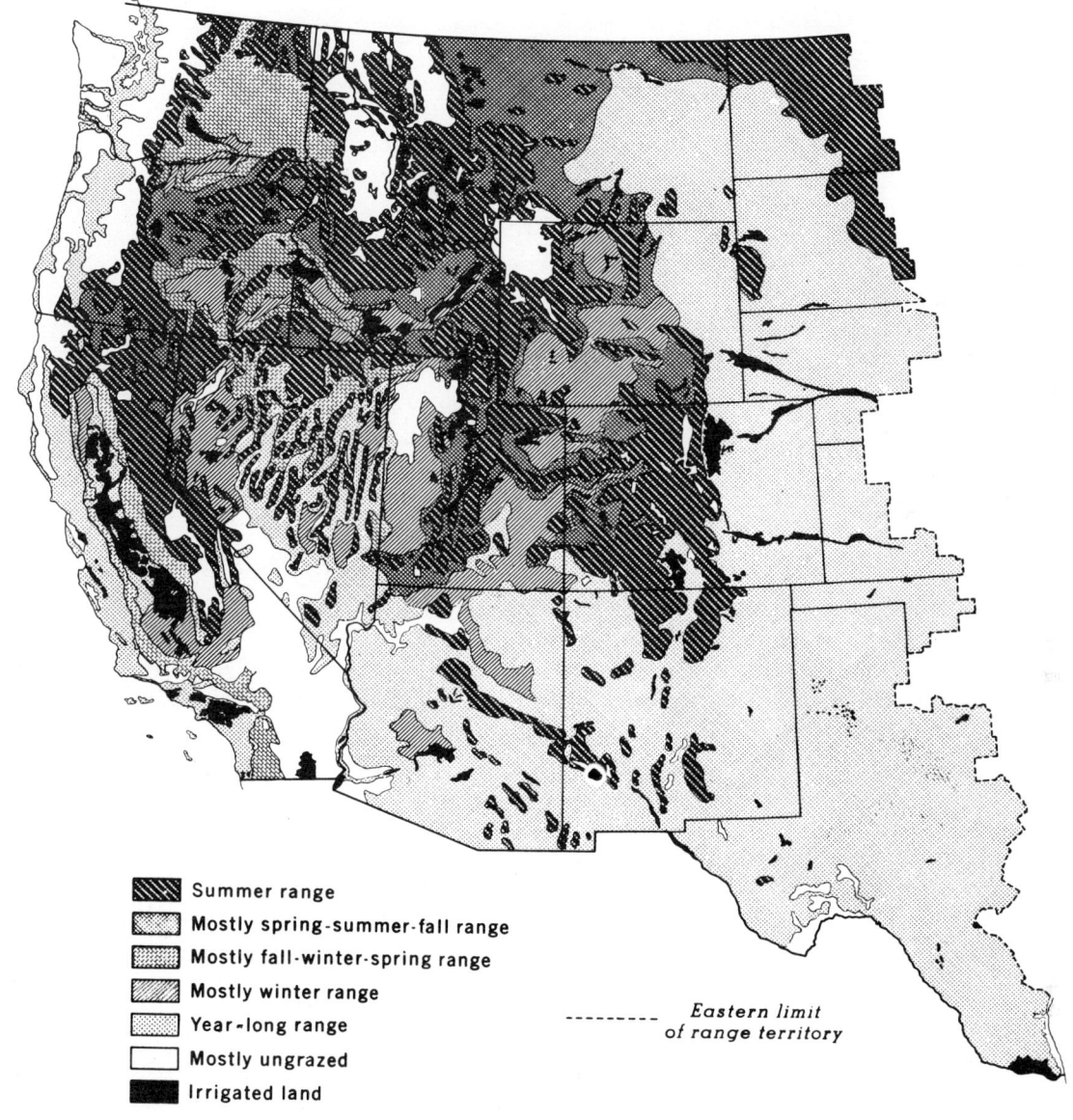

▨	Summer range
▨	Mostly spring-summer-fall range
▨	Mostly fall-winter-spring range
▨	Mostly winter range
▨	Year-long range
☐	Mostly ungrazed
■	Irrigated land

- - - - - - - - - *Eastern limit*
                   of range territory

Figure 14-5. Seasonal use of Western ranges. (U.S. Department of Agriculture)

own little land for a home ranch, although many have enough for lamb sheds and shearing pens. A band of 1,000 is considered the smallest unit for efficient operation.

Sheep usually are driven to the summer range at the higher elevations, although some operators now transport them by truck. In September or in October, depending on market conditions, the bands are brought down from the summer range and separated. Healthy lambs and old sheep are sold; the weaker lambs are held for winter feeding. Bands then are made up again and sent to the winter range.

Summer bands of the large operators number approximately 1,000 ewes with lambs; winter bands have about 2,000 to 2,500 ewes. The average band has one herder, occasionally two. With the herder is a camp tender who brings him his supplies and aids him when necessary. A herder places great reliance on his dogs for handling the band.

Under grazing control the old feud between sheepmen and cattlemen is disappearing, but at one time the feud was so bitter in some parts

Figure 14-6. The ghost town of Hamilton, near Ely, Nevada, stands as a reminder of the mining boom. (Nevada State Highway Department)

of the region that murder frequently resulted.

Sheep raising always has held a prominent position in the Intermountain West and has been the basis of many fortunes and the foundation for the development of many other enterprises. Wool sheep dominate. A very large proportion of the wool clip is marketed outside the region to West Coast and Eastern mills, although Utah has a number of woolen mills and knitting factories.

MINING

The lust for gold and silver caused thousands of prospectors to try their luck in the Basin and Range Province. Many came into the region on their overland trek to California. Others, who rounded the Horn by sea and headed for the mother lode of the Sierra Nevada, went beyond that range and into this province. Mining communities rose rapidly. Nevada mines not only brought about the settlement and development of the region but were vitally important to the nation. During the troubled days after the Civil War, American credit was sustained by the wealth pouring from the Comstock Lode.

Towns that were once great producers of mineral wealth are now either ghost towns or have fallen to the low estate of trading centers. Virginia City, Goldfield, Tonopah, Austin, and Eureka, all in Nevada, were some of the most fabulous.

The Basin and Range Province has yielded hundreds of millions of dollars in gold and silver. Today these metals are recovered chiefly as by-products of other minerals. Nevada's total mineral wealth taken from the ground since the first shafts went down about 100 years ago is a staggering $3 billion.

COPPER

Kennecott Copper is a famous name in Utah and Nevada mining registers, for this corporation has been identified with the Bingham Canyon and Ely districts for decades, mining ore from deep pits and producing blister copper in enormous volume.

Bingham Canyon, Utah. Bingham, the world's largest open pit copper mine, located approximately 28 miles southwest of Salt Lake City, produces nearly 22 per cent of the nation's copper annually. Until after 1900, Bingham Canyon was essentially a lead-silver-gold mining camp.

Mining and treating Utah's low-grade copper ore is a difficult and expensive process. Copper minerals are scattered through the rock, which is granite-like in composition. The ore contains less than one per cent copper.

Only the large size and uniform mineralization of the ore body, which allow a large-scale and highly mechanized operation, make it economically possible to recover valuable metals from such low-grade material. Because of the low grade of the ore and the losses which occur, 309 pounds of waste and ore must be moved to obtain a pound of copper.

Ore is loaded into railroad cars and hauled by electric locomotives to the Copperton main assembly yard at the mouth of the canyon. There trains are made up for movement to the Arthur and Magna concentrating mills nearby. The concentrates are reduced to copper ingots at the American Smelting and Refining Company smelter at Garfield, which lies a few miles to the north.

Ely, Nevada, district. White Pine County, particularly in the Ely-Ruth-Kimberly-McGill sectors of east-central Nevada, was greatly favored by nature with very large copper ore deposits. Because both the Kennecott Copper Corporation and the Consolidated Copper-mines Company have learned how to handle ores with a low copper content successfully and efficiently on a quantity production basis, copper mining in eastern Nevada has grown from a rather puny beginning to a position of great stability.

In contrast to Bingham Canyon, which is less than 30 miles from the well-developed transportation network serving metropolitan Salt Lake City, the Ely-Ruth district is separated from markets by barren desert. Consequently, exorbitant freight rates make the latter a marginal producer, shipping ore only when prices are high. Even so, Ruth and the nearby mines and pits have produced approximately $800 million in copper, gold, and silver.

Ore is shipped via the Nevada Northern Railroad, which runs for 140 miles from Ely to Cobre where it connects with the main line of the Southern Pacific. The entire area of copper impregnation is localized in a zone that runs roughly east and west for about seven miles and is about a mile wide.

Figure 14-7. The Utah Copper Division mine of the Kennecott Copper Corporation at Bingham Canyon, Utah, covers an operating area of 972 acres. (Salt Lake City Chamber of Commerce)

IRON ORE

Iron ore mining is of considerable importance in the Basin and Range Province. Utah ranks fourth in the nation (behind Minnesota, Michigan, and Alabama) in the production of iron ore, with an output exceeding that of all other Western States combined. Open pit mining of high-grade ores (54 per cent iron average) is carried on throughout the year in southwestern Utah near Cedar City. This ore body supplies the ore for the blast furnaces of the Columbia-Geneva Steel Division of the United States Steel Corporation on the eastern shore of Utah Lake near Provo.

About half of Utah's iron ore production is consumed within the state; about a fifth is shipped to blast furnaces near Pueblo, Colorado; and most of the remainder is sent to Fontana, California. Some ore from Utah finds its way into Eastern markets.

LEAD

Mining of lead ores in the region dates back to 1863 when Bingham Canyon first was opened up. The replacement lodes there and the prolific fissures and bedded limestone replacements of Park City, Utah, are important lead ore sources.

URANIUM

There is probably a considerable amount of uranium ore, both secondary and primary, in the Basin and Range Province, but to date this region has not experienced bonanzas comparable to those of the Colorado Plateau. The most promising prospect at the present time is that of Apex Uranium, Inc., with a group of claims six miles south of Austin, Nevada, in the Toiyabe Range. The company has found and developed a large volume of secondary uranium ores on the surface and recently discovered a strong vein of primary ore at depth.

Open pit mining is carried on in an old lake bed in the vicinity of Tonopah, Nevada, where a secondary ore of uranium is found associated with compacted sand, mud, and clay. Near Pyramid Lake north of Reno, the Homestake Mining Company of South Dakota also is engaged in developing uranium ore. In Utah alone, over 100 companies are mining and shipping uranium ore to mills.

GOLD

Gold occurs in a number of areas along the east flank of the central and northern parts of the Sierra Nevada Range. Although the current price of gold prevents large-scale mining operations, some mining still occurs. In the Diamond Mountain district, a few miles south of Susanville, California, gold is produced from quartz veins in granitic rocks and from stream gravels. More than $30 million worth of gold has been produced at Bodie, California, in eastern Mono County. The Randsburg district, which lies athwart Kern and San Bernadino Counties, contains the largest gold mines in southern California.

SALINES

Salt is secured from the brines of Great Salt Lake by the solar process; the refined material is marketed for household, dairy, and stock purposes and is used in the manufacture of soda ash and other sodium compounds. Some of the salt is impregnated artificially with sulphur, iodine, trace minerals, and phosphorus. Less than 25 per cent of some 130,000 tons produced is consumed within Utah, mostly by the livestock industry; the remainder is marketed in the other Western States. Although salt is important in its economy, Utah furnishes less than one per cent of the nation's supply.

Potash is produced from the brines underlying the Great Salt Lake Desert. It is increasingly important in commercial fertilizers and in the electrochemical industry. The process of recovery is comparable to that of salt from the lake. Potash is available also from enormous deposits of alunite with which Utah is favored. Commercial fertilizers and soil correctives have been compounded from the materials in these deposits, and alum and high-grade polishing compounds have been produced.

Salines have been extracted continuously from Owens Lake since the early 1880's; commercial commodities obtained include trona or sodium sesquicarbonate, soda ash, and borax. Commercial deposits of potash, borax, boric acid, soda ash, bromine, and phosphoric acid are produced from Searles Lake.

OTHER MINERALS

Of unusual interest are deposits of pozzolan,

a volcanic material with intrusive granites interspersed among the volcanic ash. There are about 5,000 acres containing this material near Milford, Utah. It varies from a fine volcanic ash to large aggregates known locally as pumice and perlite. Pozzolan is being used in making concrete for the Glen Canyon Dam.

Fullers earth and bentonite deposits are found in commercial deposits in south-central Utah. Some deposits are being quarried and processed near the community of Aurora.

MANUFACTURING

Geographically, the Basin and Range Province is a region situated too far from large consuming centers to attract many large-scale industries. More than 50 per cent of the area is located in a region that Americans have shown a historical tendency to avoid. In the early years of westward migration, the area bounded by the Wasatch Mountains and the Colorado Plateau on the east and the Sierra Nevada and Cascades on the west represented primarily an obstacle to be negotiated before reaching the promising Pacific Slope. Despite a dramatic rate of growth in recent years, this vast region between the mountain ranges has remained largely undeveloped. At the same time, the three states to the west of the Sierra Nevada and Cascades have been approaching economic maturity—in the sense that a great industrial complex has been superimposed upon the agricultural and extractive base. The contrast in level of development between the Pacific Coast States and the Intermountain States is readily apparent to any observer.

Manufacturing employs less than one-sixth of all persons working in nonagricultural pursuits. There has been, however, a very large over-all rate of growth. In some types of manufacturing there has been progress symptomatic of an economy freeing itself from dependence on agriculture and mining.

Although the growth of the region's industry is of more than local interest, only those industries can survive that process materials for local consumption or concentrate bulky raw materials to forms that can be shipped economically out of the region to consuming centers in the East or Far West.

The leading industries are smelting of nonferrous and ferrous metals, chemicals, sugar refining, petroleum refining, flour milling, canning, and meat packing.

NONFERROUS METALS

The Salt Lake City area is the greatest smelting center in the United States. Within 25 miles of Salt Lake City are large smelters operated by American Smelting, U. S. Smelting, and International Smelting, and two huge copper concentrating mills and a refinery operated by Kennecott. The refinery has a capacity of 384 million pounds of copper annually.

Although approximately 30 per cent of the nation's copper is produced in Utah, only three per cent of copper fabrication is in the West.

The low-grade copper ore from the Utah copper mine is concentrated at Magna and Arthur, and the concentrates are reduced to copper ingots at the American Smelting and Refining Company smelter at Garfield. In 1950, a copper refinery and a copper anode plant were constructed nearby, an event that renders feasible the establishment of a number of fabricating industries in Utah.

The International Smelting and Refining Company plant at Tooele, Utah, serves numerous mines inside and outside of Utah, handling both copper and lead ore concentrates. The United States Smelting, Refining and Mining Company plant at Midvale, Utah, treats lead, zinc, and silver ores. Not only local ores but also those from nearby states are processed here. For example, the Howe-Sound Company has established in this area a cobalt smelting and refining plant for the processing of cobalt ores from the Salmon River in Idaho; the Vitro Chemical Company has established a uranium processing plant adjacent to Salt Lake City to supply uranium concentrates to the Atomic Energy Commission.

FERROUS METALS

Steelmaking in Utah began during World War II when the Defense Plant Corporation of the Federal government built the Geneva plant, the first fully integrated mill in the West, on the shores of Utah Lake to supply West Coast shipyards with structural steel shapes. The original plant cost more than $200

Figure 14-8. Located in the heart of Utah, U.S. Steel's Columbia-Geneva Steel Division has a capacity of 2.3 million tons of ingot steel per year. (U.S. Steel Corporation)

million and consisted of nine 255-ton furnaces. It was sold to the U. S. Steel Corporation in 1947.

Two basic factors brought this steel facility to Utah: (1) large local deposits of iron ore, coking coal, and limestone; and (2) location— it is equidistant from the Pacific Northwest, the San Francisco Bay area, and Los Angeles.

At full production today, Geneva produces 2.3 million tons of steel annually. Finished steel products include plates, structural shapes, hot-rolled coils, and hot-rolled sheets. Nearby raw materials, available low-cost water, good rail transportation, and skilled labor insure low-cost steel production. Coal is hauled 130 miles by rail from Sunnyside, Utah, in the southeast; iron ore is shipped by rail from Iron Mountain near Cedar City, 252 miles to the southwest; limestone and dolomite originate at the Keigley Quarry near Payson, some 30 miles to the south. Because local demand is small, most of Geneva's finished products are shipped via the railroads to Pacific Coast markets. The corporation has integrated Geneva's economy with that of its Pittsburg, California, plant to make fuller use of its capacity.

Adjacent to Geneva, U. S. Steel's Consolidated Western Steel Division produces high-strength steel pipe at a multimillion dollar plant. Consolidated Western also provides specialized designing, engineering, metallurgical, and fabrication services required for the production of ordnance material, wind tunnels, and other highly technical military and civilian projects.

Many firms with national and international markets are located near the Geneva plant. For example, Eimco serves a world-wide market with its mining and milling equipment. Western Laundry Press, a subsidiary of American Laundry, ships commercial laundry equipment all over the world. Also represented are American Can, General American Transportation, Commercial Shearing and Stamping, Pacific Iron and Steel, Grover Tank and Manufacturing, and Chicago Bridge and Iron.

Further growth in steel fabricating is assured because of the availability of more types of finished steel, increasing demand in the growing West, and the trend toward decentralization of industry.

OTHER INDUSTRIES

Electronics and aircraft. Strategic location, space, and a dependable labor supply are among the factors that have brought some of the nation's well-known electronics and rocket engine and fuel manufacturers to this area. Among the more notable are Eitel-McCullough, Inc., world's largest maker of transmitting tubes; Litton Industries, Inc., at Salt Lake City; and Marquardt Aircraft at Ogden.

Chemicals. As a result of the availability of sulfuric acid and other chemicals, many new industries have been established in the Salt Lake area, including: the Filtrol Corporation, manufacturers of a chemical for the production of 100-octane gasoline; Western Phosphates, Inc., a subsidiary of Stauffer Chemical; Kennecott Copper and American Smelting and Refining, producing fertilizer for the region's agriculture; and Garfield Chemical and Manufacturing, which makes 1,000 tons of sulfuric acid daily.

Sugar beet refining. Because of their isolated position and the high cost of the overland haul, the Mormons erected a sugar beet factory in Salt Lake City in 1852. Although this venture failed, it paved the way for a successful enterprise at Lehi, south of Salt Lake City, in 1891. Since that time four factories have been established to process locally grown beets. Sugar beet refining is well suited to the intensive irrigated agriculture practiced in the Salt Lake area, for the growing of sugar beets is a two-crop industry. The harvested tops from an acre of beets plus the pulp that remains after extraction of sugar from the roots equal the stock feeding value of the entire product from an average acre of corn. The by-products, fed to cattle along with hay and grain, support a livestock industry.

Petroleum refining. Petroleum refining and the industries associated with it have grown at a very rapid rate in the Salt Lake City district in recent years, stimulated in part by government investment during World War II and by the rapid development of crude oil sources in the Intermountain States. For the most part, crude oil is supplied to Utah by the oil fields of Colorado and Wyoming, made available by the creation of an extensive pipeline network. However, since 1948, commercially significant quantities of crude oil have been coming from Utah's own oil fields.

There are four oil refineries in or near Salt Lake City and one at Jensen, which is in the Southwestern Interior Plateaus, Plains, and Mountains Province. These refineries represent an investment of nearly $100 million; they are subsidiaries of Standard Oil of California, Standard Oil of Indiana, Sinclair Oil, and Phillips Petroleum Company.

Flour milling. From the beginning, the economy of Salt Lake City and Utah was based on agriculture. After the weary trek of a thousand miles from the Missouri River, the pioneers found themselves pretty much on their own. Almost immediately, grain mills were established.

Today more than 90 per cent of the flour produced within the region is milled by three large concerns—General Mills and Globe Mills at Ogden, and the Salt Lake Flour Mills in Salt Lake City. The remainder is handled by many small and widely distributed mills. High protein wheat from Montana is mixed with Utah wheat to meet milling demands for baking flour. The softer wheat of the Palouse is mixed with local wheat to make low protein cake and pastry flour.

Milling-in-transit privileges allow the large concerns to compete in the California market with grain milled there. Since Utah produces about three times as much flour as it consumes, this is a distinct advantage.

Meat packing. Utah has enjoyed substantial growth in the meat packing industry, both in the process of providing for the expanding market resulting from the high rate of growth of population in the Intermountain States and in the expansion of its role as a processing way station between the Plains States and the Pacific Coast. The state now has more than 70 packing houses. Most of these, of course, are small operations that supply local markets.

The larger plants, located at Salt Lake City and Ogden, provide the bulk of the meat shipped out of the region. California's rapid population growth has in turn created a large market for meat products. Since freight costs from the Midwest to the Pacific Coast are high, it is cheaper to slaughter for the California market meat animals that have grazed and fattened in the Basin and Range Province. Many live animals are also sold to California ranchers as feeders.

TRANSPORTATION

A thin network of modern transportation facilities links the Basin and Range Province with the rest of the United States. Raw materials and semiprocessed and manufactured goods are shipped out of the region either to the Pacific Coast or to the Midwest. The bulk of the cargo is transcontinental in nature and moves through Salt Lake City following the most direct route from central California or the Great Plains.

RAILROADS

Four major lines serve the Salt Lake-Ogden area, with a number of branch, feeder, and short lines reaching strategic points in surrounding territory. The major lines are Union Pacific, Southern Pacific, Western Pacific, and Denver and Rio Grande Western. These lines prosper in this region only because they are able to carry the rich cargoes of the Pacific Coast and those of the Middle West and the East. Otherwise, service now rendered to the region would not be economically feasible.

HIGHWAYS

Six major Federal highways and a network of state and local highways serve the area. U. S. Highways 40 and 50 carry the heaviest passenger and truck traffic. In this sparsely populated region the people must rely upon the Federal government to maintain good roads through its national program.

Salt Lake City is the center of the central transcontinental highway system, with Highways 30, 40, and 50 entering from the east —Highway 50, from Kansas City via Pueblo, Highway 40 from St. Louis via Denver, and Highway 30 from Omaha through Chey-

enne. Highway 30 goes to Spokane and the Northwest from Salt Lake City. Highway 40 passes westward through Elko and Reno, Nevada, into the San Francisco Bay area. Highway 50 runs west through Ely and Carson City into the San Francisco Bay area.

Salt Lake City will be an integral intersection of the highway system being built under the new Federal Aid Highway Program.

AIR TRANSPORTATION

Five airlines—United, Western, Bonanza, West Coast, and Frontier—connect the region with the rest of the country. Salt Lake City is one of America's most important air centers. Feeder lines operating out of Portland, Spokane, Seattle, Los Angeles, Butte, and Edmonton carry passengers to this city for transfer to major East-West transcontinental flights.

POPULATION CENTERS

Salt Lake City and Ogden, Utah, and Reno and Las Vegas, Nevada, are the major population centers. Of these, only Salt Lake City has more than 100,000 people.

SALT LAKE CITY

Salt Lake City has a metropolitan area population of 383,035, with 189,454 within the city limits. It is an oasis settlement at the base of the Wasatch Mountains, a longitudinal range that juts above the plateau to heights exceeding 10,000 feet. It is located at the very center of the 11 Western States (excluding Alaska and Hawaii), which comprise an economic unit.

Salt Lake City commands one of the largest trade territories in the United States, having an average diameter of about 600 miles, extending from Grand Junction, Colorado, and Rock Springs, Wyoming, on the east, to the middle of Nevada and eastern Oregon on the west. It is the dominant financial, commercial, and industrial center of the Basin and Range Province and is the mining, smelting, and refining center of the West.

OGDEN (70,197)

Another oasis settlement at the base of the Wasatch is Ogden, located about 40 miles north of Salt Lake City. It is a railroad center commanding the best railroad pass through

Figure 14-9. Salt Lake City, Utah, is situated at the base of the Wasatch Mountains and is favored with a plentiful supply of water. It is the seat of the Church of Jesus Christ of Latter-day Saints. (Salt Lake City Chamber of Commerce)

the mountains to the east. Ogden, also important for meat packing and flour milling, serves as the trading center for the northern part of the Salt Lake area.

RENO (44,500)

This city is a playground for people from the San Francisco Bay area. It is easily accessible by a good highway. Legalized gambling and convenient marriage and divorce laws lure many people there. It is the shopping center for northwestern Nevada and for nearby communities in the mountain counties of California. Reno is also the access point for Lake Tahoe and the Sierra Nevada ski areas. Reno Ski Bowl, a huge natural land indentation on the northeastern flank of Slide Mountain, lies 25 miles southwest of Reno.

The city is located on the eastern flank of the Sierra Nevada on the Truckee River, which flows through the central business district. Mining was the prop of its early economy, followed, with the building of the Central Pacific, by the railroad era.

LAS VEGAS (44,750)

Located in the center of a vast recreation area, Las Vegas is surrounded by scenic deserts and cool mountains, and is within easy driving distance of many of the West's major national parks and monuments—Grand Canyon, Bryce, Zion, Death Valley, and the Valley of Fire, to name a few.

Las Vegas has benefited by southern California's rapid growth, since it is within 300 miles of that area and is connected to it by a good

Figure 14-10. The famous "Strip" in Las Vegas, Nevada. The city is internationally famed as a gambling, entertainment, and health center. (Las Vegas News Bureau)

desert highway. Multimillion dollar resort hotels, featuring motion picture and television stars, attract tourists from many parts of the nation to Las Vegas' gambling tables.

THE FUTURE

The Basin and Range Province has enjoyed a very high rate of growth since the beginning of World War II, a growth period that has seen significant increases in nonagricultural economic activity and improvement of economic conditions in agriculture to the extent that the average citizen of the region has received a large welfare gain. Still, the region remains sparsely populated, with only certain localities favored by much industrialization. Continued progress depends very largely on the careful utilization of an exceedingly scarce natural resource—water. Economic development in the future will depend, as it has in the past, on the progress made in harnessing the great river systems of the region.

15 | Columbia-Snake Plateaus, Plains, and Mountains

(Relief map copyright Aero Service Corp.)

THE Columbia-Snake Plateaus, Plains, and Mountains Province, popularly called the "Inland Empire," is bounded on the east and north by the Rocky Mountains and on the west by the Cascade Mountains; on the south it merges with the Great Basin of Nevada. It includes most of Oregon east of the Cascades, east-central and southeastern Washington, the Snake River Plain of Idaho and a small segment of land near the Idaho-Oregon-Washington border, and part of the extreme northern fringe of Nevada.

SURFACE FEATURES

Much of the surface is a lava plateau (one of the greatest in the world) in various stages of the erosion cycle. The area is drained by the Columbia River system, with the exception of the upper Snake River Plateau, which has internal drainage.

The underlying rock is mainly basalt, which came as repeated lava flows in sheets of from a few feet to 200 feet thick. The total thickness varies from less than an inch to 4,000 feet, averaging perhaps one-half mile. This lava buried a rough (locally mountainous) surface. Since the vulcanism, some parts have been broadly depressed and others elevated, so that the local relief varies considerably and three major landforms—plains, plateaus, and mountains—are found within the province. The time interval between the lava flows was often short, but sometimes long enough to permit soil to form.

The Columbia Intermontane Province, as the region is sometimes called, includes: (1) the Waterville Plateau Subregion, (2) the Channeled Scablands Subregion, (3) the Palouse Hills Subregion, (4) the Deschutes Plateau Subregion, (5) the Central Highlands Subregion, (6) the Snake River Lava Plain Subregion, (7) the Harney High Lava Plains Subregion, and (8) the Malheur-Owyhee Upland Subregion.

The Waterville Plateau Subregion in Washington is in the rain shadow of the Cascades, where the average annual rainfall is only about ten to 15 inches. It is a dry land wheat farming area. The topography varies from 2,000 to 4,000 feet in elevation, and two major canyons break the surface, the Columbia River and the Grand Coulee. The latter canyon now includes a man-made lake, the Grand Coulee equalizing reservoir. Grand Coulee Dam occupies the Columbia River Canyon. On the tablelands above the canyons the surface has a thin mantle of fertile soil that, with normal rainfall, is suited to winter wheat.

The Channeled Scablands Subregion is a lower plateau extending eastward from Grand Coulee Canyon to the Spokane and Palouse Rivers. It is a dry land area with ten to 15 inches of annual precipitation. The surface consists of a network of old glacial river channels, or coulees, that once carried large volumes of water southward from a great ice sheet. Bedrock, locally termed "scab rock," has been exposed by the erosion in the channels. These old water courses contain potholes, shallow lakes, swampy meadows, rocky buttes, and mesas. Between the coulees are rolling plains, low hills, and plateaus covered with rich, wind-deposited soils. On these loess soils extensive wheat farming of the summer fallow type has been highly successful, and this subregion is second only to the Palouse Hills in importance of wheat production.

The Palouse Hills Subregion, named for the Palouse River, provides the best soil and moisture conditions for wheat culture in the Pacific Northwest. It is characterized by rolling hills of loess soil at an average elevation of 1,000 to 3,000 feet.

Within the Palouse section are large, rounded knolls having a steeper slope to the east and north than to the west and south; they resemble sand dunes in shape. These broad, rounded swells rise 20 to 80 feet above valleys where there are neither streams nor channels. Here and there in the northern part are isolated buttes of older rock, outliers of the Idaho Mountains, rising abruptly above the lava plateaus. Steptoe Butte, an isolated quartzite mountain standing 1,000 feet above the plain in the heart of the wheat country midway between Lewiston, Idaho, and Spokane, Washington, is the most spectacular of these formations.

Pioneer farmers discovered the Palouse, originally a sparsely populated land covered with bunch grass, to be ideal for wheat. The soil, wind-deposited in a deep mantle over basaltic rock, is fine textured, fertile, and highly retentive of moisture. Precipitation averages 15

Figure 15-1. Palouse wheat lands south of Spokane, Washington. Wheat production is highly mechanized. (Spokane Chamber of Commerce)

to 25 inches annually. A reliable seasonal snow cover protects winter wheat from winterkill.

Two major types of farming are carried on: (1) winter or spring wheat alternating with fallow, and (2) spring wheat alternating with dry land peas. Wheat has been the only grain crop on many farms since the beginning of cultivation and units tend to be large. The disadvantage of the Palouse Hills terrain is the steep slope of some fields. Occasionally gullying and sheet erosion occur when there are heavy rains or during periods when snow cover melts rapidly. Fallow land and young grain fields often are seriously affected by rapid runoff.

The Deschutes Plateau Subregion of north-central Oregon is an old lava plateau deeply dissected by the Columbia, Deschutes, and John Day Rivers. The gently rolling terrain between the gorges and canyons rises from 1,000 feet near the Columbia River to 3,000 feet at the edge of the Umatilla Range. The plateau receives ten to 20 inches of precipitation annually, which is partially absorbed by a thin mantle of fertile, volcanic ash soil. Although low soil moisture is a risk factor, the area is farmed in large units and alternately planted to wheat and left in summer fallow.

The Central Highlands Subregion's physiographic area includes the Blue and Wallowa Mountains of Washington and Oregon and the Clearwater, Seven Devils, and Salmon Mountains of Idaho. The Blue Mountains section consists in part of somewhat glaciated mountains of old rocks, 9,000 feet high, standing above the lava. The rest of it is the plateau surface gently arched (elevation 5,000 to more than 6,000 feet) and deeply eroded, locally mature, and also called mountains. Much of this section is covered with pine forest. Streams from the mountains furnish water for irrigation on the adjacent plateau.

The Snake River Lava Plain Subregion is an arcuate downwarp 30 to 60 miles wide and about 400 miles long. It descends gently from an elevation of about 6,000 feet above sea level at its eastern end to about 2,200 feet on the west. The eastern part is a silt-covered, youthful, lava plain, featureless except for low lava domes and occasional cinder cones. Very young lava occurs in places. The western part of the plain is underlain by lake beds and alluvium as well as lava, and is partly dissected to terraces, box canyons, and open valleys. As a result of its open terrain, soils, water, and other favorable factors, the Snake River Lava Plain supports a large and growing population.

The Harney High Lava Plains Subregion of central Oregon is located in an arid country drained in part to salt lakes. A portion of it (with adjacent country to the south) is covered with volcanic dust (sand) and is known locally as the "Great Sandy Desert." These plains are mainly a flattish, youthful tract of late Cenozoic lava, ranging in general elevation from about 4,000 to 5,000 feet.

The Malheur-Owyhee Upland Subregion occupies parts of southeastern Oregon and southwestern Idaho. The Owyhee Mountains were never quite buried by lava, and now are surrounded by an eroded lava plateau sloping away in all directions. Adverse moisture conditions and lack of streams for irrigation water have kept settlement to a minimum. Consequently, this is the most sparsely populated area of the Pacific Northwest.

CLIMATE

The climate of the Columbia-Snake Plateaus, Plains, and Mountains Region is affected by both continental and maritime influences, but the continental regime dominates. The Rocky Mountain barrier to the east protects it to some extent from the cold waves that frequently sweep over the interior of the continent; yet winter temperatures as low as —20° and —25° F. have been recorded, and summer temperatures often exceed 100°. However, because of the dryness of the air the heat is rarely oppressive. The Cascade Mountains on the west serve as a barrier against the moist and mild marine climate of the Pacific Coast. Nevertheless, the precipitation in the region comes mostly in the late autumn, winter, and spring months, following the regime on the Pacific Coast, rather than in the summer as in the Western Interior High Plains Region to the east. The province is arid along its western border, in Washington; semiarid in the central Washington section and on most of the plateau south of the Columbia River, in Oregon; and subhumid to humid in eastern Washington, in most of the Idaho portions, and along the foothills of the Blue Mountains.

The prevailing moisture-bearing winds are from the southwest and west. In passing over the Cascade Range, the air currents lose much of their moisture, which is precipitated as snow or rain on the western slope of the mountains. In descending the eastern slope of the Cascade Range into the valleys below, the air becomes warmer and much drier. Its capacity for holding water vapor continues to increase until the low elevations along the Columbia River are reached—where the average annual precipitation is between six and seven inches and where there is a preponderance of dry air, clear skies, and heavy evaporation during much of the year. As the winds pass in a northeasterly direction from the Columbia River to the higher altitudes of the Big Bend Plateau, the air becomes cooler and its capacity for holding water vapor is gradually reduced. This results in a rather regular increase in the annual precipitation as the elevation increases.

The annual precipitation ranges from eight or nine inches, on the average, along the arid margin, beyond which crop production has been found to be unprofitable, to about 25 and in places possibly 30 inches along the mountain margin on the east and south. Because rainfall occurs largely in the winter and spring (when evaporation is low) and because of the practice of summer fallowing, grain is grown along the arid margin of this region with less precipitation than elsewhere in the United States, except possibly in California, where the crop is produced during the cool, moist winter. The precipitation comes in the form of both rain and snow. Most of it, however, is rain and the showers are seldom torrential. Very little water is lost as surface runoff except when rain falls or snow melts on a frozen surface.

From 30 to 40 per cent or more of the precipitation is received in the three winter months, the proportion increasing toward the west; and from 20 to 30 per cent during the spring months. Wide variations, however, occur from year to year. The winter precipitation ranges from an average of about three inches along the arid margin of the region near the Columbia River, in central Washington, to eight and nine inches along the foothills of the Rocky and Blue Mountains. During the spring the rainfall ranges from one or two inches along the desert margin, to about eight inches along the mountains. Summers are dry, with a rainfall ranging from about one inch along the Columbia River to four inches or more in some sections near the mountains. But in autumn rainfall increases again, usually in late autumn, and averages, for the three months, about two inches near the Columbia River and from six to eight inches along the mountain foothills. The normal snowfall is 20 inches in the drier and warmer portions of the region along the Columbia and Snake Rivers and 60 inches along the mountain front. Snow covers the ground in an average year from 25 days or less in the lower, warmer valleys to 50 days and more along the foothills of the mountains. The first snowfall usually comes early in November.

In winter the average daily range in temperature is only 12 to 15 degrees, like that of the Pacific Coast, but in summer the range is as great as 30 or even 35 degrees. The last killing frost in spring occurs during May, except in the river valleys, where it comes earlier; and the first killing frost in fall usually takes place in late September or early October. The frost-free season averages 100 to 120 days in length in the higher portions of the plateau in eastern Washington and Idaho; but in the Snake River Canyon and adjacent slopes and along the Columbia River below the mouth of the Snake it exceeds 180 days.

SOILS

The principal soils are the brown soils in the low precipitation zone and the chestnut, chernozem, and prairie soils in areas of increasing precipitation. The soils vary from rapidly permeable and well drained to slowly permeable and poorly drained. Most of them are deep enough to store moisture adequately, but some areas have shallow soils with inadequate storage capacity.

The soils have a very fine sandy or silty texture in the zone of low precipitation. They become finer in texture in the high precipitation zones, where most surface soils are silt loams with silty clay loam or clay loam subsoils.

Soil organic matter also varies with the amount of precipitation and ranges from about one per cent in the dry sections to four per cent or more in areas of high precipitation.

HYDROGRAPHY

The unifying factor of the "Inland Empire" is the Columbia River and its tributaries, which form a drainage basin for an area encompassing 259,000 square miles. The basin includes a considerable area both within and outside of the Columbia-Snake Plateaus, Plains, and Mountains Province. Nearly the whole of Washington, Oregon, and Idaho, that part of Montana west of the Rocky Mountains, small areas in Wyoming, Utah, and Nevada, and 39,700 square miles of mountainous country in the eastern part of British Columbia lie within the watershed. About 60 per cent of the water that passes the Grand Coulee Dam comes from river basins in Canada.

The source of the Columbia River is Columbia Lake, which lies between the Canadian Rockies and the Selkirk Mountains at an elevation of 2,650 feet. The river flows northwesterly 195 miles, turns sharply west and south around the Selkirks, and then flows southward 270 miles to enter the United States in the northeastern corner of Washington after passing through the Arrow Lakes in British Columbia.

The largest tributary of the Columbia is the Snake River, which rises in western Wyoming and drains central and southern Idaho, eastern Oregon, and the southeastern part of Washington. It joins the Columbia River in south-central Washington, 323 miles above its mouth and 274 miles below Grand Coulee Dam.

The second- and third-largest tributaries of the Columbia, the Kootenai and Clark Fork Rivers, join it in Canada. The Kootenai rises in the Canadian Rockies 75 miles north of the source of the Columbia and flows south 180 miles into the United States, passing within a few miles of Columbia Lake. After traversing a 167-mile loop in Montana and Idaho, the Kootenai returns to Canada and enters Kootenai Lake, which discharges into the Columbia River.

The Clark Fork of the Columbia River drains almost all of western Montana. From its source in the Rocky Mountains near Butte and not far from the headwaters of the Missouri River, it flows generally northwesterly 360 miles into Lake Pend Oreille in northern Idaho and then nearly 100 miles west through Idaho and north through Washington into Canada. The upper Columbia is characterized by wide variations in annual flow and by having its peak flow in summer, usually in June. Most of its water comes from snow and ice deposits in the high mountains of British Columbia, western Montana, and northern Idaho. Warm

Figure 15-2. The Snake River in Idaho. The river, surrounded by horizontal-lying black lava, drains an area of 190,000 square miles. (Union Pacific Railroad)

weather, thawing such deposits, accounts for the high summer flow, which provides surplus water for irrigation and for power to pump the water.

The demand for power, spurred by defense needs, has called attention to the seriousness of the low flow of the river in the winter, when the need for power is greatest. The tremendous sudden flooding of the Columbia and all of its tributaries in the summer of 1948, and the consequent damage to property on the lower river, demonstrated the need for co-ordinated flood control. Both the production of power and the protection of life and property can be served by the same means, namely, reservoirs in the upper basins of the river's tributaries in the United States and in Canada. Such reservoirs could be drawn upon during the winter to supplement the natural flow of the Columbia and to maintain high power production; they could be used during the summer season to contain the peak flow.

AGRICULTURE

COMMERCIAL GRAIN FARMING

The Columbia-Snake Plateaus, Plains, and Mountains Province illustrates as well as any other section of the nation the evolution of agriculture during the past century. The missionary and the fur trader broke the trail for the cattleman. The miner provided a small market for farm products. The sturdy and reliant pioneer grazed his herd on the grasslands and drove his cattle hundreds of miles to market. Then it was discovered that wheat could be grown successfully in the region. The railroads came, providing cheap transportation, and the grasslands were transformed into grain lands where the climate did not prove too dry for the crop or the slope too steep for the machinery that was used.

Wheat. Wheat was one of the first crops to be planted by those who came to the Pacific Northwest to farm. Accordingly, the expansion in wheat production closely followed settlement of the region.

The wheat region has a fairly homogeneous environment. Its mean elevation is approximately 2,000 feet. Its soils are predominantly silt loams. They lie over an ubiquitous basaltic bedrock. Precipitation, though increasing perceptibly from west to east, is nearly everywhere marginal in quantity and falls mostly in the winter season. The vegetation reflects the semiaridity and aridity of the region by ranging from sagebrush in the west to bunch grass in the east. That the outstanding adjustment made by man to this environmental complex is dry farming with wheat is not surprising. Indeed, so heavily dependent is the entire region upon this one crop that the yield and price of wheat for any given year become the vital regional index of prosperity.

Over the years the borders of the wheat lands have changed. During times of drought or low prices farms with dry or poor soil were abandoned; during years of prosperity such marginal lands were resown to wheat.

Both soft red and soft and hard white wheats are produced. The amount of precipitation is the chief factor that splits the region into the annual cropping and the summer fallow zones, which in turn can be divided into the dry farm area of eight to 12 inches of annual precipitation and the area of intermediate precipitation, 12 to 18 inches.

The annual cropping system commonly is used in the zone that receives 18 to about 25 inches of precipitation yearly. Thus, in the areas of lower rainfall, crops are grown under a moisture stress; in this zone, the lack of moisture is seldom a major factor in crop growth. Precipitation ranges from about 20 inches in the Palouse Hills Subregion of eastern Washington and northern Idaho to a low of little more than ten inches in the Big Bend area immediately east of the Columbia River. The growing season ranges from about 140 to 180 days, and both spring and winter wheat varieties are produced. It is not uncommon in this region to reseed to spring wheat the acreage that was winterkilled when it was winter wheat planted the preceding fall. But winter wheat is generally preferred because it yields better than spring wheat and because it provides some cover to retard erosion during the

winter. The topography is undulating to rolling; in the Palouse area it is so rolling that track-laying tractors were adopted when farming operations were mechanized. Some of the cropland has slopes of 50 per cent or more.

Farms in Whitman County, Washington, located in the heart of the Palouse, average 670 acres. The wheat crop in Whitman totals 12 to 15 million bushels annually, which makes it first in wheat production among counties of the United States.

Farther west, in the drier Big Bend section, wheat is grown exclusively on summer fallow. In the eastern parts where additional rainfall permits more alternatives, common practice has been to rotate fallow with wheat every two or three years, primarily as a means of weed control.

Wheat from the Columbia-Snake Plateaus, Plains, and Mountains Region yields a soft flour that is excellent for cakes and pastry; but this wheat must be balanced with a hard wheat, generally imported from Montana, for making bread. Soft white wheats suitable for pastry flour normally comprise about 90 per cent of the total wheat production. The hard red wheats are grown to a limited extent in the low precipitation areas.

Wheat production in the province increased from 94.8 million bushels in 1929 to 142 million bushels in 1951. The large United States wheat crops of 1952 and 1953, coupled with falling exports in 1955, created supplies of wheat greatly in excess of demand. Accordingly, wheat acreage allotments again became effective and the 1956 crop declined to 85.8 million bushels. Total production since then has risen, with 107.8 million bushels grown in 1959.

Two machines, the tractor and the combine, revolutionized the wheat industry. The substitution of tractors for horses on the wheat farms began in the 1920's and was almost complete by the early 1940's. A tractor with gang plows can cover 40 to 80 acres a day. With three to five cultivators or tillage implements operated as a unit, from 320 to 640 acres of fallow ground can be tilled in a long day. A tractor pulling three drills can seed 160 acres per day. The combine cuts and threshes wheat in one operation and does away with hauling bundles of grain or loose tops to the threshing machine; furthermore, the loose straw is plowed under, enriching the soil.

Power machinery and bulk handling have greatly reduced labor requirements and, as a result, the rural population. Around 1910 it took 106 man-hours to produce 100 bushels of wheat; by 1950 this had been reduced to 34 man-hours.

Wheat yields. Wheat production may be limited by lack of moisture or by the absence of plant nutrients.

Moisture nearly always is the determining factor in the zone that gets less than 12 inches of precipitation a year. Even with summer fallow, the supply of moisture usually is too small for wheat yields of more than 30 bushels an acre. Yields sometimes drop to about ten bushels in years of subnormal precipitation.

Plant nutrients, especially nitrogen, have a more dominant influence on wheat yields in the zones of higher rainfall. In the areas where moisture is less frequently a limiting factor, wheat yields average 30 to 40 bushels an acre. Yields of 60 to 65 bushels are common on better-managed, well-fertilized fields.

In areas that have more than 18 inches of precipitation, several crops are grown in rotation with wheat—peas, barley, oats, clover, alfalfa, and grass. The acreage of these crops, in relation to the amount of wheat, increases in the sections of higher rainfall.

Flour milling. The region's wheat crop, ten to 15 per cent of the national harvest, is far in excess of the requirements of the local population. Sizable quantities are, of course, withheld for seed and feed, and much is exported unprocessed. In the past, approximately two-fifths of the crop has been milled—some for domestic consumption but the greater part for shipment to grain-poor California, the East Coast of the United States, the Orient, South America, and England. Asiatic markets especially are being sought in the present decade. Milling reduces weight by approximately 25 per cent. In addition, many importing areas are deficient in mill capacity.

The export business has been largely responsible for the tidewater location of the large flour mills. Five modern terminals—two in Portland and one each in Tacoma, Seattle, and Astoria—are convenient points for the transfer of grain from box cars or Columbia River barges to ocean-going vessels. These terminals have two-thirds of the West's milling capacity. Mills are also located at the center of the Northwest flour market. A second group of mills, smaller than the first but still sizable, is located at transportation centers where grain can be collected from a wide area for milling: Spokane, Pendleton, and The Dalles. Smaller and, for the most part, older mills are scattered in villages throughout the wheat districts. Generally unable to compete with their giant rivals and ill-equipped to meet the exacting requirements of mechanized bakeries, these units have been declining in number and significance. Many of them are idle; when destroyed by fire, they are not rebuilt.

Minor grains. Production of grains other than wheat is of minor importance.

Oats are grown mainly as feed grain and forage for livestock. A small quantity is processed for human consumption. Oats are planted in the spring and mature in a shorter growing season than wheat.

Barley is in demand for feeding livestock; about 40 per cent of the annual crop is used for this purpose on the farms where it is grown. Barley is planted in the spring, using the same farming methods as for wheat, which it resembles closely.

Field corn is a minor crop because the weather during the summer is too dry for its growth. Rye does better than wheat on poor soil or inferior land and is sometimes planted for hay.

HAY AND FORAGE CROPS

Climatic and soil conditions generally encourage hay cultivation. Moreover, the sunshine and dry air of the region are favorable for curing the crop, which ranks second to wheat in total acreage harvested. Hay and forage crops are basic to the livestock industry.

Alfalfa is the leading hay and forage crop. Although grown in all sections, including dry lands with rainfall of 15 inches or more, it does best under irrigation. It produces larger yields than other legumes and ranks highest in feed value. A perennial, alfalfa continues to yield for several years before replanting becomes necessary. The Deschutes River Valley of Oregon leads in alfalfa production.

Oats, wheat, and barley are often planted

Figure 15-3. A farm scene in the Wallowa Valley, near Joseph, Oregon; the Wallowa Mountains are in the background. (Oregon State Highway Commission)

for grain hay that is cut green. This makes a good quality forage. Grain hay can be grown on lands unsuited to alfalfa, clover, or timothy.

ROOT CROPS

Potatoes. Irrigated sections of the Columbia-Snake Plateaus, Plains, and Mountains Province account for the greater share of the region's commercial potato production. Malheur, Crook, Deschutes, and Jefferson Counties in Oregon, and Garfield, Whitman, Benton and Kittitas Counties in Washington produce more than three-fourths of the potatoes marketed as a cash crop. San Francisco has long been the leading market for Oregon potatoes; Seattle, for Washington potatoes. Idaho potatoes are a major cash crop in irrigated areas up the Snake River from American Falls. The main trading and shipping center for the irrigation district is Idaho Falls. Some 240,000 acres are planted to potatoes; yields average 240 bushels per acre. Potatoes from this district rival those of Aroostook County, Maine, in both quality and quantity. Potato research follows the crop from cutting and planting the seed piece through production, harvesting, marketing, and even into the kitchen.

Seed selection, seed treatment, and improved cultivation practices have resulted in higher yields and a better product.

Sugar beets. The hot sun and deep soil mantle of the interior valleys make the cultivation of sugar beets a prominent feature of the irrigated agriculture practiced there. Fifteen per cent of the national output—two-thirds of this in Idaho—is accounted for by five regions in the Northwest: the upper Snake Valley of eastern Idaho, the central Snake Valley, the Boise-Payette district, the Yakima Valley (mostly outside the region under discussion), and the Moses Lake district—a part of the Columbia Basin Project. The extraction of sugar from the beet entails a weight reduction of 85 to 90 per cent. The refining, therefore, takes place in the middle of the growing area; the refiners try to draw most of their beets from within a 25-mile radius. Sugar beet refineries, large units representing a substantial investment and requiring a minimum planting of 10,000 acres, are spaced at a distance from one another within the same irrigated area rather than clustered at one central town.

Sugar beet production has expanded rapidly in central Washington since 1936, when sugar beet varieties resistant to curly-top disease were developed. During the past few years, average yield has been slightly more than 20 tons per acre, with many fields producing over 30 tons per acre. The acre value of sugar beets is high, making the crop suitable for expensive land.

The combination of sugar beet production with livestock feeding and the proper utilization of the manure on the beet land is probably more nearly essential for continued high yields of sugar beets than for any other commercial crop in the irrigated areas of Washington. Through feeding the beet by-products to livestock and returning the manure to the soil, more than 80 per cent of the fertility value of the beet is retained to help produce the next crop. With the exception of unavoidable losses in the refining process, none of the fertilizer constituents is destroyed in sugar production.

The Snake River Lava Plain Subregion produces sugar beets in great quantity and excellent quality. Yields in this area are among the highest in the nation, averaging 23 tons per acre, or 7.25 tons per acre higher than the national average.

The growing and processing of sugar beets account for considerable income throughout the Snake River Lava Plain Subregion. In the western part alone, where 45,000 acres of sugar beets are grown to supply factories at Nampa and Nyssa, the growers are paid more than $13 million.

As production of cane sugar has the advantage of much lower labor costs, growers and processors of sugar beets have striven to neutralize the advantage by the greatest degree of efficiency possible.

Growers use tractor-drawn six-row beet thinners; a tractor-cultivator with its variation of bars and tools; and tractor-drawn harvesters that top, dig, and deliver beets into trucks that hold from six to eight tons and dump mechanically. Beet pilers at receiving stations screen and pile beets at a rate of more than 3,000 tons a day.

Processing the beets is almost entirely mechanical. Brought into the plant by a conveyor system, they are lifted, scrubbed, shredded, and sent through the diffusers, filters, evaporators, spinners, boilers, crystallizers, and the like, that extract, refine and dry the sugar in a continuous mechanical operation.

THE COLUMBIA BASIN PROJECT

Some 50,000 years ago, giant glaciers of the last ice age blocked the flow of the Columbia

Figure 15-4. A field of sugar beets in the Boise Valley. Idaho is the third-largest beet growing state in the nation, surpassed only by California and Colorado. (Amalgamated Sugar Co.)

Figure 15-5. Grand Coulee Dam and Roosevelt Lake on the Columbia River in Washington. The dam is 550 feet high and 4,173 feet long and has a capacity of 3,918,000 kilowatts. (Bonneville Power Administration)

River at what is known today as Big Bend. The river, backed up to lake depth, eventually spilled over a surrounding hill and cut a new course through the lava-encrusted plateau. When the ice retreated, the river returned to its normal channel and left behind a coulee 800 to 1,000 feet deep, 27 miles long, and two to five miles wide, southwest of the present dam site. This long, dry chasm came to be known as the Grand Coulee, one of the world's geological wonders, which has given its name to an impressive dam.

With the opening of Grand Coulee Dam, water from the Columbia River poured through Grand Coulee for the first time since the ice age. The Columbia Basin Project, irrigated with Columbia River waters impounded by the Grand Coulee Dam, is in south-central Washington. The project area is approximately 80 miles long, north and south, and 60 miles wide from east to west. An intricate network of canals, siphons, and lateral ditches feeds water to nearly 186,000 acres of irrigated cropland on more than 2,500 farm units. When the ancient coulee is filled to a depth of 90 feet it will become the main reservoir for an irrigation system that will bring water to some one million acres—an area almost the size of Delaware—and will provide irrigation water for

13,000 to 14,000 farms of from 45 to 160 acres.

A total of 8,000 new jobs has been created to date on the farms and in the towns of the Columbia Basin Project. Larson Air Force Base and the Boeing Aircraft Company's Flight Test Center have boosted the population of Moses Lake and Ephrata; the Hanford Atomic Energy Commission development has brought considerable growth to Pasco. Ephrata is the headquarters for the Columbia Basin Project.

Soils, although variable, are well suited to irrigation farming. There are no areas of heavy, clay soils. Soil types, in general, range from deep loess to coarse sand. Those suitable for irrigation farming range from silt loams to loamy sands, and their depths vary from less than two feet to more than 15 feet.

Scanty rainfall, warm summers, and comparatively mild winters are typical of the entire area. The average annual temperature is 50.4° F. The average temperature during the irrigation season, April to October, is 62.2°. Temperatures range from an average minimum of about 20° in January to an average maximum of about 91° in July, although extremes of −33° and 113° have been recorded.

Average precipitation ranges from less than six inches in the southwestern part of the area to ten inches in the northeastern uplands. Most of the precipitation falls as late autumn rains and winter snows. Very little occurs during the growing season, a circumstance that makes it impossible to grow crops successfully without irrigation, except in areas where wheat is cultivated by dry farming methods.

The average frost-free period is 170 days, with a variation of 127 to 212 days in different sections of the area.

Lands of the basin are suited to a wide range of crops, including alfalfa, clover, small grains, corn, sugar beets, beans, and potatoes. Markets, rather than physical or climatic factors, determine the acreage of intensive crops—vegetable, fruit, seed, and specialty crops.

LIVESTOCK

Soils, topography, and climate make production of range livestock more profitable than production of crops throughout a great portion of the Columbia-Snake Plateaus, Plains, and Mountains Region. Rainfall in much of the region is low and uncertain. Cropland farming is often impossible or hazardous without irrigation. Drought, or continuous threat of drought, is a menace to serious ranching in many parts of the area. Some ranches have both dry and irrigated land, the latter furnishing the winter feed base. Others rely on feed from nearby irrigated farms. Renting pastures or buying hay is common in some areas.

Beef cattle.   Cattle ranching is widely practiced on the extensive arid rangeland east of the Cascades. Beef cattle profitably utilize great quantities of by-product feeds—pea straw, sugar beet tops, cull potatoes, cannery refuse, and the like—which are produced abundantly in the grain lands and irrigated districts. Cattle also feed on the grasses and sagebrush found on wooded and cutover lands and in rough and swampy areas.

Cattlemen sometimes lease grazing land in nearby national forests. The cattle graze in the mountain meadows during the summer and are returned to the home ranch in the fall. Fat steers are sold, and the breeding stock fed hay as needed during the winter. In spring the cows with their calves are again driven into the upland pasture.

Principal beef cattle breeds are Hereford, Shorthorn and Aberdeen Angus. The greater part of the beef cattle consists of stockers and feeders. A common practice is to transfer cattle to irrigated sections or the Willamette, Yakima, and Kittitas Valleys to be grass fed before slaughter. Throughout the cattle raising areas, particularly in districts specializing in fattening, small plants process meat for local consumption. Most beef cattle, however, are slaughtered and packed in a half-dozen large plants in Spokane, Portland, Seattle, and Tacoma. The big cities have the dual advantage of a substantial immediate market and available labor.

Sheep.   The sheep industry is much less important than cattle in most sections of the region. Sheep have been decreasing since 1931. High production costs, the problem of obtaining shepherds, and low wool prices, have tended to cause sheep ranchers to switch to cattle raising.

The Pacific Northwest is known for its top-quality wool and for grass- and grain-fattened lambs. The Chicago market pays premium prices for the spring lambs produced in this region.

Woolen mills have been processing the region's wool clip since the 1860's. Since the sheep population was at that time heaviest in the Willamette Valley, the early mills were located in riverside towns there to assure a steady supply of the pure water required for processing. These mills, located in another province, expanded in their original locations—Salem, Oregon City, and Portland. They constitute the bulk of the present woolen industry. A major share of the wool consumed by these mills is imported from Australia and New Zealand; this fleece is mixed with native fibers to impart desirable qualities of texture and strength. Much of the wool clip is shipped unprocessed to the Boston wool market.

HYDROELECTRIC POWER

Although without oil, natural gas, or coal of commercial value, the Columbia-Snake Plateaus, Plains, and Mountains Region is generously endowed with water power. As a result, more than nine-tenths of the electrical energy consumed in the region is generated by falling water. In the United States as a whole only about one-quarter is so derived; the remainder is generated by fuel. Of a 105-million-kilowatt potential in the whole country, 37 per cent is in the Northwest. At present, however, only slightly more than one-tenth of this vast potential has been developed.

Hydroelectric development in the Northwest began near the end of the 19th century. The earliest projects were developed by local private utilities and a few municipalities. By 1930, the region produced 1,341,000 kilowatts in hydroelectric plants.

In the period from 1930 to 1950, production rose to 4,792,000 kilowatts, an increase of about 177 per cent. The total power from Federal installations on the Columbia River in this period reached 2,138,400 kilowatts—518,400 kilowatts at Bonneville Dam and 1,620,000 kilowatts at Grand Coulee Dam.

The Bonneville Power Administration was established in 1937 to market power from Bonneville Dam. Later it was directed to market the power from Grand Coulee and other projects.

At first, output of the installations at Bonneville and Grand Coulee was absorbed largely by war industries attracted to the region by the abundant supply of low-cost power. However, this power supply also contributed to the increased mechanization of industry and the rise of urban domestic consumption; it was undoubtedly the major factor in rural electrification. With the end of the war, there was a temporary surplus of Federal power, but this surplus disappeared rapidly as war plants shifted to peacetime production.

The period since 1950 is marked by the growth of the Columbia River Power System, which nearly doubled its installed capacity to 4,151,000 kilowatts by mid-1956. The system is composed of the generating plants constructed and operated by the Corps of Engineers and the Bureau of Reclamation and the Bonneville Power Administration transmission grid, through which power from these projects is dispatched and marketed. Projects added to this system since 1950 are Hungry Horse, Detroit, Big Cliff, Lookout Point, Dexter, McNary, Albeni Falls, Chief Joseph, and Chandler Dams. Presently, the Northwest has an annual capacity of 11,038,610 kilowatts. The system will be expanded further by The Dalles, Roza, Cougar, Hills Creek, and Ice Harbor projects now under construction.

Of particular importance in coming years in terms of power development is the giant John Day Dam and Lock, destined to be the Columbia River's largest power producer. Construction began in 1958 and is scheduled for completion in 1968. The dam is being erected 27 miles east of The Dalles and about two miles downstream from the mouth of the John Day River. It will impound 500,000 acre-feet of water for flood storage and will ultimately have 20 huge generators capable of supplying a total of 3,105,000 kilowatts—50 per cent more power than is produced by Grand Coulee Dam.

Private companies, municipalities, and others have 16 projects under construction or licensed for construction that will add 3,400,000 kilowatts to the power pool of the Northwest by 1968. Forty additional projects are under consideration—involving an additional 5,200,000 kilowatts.

The Columbia River Power System is integrated with the other electric power facilities of the region. The Northwest Power Pool is a voluntary organization that provides the region with many benefits. It co-ordinates the operation of the member utilities, including those using steam as well as those using water power, to insure the most economic use of all power resources.

Certain industries, primarily aluminum reduction, located in the Columbia-Snake Plateaus, Plains, and Mountains Region because of the abundance of cheap power. In the case of others, such as the producers of phosphorus and ferroalloys, the availability of raw materials was also a factor. Still others, such as chlorine and caustic soda manufacturers, expanded because of the growing demand for the product in local and Western markets.

The aluminum industry came to the region because the price of power was sufficiently low to offset the high cost of freight on raw materials received and on manufactured products sent to Eastern markets. This advantage, however, is rapidly disappearing as freight rates continue to advance and as technological improvements increase the efficiency of steam generation of electricity in Eastern production centers. The price of power is higher than it was when it attracted industries originally. As a consequence, difference in power costs between this region and the rest of the nation is

Figure 15-6. The Harvey Aluminum Company reduction plant at The Dalles, Oregon. To the right of the plant is the Columbia River; Mt. Hood is in the background. (Harvey Aluminum Co.)

now less of an incentive to the location of industries in the Northwest.

Recently, the United States and Canada concluded an agreement for the joint development of the Columbia River Basin. This agreement sets in motion a $450 million Canadian water storage program—the largest public works project Canada has undertaken since the construction of the St. Lawrence Seaway. Under this agreement Canada will build, within ten years, dams at Mica Creek on the Columbia River in British Columbia, at the outlet to Arrow Lakes near the United States border, and at the outlet of Duncan Lake on the West Kootenai River. This agreement will also permit the United States to build Libby Dam, which will have a reservoir extending 42 miles into Canada on the Kootenai River.

MANUFACTURING

The Columbia-Snake Plateaus, Plains, and Mountains Province is not yet an industrialized area; nor, contrary to popular opinion, is it rapidly becoming one. The over-all rate of industrial growth remains comparatively low. Industrial growth is always cumulative; the output of one plant is the raw material of another as new factories are erected to utilize the by-products of existing ones. Industries develop to provide supplies and machinery for expanding businesses, and the interchange of ideas leads to the development of new products. Profits become a source of capital for speculative enterprises, and a reservoir of skilled labor and technical talent is formed from which different industries can draw. Apart from the industry that has grown up around forest products, there is little integration of manufacturing in the Columbia-Snake Plateaus, Plains, and Mountains Region. The industrial foundation is still too narrow for the cumulative effect to have gained momentum.

Figure 15-7. Forest cover east of the Cascade Mountains in Oregon. This section was last cut over in 1924. (U.S. Forest Service)

Most important among the forces inhibiting industrial growth in the area is the smallness of the local population (and therefore the local market), combined with the remoteness from, and the high cost of reaching, the national market. The slightly more than five million residents of Washington, Oregon, and Idaho are surrounded by sparsely populated territory that offers little as a supplement to the local market. The manufacturer desiring to produce for more than the immediate population is forced to go far afield. To sell his product nationally, he has to buy more transportation miles than his competitor in any other part of the country. The manufacturer in the Midwest can reach more than half of the national population and more than two-thirds of national industry within a radius of 500 miles. To reach an equal market from his position, the manufacturer from the Inland Empire must ship his product 2,000 miles. Consequently, the only items from the area sold on the national market, outside of processed raw materials, are those for which transportation is not an important cost. Such products are of high value in relation to weight, are self-transporting, or are of a quality for which the customer is willing to pay the extra money.

Forestry, farming, and mining are the bases of industrial development of the region.

FOREST PRODUCTS INDUSTRIES

East of the Cascades the lumber industry differs substantially from that in the western zone. The difference is a consequence of the kinds of trees present and the prevailing land forms. The interior uplands, too dry to support the dense stands of fir, cedar, and hemlock of the coast, are forested predominantly in pine, of which the Ponderosa and Idaho white are most valuable. The former prevails on the Okanogan Highlands, and the Blue, Bitterroot, Selkirk, and Rocky Mountains. At higher altitudes in central Idaho, Ponderosa is replaced by lodgepole pine, and in northern Idaho by Idaho white pine. The forests, however, are largely of mixed species and, although one tree may predominate, solid stands such as those of Douglas fir or hemlock found on the western slopes are lacking. Interspersed with the dominant species are Western larch, Douglas fir, sugar pine, Pacific white fir, and grand fir.

The relative dryness causes trees to grow more sparsely and more slowly and the yield per acre of forest land is correspondingly small. As a result, the region is not able to support a lumber industry of the proportions existing west of the Cascades; it accounts for only one-fifth of the Pacific Northwest's output. Because the available timber is spread over a wide area, the mills are dispersed throughout the region. These mills, especially the larger ones, tend to be at lower altitudes than the forests, frequently at the edge of the woods, and—if possible—on a railroad.

Small, privately owned tracts of timber and small mills are less common than in the Douglas fir country, for the timberland not in the national forests or Indian reservations was bought up originally by a few big companies with headquarters in St. Paul or Chicago. These operators generally have cut more than the annual growth, with the result that the once-important lumber towns of Spokane and Klamath Falls are now sawing only a fraction of the timber they once handled.

The importance of the forest industry is readily evident. In Idaho more than 50 per cent of all manufacturing industry wages is earned by producers of forest products. Furthermore, good forest management helps sustain other facets of the economy, for the forest areas are also the watersheds that supply water for irrigation and to generate power.

Although the nation's greatest remaining stand of white pine is in the northern part of the state, southern Idaho (south of the Salmon River) has sizable stands of Ponderosa pine. Idaho's forests include Douglas fir, white fir, red fir, Engelmann spruce, cedar, larch, and lodgepole pine.

In southern Idaho, there are some 60 sawmills, scattered from Riggins on the Salmon River south to Boise and Caldwell and east to Wendell. Largest is the Boise Payette Lumber Company, which processes about half of the total cut in the forest areas south of the Salmon River. More recent operations are the Salmon River Lumber Company at Riggins and the Caldwell Lumber Company, which operates a planing mill at Caldwell and a sawmill at Horseshoe Bend. The Price Valley Lumber Company is at Tamarack; the Sawtooth Company, at Mountain Home. These and other lumbering enterprises in the area are keenly interested in new methods to sustain the yield and cut the cost of operation.

The Boise Cascade Corporation has constructed a $1 million plant for making corrugated containers in Burley, Idaho, and a similar plant at Wallula, Washington. In 1959 a pulp and paper mill also was constructed at Wallula; a $5 million expansion program has been scheduled recently.

FOOD PROCESSING

Ranking second in importance to forest products is food processing—frozen food plants, canneries, sugar beet refineries, meat packing plants, and dairies.

Growing conditions for fruits and vegetables are ideal in the interior valleys. Fruits and vegetables are produced in excess of local needs and are of sufficiently high quality to overcome the freight barriers that separate the region from the major Midwestern and Eastern markets. A large portion of the fruit is kept in cold storage plants and cellars and shipped fresh during the ensuing year. The fruits and vegetables not sold fresh on the local market are either canned or frozen. The pea crops of the Palouse district have brought a dozen canneries to Walla Walla, Pendleton, and other towns in the foothills of the Blue Mountains.

The canning operations are located close to the area of production, with a 30-mile radius considered the maximum distance that most products may be transported economically. Certain items, such as pears and apples, can be hauled greater distances, and a plant may draw on several producing areas to secure its supply. Frozen food plants and canneries are very heavy users of water. Water of good drinking quality is required for cleaning the raw product; for steam, brine, and syrup; and for cooling and cleaning the cannery.

Because of the seasonal nature of the canning industry, a large number of temporary workers is needed during the packing season.

Sugar beet refining, which has been discussed previously, is dependent on government acreage allocation. The question of establishing a refinery in the area, then, is dependent on allocation of a sufficient number of acres of land for the growing of sugar beets.

The raising of livestock is an important enterprise in the region and meat processing plants are found where livestock production warrants it. A meat packing plant has high overhead costs and the competitive nature of the industry forces it to operate on a relatively small margin of profit. Profits result from efficient and continuous operation at or near capacity. Spokane is the only major city within the region where meat packing becomes more than a local operation.

ALUMINUM REFINING

In the early years of World War II, Alcoa built and operated a huge government-owned reduction plant at Spokane, Washington, the first such plant in the region. This facility was later purchased as surplus from the War Assets Administration by Henry J. Kaiser.

The Harvey Machine Company, a new producer, has completed a $65 million aluminum reduction plant at The Dalles, Oregon; its production capacity in 1961 was 75,000 tons. A new aluminum pig plant is scheduled to start production in 1963. Capacity will be 75,000 tons per year. Arrangements have been completed for freighting alumina from Japan to the plants. Bauxite is mined in Malaya near Singapore and shipped to Japan where it is refined into alumina.

ATOMIC ENERGY

The city of Richland, Washington, mush-

Figure 15-8. An aerial view of a section of the Hanford plutonium plant in Washington. (General Electric Co.)

POPULATION

The Columbia-Snake Plateaus, Plains, and Mountains Region is one of the least populated areas of the United States. With a few outstanding exceptions, such as Benton County, Washington, growth in the last decade has occurred mainly in areas where people already clustered. The population of the region is still more rural and less urban than the national average.

The wheat districts have experienced a consistent decline of their rural population since 1910, a situation brought about primarily by the increase in the size of farms operated and by increased mechanization.

Districts that have experienced a continuous expansion of irrigated lands since 1890 have had a marked increase in rural population during most decades; the increase during the last two decades reveals the influence of the Grand Coulee Dam development and the Columbia Basin Project. The population of the Inland Empire will continue to experience substantive growth near the Columbia Basin Project, the Hanford atomic energy works, and in some southern Idaho counties.

POPULATION CENTERS

Spokane (182,000). The most important city of the province, Spokane had its origin with the erection of a sawmill at the falls of the Spokane River in 1871. Four transcontinental railroads now meet at Spokane, making it a major transportation center and the central distribution point for the Inland Empire. Spokane is the economic capital, not only of eastern Washington, but also of northern Idaho and Montana as far east as the Continental Divide.

Boise (41,271). The capital city and financial center of Idaho, Boise is located on the main line of the Union Pacific Railroad. It occupies a key position as the wholesale and retail distribution center of the Snake River Lava Plain Subregion. Boise's trade area extends from Glenns Ferry, Idaho, on the southeast, to Weiser, Idaho, on the northwest. The city is the shopping center for 26 communities in 11 counties, an area of more than 238,346 persons.

roomed as a direct result of activities at the plutonium plant built during World War II at nearby Hanford. The Federal government took over 631 square miles of Benton County, Washington, to go into the business of manufacturing plutonium.

General Electric assumed control of the Hanford plant in September, 1946, when the Atomic Energy Commission relieved the Army of its control. The total plant investment at Hanford at present exceeds $1 billion and the annual payroll in Richland totals more than $56 million.

Plutonium 239 is the end product and involves three major steps, which call for extensive plant facilities, costly scientific equipment, and highly trained personnel. First, cylindrical uranium slugs are canned in aluminum jackets. Second, uranium is irradiated in the reactors of "piles." Third, plutonium is extracted from the irradiated slugs of uranium.

Thirty miles north of Spokane, near the town of Ford, the Dawn Mining Company has a $3 million uranium processing mill with a daily capacity of 400 tons. Recent uranium discoveries in the region made the plant feasible.

Part VI | PACIFIC SLOPE MOUNTAINS AND VALLEYS

The Sierra Nevada-Cascade Mountain Ranges separate most of California, western Oregon, and western Washington from the Intermountain West. Partially screened off from the continental winds of the interior, these Pacific Coast areas enjoy a very mild climate for their latitudes. The marine effect may be seen in the profuse natural vegetation mantling the slopes of the Coast Ranges and the western slopes of the Sierra Nevada-Cascades. The variety of agricultural crops—ranging from subtropical citrus and vine products to a vast array of deciduous fruit and nut crops, grains, and vegetables—exists as a result of the long growing season and ample precipitation or available irrigation water.

Settlement patterns, land uses, and climates are sufficiently varied within the Pacific Slope Mountains and Valleys to justify a division into the Sierra Nevada-Cascade Mountains and Valleys Region, the Central Valley of California Region, the Coastal Mountains and Valleys of California Region, and the Puget-Willamette Lowland and Coastal Mountains Region.

16 | Cascade-Sierra Nevada

Mountains and Valleys

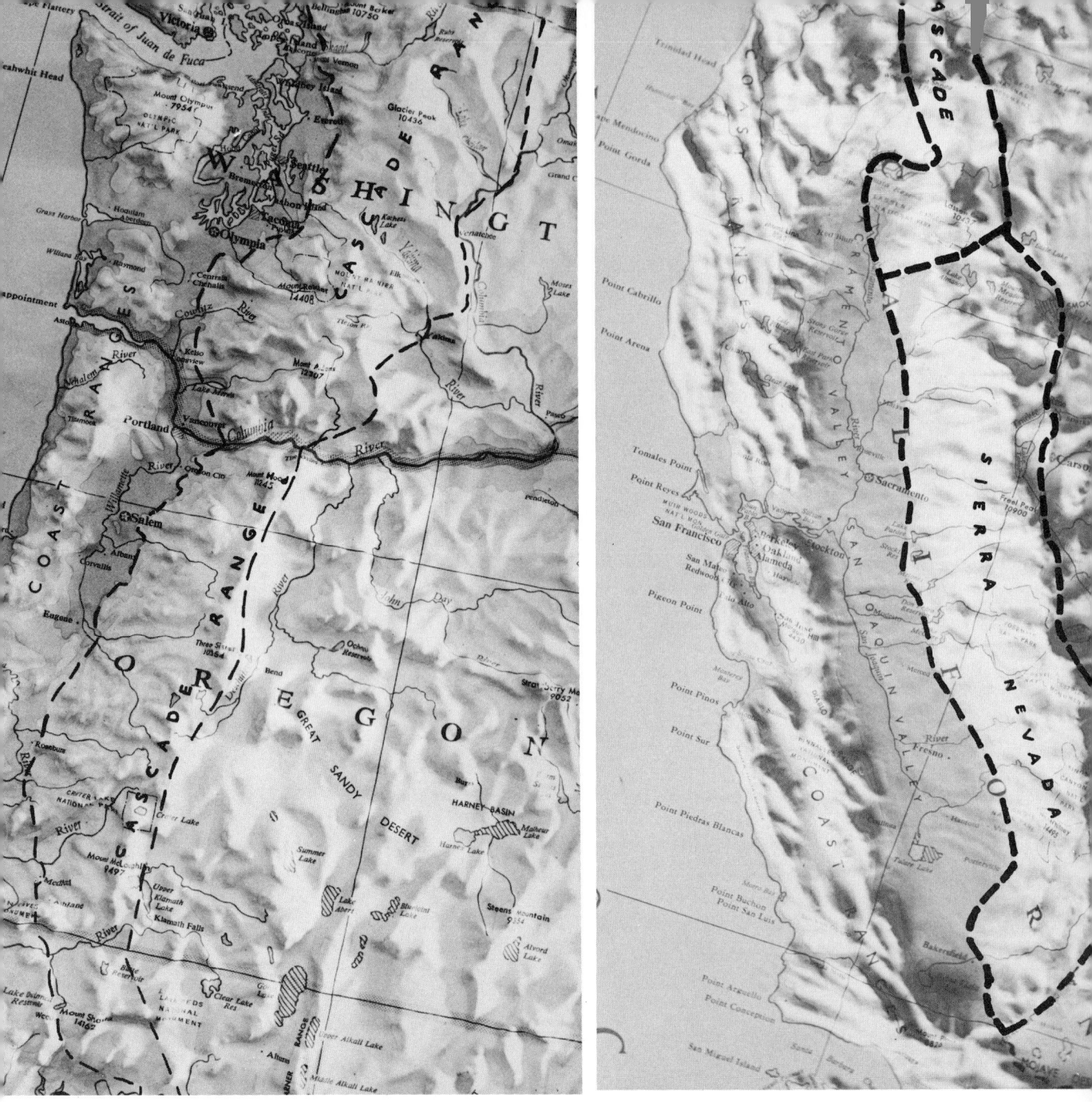

(Relief map copyright Aero Service Corp.)

THE Cascade Mountains and the Sierra Nevada are usually considered to comprise one province because they make a continuous highland separating the Columbia-Snake Plateaus, Plains, and Mountains Region and the Basin and Range Province on the east from the Central Valley of California Region and the Puget-Willamette Lowland and Coastal Mountains Region on the west. Since the Cascade Mountains and the Sierra Nevada have different histories, they will be considered as separate subregions here.

THE CASCADES

SURFACE FEATURES

The Cascade Mountains rise east of the Willamette-Puget Lowland like a broad, giant wrinkle of the earth's crust. The subregion begins just north of the Canadian-boundary line and extends southward for some 500 miles to the Feather River in northern California. It varies in width from less than 50 miles at the California border to about 120 miles at its northern extremity.

Northern Cascades. The northern Cascades, situated in northern Washington and adjacent British Columbia, consist of metamorphosed Paleozoic rocks with granite batholiths. In general, they are carved into sharp peaks and rugged ridges of a height (6,000 to 8,000 feet) suggesting an uplifted peneplain deeply and maturely dissected by water and ice. The U-shaped valleys are very deep. In one of the valleys lies Lake Chelan, with a bottom 400 feet below sea level.

A series of volcanic peaks tower above the general summit of the northern Cascades. The most noteworthy of these are Mt. Baker (10,-778 feet) and Glacier Peak (10,438 feet).

Glaciers have profoundly affected the relief features of the projecting ridges and have smoothed the surface of the exposed bedrock. Sometimes the broadening of the valleys by glaciation removed the lower part of tributaries, leaving them as "hanging valleys" from which beautiful waterfalls cascade into the main valley. Lakes were also formed, both by glacial erosion and by piles of debris blocking drainage. Hundreds of lakes are scattered among the mountains and in the area around them.

Central Cascades. The middle section of the Cascades, extending from southern Oregon almost to the latitude of Seattle, is a continuous range cut only by the Columbia River. The altitude throughout is 6,000 to 7,000 feet. The northern part has a horizontal skyline like the Sierra Nevada, but this gives out toward the south. Above this general level rise isolated volcanoes, such as Mt. Hood (11,245 feet), Mt. Adams (12,307 feet) and Mt. Rainier (14,410 feet). The latter peak has one of the most extensive glacier systems in the United States.

Near the southern end of this section is 6,177-foot high Crater Lake, occupying the caldera of an old volcanic cone. Located within a national park, the lake is six miles wide and 2,000 feet deep.

South of latitude 44° the western boundary of the central Cascades borders the Oregon Coast Range and the Klamath Mountains; north of 44° it abuts the Willamette Valley.

The northern and central Cascade Mountains have very heavy winter rains on their windward (west) sides. They also have the finest coniferous forests in the United States.

Southern Cascades. The southern Cascades extend north 150 miles from the 40th parallel to southern Oregon. It is the narrowest part of the subregion and very irregular in height. It is not a range made by uplift but a belt of closely set volcanoes (120 in the first 50 miles at the south end) of all ages, from active to old and much eroded.

Within California the Cascades are rather ill-defined and, except for a few scattered volcanic cones, can scarcely be distinguished from the Modoc country to the east. They extend from the Oregon boundary southeastward to the Feather River.

Surface configuration in the southern Cascades bears almost universal evidence of former volcanic activity. Lava flows are visible wherever streams have cut valleys sufficiently deep to produce rapid erosion. Such flows are also apt to be apparent on the sides of the larger valleys; the Pit River, principal stream of the region, has eroded spectacular canyons.

With the exception of a few high summits, elevations above the local valleys are not great. Altitudes vary considerably, from low elevations of 6,000 to 8,000 feet to high elevations

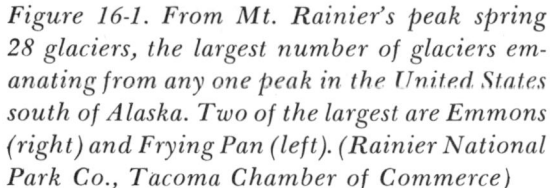

Figure 16-1. From Mt. Rainier's peak spring 28 glaciers, the largest number of glaciers emanating from any one peak in the United States south of Alaska. Two of the largest are Emmons (right) and Frying Pan (left). (Rainier National Park Co., Tacoma Chamber of Commerce)

Figure 16-2. Crater Lake, in Oregon, is one of the scenic attractions of the central Cascades. The lake, formed when Mt. Mazama was destroyed by volcanic action more than 5,000 years ago, covers an area of 20 square miles. (Oregon State Highway Commission)

ranging from 10,000 feet to slightly over 14,000 feet above sea level.

Two peaks, Mt. Shasta, and Mt. Lassen, are outstanding. Mt. Shasta sends its ancient volcanic mass up 14,162 feet above sea level and dominates the surrounding territory. Mt. Lassen, over 10,000 feet high, holds the distinction of being the only active volcano in the United States (excluding Alaska and Hawaii). Its last major eruption occurred in 1915.

WATER POWER

The Pacific Northwest has historically met its power requirements almost entirely by hydroelectric means.

The Pacific Ocean provides a limitless reservoir of water. Prevailing winds absorb the moisture evaporated from the ocean by the sun and deposit it inland over the Cascades. In gravitating back to the ocean, this water must traverse a rugged terrain with rock formations of widely varying hardness and resistance. A rapid runoff, numerous waterfalls, and deep gorges and canyons, are the general results.

Such a fortuitous interaction of geographical and meteorological forces provides the Pacific

Northwest with one of the largest concentrations of hydroelectric potentiality on the North American continent. The Northwest had a capacity in its power pool of more than 13 million kilowatts in 1960. This compares with a national total of 183 million kilowatts. The aggregate power potential of the area, including the Columbia River tributaries of western Montana, is estimated at 39.4 million kilowatts, approximately 37 per cent of the total hydroelectric resources of the nation. Most of this power potential, however, lies outside the Cascades Subregion.

The rivers of the Cascades Subregion have been harnessed and supply much electric power. The Skagit, Snoqualmie, White, Green, Lewis, Chelan, Clackamas, Umpqua, and Rogue Rivers in the northern and central Cascades are power suppliers. These streams have their highest flow in winter and early spring, and complement the summer maximum flow of the Columbia River. Power plants built on the lesser rivers have the effect of stabilizing seasonal power on the Columbia.

In addition to serving as a source for hydroelectric power and for irrigation water, Cascade streams furnish such centers as Seattle, Tacoma, Portland, and smaller cities with their municipal water supplies.

The Pit, McCloud, and Sacramento Rivers of the southern Cascades have been harnessed behind Shasta Dam for both hydroelectric power and irrigation. Shasta Dam, situated 12 miles north of Redding on the Sacramento River, is one of the largest and highest concrete structures in the world, second in its class only to the great Hoover Dam on the Colorado River.

LUMBERING

Lumber and forest products dominate the economy of the Cascades Subregion. Once exclusively an exporter of green timber and logs, the area's economy has within the last generation been evolving into one centering on forest products. Lumbering, however, is still the dominant economic activity.

The West Coast forest belt lies between the Cascade Mountains and the Pacific Ocean, covering an area roughly 1,000 miles long and 140 miles wide. The Cascade Mountains slopes and foothills comprising the eastern outlier are densely wooded and used for timber production and watershed purposes.

The Cascade Mountains form a barrier to coastal storms. Precipitation ranges from 40 inches in the lower foothills to as high as 130 inches in the mountains. On the eastern slope, precipitation is greatly reduced, for the air has lost a considerable portion of its moisture on the west. These physiographic and climatic conditions affect the forest growth. On the western slope, four primary species dominate—Douglas fir, West Coast hemlock, Western red cedar, and Sitka spruce—to produce some of the most luxuriant forests in the United States. Other species found in lesser volume are silver fir, noble fir, and white fir. On the eastern slope, precipitation is sparse and temperatures fluctuate widely. Ponderosa pine predominates, but Western larch, white fir, lodgepole pine, and Sierra juniper are also important. Douglas fir, West Coast hemlock, Western red cedar, Sitka spruce, and Ponderosa pine are the subregion's principal commercial trees.

Early logging in the Douglas fir region was primitive. Bull teams were in general use until the turn of the century. Several years later, high-speed logging was developed. Because of the rough terrain and because a huge volume of privately owned timber was accessible to water transportation in the Puget Sound,

Figure 16-3. Mt. Lassen, the southernmost peak in the Cascade Range, rises 10,453 feet above sea level. Once an active volcano, its last eruption was in 1915. It is now a part of Lassen Volcanic National Park. (California Division of Highways)

Figure 16-4. Bonneville Dam on the Columbia River, about 40 miles east of Portland. Used for hydroelectric and navigational purposes, it also has fishways to permit salmon to ascend the river. Locks enable barges to move upstream. (Bonneville Power Administration)

Figure 16-5. Shasta Dam is 602 feet high, two city blocks thick at its base, and approximately 3,500 feet long. Behind it, 4.5 million acre-feet of water back up in the canyons of the Sacramento, Pit, and McCloud Rivers to form Shasta Lake, with a shoreline of 365 miles. In the left background rises Mt. Shasta. (Redding Chamber of Commerce)

Grays Harbor, and Columbia River territories, only a moderate amount of logging occurred in the Cascades.

The boom in truck and tractor logging in the late 1930's and the greater demand for lumber during World War II stimulated timber cutting. Today, more than 250 million board feet of lumber are marketed from this region annually. The fine-grained Douglas fir is widely used in the construction of houses, bridges, and ships.

Much of the timber in the northern part of the Cascades is noncommercial, principally because rugged and rocky terrain makes extraction difficult and costly. Moreover, lodgepole pine predominates, a species that does not command as high a price as Douglas fir and Ponderosa pine. The noncommercial area includes western Whatcom and Skagit Counties,

nearly all of Chelan County, and all of northwestern Okanogan County.

Ponderosa pine is the leading species by acreage on the eastern side of the Cascades. Its chief market is in the East and South where it is used in home construction. Principal local uses include sash and doors, box shook, and interior finish. A considerable factor in the success of the fruit growing industry of eastern Washington is the availability of Ponderosa pine for boxes.

Western red cedar is in great demand for use as shingles, shakes, and posts. It is found in the river valleys and stream bottoms within the Cascades Subregion. Another important tree to the lumber industry in Washington is Western hemlock. Stands are common on the cool western slopes of the Cascades. The tree does not have the qualities of Douglas fir, but is suitable for many uses—one of the most important being pulpwood.

Future outlook. The Cascades Subregion contains one of the last great stands of virgin timber in the United States. Moreover, environmental conditions are extremely favorable to rapid tree growth. Studies show that in a dense forest a Douglas fir will attain a height of from 90 to 110 feet and a diameter at breast height of from ten to 30 inches in 100 years.

In the days of cheap timber and forest products, very little attention was paid to the replenishment of the forest. The last 15 years have brought about a significant increase in the value of both timber on the stump and its manufactured products. This has encouraged Cascades forest owners to establish tree farms and adopt other long-range, scientific forestry practices.

MINING

Coal. Coal is the only mineral fuel presently found in large-scale commercial quantities in the Pacific Northwest. The major coal belt lies on the western flank of the Cascades, extending from Mt. Baker in the north to the Columbia River in the south. Another coal belt, small in area but highly concentrated and rich in deposits, is situated east of the Cascades in Kittitas County. Together these two areas have an estimated 63.4 billion tons of coal. A third of this amount—21.1 billion tons—is recoverable. At the present rate of consumption, these reserves are sufficient to supply the area for many years.

The coal mining industry in the subregion has undergone a gradual decay for the last 35 years, with the exception of a temporary recovery during World War II. Annual output

Figures 16-6 and 16-7. In the Pacific Northwest, Douglas fir trees are harvested by clear cutting of selected patches on commercial tree farms (right). A system of logging called "forest area selection" is used—islands of trees are left unharvested to serve as seed sources. Logs are dragged to a loading area by high-lead cables and tractors. There a shovel loader stacks them on logging trucks carrying up to 60 tons of logs apiece (left). (Weyerhaeuser Timber Co.)

Figure 16-8. The Wenatchee Valley of Washington is a major producer of apples. Fertile soil, abundant sunshine, and irrigation combine to produce fruit of high quality. (Wenatchee Chamber of Commerce)

dropped from 4,128,000 tons in 1918 to the present 685,000 tons. This decline was caused by the high cost of production, inefficient marketing, and loss of markets to imported coals and to nonsolid fuels. Total demand for coal in the area has increased somewhat since 1940, but the rate of per capita consumption has declined. Most of the tonnage is used for government institutions, for industrial heat, and for power purposes.

Iron ore. Although several million tons of iron ore have been located in the Cascades Subregion, only a few thousand tons are mined annually. In addition to the fact that the iron ore is of a low grade, a scarcity of coking coal creates a handicap for iron smelting. Some exports of iron ore to Japan are made from deposits in Whatcom and Okanogan Counties.

Other metals. Gold first was mined in the northern Cascades near Blewett in Kittitas County. Chelan County leads in gold production, with important mines at Holden and near Wenatchee. The total value of gold produced from this region amounts to about $1.5 million annually. Copper ores are widespread in the mineralized districts of Washington. The largest copper mine in the state is at Holden, near the head of Lake Chelan. Ores are concentrated and then shipped to the Tacoma smelter. Copper has also been produced at Index and other places in Snohomish County. Zinc is found with gold and copper at the Holden operation.

AGRICULTURE

Agriculture plays a secondary role in the economy of the Cascades Subregion. The heavy precipitation, dense vegetation, and acidic soil favor forestry and forest products. A small number of livestock, poultry, and dairy enterprises are scattered throughout the western side of the Cascades. Grazing is negligible here because of the lack of grasses and the unpalatability of most of the shrubs. Some summer grazing occurs in the lower foothills. On irrigated farms, fruit is grown, but generally not on a commercial scale.

Agricultural possibilities improve only in the Ponderosa pine region. This area occupies the eastward, shadowed slope of the range, where the forest cover is less dense and the soil, still a podzol, is less arid. The undergrowth, more of a grass than a shrub, encourages agriculture. Here in the foothill valleys of Washington and Oregon cultivated agriculture is practiced; grazing prevails on the grassland slopes.

The growing season varies considerably throughout the region as a result, partially, of differences in elevation. Frost-free days vary from 120 to 200 in the eastern foothills area, for example, while central Oregon has less than 80 days without frost.

Commercial agricultural production is confined largely to the protected valleys—Wenatchee, Yakima, Hood River, and Rogue River. These are the core areas and production radiates outward from them. The Wenatchee Valley is predominantly an apple producer; its apple crop is supplemented by dairying, ranching, and a very minor marketing of field crops. Five per cent of the cling peach crop also is grown here. The Yakima Valley excels in the production of fruits and nuts—yielding about a fourth of the state's apples, three-fourths of its peaches, and minor quantities of grapes, walnuts, and filberts. Yakima field crops are valued at approximately $25 million. Corn for grain leads, followed by spring wheat, winter wheat, and oats. Hops and potatoes are grown on a large scale. The Hood River Valley in the

Figure 16-9. The Hood River Valley, with Mt. Hood, the highest point in the Oregon Cascades, in the background. The valley's 200 square miles of irrigated fruit farms produce about one-half of Oregon's annual commercial crop of apples and pears; over two million boxes are packed annually. (Hood River Chamber of Commerce)

eastern Cascades is comparable to Yakima Valley as an apple producer. Principal varieties are Delicious, Winesap, Jonathan, Rome Beauty, and Yellow Newton. All but the Jonathans are winter apples that are kept in cold storage and sold during the October to March period. This area leads the world in the production of Anjou pears. Peaches, cherries, walnuts, and filberts also contribute in making the area an important fruit and nut producer. Ninety-four per cent of the agricultural income of Hood River County is derived from fruit.

Field crops and livestock production occupy the bulk of the land devoted to agriculture south of the Hood River. Barley leads among the small grains, followed by oats, spring wheat, and minor production of winter wheat.

The cropland of the Rogue River Valley has attained a greater intensity of use than any other farming area in Oregon. About 30 per cent of the land is now irrigated and much of it is in intensive crops. Over 11,000 acres are planted to pears. Peaches and apples are also important. Dairying is second to fruit in importance, followed by livestock and livestock products. Grain, hay and seeds, poultry, truck crops, and swine also are well represented.

RECREATION AND TOURISM

The Cascades Subregion offers many natural attractions. Snow-capped peaks, mountain streams, and national forests provide the setting for a variety of outdoor activities.

Majestic Mt. Hood offers many opportunities for outdoor recreation. Timberline Lodge, the Skiway cable bus, skiing and ski lifts, camping, hiking, and magnificent scenery attract visitors from all over the world. The Mt. Hood loop highway trip is one of the most beautiful in the Pacific Northwest.

Mt. Rainier National Park centers upon Mt. Rainier, an extinct volcano 14,408 feet high. It is the most frequently visited of the three national parks in the Cascades, catering to over 750,000 sight-seers annually. Established in 1899, the park covers an area of 377 square miles. On its slopes are 28 glaciers, the largest such system in the nation.

The northern Cascades contain five national forests: Gifford Pinchot, Snoqualmie, Wenatchee, Mount Baker, and Chelan. In the central Cascades of southern Oregon is Crater Lake

National Park. Rogue, Deschutes, and Willamette National Forests in the Oregon Cascades offer additional recreational opportunities.

The southern Cascades are noted for the "Shasta Cascade Wonderland," a recreation area of great scenic beauty, comprising some 25 million acres in northern California.

THE SIERRA NEVADA

SURFACE FEATURES

The Sierra Nevada is a bold mountain mass that forms the backbone of California. In shape the range resembles the state's own outline. Lying almost wholly within California, the Sierra Nevada Mountains are some 400 miles long and average nearly 80 miles in width. The western side of the range rises gently from the flat Central Valley and its eastern front is a dramatic series of sharp cliffs and steep, high mountains.

On the south the range is separated from the west-trending Transverse Ranges by Tejon Pass; to the north, the relatively recent lava flows from Mt. Lassen and the Modoc Plateau prevent precise determination of the Sierra Nevada. The range here blends into its northern neighbors.

Elevations gently diminish the farther one moves north and south from Mt. Whitney (14,496). Several peaks north of Whitney, however, and along the eastern margins of Sequoia and Kings Canyon National Parks, rise above 14,000 feet. Summits towering above 13,000 feet may be found as far north as Yosemite National Park.

Numerous rivers and streams drain the mountains, most of them flowing westward or southwestward to empty into the Sacramento or San Joaquin Rivers. The larger rivers have cut spectacular canyons into the mountains—canyons that deepen toward their mouths. The Tuolumne, Merced, Kings, Feather, and Kern Rivers—as well as the San Joaquin River itself—have eroded gorges from 3,000 to 5,000 feet deep. Best known of these is Yosemite Valley, where the preglacial Merced River slashed a deep canyon that later glaciers carved into a nearly flat, U-shaped valley with sheer cliffs of breathtaking grandeur. The beds of streams tributary to the Merced today are in hanging

Figure 16-10. The eastern fault scarp of the Sierra Nevada Mountains north of Mt. Whitney, with Owens Valley in the foreground. The high peak in the background is Mt. Tom. (Mary Hill)

valleys. These streams, when flowing, fall to the floor as cascading waterfalls that, from the crest of the highest to the base of the lowest, measure nearly half a mile. There are few other valleys of appreciable size within the central or southern Sierra Nevada Subregion.

In the north, Sierra Valley, Indian Valley, and smaller valleys support irrigated agriculture. The lower and gentler slopes that merge into the Central Valley Region allow the dry farming of grain in some sections and the production of irrigated fruit in others.

CLIMATE

Water has been called the "white gold" of California. It is a treasure over which the Sierra Nevada is guardian, for it is the long western slope of the mountains that intercepts winter rains and snows to account for nearly half the state's total runoff.

The maximum amount of moisture falls

above the 3,500-foot level of the western slopes. From here to the crest of the range the rainfall increases at a rate of approximately one inch to every 75 to 100 feet.

The Sierra Nevada Subregion is favored by more snow than most other areas in the United States. Norden, a fairly representative station at an elevation of 6,861 feet near Donner Summit, has a mean seasonal snowfall of slightly more than 400 inches—enough, when melted, to provide 50 inches of water.

This heavy snowpack and the heavy rains common during the winter months in the lower reaches of the range are vital to the California economy, for they provide the water to fill the area's rivers and streams. Many of the streams and rivers lead into reservoirs where their water is banked for use in the hot, dry, almost rainless summer months.

Most of the large surface storage developments in the subregion are planned to serve

Figure 16-11. Kennedy tailing wheels in the Sierra Nevada Mountains. Such relics of gold mining days are found throughout the Sierras along California's Gold Highway 49. (Mary Hill)

primarily as storehouses for water that will be used in agriculture in the Sierra Nevada foothills and in the Central Valley Province and in industry and as domestic water in the cities and towns. However, it is becoming apparent that large reservoirs can and do serve many purposes. They are a source of hydroelectric power, they help control floods, and they form vast vacation playgrounds.

MINING

Although the colonization of California was begun as far back as the time of the American Revolutionary War by Franciscan missionaries from Spain and Mexico, it was gold that precipitated the state's sudden growth and development.

The discovery of gold at Sutter's Mill in El Dorado County in 1848, though not the first discovery in the state by any means, ignited

excitement that amounted to a national furor. Within a few months would-be miners were swarming through every creek and gulch from the Cosumnes River to the Mokelumne River, from the edge of the Central Valley to the crest of the Sierra Nevada.

Mining camps sprang up rapidly in the placer and surface mining areas—lawless, hard-living boom towns such as Drytown, Fiddletown, Plymouth, Volcano, Sutter Creek, Jackson, Grizzly Flats, Chili Bar, Fairplay, Angels Camp, and Cherokee Flat. Deep mines came later—the Argonaut, Kennedy, Oneida, Keystone, and Lone Star were a few. From these mines and others in the mother lode came the gold that was to finance the growth of America for the next century. Then, almost as suddenly as it had begun, the Age of Gold ended.

Towns bloomed and faded within months—sometimes even within weeks or days. What was once a populous tent city would disappear so completely that even its erstwhile residents were hard put to recall its location. More permanent towns, too, grew and flourished.

Most of the towns in the gold country have had several lives. From tent cities they grew to collections of board-and-batten shanties, with here and there a more pretentious wooden structure—a church, a miners' hall, a saloon. But the lower Sierra Nevada foothills have long dry seasons; all except the major streams run dry and the countryside becomes a tinder box. Fires, both accidental and deliberate, razed the villages—some of them several times.

Few of those who followed shining dreams of wealth had any idea of the back-breaking labor that would be required to make their dreams realities. Some, it is true, found riches quickly; most spent it just as quickly. But of the great horde that poured into the new diggings, few were lucky; most of them made daily wages or less.

Today most of the gold mines of the Sierra Nevada Subregion are closed, for the price of gold is not high enough to cover the cost of the labor to mine it. Now and then, one or two hydraulic mines wash a few hundred yards of gravel. Skindivers and recreational prospectors swarm the rivers in the spring and summer, but the total amount of gold they mine is not great.

Most of the gold that comes from California today is taken from river beds by dredges—

large floating power shovels that scoop up gravel from the river bottom, run it through concentrating machines mounted upon the floating barge, and shoot the unwanted gravel out the rear to be stacked in large piles along the shore.

Metals mining, however, is not altogether dead in the Sierra Nevada. For years the Pine Creek mine, located on the east side of the range near Bishop, was one of the nation's leading tungsten producers; the Leviathan mine, near Markleeville, still provides work for many of the men of sparsely populated Alpine County. Other mines are worked now and then, depending upon the market for their ore.

Mines of a different sort are today's major bulwark of the mining industry—limestone and gravel quarries producing materials for the construction industry; clay pits, where fine clays for ceramic wares are extracted; and sand mines that produce sand of a quality good enough for plate glass.

The mines of Amador County, for example, once dominated by such gold mines as the Argonaut and the Kennedy, still yield more than a million dollars worth of raw materials each year. Over half of the output is sand and gravel; a third is clay; the remainder is lignite coal (produced for its wax content, not for fuel), and stone, gold, and silver.

LUMBERING

Since the days of the Gold Rush, lumbering has been economically important in the Sierra Nevada Subregion. The first sawmills were established shortly after the discovery of gold to provide rough lumber for miners' shacks and other purposes. Lumber continued to play an important part in the development of the mines and also in the agricultural, industrial, and residential aspects of life in California.

Although the industry is gradually shifting to the north coastal area of California, the Sierra Nevada Subregion is still the second-largest lumber producing region in the state. Fortunately, the forested mountain slopes lie fairly close to communities of the Central Valley Region, so that accessible timber can be hauled down to market at a distinct profit. Only a small portion of the cut reaches the coastal cities, which are more cheaply supplied by the coastal forests of northern California and southern Oregon.

Lumbermen classify the Sierra Nevada Subregion as the pine region. Major species found there are the sugar pine, Ponderosa pine, Jeffrey pine, white fir, Douglas fir, and incense cedar. The pine type covers about one-quarter of the commercial forest land and is found principally at elevations of from 1,000 to 5,000 feet. The Douglas fir type is found at elevations of 4,000 to 7,000 feet, chiefly on the western slopes of the mountains.

Three-fifths of the timber stands are government owned. Most of this commercial forest land is within the national forests. Timber companies, railroads, recreation areas, ranchers, farmers, and individual residents own the rest of the timberlands.

AGRICULTURE

The raising of cattle and other livestock constitutes the chief agricultural activity of the Sierra Nevada Subregion. If the cattle are kept in the mountains all year they eat cut meadow hay during the winter months. Many of the larger ranches have lands in the Central Valley Province where they can winter the cattle.

The chief outlets for the subregion's cattle are the packing plants, smaller slaughterhouses, and feeder ranches of the Sacramento Valley. Stockton and San Francisco are the chief markets.

Numerous high valleys in the Sierra Nevada Mountains are used for summer grazing. One of these, Sierra Valley, once the floor of an ancient lake, contains alluvial soil 120 feet deep at some points. The valley is the source of the Feather River, which, after meandering many miles, plunges down through its namesake canyon near Portola. Hay, wheat, oats, and barley grow in Sierra Valley. Because of high winds and a frost-free period of less than 90 days, the soil cannot produce fruit and other crops that might otherwise be expected to thrive there. Formerly these high valleys were given over entirely to dairy farming and produced large quantities of butter for shipment to the Sacramento Valley and the San Francisco Bay area. Since World War II, the land has pastured beef cattle and sheep brought up from the lower valleys in the summertime.

Figure 16-12. A ranch headquarters in Amador County, California, in the rolling-to-rough foothills of the western Sierras. (U.S. Department of Agriculture Soil Conservation Service)

Indian Valley, northwest of Sierra Valley, at an elevation of almost 3,500 feet, has numerous ranches that raise sleek, purebred cattle and hardy sheep on some 34,000 acres of meadowland.

Orchard crops, first planted by gold miners, still cover some Sierra Nevada foothills. Most of the trees are Bartlett pears, with plums and peaches next in number.

RECREATION AND TOURISM

The historic gold mining regions, the matchless scenery of the Sierra Nevada Mountains, and a climate favorable to both summer and winter sports, lure thousands of vacationers, sportsmen, and tourists to the Sierra Nevada Subregion.

The outstanding scenic attractions of the area—its magnificent mountains, valleys, forests, lakes, and streams—have stimulated the establishment of many public and private recreation areas. Major resorts are centered at such localities as Yosemite Valley, Lake Tahoe, and along Highways 40 and 50. Small resorts and private summer homes are scattered throughout the entire subregion. Because they are easy to reach, comfortable, and set in healthful surroundings, these recreation areas probably will attract a large percentage of permanent residents in the future.

Yosemite Valley is a magnificent gorge known the world over. The valley, scooped out by the combined action of glaciers and the Merced River, is seven miles long, a half-mile deep, and a mile wide. The waterfalls of the valley are spectacular. Upper Yosemite Falls drops 1,430 feet at one leap, a height equal to about nine Niagaras. Lower Yosemite Falls, the lower stage of the same stream, drops 320 feet, the equivalent of two Niagaras. The waterfalls are fed by melting winter snows and reach their maximum flow in the months of May and June.

A vast domain of granite peaks speckled with innumerable lakes and with high mountain meadows whose vivid green is emphasized by colorful wild flowers during July and August stretches to the north, east, and south of Yosemite Valley. Living glaciers nestle in the shadows of the highest peaks. There are some 700 miles of trails, and fishing may be enjoyed in many of the streams and lakes.

Near the south entrance of Yosemite National Park, is the Mariposa Grove of giant sequoias, one of the major points of interest. The grove contains about 200 trees of enormous size and great age, some of them estimated to be more than 3,000 years old.

Kings Canyon National Park is one of the newest of the national parks. The Kings River flows through most of its length, its three forks roaring swiftly down from the 12,000-foot heights of the Central Sierra Nevada through a canyon whose nearly vertical walls are almost twice as high as any part of the Grand Canyon of the Colorado River. Kings Canyon, one of the most rugged known, attains at one point the greatest depth of any gorge in North America, 8,000 feet.

Sequoia National Park, the nation's second oldest national park, lies just south of Kings Canyon. The special features of this park are

Figure 16-13. Yosemite Valley, California. This U-shaped glacial valley, famed for its waterfalls and big trees, attracts visitors from all over the world. (National Park Service)

its vast forests and its awe-inspiring views of the Great Western Divide. The General Sherman Tree, reported to be one of the oldest and largest living things in the world, grows here. It is 36 feet in diameter at the base and as high as a 20-story building.

Lake Tahoe, the largest and one of the most beautiful lakes of the Sierra Nevada, is a major resort for summer visitors and is especially accessible to the people of central California. Because part of the lake is in Nevada—not far from Reno and Carson City—the area is quite often part of the "package" vacation offered by gambling casino entrepreneurs of that state.

Not far from Lake Tahoe, U.S. Highway 40 crosses the Sierra Nevada over Donner Pass, and so provides access to one of California's foremost winter sports areas. Some of the best skiing in the world is to be found in these hills. The major ski areas are Squaw Valley, Sugar Bowl, Soda Springs, Donner Summit, Olympic Hill, and Rainbow Tavern.

The mother lode section, a recreational area of romantic tradition and natural charm about 150 miles from San Francisco, covers eight counties. Abandoned mine shafts and ruined buildings and towns stand as ghostly remnants of the turbulent Gold Rush.

Figure 16-14. The General Sherman Tree, Sequoia National Park. (National Park Service)

17 | *Central Valley of California*

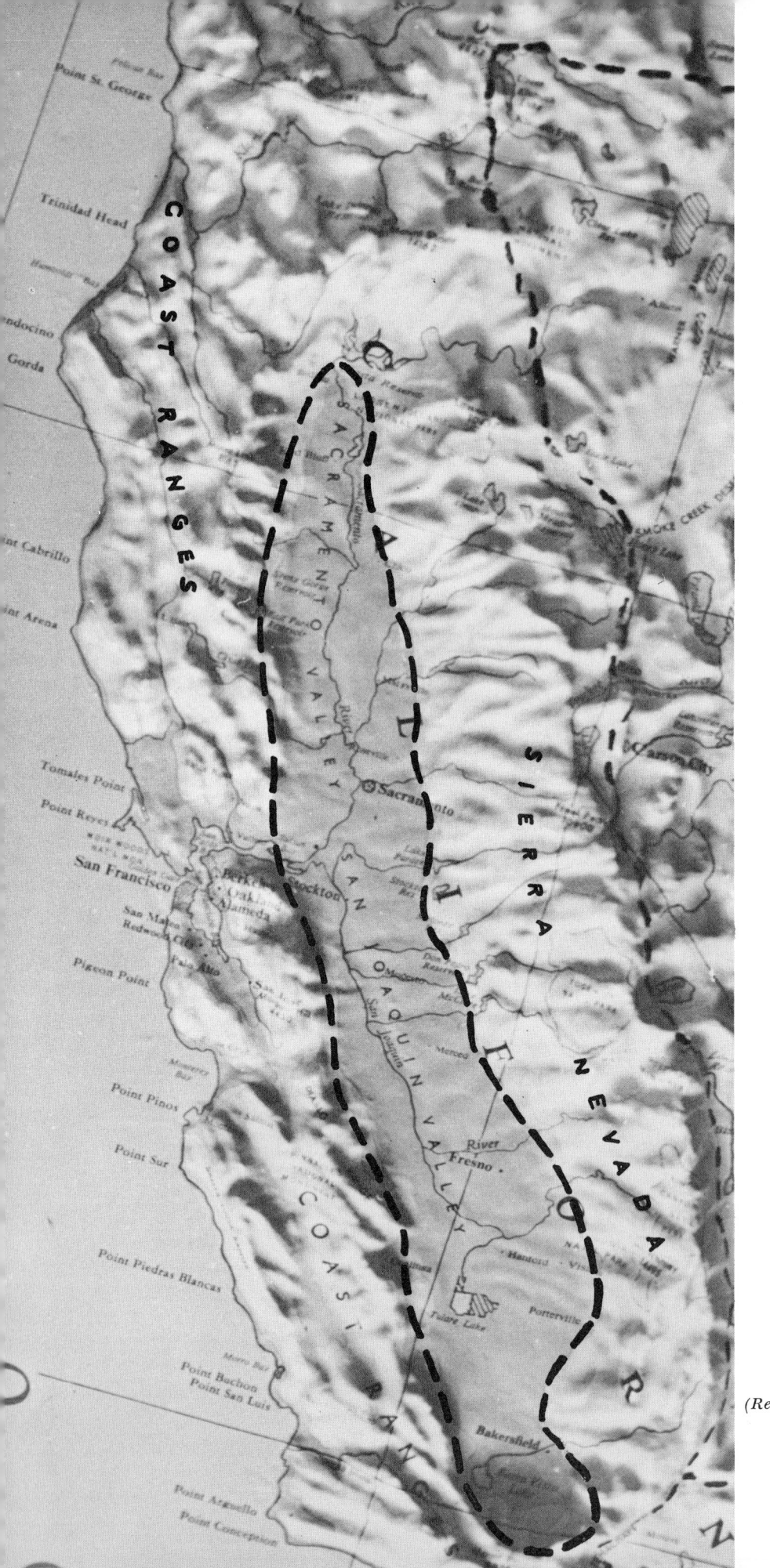

COAST RANGES

SACRAMENTO VALLEY

SIERRA NEVADA

SAN JOAQUIN VALLEY

COAST RANGES

Point St. George

Trinidad Head

Mendocino
Gorda

Point Cabrillo

Point Arena

Tomales Point

Point Reyes

San Francisco
Berkeley
Oakland
Alameda
San Mateo
Redwood City
Palo Alto

Pigeon Point

Stockton

Sacramento

Point Pinos

Point Sur

River
Fresno

Hanford

Point Piedras Blancas

Tulare Lake

Porterville

Bakersfield

Point Buchon
Point San Luis

Point Arguello
Point Conception

(Relief map copyright Aero Service Corp.)

THE Central Valley is an area some 450 miles long by 50 miles wide embracing all or part of 20 California counties—nearly half the length of the state. It is sometimes called the Sacramento-San Joaquin Valley after the two rivers that converge upon the Carquinez Strait from north and south, respectively.

SURFACE FEATURES

The region should not be thought of as one continuous expanse of level land, for it contains sufficient surface irregularities to provide considerable topographic variety. Between Red Bluff and Redding, in the north, it becomes quite hilly, and then widens out again at Redding itself. The low hills that surround most of its margins grade almost imperceptibly into the Coast Ranges to the west and the Sierra Nevada to the east. All moisture falling within the region either evaporates, is consumed, or flows out to the Pacific Ocean through the Carquinez Strait and San Francisco Bay.

The most conspicuous landform within the region is the buttes of northern Sutter County. These old volcanic cores rise 2,000 feet above the nearly level surrounding terrain. Just north of the mouth of the Sacramento River are the Montezuma Hills; near Coalinga, the Kettleman Hills stand virtually detached from the central Coast Ranges, to which they properly belong. Still another isolated bit of steeply rolling country, the Elk Hills, lies northwest of Buena Vista Lake.

On the eastern side of the Central Valley Region, and particularly south of Stockton, the land rises gently to the base of the Sierra Nevada. Here the many streams that issue from the mountains have deposited huge alluvial fans across the valley floor, pushing the course of the San Joaquin River several miles west of the valley's center. The fan of the Kings River has even dammed the southern valley, transforming it into an internal drainage basin with no normal fluvial outlet.

Though most of the valley is devoted either to farming or to urban use, there are still considerable areas of grassland, and to the far north and on the Sutter Buttes there are several large blocs of hardwood trees mixed with the grasses.

AGRICULTURE

The Central Valley's ranches, orchards, vineyards, and dairies each year produce nearly $1 billion in staple and specialty products. The chief reasons for its productivity are level land, good soils, a long growing season of some seven to nine months, and highly developed water supply systems.

Agriculture is an intensive, specialized, and heavily commercial enterprise. The techniques and machinery used by Central Valley farmers are among the latest and most scientific in use anywhere.

Farming in the Central Valley is organized differently than elsewhere in the nation. Large land holdings of a few hundred to more than a thousand acres are operated as food factories. Capitalization is high, and the superintendents and foremen work from central administrative headquarters rather than from individual farms. The smaller operators usually concentrate upon the raising of one crop. This pattern, which is the result of such factors as distance from market, fluctuation of prices, and the uncertainty of yearly yields, has led to the formation of co-operatives designed to make transportation cheaper by mass shipments to Middle Western and Eastern markets. The grower does not necessarily own all the land he plants to crops. On the contrary, in many instances he studies market needs, rents suitable acreages, and then plants accordingly. Out of this procedure the "risk specialist" has been born, the grower-shipper whose knowledge of the uncertainties involved is the greater precisely because he does so specialize.

In the early years of stock raising and of grain production the field hands were hired on a long-term basis, and only a few of them were migratory. As agriculture became intensified, outside sources of labor became more important, so that today seasonal employees are the usual help of the valley's farm owners, despite the problems they bring.

The seasonal worker is always on the move, harvesting the various crops as they mature in one region after another; he is never able to remain in one place long enough to establish himself as a citizen. He lives apart from the local residents, usually in barracks or work camps behind the fields and orchards, and sometimes in crude shanties he himself has built along a river bank. The migratory worker will work for low wages, and—because the available labor pool is often large—he has little bargaining power. The local townspeople treat him as an outsider; local governments feel no responsibility for his welfare. No one knows how to help him with his problems and few people care. Still the local farmer seldom can get along without his help. Mass farming has created an underprivileged agricultural proletariat at precisely the time when the lot of the industrial worker has improved.

The northern part of the Central Valley is noted for general farming, field crops, and some dairying. Intensively cultivated truck crops are raised by efficient, large-scale methods in the Sacramento-San Joaquin Delta. The Sacramento Valley also markets sizable crops of peaches, prunes, almonds, pears, walnuts, olives, and some citrus fruit. Livestock, particularly cattle and sheep, are wintered in and around the Sacramento Valley, and summer either in nearby private range lands or else in the mountain national forests. The pasture of cattle on grain stubble and their feeding on a year-round diet of such crop residues as sugar beet tops are becoming increasingly important.

Its longer growing season has made the San Joaquin Valley more versatile agriculturally than the Sacramento. The largest enterprises in the San Joaquin are such field crops as grain, alfalfa, cotton, and sugar beets; fruit crops; nut crops; vegetables; dairying; and livestock feeding.

FIELD CROPS

Cotton.   The chief cash crop of California, cotton is the most important of the Central Valley's field crops, even though Federal acreage allotment has forced cotton farmers to find alternate crops for that part of their land that can no longer be planted to cotton. Because of irrigation, and because of an even climate that is warm without being highly humid, local growers have been able to produce cotton of a more uniformly high grade than can be grown in most other cotton producing areas. Yields per acre are exceptionally high, averaging well over a bale and a half. Some years farmers have reported an outstanding average yield of nearly 900 pounds of lint per acre. This high figure

could not have been reached without mechanization. Consequently the vast majority of the growers use cotton picking machines to harvest their crop. Each machine can harvest about 800 acres a season—equivalent to the work of 25 men. In addition, every big grower has an arsenal of machinery for use in planting, thinning, weed killing, and fertilizing.

Acala cotton, strain 4.42, is the only variety grown on a mass basis. The breeding and seed distributing program developed jointly by the growers and by the U.S. Department of Agriculture's Valley Experimental Station was concentrated upon this strain. It proved so successful that the state legislature restricted all planting to Acala 4.42. Heavy yields, together with the uniform staple fiber, have made the growing of cotton highly profitable.

Rice.   Rice, the newest Central Valley commercial crop of major significance, is now a multimillion dollar enterprise. Although the Sacramento Valley is the greater producer, the San Joaquin also has a considerable acreage. The environmental conditions of level land, fertile topsoil, impervious subsoil, abundance of water, and high temperatures (over 70° F.) are all favorable to rice production.

The pattern of rice planting is similar to that of cotton. In the beginning the crop was cultivated and harvested by the hand methods still practiced in some of the Southern States. Then the development of machine methods made a higher and more economical production possible, and so produced a more stable economy.

Rice farming is expensive, difficult, and risky; it requires large-scale mechanization in order to be profitable. The fields are prepared for mid-April planting by plowing and leveling the ground as soon as it dries after the winter rains. Levees are rebuilt and repaired by mechanized graders called "dikers." The field is flooded before planting, thus killing the weeds with water. The planter moves over them at a height of 40 feet and a speed of 100 miles an hour. Specially-equipped biplanes flying a line between flagmen stationed at each end of a field can spread 900 pounds of seed over five acres in about five minutes. The seed, soaked and starting to split, hits the water as it is germinating.

Harvesting is done by self-propelled combines that reduce a stand of rice to bulk form

Figure 17-1. Irrigating alfalfa by flooding in Madera County, California. Note the cattle grazing in the background. (U.S. Department of Agriculture)

in one brisk operation. Standing by are tractor-treaded "bank out" wagons that take loads from harvesters to trucks. The heart of the harvesting operation is the dryer, a cluster of silos with a rectangular pinnacle at the end. The pinnacle does the drying. Trucks deliver the field rice to a conveyor that boosts it to the top of the drying apparatus. From there the rice filters downward while heat is blown through it (reducing its moisture content to 14 per cent), after which it is stored in the silos. The modern rice dryer gives the farmer a final bit of leverage on the elements. He is able to harvest his crop slightly green without fear that moisture will spoil it.

The Rice Growers Association, organized in 1921, markets most of the crop, partially remedying the danger of oversupply during bumper crop years. Since the United States and its territories normally consume the same amount of rice every year, no major increase in production for domestic use is to be expected. Recent government quotas have caused a decline in the acreage devoted to rice. Since other foreign markets are negligible, the Asiatic market is a dominant factor in the economy of the crop.

Barley. Well adapted to the dry conditions of the Central Valley and one of the chief grain foods raised there, barley also is grown as an irrigated crop in the cotton area, where 50 per cent of its acreage is sown. Dry land plantings, making up the rest of the acreage, are to be found along the foothills on both sides of the Central Valley. The income from barley used as a livestock and poultry feed is sizable, though its cash sale in the form of grain is relatively small. Only about 25 per cent of the crop is sold locally or for export; this is used to produce malt liquors, alcohol, and distilled spirits.

Wheat. Irrigated or dry farmed, wheat no longer dominates the region's agriculture as it did at the turn of the century, for it has been replaced by barley and other grains better adapted to growth under arid conditions. The soft wheat variety grown here cannot compete with the hard winter wheat produced in the southern Great Plains or the hard spring wheat of the northern Great Plains.

Oats. Oats are grown on nonirrigated land or where soil and other conditions are unsuited to higher value crops. Twenty-five per cent of the state's total, 45,000 acres, is sown in the Sacramento Valley, both as a regular and rotation crop. Oats are used there chiefly as livestock feed.

Alfalfa. Alfalfa is widely planted, chiefly to make hay; it fits well into the rotation program, where it is alternated with other field crops and vegetables. Alfalfa can grow only where the land is perfectly level, for if there are any depressions the plants are scalded out by accumulated irrigation water and Bermuda grass. As a result, alfalfa is grown only on the valley floor, primarily on loamy soils.

Seed. The production of both certified and uncertified seed—from barley, clover, and oats to orchard grass, Sudan grass, and fescue—is a major activity in the Central Valley.

Sugar beets. Producing excellent yields, both in tonnage and in sugar content, sugar beets are not only ideally suited to the rotation program but also provide a good cash crop. They can be grown successfully on the same land for at least two years in succession.

They are a flexible crop involving less risk from both disease and weather than other crops. Usually planted in February or March, the beets are harvested from mid-August on. As it crawls along the rows, the harvester simultaneously loosens the soil, spikes the beets on two huge wheels, tops them by means of a set of blades, and dumps them on a conveyor belt that carries them to a waiting truck. The average yield per acre is approximately 20 tons.

FRUIT CROPS

Grapes. Grapes grown for raisins have long been one of the bases of the Central Valley's economy. Although grapes are grown for all purposes, the area near Fresno produces more raisins than the rest of the state combined.

During the early period of the industry the growers marketed their own crops of raisins, but with expansion the commercial packer appeared on the scene. As the economic pattern fluctuated, the packer left more and more of the financial risk to the grower. To combat this the grower turned to the co-operative. After many attempts, the California Associated Raisin Company was organized in 1912; this was the forerunner of the present Sun-Maid Raisin Growers of California.

Sun-Maid is a nonprofit organization whose members deliver their raisins under a uniform crop contract. The contract provides that the raisins be received, graded, stored, and eventually processed and marketed. The net proceeds, less appropriate withholdings to assure working capital reserves, are then returned to the growers in proportion to the amount of their deliveries. The basic operating principles of the organization are the establishment of quality standards for raisin packs, grower ownership of packing facilities, and grower control of distribution.

Sun-Maid is the largest dried fruit packing establishment in the world. As many as 1,000 tons of raisins can be packed and shipped from its plant in a single day, and more than $25 million have been spent on national advertising. The advertising of Sun-Maid in foreign countries, together with the uniformly high quality of the product, has made the brand name famous throughout the world.

The word "raisin" is a shortened form of the French *raisin sec,* or "dry grape." Therefore any dried grape has the right to the name "raisin." By usage, however, the term has been limited to a few varieties. Three of these, the Thompson Seedless, Black Corinth, and Muscat of Alexandria, produce nearly all the raisins used in international trade.

Successful raisin grape cultivation demands a dry and relatively hot ripening season to facilitate drying the fruit; mild winters, since even during their dormant season most varieties are apt to be damaged by temperatures appreciably below 32° F.; and freedom from killing frosts. All these factors are to be found within the San Joaquin Valley.

Raisins are a key factor in the price structure of the whole grape industry, since all those grapes that are not sold either to wineries or in the fresh grape market are used to make raisins. At least one-third of the state's grape crop is used for this purpose.

Though co-operative marketing has been helpful, it has not been able to solve all the problems of raisin production and sale. Only about 70 per cent of the raisin pack is consumed in the United States. The loss of the prewar European export market, which absorbed about a quarter of the total raisin production, is the chief cause of the slump felt in the raisin industry since the war. The co-operative has been left with a burdensome surplus of raisins.

The domestic demand for raisins, like that for rice, is stable. In order to induce buyers to eat 30 per cent more raisins, which is that portion of the pack exported during recent years, the growers would have to cut their prices by much more than 30 per cent, a procedure that would be virtually impossible.

Along with raisin varieties, table and wine grapes exist in large plantings. The principal table varieties are the Almeria, Emperor, red and white Malaga, Ribier, Cardinal, Thompson Seedless, and Muscat. The principal wine varieties are Alicante Bouschet, Carignone, Malvoisie, Grenache, Mission, and Palomino.

Citrus fruit. The Central Valley's citrus industry is second in importance within California only to that of the south coastal region, and threatens to surpass the latter in orange production as urban subdivision and industrialization reduce citrus acreages. Many Los Angeles County and Orange County growers have sold their southern California holdings at a high profit per acre and have purchased new plots in the southern Central Valley, where land values are considerably lower.

Orange groves are clustered along the foothills from Orange Cove south to Rich Grove in Tulare County. Climatic extremes cause the fruit to ripen earlier here than it does in the coastal portions of the state, with the result that it can be put on the market before the crop of the southern Coastal Mountains and Valleys Province is ready. Since 1943, navel oranges have increased in acreage and now make up 65 to 75 per cent of the total crop. Tulare County is the undisputed leader in the production of this variety. In the same period, Valencia plantings declined 25 to 35 per cent.

Growing oranges is not a get-rich-quick business. It takes about eight years for an orange grove to come into fruit; irrigation water is expensive and picking, processing, and marketing procedures may be troublesome (even though handled by such co-operatives as Sunkist). Oranges are picked by hand, which is laborious and expensive. Furthermore, state laws direct that navel oranges cannot be harvested until they have attained a certain specified sugar content and a characteristic orange color. Frost is always a danger. During the cold winters of 1948, 1949, and 1950, it caused a loss of as much as 70 per cent of the crop. The newest challenge to the California orange industry is the flood of frozen juice concentrates from Florida, where a cheaper labor supply makes a cheaper product possible.

There are, however, compensations for these apparent difficulties. Modern methods have assured at worst only a small loss on the fruit once it has been harvested, since oranges not sold on the market, including even culls, can be turned into juice. Oils are extracted from the skin for use as flavoring, and the peel and pulp are dehydrated and used as livestock feed.

Lemon acreage is found almost exclusively on the higher ground east of Terra Bella. Although plantings are small, output compares favorably with other lemon districts when ample protection is provided against wind and cold. The value of the lemon crop is over $1 million annually. Lemon trees are extremely sensitive to the hot, dry summer climate, which means that frequent irrigation is necessary during summer months.

Peaches. The climatic conditions of the San Joaquin Valley are well suited to peaches, which thrive on low humidity, abundant sunshine, and rather high temperatures during the growing season. In the peach producing areas winter temperatures seldom drop low enough to cause crop damage, though spring frosts are occasionally harmful.

Nearly all peaches raised for drying are grown in the Central Valley, chiefly in Stanislaus, Merced, and Fresno Counties. The Muir and Lovell types predominate, though some Elbertas have been dried in recent years.

The production of peaches for canning is concentrated in a few districts; 50 per cent of the tonnage is grown in the Sacramento Valley. A little more than 30 per cent is raised in the Modesto district, which includes Stanislaus, San Joaquin, and Merced Counties; three per cent in the upper San Joaquin Valley, in Madera and Fresno Counties; and about eight per cent in the Tulare-Buena Vista area.

Nectarines. Nectarines are grown in the peach area. Peach and nectarine trees resemble each other in appearance, growth responses, bearing habits, and in certain other general characteristics. The nectarine fruit differs from the peach only in its lack of pubescence, its usually smaller size, its greater aroma, and its more distinctive and richer flavor. At present most of the nectarines are shipped to local and distant markets as a dessert fruit. Although they make an excellent dry product, few nectarines are dried commercially at the present time; nor are they extensively canned for market, largely because the varieties now grown do not can well.

Figs. Over 80 per cent of California fig acreage is to be found in the Central Valley. More than half of this, 15,000 acres, are in Fresno County, where the crop is localized on hardpan ground northwest of Fresno near Reedley. The next largest planting, one of over 7,000 acres, is in the Planada district of Merced County. The remainder of the valley has only small acreages scattered throughout the peach belt.

Although most figs are dried before being marketed, an increasing tonnage of fresh figs is packed and shipped by air to distributing centers throughout the nation. Adriatic, Calimyrna, Kadota, and Black Mission are the chief varieties.

OLIVES

The rather sensitive olive tree requires warm temperatures, an absence of severe frost, low humidity, and winds of low velocity if it is to flourish. It is therefore limited as a commercial crop to those areas that have six months of temperatures above 68° F., including three or more months of temperatures above 80°.

Excessive humidity is disastrous to the olive tree. Heavy rains impede flowering and continued dampness is favorable to disease. The tree can survive drought, long hot periods, and dry soil conditions because its small, leathery leaves have water-retaining cuticles on their upper surface and peltate hair masses to pro-

tect the numerous small depressed openings on their undersides. It is widely and incorrectly believed that the olive tree does not need much water, largely because it seems to thrive under dry soil conditions in Mediterranean areas. At first, California olives were raised without irrigation, as they had been in Europe, for the planters were unaware that the dry planting of the Mediterranean was dictated by necessity, not choice. Irrigation experiments have shown that olive trees require as much moisture as other trees, if not more, if they are to produce their best.

Olive culture is concentrated in Tulare County, but continues as far north as Corning and Red Bluff. The Mission variety dominates, but others grown include the Manzanillo, Sevillano, Ascolano, and Barouni.

NUTS

Almonds. Almonds are an important money crop in the Central Valley. Somewhat resembling the peach in manner of growth and character of the leaves and flowers, the almond tree is the earliest commercial deciduous fruit species to bloom in California, and commonly produces a profusion of flowers in early February. The first leaves, which appear about the time the last petals fall, develop rapidly into full foliage.

The exacting climatic conditions under which almonds can be grown limit the trees to relatively small areas. The hot interior valleys of California, which have comparatively dry atmospheric conditions, seem well suited to the growth of almond trees. Trees there are less subject to disease than are those planted along the coast. Adequate water for irrigation and an absence of severe spring frosts favor almond culture. Orchard heating is a common practice even when frosts are light.

The trees are grown with varying degrees of success upon soils of all possible types, from the lightest sands to heavy adobe. The yield per acre is the important factor in determining whether or not the orchard is profitable, for the cost of production per pound commonly runs higher in orchards with low yields. The average yield is much lower than is generally realized: the state average for the last 31 years was 357 pounds per acre. Several other factors, such as the amount of the initial investment

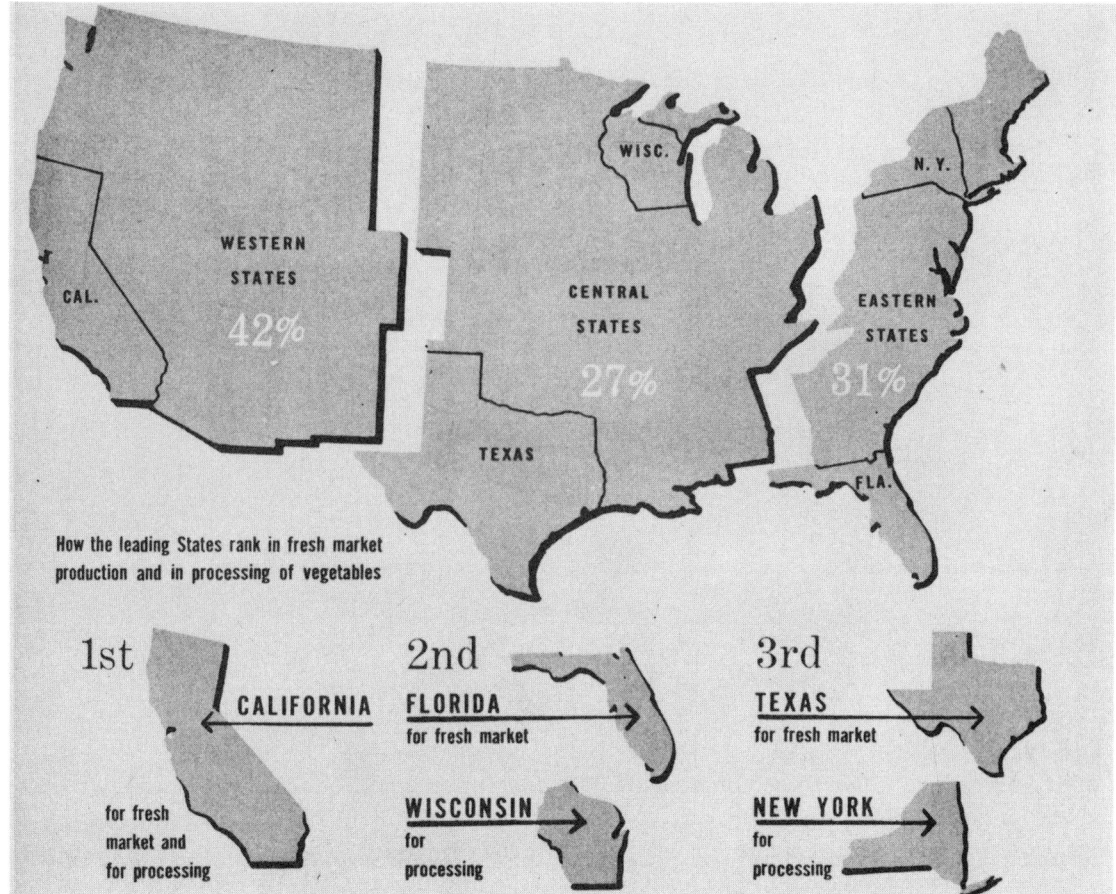

Figure 17-2. Regional contributions to the national commercial vegetable crop and the ranking of the major producing and processing states. (U.S. Department of Agriculture)

and the expense of developing the orchard before it reaches productive maturity, the cost of upkeep after the orchard begins to bear commercially, the cost of marketing, and the demand reflected in market prices, affect profit and loss.

Walnuts. Most of California's walnut crop is now produced in the Central Valley. Loss of acreage in southern California, chiefly because of urbanization, has led to an expansion of the industry in the San Joaquin Valley, particularly in Merced, Stanislaus, and San Joaquin Counties. Income from the walnut crop has increased greatly and, as a result, walnuts have become extremely popular with local farmers. A multimillion dollar plant at Stockton handles the harvest of walnuts from the Central Valley.

TRUCK CROPS

Truck crops, although of far less monetary importance than field, fruit, or nut crops, are vital to the economy of the region. More than 25 different varieties of vegetables are grown, bringing in nearly $100 million annually. Three-quarters of the entire California potato crop is produced in the Central Valley, with Shafter the state center for the production of seed potatoes. Other producing areas include Terrabella and the section from Porterville west to Woodville. The output is so great that individual growers ship entire trainloads to Eastern markets.

Tomatoes, both fresh and processed, are one of California's three most important vegetable crops, ranking after lettuce and potatoes. About 25 per cent of the nation's fresh market tomatoes are grown in the state; summer and fall tomatoes are raised in virtually every agricultural area.

Many of the tomatoes grown for canning are raised in the Delta area. Since soil, climate, and farm operations are all favorable, almost 40,000 acres are devoted to this crop. Late va-

Figure 17-3. Sprinkler irrigation of potatoes in Kern County, California. (U.S. Department of Agriculture Soil Conservation Service)

rieties thrive there, their roots reaching down six feet or more. For roots to extend to this depth, a soil that contains plenty of available water and is free from hardpan or other impervious layers is needed. Such soil occurs extensively in the Delta. Special equipment for leveling the ground, diskers that prepare the soil for tomatoes, and transplanting machines are all profitably used by the local farmers. Abundant irrigation water assures a high yield.

Asparagus grows best in so-called soft land. Therefore it does extremely well in the mucky peat soils of the Delta. Sea breezes from San Francisco Bay moderate temperatures, and low-cost, controlled irrigation water makes good commercial yields possible. The delta of the Sacramento River was the first large-scale asparagus producer in the state, the first plantings dating back to 1896. Today this area produces over 90 per cent of California's output, which is one-half of the nation's total output.

The delta of the San Joaquin River is a very important asparagus area. Sacramento County, which once led in this field, ran out of new land to plant to it in 1929. Land planted to asparagus remains productive for ten or 12 years only; any replanting after this period produces an infestation of rattail grass. The cost of fumigating the soil and of hiring labor to cut the rattail grass from the land makes continued asparagus culture after that length of time unprofitable. Sacramento County used to have a monopoly on white asparagus, which thrives on peaty soils since a mound of peat surrounding the asparagus shoot is the cause of the white color. When the canning of green asparagus became practicable it destroyed the white asparagus market, and caused many asparagus farmers to move from the Sacramento to the San Joaquin part of the Delta.

Asparagus packing sheds and canneries in the cities that fringe the area process and market most of the crop. A small percentage is sold as a fresh vegetable.

LIVESTOCK AND LIVESTOCK PRODUCTS

Since a substantial portion of the irrigated land of the Central Valley is used to produce forage, the raising of livestock is one of the important agricultural activities in the area. The more profitable operations, however, are limited to the importing, fattening, and finishing of already fairly mature cattle.

Beef cattle are raised on natural ranges in the foothills of the Sierra Nevada, the Coast Ranges, and, to a lesser extent, on the irrigated alfalfa pastures of the valley floor. There are several large feedlot operations where feeder cattle are fattened into finished beef on the byproducts of such local processing plants as cottonseed oil mills.

Dairying is highly specialized, particularly where market milk production is concerned. Many farms have small dairy herds, predominantly of Holstein stock. Milk is sold locally—large quantities are shipped to the Los Angeles and San Francisco Bay areas. Milk, cream, condensed milk, and dried milk are the chief dairy products.

Two types of sheep operations are carried on in the region. There is the small flock owner who pastures his animals on irrigated pasture and the large operator who moves his sheep from one available food supply to the next throughout the year. The larger flocks graze on barley stubble, irrigated pasture, and alfalfa and on the various ranges. The large operators prefer alfalfa fields during lambing, which occurs in late autumn. The sheep are usually kept on the valley floor until May, after which time they are trucked or shipped to the higher ranges in the mountains, often as far away as Nevada.

Although hog production has almost limitless potentials, it remains a minor stock enterprise at the present time, primarily because of the unsatisfactory price balance between the cost of feed and the market price of pork. However, since there has been a cutback in cotton acreage, it is possible that new plantings devoted to corn will lower the price of feed and encourage the raising of hogs.

The poultry industry, which includes the production of eggs, broilers, fryers, and turkeys, has increased tenfold during the past decade. Turkeys and fryers alone produce an estimated $35 million profit. Ideal climatic conditions, an adequate supply of locally grown, locally milled feeds, and excellent marketing facilities make this business commercially attractive.

Turkeys are raised chiefly in a strip along the eastern foothills stretching from Fresno north through San Joaquin County. Chickens are raised in widely scattered areas on the poorer soils of the valley floor. Eggs, both for hatching and for fresh consumption, are of increasing commercial importance.

WATER

The maintenance of a constant water supply is essential to the agriculture of the Central Valley Region. The sequence of dry summers and wet winters results in a seasonal and regional unevenness of stream flow, and this in turn means that the summer crops have to be artificially irrigated during the period of greatest evaporation and lowest measured stream volume.

These regional and seasonal inequalities of water distribution present a serious problem. The northern end of the Central Valley is near the normal northwestern storm tracks and receives the most rainfall, but there is a gradual decrease of precipitation of from 37.3 inches at Redding in the north to a little more than 5.5 inches at Bakersfield in the extreme south. This appreciable difference in average precipitation between the northern and southern ends of the region has a profound effect upon the amount of irrigation water required in any one place. For example, grain is successfully produced without irrigation in the Sacramento Valley but demands irrigation in the San Joaquin Valley and Tulare Lake Basin. Temperature differences also have their effect on the amount of water required and therefore on the crop pattern. The short, mild winters and long, warm growing seasons of the southern portion of the valley floor permit year-round production of crops. Potatoes and grain are grown during the winter, diverse field and truck crops during the summer.

The Sacramento Valley, which occupies one-third of the agricultural lands of the Central Valley, has within its drainage basin two-thirds of the water supply. Stream flows here reach their crest in late winter and spring. This means that the greater part of the valuable water is allowed to flow unused into the Pacific, sometimes causing destructive floods along the way. In summer the low river stages are often inadequate either for irrigation or for navigation upstream from Sacramento, a circumstance that greatly limits widespread distribution of crops.

Each year, during the summer months, when the fresh waters of the San Joaquin and Sacramento Rivers are too low to repel the incursion of ocean tides, the fertile farm area of the Delta is threatened by an inflow of salt water from San Francisco Bay. Thousands of acres of rich irrigated land face permanent damage, and the cities and industries of the Delta and northern San Francisco Bay areas find themselves confronted with inadequate fresh water.

Figure 17-4. Folsom Dam, built in 1955, has a capacity of 162,000 kilowatts. It stores the waters of the American River, forming Folsom Lake, a popular fishing and boating spot for people in the Sacramento area. (Bureau of Reclamation)

The San Joaquin half of the Central Valley, on the other hand, has two-thirds of the agricultural lands and only one-third the water supply, so that during the irrigation season there is not enough water to meet crop requirements. A large portion of these lands, therefore, are irrigated by pumping, with the result that there has been a serious overdraft on the subsurface water supplies as more and more land has been brought under cultivation. Thousands of acres have had to be abandoned because of the water shortage, and other thousands are threatened. There are, as a result, tens of thousands of acres in this area that could be made productive if water could be obtained.

Although the desirability of some valley-wide plan for the development of water resources was recognized at an early date, the need for one has only recently become pressing. Actual development has been carried on in lo-cal, unconnected projects by individuals, cor-porations, and co-operative groups.

Litigation between those who support English common law's riparian rights (under which doctrine owners of lands bordering streams own all water rights) and those who support the Spanish doctrine of the right to appropriate water has gone on for decades in California. The fruit growers fought the cattle ranchers and wheat farmers in the courts, and the courts themselves have handed down contradictory verdicts, deciding now on behalf of undiminished natural stream flow, now in favor of appropriation, and again on some compromise between the two. In 1928 the new principle of "most beneficial use" was established in California. This was clearly in favor of irrigation. At present about 4,750,000 acres, approximately 57 per cent of the presently cultivated lands in the Central Valley, are irrigated annually. With virtually all the stream flow put to irrigation, the necessity of storage reservoirs in the mountains to retain winter rains and snow runoff is now immediate.

One of the most comprehensive plans for the storage of irrigation water is the Central Valley Project. Under the guidance of the U.S. Bureau of Reclamation, the ultimate aim of this program is to put all the water resources of the region to beneficial use. It aims at doubling the amount of irrigated land by constructing 48 dams, 20 large canals, powerhouses, and other works. The total program, both immediate and future, would provide water for 3,040,000 acres of irrigated land and produce eight billion kilowatt-hours of power a year.

This development, when completed, will be largely self-liquidating financially, and is expected to double the number of farms in the Central Valley, add $200 million a year to its crop income, assure an adequate supply of

water for domestic use, expand industry by offering it low-cost power, provide flood and salinity control, and provide recreation areas on and near the man-made lakes that will rim the valley.

It is quite apparent that the continued growth and prosperity of California are dependent upon the co-operative and prompt efforts of local, state, and Federal agencies to provide sufficient water to meet the ever-expanding needs of the state. The state-sponsored California Water Plan has already proposed further water development plans both for the Central Valley and for the state as a whole. The plan calls for 15 million acre-feet of new reservoir storage capacity in the Sacramento River Basin. Some seven million acre-feet could be located in foothill reservoirs tied in to the California aqueduct system. This new storage capacity would be placed in 85 reservoirs designed to irrigate both the uplands and the valley floor, to provide power and recreational

Figure 17-5. The Friant-Kern Canal, main irrigation artery for the rich San Joaquin Valley agricultural empire, bisects orange groves and pastures as it flows south from Friant Dam. It is part of the Central Valley Project. (Bureau of Reclamation)

facilities, and—particularly when co-ordinated with the ground water storage capacity—to regulate stream flow in such a way that seasonal or other surpluses could be used for export.

The Feather River Project is the first unit of the California Water Plan. Costing about $2 billion, it involves the construction of a dam on the Feather River 1.7 miles below the junction of that stream's north and middle forks and 5.5 miles above the city of Oroville. There will be a power plant at the dam site and an afterbay dam and power plant a mile above Oroville. Other works scheduled to be built during the next five years include diversion of the Trinity River into the Sacramento Valley, large conveyance canals to serve the Sacramento Valley, and distributive systems to be constructed in the San Joaquin Valley.

WATER FOR RECREATION

Besides the man-made bodies of water previously mentioned as recreation resources, the 1,000 miles of navigable inland waterways that connect Stockton to San Francisco Bay afford a variety of opportunities for recreation and sports. All kinds of boating are possible there. Swimming, fishing, and hunting are other popular sports. The Delta, in this sense, is comparable to the Everglades of Florida or the lakes and waterways of Ontario.

MINERALS

PETROLEUM AND NATURAL GAS

The barren mountains and deserts that cover the southern part of the Central Valley Province are so forbidding in appearance that until recently their mineral wealth as well as their agricultural potentialities remained unexplored and undeveloped.

Despite the discovery of oil in 1864, activity was limited until 1910. The oil boom began in that year when the Lakeview gusher blew in. Taft became the capital of the West Side oil empire. Other fields have been brought in throughout the county.

Although production is declining in many of the older fields, new areas are constantly being opened, so that the total output remains more or less constant from year to year. The Elk Hills Naval Reserve is potentially an important oil field, but only such oil is taken out of it as is needed to keep the wells in condition.

Kern has several refineries with a capacity of more than 100,000 barrels a day. These are complemented by plants devoted to skimming and cracking crude oil and to producing lubricating oil, asphalt, and road oil. All of California's major oil companies, as well as a number of independent operators, draw petroleum from the area. Most of the crude petroleum is brought to refineries in the San Francisco Bay area by pipeline through the valley, but some of it is refined locally and piped directly to the coast for loading on tankers.

Part of the famous Kettleman Hills North Dome oil and gas field, one of the most important oil pools in the state, is located on the west side of the Central Valley, near Coalinga. Another oil field here is the Kettleman Middle Dome.

The Sacramento Valley has the state's largest gas field. It underlies parts of Sacramento, Solano, and Contra Costa Counties. California's nearly ten million cubic feet of recoverable natural gas place the state sixth nationally in natural gas reserves.

OTHER MINERALS

The structural minerals produced in the Central Valley include sand and gravel, stone, slate, and several other products. Since they are all basic building materials, their use will continue to increase as the state expands. Industrial minerals—clay, asbestos, diatomite, lime, pumice, and pyrites—are important to manufacturing industries within the region.

POPULATION

The Central Valley Region has nearly 100 incorporated cities and towns, the largest of which are Bakersfield, Fresno, Sacramento, and Stockton. The 1960 population of the region was over two million.

POPULATION CENTERS

Bakersfield. With a metropolitan area population of 200,000, Bakersfield dominates local wholesale and retail trade and is important not only to its own agricultural area but also to the state economy as a whole. The city spreads out along the south bank of the Kern River in the narrow southern end of the Central Valley. Petroleum from the surrounding foothills has made Bakersfield an important production and refining center and an important manufacturer of tools for the oil industry. The environs of the city have a strikingly varied appearance—with derricks, cotton and alfalfa, pastures, vineyards, orchards, and apiaries jostling for space.

Component aircraft parts for Lockheed's Super-Constellation are subassembled at Bakersfield, which represents an overflow of industry from the crowded Los Angeles metropolitan district. Inexpensive industrial power, extensive raw materials and resources, and plenty of available space will undoubtedly attract more and more industries to the area.

Fresno. This city has a metropolitan area population of 241,000. It lies in the approximate center of the state and is served directly or indirectly by the transcontinental railroads, two transcontinental airlines, and all the principal trucking concerns and bus lines operating in the San Joaquin Valley. It is one of the most important Central Valley centers for incoming and outgoing traffic, and is principally an agricultural clearing house for the distribution of fresh and dried fruits, raisins, wine, cotton, livestock, and dairy products. Fresno also is a center of the petroleum industry; of the drug, grocery, hardware, electrical appliance, and variety store trades; and of the logging and lumber industries. In addition, it is a hub of the tourist and travel traffic.

Sacramento. Sacramento, the capital city of California, is the largest city in the Central Valley and the sixth largest in the state. It had a 1960 population of 191,667, and a trading area population exceeding 500,000.

Sacramento combines industry, commerce, governmental activities, and agriculture in a balanced economy. Its residents enjoy one of the highest per capita incomes in the nation. The chief industrial employer is the Aerojet-General Corporation, which manufactures solid rocket fuels.

Sacramento is strategically situated at the principal north-south and east-west traffic crossroads of California. The city is on the main

Figure 17-6. Sacramento, California, with the Sacramento River in the foreground and the Capitol and other state government buildings right of center. (Sacramento Chamber of Commerce)

lines of two transcontinental railroads, the Southern Pacific and the Western Pacific, and is connected with the Atchison, Topeka, and Santa Fe by the rails of the California Traction Company. The east-west main lines of the Southern Pacific and Western Pacific Railroads pierce the Sierra Nevada barrier northeast of Sacramento, and as a result all transcontinental rail traffic over the central overland route moves through the city. The north-south main line of the Southern Pacific intersects these transcontinental lines at Sacramento, and the Sacramento Northern Railroad provides freight service from Oakland through Sacramento to Sacramento Valley points.

Fourteen airfields and airstrips in the area provide service for all types of aircraft. The Mather and McClelland Air Force installations are included among these. These Air Force bases employ a substantial staff of civilian personnel to maintain, repair, and rebuild aircraft. Several airlines serve the city.

For more than 30 years a deep-water channel connecting Sacramento with the Pacific Ocean, and so with the ports of the world, has been in the discussion stage. Now Sacramento has initiated a project that will provide it with a deep-

Figure 17-7. Stockton, California, owes much of its success as a trading center to its deep-water shipping facilities. (Greater Stockton Chamber of Commerce)

water port connected by a 30-foot channel with Suisun Bay some 40 miles away. A port district has been organized and land acquired for clearing basins and wharves. A grain elevator and several warehouses are already built and railroad facilities have been installed.

Stockton. An inland seaport with a popu-lation of 86,321, Stockton is the transportation center for the Central Valley. Seventy-seven nautical miles directly east of the Golden Gate on the banks of the San Joaquin River, it is reached from the Pacific Ocean by a 32-foot-deep ship canal completed in 1933 at a cost of more than $10 million.

One of the largest general cargo terminals on the Pacific Coast, the port can berth eight ocean-going vessels at one time. It has 422,174 square feet of transit sheds, 181,620 square feet of brick warehouses, an oil terminal, cotton compress and warehouse facilities, a lumber terminal, grain elevator conveyors and a grain warehouse, gear sheds, and 244,064 square feet of improved open storage.

A belt line railroad connects the port of Stockton directly with the Santa Fe, Southern Pacific, and Western Pacific, the three trans-continental railroads intersecting at Stockton. More than 20 steamship lines offer a direct call service from the port to and from intercoastal, European, South American, and Far Eastern ports.

The commodities moving through the port embrace almost all items produced or con-sumed in the entire Central Valley, including: agricultural implements, machinery, pipe, steel, iron, chemicals, lumber, petroleum, grains, beans, wines, canned fruits and vegeta-bles, dried fruits, and a host of other goods.

18 | *Coastal Mountains and Valleys of California*

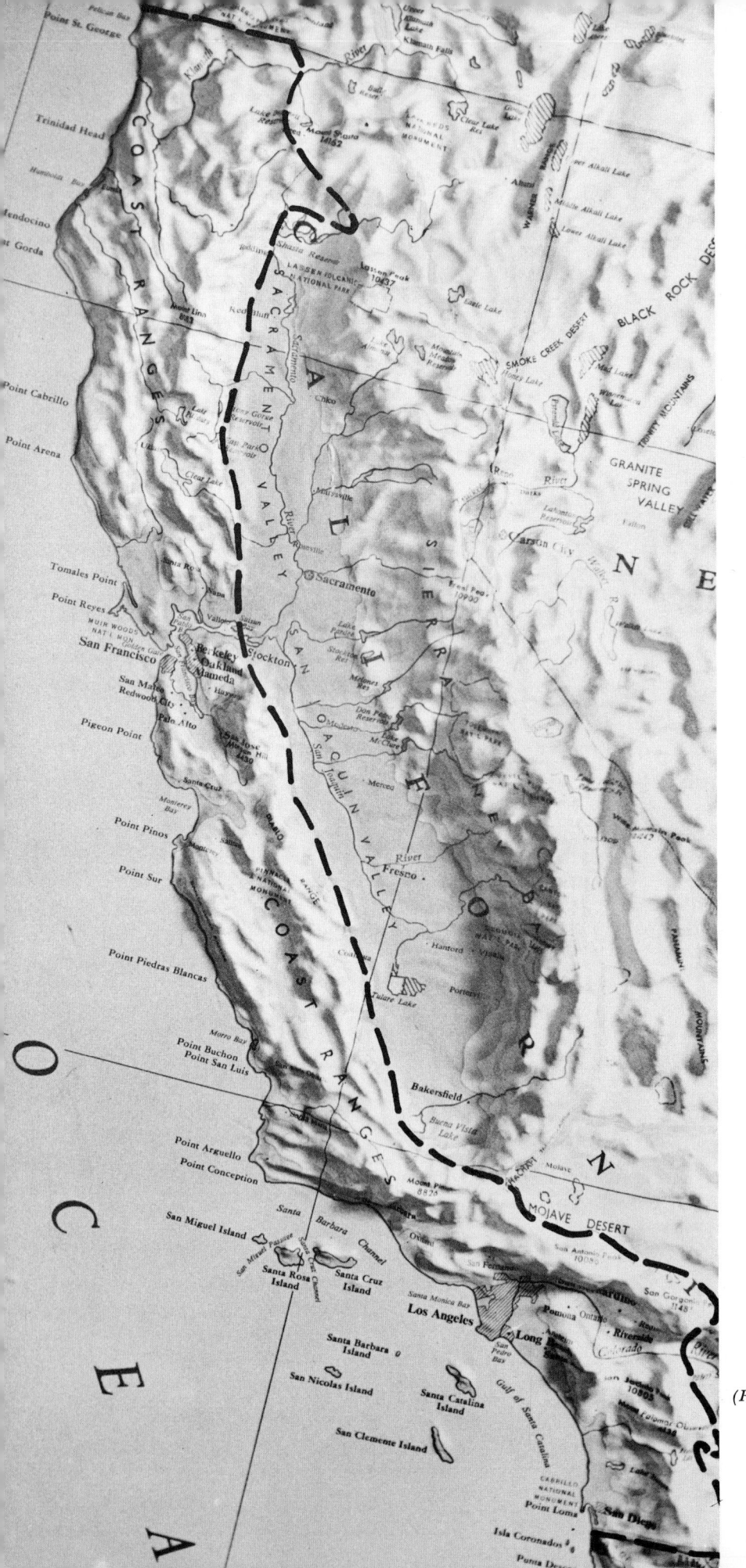

(Relief map copyright Aero Service Corp.)

ALONG California's 1,200 miles of Pacific Ocean coastline lie a series of rugged hills and mountains. Between ridges and ranges, and between these ridges and ranges and the ocean, are found small valleys and plains; it is here that 80 per cent of California's population lives. It is unlikely that the relative population distribution will change significantly in the future.

Two subregions within the Coastal Mountains and Valleys of California Region, South Coastal California and the San Francisco Bay Area, contain most of the people. Between them is a less developed subregion, the Central Coastal Mountains and Valleys, and north of the Bay Area Subregion is another subregion, the Coastal Mountains of Northern California.

SOUTH COASTAL CALIFORNIA

The South Coastal California Subregion is dominated by Los Angeles and San Diego, with Santa Barbara, an internationally known resort town, to the north. The area itself is much larger and much more diverse than any of these places.

SURFACE FEATURES

The northern border runs from Point Arguello along the northern slopes of the Santa Ynez Mountains to the western extremity of Antelope Valley. From here the San Gabriel, San Bernardino, San Jacinto, and Laguna Mountains stretch to the Mexican border on the south. Their continental edges form the eastern boundary of the region. In the various noncontiguous terraces, valleys, and basins on the coastal side of these mountains lives the bulk of the local population. The greatest concentration of economic activities occurs in the largest of these gently sloping areas, popularly called the Los Angeles Basin. Actually it is not one drainage basin but includes the combined basins of the Los Angeles, San Gabriel, and Santa Ana Rivers.

CLIMATE

Because of the wide variety of landforms and because of their various exposures to the sea, this subregion has a great climatic range. At San Diego, near the southern border, the annual rainfall averages 10.1 inches, while at Nellie, only 50 miles northeast, precipitation is 48.2. Even in places along the coast which might be presumed to have a somewhat similar climate, the rainfall varies—from San Diego's low (10.1 inches) to 18.9 inches at Santa Barbara. Inland, the variation is equally marked, ranging from a high of 24.8 inches at Sierra Madre, near Monrovia, to a low of 11.5 inches at Riverside. Snow is rare in the plains areas, but it is normal higher up. Winter is the season of maximum precipitation, whether snow or rain; indeed, summer rain is almost unknown in the river basins and along the coast, though occasional thunderstorms wet the higher mountains.

Near the Pacific, where ocean breezes prevail, temperatures vary slightly from season to season. Santa Barbara has a January average of 53° F., and July is only 13° higher. San Diego has the same annual range but is 9° warmer. As one moves inland this slight fluctuation becomes more pronounced, since land not immediately associated with maritime air heats and grows cool at a faster rate. On the whole, however, the area might be described as having a cool climate presided over by a warm sun, so that even when temperatures range higher than usual the relative humidity generally remains low.

Though the combination of an equable climate and attractive landscape has served to attract a large population, it has also resulted in the distasteful phenomenon popularly called smog. "Smog," a word coined from the words "smoke" and "fog," does not really define the problem. "Air pollution" is a better term, for analysis shows that the air in Los Angeles contains a complex mixture of solid particles, gases, and liquids as well as water and smoke.

NATURAL VEGETATION

The vegetation of this region is as varied as the complexities of the local climates and landforms would lead one to expect, and this is particularly true in those portions of the region that have been neither cultivated nor urbanized. The dry and relatively untimbered mountain slopes are covered with chaparral, a catchall term for scrub hardwoods and such shrubs as manzanita and chamise when they grow in the same place. Chaparral is scrub growth that is low, dwarfed, or straggling.

Though of no direct economic value in itself, chaparral is important because it helps the soil of the mountain watersheds to retain moisture and it prevents soil erosion. Because of the importance of water in the subregion, these watersheds are vital.

Below the level of the chaparral lies a narrow zone of coastal sagebrush, which is limited to the area of Pacific drainage. To the east of the Laguna and San Jacinto Mountains, where the drainage is continental, the chaparral is met by desert vegetation instead of sagebrush; juniper and piñon pine flourish on the north slopes of the San Bernardino and San Gabriel Mountains. In the whole region, scattered groups of conifers occur above the chaparral— chiefly such species as fir, Douglas fir, lodgepole pine, whitebark pine, Ponderosa pine, Coulter pine, and bigcone spruce. However, such growth is sparse. There are also rare stands of Bishop pine on the Santa Barbara and Santa Rosa Islands.

Small patches of grassland are widely dispersed over the lower elevations of the subregion, but the woodland-grassland complex is not common, occurring only northeast of San Diego, in the Julian area, and near Ojai.

WATER SUPPLY

For a long time now the availability of water has been the most important factor in the economic growth of the South Coastal California Subregion, for the region is a dry one and local water supplies have not been sufficient to maintain a large population.

As a result of the rapid growth that followed the establishment of railroad communication with the eastern United States, the city of Los Angeles found local water supplies to be inadequate to its needs. The first attempt to deal with the problem was the construction of the Los Angeles Aqueduct in 1913. From the Owens River, 233 miles away, it brought water across the Mojave Desert to the San Fernando Valley. An extension of this system into the Mono Lake drainage basin was opened in 1940. This system produces 305,000 acre-feet of water per year, and recently Los Angeles has been using it at near capacity. Since the Owens River Aqueduct supplied only the city of Los Angeles, surrounding communities were faced with the possibility of a water shortage. Therefore

a study of the Colorado River as a possible water source initiated by Los Angeles was taken over by the Metropolitan Water District. Construction of the Colorado River Aqueduct was completed in 1941. This 280-mile aqueduct delivers water to the city of Pomona, from which point it is distributed to other communities within the basin.

The Colorado is the major source of water for most of southern California. Withdrawals heretofore have been governed by various compacts negotiated among the seven states in the river basin. California now makes the largest withdrawals, 4.4 million acre-feet a year.

In 1960, a Supreme Court decision awarded a larger share of Colorado River water (3.8 million acre-feet) to Arizona so that it could proceed with a giant irrigation project. Stunned by the loss of Colorado River water, California voters approved a $1.75 billion state-wide water bond program to provide sufficient water for growth. A dam will be built on the Feather River that will store 3.5 million acre-feet of water from the northern Sierra Nevada. This water will be released as needed during the dry months. It will flow down the Feather and Sacramento Rivers to the Delta east of San Francisco. The water will then go into a 638-mile network of canals and conduits to southern California.

In San Diego County, where ground water is a less important source of supply, the problem has been met somewhat differently— by the construction of more surface reservoirs. Today the total storage capacity of the county is over 675,000 acre-feet, with nearly 200,000 acre-feet forming Lake Henshaw.

AGRICULTURE

The original Spanish settlements of the subregion—Mission San Gabriel (1771), Pueblo Los Angeles (1781), and Mission San Fernando (1791)—were agricultural communities using ground water for irrigation. Irrigated lands did not increase markedly under Mexican occupation; in fact, the mission lands became large cattle ranches after the Mexican government secularized the missions in 1833.

In the middle of the 19th century, groups of Mormons moved into the San Bernardino Valley; before long they had several hundred acres under irrigation. Soon many fruit, nut,

Figure 18-1. Farm land west of Puente, Los Angeles County, includes a contour-planted avocado grove on a very steep slope (left foreground); citrus groves, some contour planted (center); pastures and grain land (background); and a newly developed bench terrace. Caring for the excess runoff that accumulates on the pasture land and sweeps down over the leveler slopes planted to citrus, is one of the major problems of this area. (U.S. Department of Agriculture)

and vegetable crops were produced. At first the market for these crops was small. Some nonperishable produce was shipped north to San Francisco, but that was about all.

In 1876, when the Southern Pacific Railroad was completed, important commercial shipments to the eastern United States became practicable. Nine years later, the Atchison, Topeka, and Santa Fe Railroad began operations, and the area and its economy started to grow rapidly. The agricultural hinterland of San Diego was opened up by the San Diego and Arizona Railroad in 1919.

Agriculture continues to play an important role in the economy of the Los Angeles Basin. Recently, though Los Angeles ranked first among the nation's counties in value of farm products in the period from 1909 to 1949, an obvious change has been taking place. During the period from 1949 to 1960, the expansion of industrial and residential areas removed from cultivation large acreages of fertile farm lands. The loss of fruit and nut orchards has been particularly marked. There were 96,000 acres under cultivation in 1940, and in 1955 this figure had shrunk to 45,000. In 1940, that part of Los Angeles County which is south of the mountains contained some 464 square miles of land devoted to agriculture. By 1954, these had dwindled to 351. The change will continue to be rapid; the County Regional Planning Commission estimates that by 1975 even these farm lands will have disappeared.

Agricultural land in and around San Diego also has been driven out by expanding city development projects. Higher land values, higher

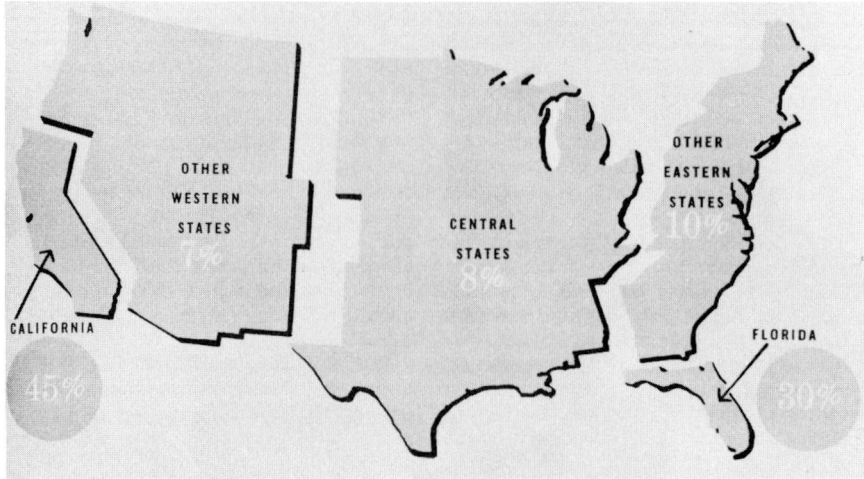

Figure 18-2. Fruit production in the United States. (U.S. Department of Agriculture)

taxes, and other problems related to this transition have brought about an intensification of agriculture and a concentration upon the growing of high value crops in prime soil.

Dairy and livestock products. One reason agriculture has remained an important industry in the subregion is that the loss of land suitable for fruit and nut cultivation has been offset by a large increase in the local demand for dairy, meat, and poultry products. Indeed, dairy products today are more valuable than are the subregion's citrus crops. This industry has been made possible by the technique of treating dairy farming and meat animal raising as a factory operation. The animals are stall-fed, as an adjustment to the problem of space in an urban area. Since this type of feeding does not permit the animals excessive exercise, it insures a maximum yield of meat or milk per animal. The large, gently sloping land areas formerly occupied by farms are no longer needed, and agriculture no longer competes with urbanization for the use of the land.

Livestock, primarily beef cattle and sheep, are fattened locally for the slaughterhouse. More than 500,000 head of cattle are necessary to satisfy the basin's annual meat requirements, so that the area has become one of the more important national centers in this field. Chickens also play a major role in the economy, as they, too, can be housed in a relatively small space and provide an appreciable profit in the local market. Some 13 million of them stock the local poultry farms.

This rise in animal production in South Coastal California is well illustrated by the record of Los Angeles County, which recently ranked first in the nation in value of livestock on farms, first in value of dairy products sold, and third in poultry and poultry products sold. Concentrations of various livestock enterprises are scattered throughout much of the basin and are symbiotic with crop raising, since some of them take advantage of such by-product supplemental feeds as citrus pulp.

Fruit production. The income from fruits, nuts, and berries ranks second only to dairy-livestock production. The amount of land devoted to citrus plantings is still considerable, despite the decline in acreage under cultivation. Though orange acreage has declined, yields have remained high, for land lost to other uses was often in groves of marginal importance. New plantings have remained low but do not reflect the increased intensification of yield.

Citrus production represents nearly one-half the value of agricultural crops in the South Coastal California Subregion. The amount of money spent by the citrus industry in this area for such necessities as crates, paper, fuel oil, chemical sprays, and various fertilizers, and for labor, transportation, and marketing is staggering.

In order to flourish, citrus crops require a very special set of conditions. Therefore, suitable land is at a premium and exists in relatively few sections of California. In the Los

Figure 18-3. A southern California orange grove with a snow-capped mountain for a background. Photographs such as this have lured millions of tourists and new residents to the area. (Sunkist Growers)

Angeles Basin, water requirements vary from 18 inches to three feet. The salt and alkali content of the irrigation water must be low, and the general atmospheric temperature high. The land must slope gently, in order to provide adequate air drainage—so that cold air may pass easily beyond the trees and settle in the lower portions of the basins. There must be an absence of severe frost and of high-velocity winds; the soils must be well drained and reasonably fecund.

The natural conditions of the Los Angeles Basin are more favorable to orange growing than are those in other parts of the state. Therefore, despite the real estate problem, oranges are apt to be found on whatever agricultural land remains there. The greatest concentration of groves is in northern Orange County, but considerable acreages also exist below the southern slopes of the San Gabriel and San Bernardino Mountains. However, leadership in this field, chiefly because of the problem of urbanization, will probably soon shift to the San Joaquin Valley in the Central Valley Region.

Lemon growers, driven from the Los Angeles area by land subdivision, have expanded the lemon industry near Ventura and Santa Barbara. The Ventura area is by far the top producer. Two-fifths of the acreage devoted to lemons here occurs in the Oxnard Plain; two-fifths is farther inland in the Santa Clara Valley to a point west of Santa Paula. The remaining lemon acreage is scattered, with the biggest concentration in the Ojai Valley. Some 8,000 acres spread above the sloping fans of land adjacent to the ocean in Santa Barbara County.

Unquestionably, southern California could not compete in Midwestern and Eastern markets with citrus from Florida and Texas on the

Figure 18-4. Los Angeles, California, with the Civic Center in the middle of the picture and the San Bernardino Freeway on the right. (Los Angeles Chamber of Commerce)

grounds of a favorable physical environment alone. The California Fruit Growers Exchange, which dates back to 1885, is a co-operative attempt to make such competition favorable through advertising, control of quality, and systematic marketing. Its efforts have been quite successful.

MANUFACTURING

Although manufacturing played no real part in the economy of the South Coastal California Subregion until after 1900, it has a long history there, for the Spanish friars of the late 18th century missions trained the local Indians in various arts and crafts. During the Civil War, local industries were forced to produce because of the virtual collapse of trade with the East. Major items included furniture, wine, distilled liquors, leather goods, food products, clothing, boots and shoes, and a variety of chemicals.

Since this area had neither coal nor accessible iron ore deposits, its industrial development remained negligible until sources of power were opened up during the early years of this century. These sources of power included natural gas, the generation of hydroelectricity, and, most important of all, the local petroleum industry.

The period of modern development begins with the establishment of Los Angeles as the world's motion picture center during the early 1900's. With the establishment of the motion picture industry, a few nationally known firms opened branch plants there.

Though the industrial growth of the subregion today shows signs of decentralization, it is still highly localized in Los Angeles and San Diego Counties, where over half of the state's manufacturing is found. At the end of World War I, about 85,000 people were employed in factories. Between the wars, growth was steady but far from spectacular. After World War II, according to the 1947 Census of Manufacturers, Los Angeles County alone had 350,000 industrial workers, and by 1955 this figure had doubled. Los Angeles has grown more rapidly than the nation's other industrial centers; today it ranks third in the country in number of employees and value of goods produced. It ranks first in the manufacture of aircraft and aircraft parts; in motion picture production; in the manufacture of pumps and compressors, refrigeration equipment and other refrigeration machinery, and heating and plumbing equipment; and in the canning of sea food. It is one of the national leaders in such assorted industries as jewelry and silverware and in concrete and plaster products.

In addition to its importance in these fields, Los Angeles also supports a large number of smaller industries that help to give it a great degree of diversification. Such industries were attracted by the huge labor pool and the growing market, which together increasingly counterbalance the disadvantages of having to import most of the essential raw materials and much of the power.

Population and climate have attracted manufacturing to the San Diego area also. Much of this growth may be attributed to defense industry—in particular to aircraft manufacturing, electronics, and the activities of the Navy.

The motion picture industry. Los Angeles and its vicinity leads the world in motion picture production. The gross annual earnings of this industry amount to $2.25 billion, $1 billion of which is derived from overseas markets. Over 800 companies are engaged in the production and distribution of films, and these companies employ a total of from 25,000 to 30,000 people.

The industry was first attracted to southern California by the mild climate and by the wide range of natural settings easily available. Lighting conditions were particularly good for the primitive equipment of the time. As equipment improved mechanically, the industry moved indoors and large studios were built in the 1930's. Today, with improved technical equipment, the industry has moved out on location again, in most cases away from the Los Angeles area altogether. Probably because of competition from television, major producers are concentrating on a few extremely costly films per year. But they also have entered the field of television films themselves. These films are made mostly in the Los Angeles area.

Television. Los Angeles is second only to New York City as a television center. Increasingly the industry is shifting to the West Coast to make use of the talent centered there as a result of the movie industry. Most of the major

Figure 18-5. The central manufacturing district of Vernon, California. Within a five-square-mile area are some of the biggest names in American industry. In 1,200 different plants and businesses work more than 70,000 employees from the many cities and towns of Los Angeles, Orange, and San Bernardino Counties. (Los Angeles County Chamber of Commerce)

Figure 18-6. Coyote oil field near La Habra, California. The lack of space between derricks is indicative of poor planning and control in oil recovery. (Standard Oil Co. of California)

struction, maintenance, and heating. The huge supply of skilled and semiskilled workers trained during World War II simplifies the labor problem. Until recently there was ample room for the enormous amount of floor space required for assembly. The weather is generally favorable for flying, and huge testing grounds for research are available in the nearby Mojave Desert.

The largest single concentration of parts manufacture and assembly is around the Los Angeles International Airport, near the towns of Inglewood, El Segundo, Hawthorne, and Torrance. The North American and the North-rup plants and two Douglas plants are here; each hires from 10,000 to 30,000 workers. Within a six-mile radius of the airport are the Douglas plant at Santa Monica, many parts suppliers, producers of highly technical equipment, and experimental laboratories.

Located farther away are the Douglas Long Beach plant and the Lockheed plant at Burbank, each of which employs more than 20,000 workers. Subsidiary manufacturers are scattered within the basin, from Riverside to Santa Monica and from Santa Ana to San Fernando.

The aircraft and parts industry accounts for 80 per cent of all wage and salary factory workers in the San Diego metropolitan district. Convair, a division of General Dynamics Corporation, is easily the largest of these operations, having over 23,000 employees. Rohr Aircraft, Ryan Aeronautical, and Solar Aircraft are of national importance and have recently enlarged their facilities. These three are primarily makers of a wide variety of parts and electronic equipment for aircraft. Convair, on the other hand, produces both jet and piston aircraft. Production is centered near Lindbergh Municipal Airport, at the north end of San Diego Bay, though Rohr is located on the bay shore at Chula Vista.

Electronics. California is a leading state in the production of electronic products. The Los Angeles metropolitan area and San Diego have become important electronic centers. More than 500 plants turn out in excess of $1 billion worth of electronic equipment annually, the bulk of it for the aircraft and guided missiles industries.

Automobile assembly. In the past two dec-

film studios devote part of their equipment and floor area to the production of television programs, and the two best-known networks, CBS and NBC, have major facilities in Hollywood and Burbank. In addition, many relatively small companies are engaged in making TV films, utilizing techniques worked out in movies, radio, and television itself. Production of radio shows is still an important industry in Hollywood.

Aircraft. The manufacturing of aircraft is easily the leading industry of the Los Angeles Basin, employing more than 200,000 persons— nearly 30 per cent of all the industrial workers in the area.

Several factors help to explain this concentration of aircraft parts manufacture and assembly. The climate permits low-cost con-

ades the Los Angeles Basin has become second only to Detroit in the assembly of automobiles and in related industries. The largest automobile manufacturers each have at least one plant in the basin, and the Big Three have two or more each.

There are more automobiles per family in the Los Angeles area than in any other large urban concentration, and the cars are used more. Tires are consumed rapidly; the area is second only to Akron, Ohio, in tire and tube manufacturing, an industry which blossomed here during World War II because petroleum, essential to the fabrication of synthetic rubber, was readily available.

Petroleum. Successful drilling in western Pennsylvania stimulated similar activity in southern California, and the first commercial well came into production in Pico Canyon in 1875. Ten years later, the first field of any major significance in California was brought in at Puente Hills, east of Whittier. Many other fields had followed by 1900, but it was not until

after the completion of the Panama Canal in 1914, when local drillers found that they had a transportation advantage over the Midwest as far as Atlantic Coast markets were concerned, that production increased greatly. The discovery of new fields at Signal Hill and Santa Fe Springs caused production in Los Angeles County to soar from 114 million barrels in 1921 to 157.8 million in 1923. Peak output was reached in 1929, after which there were serious declines until the discovery of the Wilmington field in 1936. Today Wilmington is the leading field of the basin, followed by Huntington Beach in Orange County. Because of the population increase in the region, there is a distinct contest between those who would use the land for drilling and those who would use it for residences. Some land developers even find it more profitable to subdivide for housing than to drill for oil. In the past, both were often tried at the same time.

Failure to practice proper spacing of the wells, proper pumping, and other conservation

Figure 18-7. El Segundo, one of southern California's largest oil refineries. (Standard Oil Co. of California)

Figure 18-8. Kaiser Steel Corporation's Fontana plant, with four blast furnaces on the left and the open hearth building containing nine furnaces on the right. (Kaiser Steel Corp.)

measures has resulted in the waste of millions of barrels of crude oil, and most of this will probably never be recovered. Land subsidence presents the industry with another serious problem, particularly in the Wilmington-Harbor Island area, where not only is some of the land sinking below sea level but persistent earthquakes, although minor, cause considerable damage to well casings. Local refineries now process most of the subregion's oil.

In 1952, the subregion produced three per cent of the world's petroleum. At the moment, production has leveled off and is likely to decline as soon as the present pools have been depleted. South Coastal California is now becoming an importer of petroleum.

Iron and steel. Because it is the Pacific Coast's only completely integrated steel mill, the Henry J. Kaiser Fontana plant has a significance out of all proportion to its size, if size is measured by the number of workers employed or by the total value of the goods manufactured. At first largely a war measure, the operation now appears to have assumed a permanent place in the economic structure of southern California. Forty-five per cent of the Western States' demand for steel is centered in the Los Angeles Basin. Fontana does not have the capacity to supply this demand. The original blast furnace has been supplemented by three

more pig iron producers. Nine open hearth furnaces convert the pig to steel, which is then rolled to the desired shape. Kaiser will probably expand Fontana's steelmaking facilities still further.

This plant operates under the disadvantage of having higher fixed charges than any other integrated mill in the United States. It also has proportionately higher fuel and raw material costs, for the iron ore must be brought from Eagle Mountain, 164 miles away by rail, and 85 per cent of the coal comes from leased deposits over 800 miles away in east-central Utah and the other 15 per cent comes from Oklahoma.

Despite these expensive rail hauls, Fontana seems to be turning a profit. Cheap local scrap cuts down on the need for basic raw materials and the nearness of an expanding market cuts down costs at that end.

Shipbuilding. Shipbuilding is an important San Diego activity. It employs about 5,000 workers. The industry specializes in small craft, such as private yachts, ocean-going fishing boats, rescue tugs, mine sweepers, refrigerated barges, and landing craft. The U.S. Naval Repair Base provides a cognate activity.

The Navy, in its total activity, is second only to aircraft as an employer in San Diego. It normally hires between 15,000 and 20,000 civilians. A conservative estimated value of naval and military facilities in San Diego County is $500 million.

TRANSPORTATION

Shipping. One cause of the rapid population growth within the Los Angeles Basin is the man-made harbor at San Pedro Bay. The 41-mile frontage includes turning basins, wharves, belt line railroads, and other facilities for the accommodation of both passengers and cargo shipments.

The volume of world trade passing through Los Angeles during the past decade has continued to keep pace with the local industrial expansion in satisfying the demands of the steadily augmented population. During the postwar years more than $30 million worth of harbor improvements have been made, greatly facilitating the handling of this increased trade.

Los Angeles has made a strong bid for the trade of the Pacific. Japan is now its leading market in value, importing large quantities of cotton, petroleum, and other goods. Canada, West Germany, France, the United Kingdom, and Mexico are also important customers, in the order named. Western Mexico, in particular, is extremely dependent upon the Los Angeles trade. Los Angeles leads the Pacific Coast in number of ships serviced and in tonnage passing in and out of the port.

San Diego's harbor has been developed into California's third largest port (after San Francisco and Los Angeles). The chief imported items are iron, steel, newsprint, bananas, fish, limes, and fertilizers. The exports, whose value far exceeds that of the imports, include cotton from the Imperial Valley, waste paper, machinery, and tallow. The port is used by San Diego and Imperial Counties, by southwestern Arizona, and by northern Baja California. Its trade is thus not only interstate but international.

Figure 18-9. San Diego, California, looking westward to the Pacific Ocean over San Diego Bay. In the center is the new $10 million Marine Terminal, with complete facilities for all types of cargo. (San Diego Chamber of Commerce)

Figure 18-10. Santa Barbara, California, with the Santa Ynez Mountains in the background. Santa Barbara is a world famous resort. (Santa Barbara Chamber of Commerce)

Railways. The railroads have been instrumental in the emergence of modern industrial southern California. Though they began in the transport of perishable fruits to points east of the Rockies, the railroads now bring in parts for assembly, needed raw materials, and other goods, and export—in addition to citrus crops —electronic equipment, sports clothing, defense weapons, modern furniture, and other products.

Air transportation. Los Angeles is one of the nation's leading air terminals. In 1960, more than 3.5 million persons used the facilities of the International Airport at Los Angeles. Transcontinental service is provided by United, Trans World, American, Western, Continental, and National Airlines; Pan American travels to the south and west. Several foreign lines also land here, along with local feeder lines. In addition, many commuters use small private aircraft, especially for daily or weekend trips to homes in the Mojave Desert and around Palm Springs.

FISHING

Los Angeles is the center of the southern California fishing industry. Over 2,000 commercial boats, which fish coastal waters as far south as Peru, are based in Los Angeles and service the fresh fish markets and the 11 local canneries. The canneries, which have grown out of the establishment of a small sardine processing plant in San Pedro in 1893, have provided the greatest stimulus to the growth of the fishing industry. Terminal Island, or "Fish Harbor," a man-made basin, is the major site of canning operations. Here approximately 8,500 cannery workers, who draw an annual payroll of $15 million, pack nearly 12 million cases of fish for the world market. The wholesale markets of San Pedro handle most of the fresh fish trade. The major commercial species fished are tuna skipjack, tuna yellowfin, mackerel, and anchovy. The pilchard, or sardine, provided the largest tonnages landed between 1934 and 1944, but since that time there has been a steady, unexplained decline of the catch for this fish.

San Diego also holds a high position in commercial fishing, particularly for various species of tuna.

Sport as well as commercial fishing is important in southern California waters, and perhaps is destined to become even more important as commercial fisheries dwindle.

TOURISM

By making the most of its resources, the South Coastal California Subregion has become the tourist center of the West. The attractions are chiefly man-made and range from the Rose Bowl Parade to Disneyland. Formerly oriented toward the winter season, and based upon cli-matic advantages, local tourism is now a year-round, $500 million business. Well-advertised vacation possibilities such as swimming in the surf at ten in the morning and skiing in the mountains after lunch; mild climate with a high percentage of sunshine per year; the glamor of Hollywood; and the horse races at Santa Anita, Del Mar, and Hollywood Park, appeal to tourists and potential residents alike. The region has been cannily publicized.

POPULATION

The subregion, which had approximately nine million inhabitants in 1960, is the second-largest center of population in the United States. The population increases by about 700 persons per day, making an annual gain equivalent to the total population of such metropolitan areas as Spokane or El Paso. Nearly three-fourths of those arriving in California settle in South Coastal California to work in the numerous industries that have migrated to the subregion because of the market and labor to

Figure 18-11. Disneyland, in Anaheim, California, is one of the West's most famous man-made tourist attractions. (Kelly's Industrial Photo Services, Inc.)

Figure 18-12. La Jolla, California, is one of the most notable residential cities in southern California. (Historical Collection, Union Title Insurance Co., San Diego)

be found there or because they like the site.

From 1958 to 1960, the greatest expansion has occurred along both ends of a southeast-northwest axis running from Orange County through the San Fernando Valley.

To meet the housing requirements of this tremendous growth, subdividers and building contractors have expanded their activities to a degree formerly unknown in America. About 135,000 new homes are built near Los Angeles each year, almost all of them in subdivisions. The transportation difficulties caused by these low-density developments are a colossal compound of the difficulties found in other urban areas of the United States. Other problems are no less serious. For example, in Los Angeles County an average of one new elementary school opens every Monday morning, a junior high school every two weeks, and a high school once a month. Yet, the demand is greater than the facilities.

Statistics indicate that the population of the Los Angeles Basin—seven million—will be doubled by 1985. At the turn of the century there were only some 200,000 people there.

Population growth in San Diego was slow until the end of the 19th century; in 1880 the city consisted of fewer than 3,000 people. A direct railroad connection between San Diego and Los Angeles was opened in 1885. This railroad and the initiation of several water development projects brought San Diego's isolation to an end; in 1930 the population reached 150,-000. By 1960, San Diego had 573,224 people within its city limits and 836,175 in the metropolitan area.

SAN FRANCISCO BAY AREA

San Francisco Bay itself is the linking factor of this key area, the second largest metropolitan center of California. Occupying a strategic position on the coast, and with the best natural harbor, the bay forms the chief transportation route for the agricultural wealth of the Central Valley Region. From the bay these goods are distributed to other parts of the state, to the nation, and throughout the world.

SURFACE FEATURES

At this latitude the Coast Ranges become three well-defined mountain axes. To the east lies the Diablo Range, which continues on the other side of Suisun Bay as the Vaca Mountains, which stretch east of Napa Valley. Between the Diablo Range and the west stands the northern end of the Mt. Hamilton Range, paralleling and balancing the Sonoma Mountains that separate the Napa and Sonoma Valleys at the northern end of San Francisco Bay.

To the west, the Santa Cruz Range lies south of the Golden Gate, and the range dominated by Mt. Tamalpais rises to the north of it. The valleys lying between these ranges open out to San Pablo and San Francisco Bays; they are characterized by some of the most fertile and highly cultivated land in the state. The larger valleys, in order, are: the Santa Clara, into which the southern arm of San Francisco Bay extends; the Sonoma, which stretches northward from San Pablo Bay; and the Napa. The Sonoma Valley is nearly 100 miles long; in some places it attains a width of eight to 12 miles. The Santa Clara Valley, with its extension into the Central Coastal Mountains and Valleys Subregion, is even larger. The bottom lands of these two valleys are almost level and were produced by sediments deposited in the ocean's long, narrow estuaries during the last great coastal submersion. The lowlands around San Francisco Bay that slope gently back into the surrounding hills are of the same origin, though they have been modified by stream action. However, in the Carquinez Strait, the eastern extension of the bay, the mountains come abruptly down to the water. This suggests a differential movement of the mountains in relation to the floor of the Central Valley.

Land features of the San Francisco Bay Area Subregion are those characteristic of a drowned area. As the land sank in relation to the ocean, the sea entered the Golden Gate and flooded the lower portion of the Sacramento-San Joaquin river system. The configuration of the bays, islands, and in particular of the filled-in valleys between Sausalito and San Rafael, all demonstrate this last phase of the physiographic history of the subregion.

The bay itself, which is one of the best natural harbors in the world, has a surface area of about 400 square miles, if one includes the partially separated northern portion known locally as San Pablo and Suisun Bays. Its axis generally conforms to the northwest-southeast trend of the Coast Ranges and is about 42 miles long, with a width varying from five to 13 miles. A narrow water passage, the Golden Gate, connects the bay with the Pacific Ocean. Divided by the Golden Gate, the Coast Range hills and mountains that border the shoreline of the ocean thus form two peninsulas. Marin County, to the north, is dominated by Mt.

Tamalpais, with an altitude of 2,604 feet. The northern region has a wide range of climate and surface configuration, therefore an equally wide range of vegetation. Dense redwood stands cover some hills, whereas chaparral, grasses, or various combinations of forest, brush, and grass are found on others.

The tip of the peninsula south of the Golden Gate is occupied by San Francisco. Farther south, the heavily wooded Santa Cruz Mountains separate the bay from the ocean and, rising to elevations of 3,200 feet, shelter the inland peninsular cities from the winds and fog of the rugged littoral. They are underlain by the San Andreas Fault, famous for its earthquake potential. On the mainland side of the bay, the Berkeley Hills rise behind the towns of Oakland, Berkeley, and Richmond. Beyond these hills, moderately rolling to steeply sloping hills surround Mt. Diablo, a scenic landmark 3,849 feet high. The Santa Clara Valley is directly south of the bay, protected by the Santa Cruz Mountains to the west and the Mt. Hamilton Range to the east.

CLIMATE.

The San Francisco Bay Area Subregion is noted for its moderate temperatures, relatively light precipitation in the lowlands, and summer fog along the coast. The mean annual temperature in San Francisco is 56.5° F., with an annual range of only 12°. North and south of the city the fluctuation increases to nearly 30°. This temperature differential is caused principally by summer fogs blown in from the ocean by breezes that spring up in the afternoon and evening. On the leeward side of the Santa Cruz Mountains these fogs usually dissipate during the morning. Since they are more frequent in the less hilly, northern part of the peninsula, San Francisco has about ten per cent fewer hours of sunshine than does San Jose, 50 miles to the south.

Precipitation varies widely throughout the area. In general it increases with elevation but decreases farther inland from the coast. Mean seasonal precipitation for the entire area is 23.4 inches; that for the valley lands is about 20. From San Francisco and San Jose, both in the lowlands but one exposed to the sea and bay and the other inland, the precipitation decreases from 22 to 14 inches. Variations of 50 to 200 per cent in mean seasonal precipitation are not uncommon. Approximately 90 per cent of the rainfall occurs during the six months from November to April.

SETTLEMENT

At present the San Francisco Bay Area Subregion has a population of four million and continues to grow at the average of about 10,000 people a month. It currently accounts for nearly 25 per cent of the families and retail trade in the state, 30 per cent of the salaries and wages, 50 per cent of the water-borne commerce, and 40 per cent of the bank debits.

Since the Gold Rush of 1849, the San Francisco Bay Area has drawn hundreds of thousands of people to its fertile plains and valleys. The economic bases of prosperity were shipping and foreign commerce. By 1885, early settlement centered upon the waterfront activities of San Francisco itself, and the city remained the major center of population right through 1940. However, the present dispersion began to develop as early as 1920. The region's urban core has expanded until the fringe urban concentrations have almost merged with it.

Despite this tendency toward dispersion, San Francisco, Oakland, and Berkeley are still the giants of the area. These three cities contain nearly half of the subregion's population. They form a center for the many administrative, financial, and distributive activities of the area. Although San Francisco has lost its earlier monopoly on ocean shipping, it remains one of the principal gateways to the Orient. The concentration of brokerage, banking, and insurance offices there makes it the financial capital of the state. A shortage of raw materials formerly restricted local manufacturing to the assembly into finished goods of parts fabricated in the eastern United States. The greatly increased population and the stimulus provided by wartime and defense production have brought basic industry into the subregion. A large part of this heavy manufacturing spreads out around Oakland's rail terminus, which includes the services of three transcontinental railways and a deep-water port. Around the eastern and western shores of the bay is a zone of industry that includes oil refineries, wharves, docks, warehouses, power plants, food processing plants and canneries, breweries, furniture manufacturing establishments, paper mills, and chemicals, primary metals, fabricated metals, electrical machinery, and other plants. New ones are being added all the time.

SAN FRANCISCO

Despite industrial and residential dispersion, San Francisco is still the heart of the Bay Area Subregion. The city forms the center of a hybrid economic pattern, halfway between the nucleated urban areas of the East and the vast low-density sprawl of Los Angeles. It is supplemented by strings of suburban communities, some north of the bay, some down the southern peninsula, each of which preserves its social if not its geographic identity.

Ocean commerce established San Francisco during the Gold Rush and kept it going until the greater structure of manufacturing and local business grew up. Today, San Francisco's foreign trade accounts for more than $750 million a year. This figure does not include military shipments. Known for its versatility as a general cargo port, the harbor meets waterfront requirements for the handling of all kinds of import and export cargo. More facilities are being planned. San Francisco's importance in international commerce will be enhanced still more by the completion of the $2 million World Trade Center now rising on the waterfront.

The city is not only the undisputed financial and insurance capital of the West, but ranks second in the nation in these fields after New York City. Seven of the nation's 100 largest commercial banks have their home offices here; and the 12th Federal Reserve District, with headquarters in the Federal Reserve Bank of San Francisco, is third in the nation in volume of business as measured by bank debits. Nearly three-quarters of the fire, marine, and casualty insurance companies authorized to transact business in California have their headquarters in the city.

Many of the large manufacturing firms that have main offices or distribution and warehouse facilities in San Francisco produce part or all of their products in plants located either within the metropolitan area or within the state. Industry forms an integral part of the city's economy. Investment in new companies and expansion of existing facilities amounted

Figure 18-13. San Francisco and its two great bridges are shown in this aerial photograph. Part of the eight-mile-long Bay Bridge to Oakland is in the foreground and the Golden Gate Bridge, the world's largest suspension span, is at the upper right; the broad Pacific lies beyond. Some of the 45 deep-water piers that serve San Francisco can be seen. (San Francisco Chamber of Commerce)

to over $100 million in the past five years. Tidelands in the southern part of the city provide industry with hundreds of acres contiguous to excellent freeways and railroads. Food processing ranks first in the city's industrial economy, producing such items as canned fruit, vegetables, and sea food; beer; soft drinks; coffee; and dairy products. Fabricated metals are second: tin containers, rolled steel products, and builders' hardware. Some 334 firms engage in the making of apparel and allied products. Paper and paper products, chemicals, and transportation equipment also rank high in terms of product value and numbers of workers employed.

San Francisco's future as a central city might be compared to that of New York City's Manhattan. Having grown at the same period and

in the same way as did the large Eastern cities, San Francisco is more like them than such post-1900 boom towns as Seattle, Portland, Los Angeles, and San Diego.

The city's present population of 740,316 cannot be expected to increase greatly in the future, though some demographers prophesy one million by the year 2000. This, however, should be the ceiling, for the limited land area within the city limits has already developed one of the highest population densities west of Chicago. In 1950, only 1,800 acres of potential residential land were available, enough to accommodate about 31,000 dwelling units. Since then, almost all this land has been built upon. Because the city and county are surrounded by water on the west, north, and east, and have a land barrier to the south, further expansion is virtually impossible. As is the case with most major cities, including Los Angeles, the fringe area around San Francisco's central business section has lost population since 1930, for even when slum housing is removed from such districts, the space is apt to be partially filled by nonresidential offices, shopping centers, freeways, parking, new industries, public buildings, and other structures serving the region as a whole. People forced out of the fringe area usually migrate all the way to the suburbs, where prices are more likely to be within their incomes. Although San Francisco's population declined between 1950 and 1960, that of the surrounding area grew rapidly.

Two-thirds of all the people in the San Francisco Bay Area live in cities within a 50-mile radius of San Francisco, half of them in 12 contiguous central cities. San Francisco and its southern peninsula, from the Presidio to Los Altos and Mountain View, are an almost uninterrupted 45-mile urban strip. Much of this growth has occurred since World War II, with four out of every ten persons newly settled in the region since 1940.

THE PENINSULA

It took a tragedy to launch the movement south from San Francisco on the Peninsula. The earthquake and fire of 1906 forced hordes of homeless people into the vegetable fields of Daly City and Colma on the San Francisco county line. The natural allurements of the land coaxed further migration, and this crystallized into a string of towns along the eastern foothills. For every person in San Mateo County in 1900 there were 25 in 1960. The Peninsula, which once meant the gracious estates of Woodside, Hillsborough, Burlingame, and Atherton, came to include a sequence of towns with modest but comfortable ranchstyle houses.

Immediately south of San Francisco, against the mountain that separates the city from the Peninsula, lies South San Francisco. It was earmarked for industry as early as 1892, when G. F. Swift established his Western Meat Company there, at Point San Bruno. Swift was followed by the Armour and the Dubuque packing plants and the two steel plants of Consolidated Western and Bethlehem Pacific. These and other industries now employ about 26,000 people.

The other Peninsula communities grew up with a marked suspicion of industry. Burlingame, San Mateo, Redwood City, and Palo Alto developed relatively early as residential towns, taking advantage of their contiguity to the Southern Pacific Railroad, operator of a commuter service. Newer residents not only swelled these established communities but developed others in San Bruno, Millbrae, South San Mateo, Belmont, San Carlos, Menlo Park, East Palo Alto, Los Altos, and Mountain View.

Concern for maintenance of their residential character prompted city planners of the Peninsula to seek industries that did not produce noise, offensive odors, and smoke. Electronics concerns were encouraged, and there are now more than 20 plants devoted to electronics in the area between San Bruno and Palo Alto.

On land belonging to Stanford University in Palo Alto, a light industry tract has been opened. This industrial park already contains electronics manufacturers, research laboratories, a film processing laboratory, textbook publishers, and others attracted by the climate, the favorable location, and the research opportunities offered by the nearby university.

THE EAST BAY INDUSTRIAL COMPLEX

As with every major metropolitan area, Oakland's economic activity is centered upon industry. A graph tracing the general and industrial growth of the East Bay would show two parallel lines rising steadily.

To understand fully the industrial growth of the area it is necessary to understand its topography. Since the bay itself largely determines the location of transportaion routes between the population centers, the combination of topography and available transportation has affected every aspect of regional development —residential, commercial, and industrial.

The East Bay is rigidly confined by San Francisco Bay on the west and the Berkeley Hills on the east and is essentially oriented on a shoreline north-south axis. Oakland was founded because of its location at the confluence of early transportation routes.

Essentially, early enterprises merely served the demands of the local residents; but by 1900, as the transcontinental railroads expanded and coastal and Pacific shipping began to amount to a considerable annual tonnage, Oakland had become an important industrial and transpor-

Figure 18-14. Aerial view of Oakland, with San Francisco to the upper left. The large modern building right of center facing Lake Merritt is the new Kaiser Center. (Oakland Chamber of Commerce)

tation center serving an ever-widening area. A commercial agreement worked out in the 1870's by which the area traded its surplus grains for shiploads of scrap iron from Europe did much to promote this growth. Within a decade a machinery shop and foundry industry had sprung up.

During this period industries turning out textiles, paints, ceramics, canned goods, boxes, baskets, and soap were established. By 1900, there were 83 major factories employing 5,800 people.

The chief factors contributing to the enormous industrial development that has taken place since 1900 are: (1) rapid residential development as a result of improved and consolidated transportation; (2) the opening of the Panama Canal, which gave Oakland an added importance as a shipping point for the Western States, coastal trade, and the Pacific basin by extending the trade routes to the Eastern Sea-

board; (3) electric power and fuel oil cheap enough to nullify the local lack of raw materials; and (4) World War I, which pushed the Pacific Coast, and Oakland in particular, into the front ranks of shipping, shipbuilding, and their associated industries.

A study of the East Bay industrial expansion reveals two advantageous characteristics: a tendency toward diversification rather than toward a single industry, and a preponderance of small industries employing 100 men or less, partially balanced by a number of big industries.

Today the East Bay extends in a narrow 25-mile length of solid urbanization from San Pablo to Hayward, and the fringes of its central city, Oakland, now merge with what were once outlying towns. The population of this area, including Alameda and Contra Costa Counties, increased from 513,911 in 1940 to 1.5 million in 1960. The war years were undoubt-

Figure 18-15. The Standard Oil Company refinery, Richmond, California. Crossing San Francisco Bay here is the Richmond-San Rafael Bridge. Richmond is one of California's most important refining centers. (Standard Oil Co. of California)

edly chiefly responsible for this rapid expansion, for it was then that military installations began to provide major employment opportunities. Considerable employment is offered by Hamilton Field, Mare Island, Benicia Arsenal, and Travis Air Force Base on the northern end of the bay. The Naval Training Center at Treasure Island, the Alameda Naval Air Station, the Hunter's Point Naval Shipyard, and the Oakland Naval Supply Depot furnish defense employment in the other areas.

It was only during and shortly after World War II that heavy basic industries expanded sufficiently to make any great change in the region's economy. But, during the past few years, $160 million have been invested in new industries or plant expansion in Contra Costa and Alameda Counties, and this does not include $100 million spent on new public utilities.

The expansion of the primary metals industry furnishes a noteworthy example of this growth. Of some 34 new plants, more than half are in Alameda County.

Petroleum makes up three-fifths of all the cargo passing through the Golden Gate, feeding four huge refineries in the subregion. The chemical industry, closely allied to petroleum products and concentrated in the same general area, also has mushroomed.

THE SANTA CLARA VALLEY

In recent years a new kind of urbanization has taken place, of which the Santa Clara Valley is a good example. Residential subdivisions here are scattered among the farms and orchards in a disconnected pattern. Separated from each other and often at great distances from established urban centers, these developments could not exist without automobiles.

That portion of the Santa Clara Valley that lies within the San Francisco Bay Area Subregion surrounds the southern arm of San Francisco Bay and stretches southeastward between the Coast Ranges. On its eastern side the Mt. Hamilton Range rises to a height of more than 4,000 feet. On the west the Santa Cruz Range is lower but more rugged. Beginning at the bay's south end, where it is about 20 miles wide, the valley extends to Coyote Narrows some 25 miles south, where the east and west mountain ranges almost converge.

The valley consists of rich alluvial soil and is drained by the Guadalupe and Coyote Rivers. The sedimentary deposits making up the valley floor consist of irregular bodies of clay, gravel, and sand, with a predominance of clay. Gravel and sand layers embedded in the clay form a complex of large underground reservoirs, or aquifers, for water percolated down through the upper, fan-shaped deposits. These water-bearing alluvial deposits dip toward the center of the valley floor. Along the bay margin of the valley, an extensive layer of impervious clay prevents the water from escaping to the surface.

Average rainfall in the area is 15.56 inches on the valley floor, up to 25 inches in the foothills, and 40 inches in the mountains. The precipitation varies considerably from year to year, and during a dry year this causes considerable hardship to the farmers. Temperatures are never extreme: the January average for valley and foothills is around 48° F., and the July average about 67°. Growing seasons range from 260 days in the center of the valley to 313 in the western foothills.

Fruit and nut crops. The Santa Clara Valley is an ideal area for fruit growing. The winter weather is neither warm enough to impair the productivity of deciduous fruit trees nor cold enough to damage them. Summer weather is hot enough to ensure the ripening of fruit with a high sugar content, but is not so hot that it will injure the crop. From June to September the valley receives 82.4 per cent of the possible available sunshine, an important factor in the growing of high-quality fruit. The comparatively low humidity retards the growth of fungus diseases and facilitates drying of fruit in the open air, though at the moment most prunes are dried in artificial dehydrators.

The advantages of warm sun, sheltering mountains, fine alluvial soils deposited by centuries of runoff from the hills, natural underground reservoirs of water, and the moderating influence of San Francisco Bay at the valley's open northern end, have played a part in making this area one of the world's fine fruit producing regions.

Prunes. For nearly a half-century the Santa Clara Valley has been known as a prune center, and growers claim that one out of every three prunes raised in the world comes from the valley. Prunes are the largest and most important valley crop, with an annual value in excess of $17 million.

Medium-sized, oval, and somewhat necked, the fruit has a small smooth pit, a purplish skin, and gold-yellow flesh. Its only defect is that it tends to grow smaller than one would wish during a heavy crop year. Prune orchards are located in most sections of the valley that are not urbanized.

Apricots. Acreage devoted to this crop is for the most part concentrated on the higher parts of the alluvial fans of the piedmont and on those adjacent foothill slopes where suitable soils and proper air drainage are available. A very delicate fruit, susceptible to spring frosts

Figure 18-16. Varied land use in the northern Santa Clara Valley results in a pattern like a patchwork quilt. Note the building pattern along horizontal lines and the small farms surrounded by housing subdivisions in this San Jose scene. (San Jose Chamber of Commerce)

Figure 18-17. Fremont Peak State Park, in the Coast Ranges near historic Mission San Juan Bautista. Along the coast, from San Francisco Bay southward, the Coast Ranges extend in a general northwest-southeast direction. Between the various ridges of the mountains are elongated fertile valleys noted for stock raising and dairying. (Mary Hill)

and those rains that may occur during the blossoming and fruit forming period, the Santa Clara Valley apricots flourish in a climate plagued by neither hazard; they are noted for their firmness and size, and particularly for their flavor.

Cherries. These are concentrated to the northeast and to the west of San Jose. Red Bings, Black Tartarians, and reddish-white Royal Annes are the main varieties grown.

Other crops. In addition to the crops mentioned, the valley is noted for its strawberries, walnuts, and pears.

Diversity has been the salvation of the valley's agriculture during many of the past years. While highly specialized crop areas suffer when their single crop economies decline, Santa Clara has buffered itself with nearly 50 economically important crops.

Food processing industry. Before World War II, virtually the only industries in the orchard-filled valley were those directly connected with food processing and distribution. There were canners such as Libby and Del Monte; packers such as Sunsweet; wineries such as Paul Masson and Almaden; the Pict-Sweet frozen food plant; and San Jose's own nationwide corporation, Food Machinery and Chemi-

cal, devoted to the manufacture of equipment for farms and canneries.

Still a leading industry, the valley's canneries, frozen food plants, and dried fruit packers combine to turn out more tonnage of fruits and vegetables than any other similar district in the world.

The canneries in the area annually process more than 30 per cent of the entire state crop of fruits and vegetables. Though the valley itself produces only a small part of the food to be processed, the strategic location of the packing plants near the chief rail, highway, and water routes of northern California attracts the produce of every farm district north of the Tehachapi Range, providing almost year-round employment for local workers.

The total production of the state's industry furnishes about one-fourth of the nation's canned, preserved, and frozen food supply. California packs almost all the peaches, fresh figs, olives, and apricots in the United States and about half the fish, plums, sweet cherries, asparagus, and spinach. It also leads in tomato processing and the packaging of frozen strawberries. Other products include snap beans, artichokes, tomato aspic, hominy, spiced pears, French fried potatoes, and chili sauce.

The frozen fruit and frozen vegetable packers of the valley have an increasing influence upon the food processing business. Their production percentages closely parallel, and in some cases surpass, those of the canning industry.

New industries. It was only during and after World War II that industrialization came to the Santa Clara Valley. The abundance of land for expansion, excellent and extensive transportation facilities, adequate utilities, the pool of skilled labor, and an ideal climate have attracted over 250 industries.

One of the first industries to be established was the giant Permanente Company near Cupertino. Built to take advantage of local raw materials, and designed to supply cement to Shasta Dam, it now claims to be the largest cement plant in the world. Before the end of the war, International Business Machines had constructed a half-million dollar plant near downtown San Jose. It manufactures IBM cards. At the south end of town, the Monarch Match Company built a plant to turn out paper book matches. In the same area, International Minerals and Chemicals constructed a $3 million enterprise to produce a food seasoning, and General Electric has a $3 million establishment turning out electric motors there.

At first the new industries tended to cluster close to the San Jose-Santa Clara area. Later they spread out into the orchards and into the smaller towns. Du Pont installed a research laboratory at Cupertino. Ferry-Morse Seeds established a new facility at Mountain View. Kaiser built a new aluminum foil plant at Permanente.

The Ford Motor Company opened a $50 million assembly plant at Milpitas in March of 1955. Its plans call for an ultimate investment of $100 million and it will ultimately employ 4,000 to 5,000 workers. International Business Machines constructed a modern, campus-like research and manufacturing facility in an agricultural area six miles south of downtown San Jose.

Figure 18-18. Irrigating double rows of lettuce in the nearly level Salinas Valley. Irrigated agriculture dominates in the valley. (California Agricultural Extension Service)

On a 275-acre site close to the Navy's famed Moffett Field, a new plant was opened in 1957 by Lockheed Aircraft Corporation's Missile Systems Division. A separate organization of the corporation, it engages in research and develops, tests, and manufactures unmanned weapons systems.

Clearly, the scale on which economic activities are now conducted has transformed the Santa Clara Valley from an agricultural to an industrial society, from farms and orchards to factories and cities. It is only a matter of time before the entire north end of the valley, from Coyote to San Francisco Bay, becomes a solid residential-industrial strip interrupted only occasionally by open land.

THE NORTH BAY

The North Bay section includes all of Marin and Napa Counties as well as portions of Solano and Sonoma Counties. The four counties are still predominantly rural; a large percentage of the population is associated either directly or indirectly with agriculture or lumbering, the exception being those people who commute from Marin County to San Francisco or who work in the Vallejo shipyards. Although the first ripples are now apparent, the flood of urbanization has not yet broken over the north coast shore of the bay. However, it is anticipated that the small towns and cities to be found there will have become important metropolitan subcenters before 1980. As a result, the populations of Marin, Solano, and Sonoma Counties may more than quadruple. Although the actual numbers of people who will cause this large percentage increase will be comparatively small when compared to those in the southern counties, taken together, the population of the four northern counties will then equal the entire population of the San Francisco Bay Area as it stood in 1920.

The Napa Valley is the primary American source of top-quality wines, and might therefore be compared to the Bordeaux, Burgundy, and Rhineland regions of France and Germany. Most of the Napa product consists of the dry table wines best known by such generic names as Sauterne, Burgundy, Claret, and Chianti. But though many of the wines have been imported, the new growing conditions have given them a different flavor from that of their place of origin. In general, California white wines are lighter and less musky than their European counterparts whose names they somewhat deceptively bear; the red wines are harsher, but also less tangy and with less body. This does not mean they are inferior. The best of them, usually available in small quantities from limited small vineyards, are the equal of European wines—but they are different. In addition, a few grape types and hybrids have been developed locally.

Although the soil and climate have much to do with the production of these wines, the skill, care, and infinite patience of the better vintners count for even more.

CENTRAL COASTAL MOUNTAINS AND VALLEYS

SURFACE FEATURES

The Central Coast Ranges extend for some 200 miles between Point Arguello on the south and Pescadero on the north. They are characterized by the occurrence of several parallel ranges oriented in a northwest-southeast direction and confined to a belt averaging 50 miles in width. The various ridges rise to elevations of between 2,000 and 4,000 feet, and occasionally to as much as 6,000 feet. Between the ridges are narrow, elongated valleys of some agricultural importance.

North of Monterey Bay, the Coast Ranges are called the Santa Cruz Mountains. They form a broad elevated block between the Santa Clara Valley on the east and the Pacific Ocean on the west. The highest of the Santa Cruz peaks, Loma Prieta (3,798 feet), lies in the southeastern portion of the range, where elevations decrease gradually until they become a broad low depression occupied by the Pajaro River. This river drains the San Benito Valley. After cutting a narrow canyon through that low pass separating the Santa Cruz Mountains from the Gabilan Range, it passes directly out to the ocean at Monterey Bay.

The Gabilan Range extends for about 60 miles southeast and then blends in with the Diablo Range. It is famous as the site of Pinnacles National Monument, once an area of recurrent volcanic activity but now a region of rocky crags, caves, columns, pillars, and deep

Figure 18-19. Santa Cruz and environs. The tip of the Monterey Peninsula is to the upper right, across Monterey Bay. (Santa Cruz County Advertising Committee)

canyons. A trail to the southern part of the monument leads over Chalone Peak, whose summit is 3,287 feet above sea level.

The Santa Lucia Range begins on the picturesque coast south of Monterey Bay, extends southeast along the ocean for 100 miles, and then blends with the San Rafael and other mountains situated in Santa Barbara County. This range is one of the most rugged in the coastal part of California; its crest is from 3,000 to 5,000 feet high and its cliffs rise jagged from the sea—or a few miles inland at the most. The highest peak, Junipero Serra, is at 5,844 feet above sea level. The northern part of the range is known as the Big Sur. It is wild, desolate, fog-swept, but not unpleasant.

One of the most attractive land features within the region is Morro Rock, the last of a series of volcanic peaks stretching from San Luis to the sea. It is a 576-foot monolith, a smaller Gibraltar or Mont St. Michel, detached from the land and standing in the sea. It guards the entrance to the only land-locked bay between San Francisco and Los Angeles—Morro Bay, a vast expanse of shallow water and tidal basins, with a long, sandy peninsula jutting into it and surrounded by hills.

The portion of the Coast Ranges that lies to the extreme southeast forms a rugged complex known as the San Rafael Mountains. They are characterized by deep canyons containing little or no bottom land. From them flow four principal rivers, the Sisquoc and Santa Ynez westward, and the Ojai and Sespe southward.

The Santa Ynez Range, which borders the coast eastward from Point Arguello, is regular and continuous in formation. To the north is the valley of the Santa Ynez River. To the south, a narrow strip of hilly to rolling land separates the range from the ocean.

ECONOMIC DEVELOPMENT

Agriculture is the major economic activity of the Central Coastal Mountains and Valleys Subregion. Lands in the large valleys between the Coast Range ridges and on the coastal plain have been extensively irrigated wherever ground water supplies permit. Stock raising is carried on in many of the smaller valleys and most of the foothill grass lands. Those crops suitable to a cool climate, such as lettuce, artichokes, peas, and Brussels sprouts, grow on the coastal terraces of some of these irrigated areas.

The Salinas Valley is the largest intermontane valley in the Coast Ranges. The northern (lower) end of the valley produces great quantities of vegetables: lettuce, carrots, beans, onions, artichokes, broccoli, tomatoes, and garlic. The southern (upper) portion of the valley specializes in sugar beets, barley, wheat, alfalfa and dry beans.

The valley's vegetable industry got under way in 1920, when the search for new agricultural land was accelerated by the gradual disappearance of the Los Angeles area as a vegetable producer for Eastern markets.

The valley's physical environment favors the production of iceberg lettuce, in particular. The prevalent summer fog, which serves to maintain a low, even temperature despite the hot sun of summer, is the controlling factor that makes the growing of iceberg lettuce feasible. Early spring, late spring, and summer plantings make it possible for the valley to supply from 45 to 50 per cent of the national commercial head-lettuce crop from April through November.

The Salinas River drains into Monterey Bay, an inlet of the Pacific Ocean formed by a pronounced indentation of the California coastline. The bay extends north and south for nearly 30 miles from headland to headland and bites inland about a third as far. It is primarily a resort area, and its variety of physiographic conditions concentrated within a relatively small area attracts both tourists and real estate developers.

COASTAL MOUNTAINS OF NORTHERN CALIFORNIA

The Coastal Mountains of Northern California Subregion, which constitutes the north-western portion of the state, extends from Oregon southward to the Russian River. It stretches as far east as the western foothills of the Sacramento Valley. In the north a section probes into the Cascade-Sierra Nevada Mountains and Valleys Region, separating Mt. Shasta from Lassen Peak. It is wild, undeveloped, little visited, and stormy land. The population is sparse and the townships are few.

SURFACE FEATURES

The topography consists mostly of mountainous terrain, since the Coast Ranges extend through the subregion from north to south. They fall steeply to a sea that is never still and always treacherous. As the name would indicate, these mountains consist not of one dominant axis, but of several running parallel and frequently separated by deep valleys. Northward, their composite character disappears; the broad valleys give way to canyons and the regular ranges to a wide group of rugged but irregular mountains. This northern group of mountains, which straddles the California-Oregon border, has been named the Klamath Mountains. No definite limit, however, has been established for the Coast Ranges' northern boundary, except one based on geologic grounds, for the Coast Ranges blend imperceptibly into the higher, more rugged terrain of the Klamath. The taller peaks in this district reach over 8,000 feet, and many exceed 6,000 feet.

Throughout most of their length the Coast Ranges have a regular northwest-southeast orientation and run nearly parallel to the coast. The slight discrepancy between shoreline and mountain range accounts for the more important littoral irregularities. Where a mountain range juts out to the ocean, there is a more or less prominent cape; the coast itself is indented between one cape and the next. The resultant bold coastline is particularly notable near Mendocino and Point Arena.

The subregion's 300-mile coastline has few harbors, and none of them, with the exception of Humboldt Bay, are large enough to accommodate any but small craft.

LUMBERING

Lumbering is the outstanding industry of the subregion. All along the Redwood High-

Figure 18-20. The commercial fishing fleet in the port of Eureka on Humboldt Bay, 283 miles north of San Francisco on the Pacific Coast. (Greater Eureka Chamber of Commerce)

way, from a point about 120 miles north of San Francisco to beyond Crescent City and far back into the hidden recesses of the Coast Ranges, scores of small sawmills have sprung up, many of them on a 24-hour operation. Recently, however, larger and less wasteful companies have come to be the prevalent type.

The subregion contains more than a quarter of California's commercial forest land and produces at least 35 per cent of its merchant timber. From the standpoint of growth potentials, this is one of the outstanding timber areas of the world. It is known as the Douglas fir-redwood subregion. Stands of fir grow at elevations of 5,000 to 6,000 feet; they are divided equally between public and private ownership.

The redwood of the Coast Ranges attains an average height greater than that of the Sierra species, sometimes reaching to 350 feet. The tallest known tree in the world is a coast redwood on Dyerville Flat in the Humboldt Redwoods State Park—364 feet tall.

These redwoods are slim trees, however, seldom attaining a girth of more than 16 feet. They are well suited for building materials and have been adapted to many uses, right down to their bark and sawdust. The redwood industry is among the most important in the state, with the species ranking third as a source of California lumber and accounting for nearly a fifth of the total volume produced.

The Coastal Mountains of Northern California Subregion has one of the last major blocks of virgin timber in the United States. This timbered stand is not only extensive and dense but has the greatest rate of growth of any in the nation. Under good forest management the subregion will be capable of maintaining a high level of production of wood and wood products indefinitely.

Figure 18-21. A lumber mill at Scotia in the Coast Ranges of northern California. This area of extensive and dense forests is important to the construction industry in more populated regions of the state. (Mary Hill)

RECREATION AND TOURISM

The subregion offers superb recreational facilities to those interested in hunting, fishing, mountain climbing, camping, or simply the enjoyment of scenery. Development of these recreational facilities has been greatest in the coastal redwood belt and along the lower reaches of the Russian River, largely because these regions are easily accessible from the densely populated San Francisco Bay Area Subregion, whereas much of the rest of the region is scarcely accessible at all.

19 | *Puget-Willamette Lowland*

and Coastal Mountains

(Relief map copyright Aero Service Corp.)

THE Puget-Willamette Lowland and Coastal Mountains Region includes those portions of Oregon and Washington that lie seaward of the western base of the Cascade Range and that part of British Columbia which includes the city of Vancouver and Vancouver Island.

SURFACE FEATURES

At the southern extremity of the region, lying athwart the California-Oregon border, are the Siskiyou and Klamath Mountains, which link the Cascades to the Coast Ranges of Oregon and California and separate the Willamette Valley from the Sacramento Valley. These are rugged mountains. No highway connects the interior to the coast for the first 75 miles north of the California border. No one peak predominates, but as a whole, this is the highest part of Oregon's coastal ranges.

The inland Siskiyou Mountains rise to nearly 7,700 feet above sea level, but near the coast in southern Oregon the high points tend to be about 3,500 feet in elevation. The crests gradually become lower to approximately 1,700 feet near the mouth of the Columbia River and even lower in southwestern Washington. In fact, the latter are really hills. These hills terminate at the Chehalis River, where the foothills of the Olympic Mountains take their place. Soon, however, the hills merge into mountains toward the interior of the Olympic Peninsula—rough, glaciated Alpine peaks rising to a maximum elevation of 8,000 feet.

Vancouver Island is actually an extension of the Coast Ranges of Oregon and Washington, but separated from them by the Strait of Juan de Fuca. With elevations above 6,000 feet, parts of the island are perhaps even more rugged than the Olympics. They are certainly more inaccessible. As along the littoral of Oregon and Washington, there are coastal lowlands, plains, and terraces varying in width from a few feet to a few miles.

The lowland portion of the region is less continuous than the mountains. North of Roseburg, Oregon, the Willamette Valley widens to 50 miles and much of its surface is rolling, like the prairies of Iowa. The woodlots here are dominated primarily by coniferous varieties, but the agriculture also resembles Iowa,

in that general farming is the rule. There is flat land, too, and the lowlands along the meandering Willamette River are frequently flooded.

North of the Willamette Valley the trough is not as much like a valley. Between Portland and Olympia the terrain is rolling to hilly, with flat land of consequence to be found only in the narrow floodplains of the major streams. North of Olympia, the surface configuration becomes somewhat more subdued, yet only the wide valleys are along the lower portions of the rivers. Across the international boundary the floodplains and delta of the Fraser River form an extensive, nearly flat lowland of approximately 900 square miles.

CLIMATE

The Puget-Willamette Lowland and Coastal Mountains Region has the greatest contrasts in precipitation of any part of Anglo-America. The area of extreme contrast is centered on the Olympic Peninsula, whose southwest facing slopes may receive up to 200 inches of precipitation annually. A small area on the leeward, east facing slope, with less than ten inches of rain per year, is mantled by scrub vegetation.

The average annual rainfall of the large cities is not great. Victoria has 30 inches, while the more exposed Vancouver receives 59 inches annually. Seattle gets 32 inches; Tacoma, 38 inches; Portland, 39 inches; and Salem, 40 inches.

Throughout the region, winter rain and snow exceed summer precipitation. Extended periods of summer drought similar to the Mediterranean-type dry spells of California often occur. On the other hand, one may see Mt. Rainier from Seattle only rarely in July and August.

Snow has fallen everywhere within the region, but rain is much more common during winter in the lowlands. All the higher mountains receive copious blankets of snow, however. Annual snowfall is especially great in the mountains of Vancouver Island.

Temperatures are much modified by the proximity to the Pacific Ocean and by the year-round westerly winds that move predominantly maritime air over the region during all seasons. Summer readings have gone above

Figure 19-1. Oregon's 400-mile seacoast presents a striking panorama of imposing headlands, sandy beaches, and rocky shoreline. (Oregon State Highway Commission)

100° F. and the thermometer has dipped to below 0° in every county, but more common are summers when it is never really too hot and very few bitterly cold winters.

SETTLEMENT

In 1515, two years after Balboa discovered the Pacific Ocean, some of his followers sailed up the coast as far north as Oregon, but it was not until 1578 that Francis Drake explored and laid claim to this coast for England. Two centuries later, in 1775, the Spaniard, Bruno Heceta, landed on the Olympic Peninsula and became the first white man to set foot on Washington soil. In 1792, George Vancouver discovered, named, and explored Puget Sound itself. Many of the names he chose have remained unchanged, including Hood Canal, Mt. Baker, and Mt. Rainier.

In 1793, Alexander Mackenzie, of the North West Company, on his epochal journey from coast to coast, made his way into what is now British Columbia. Two years later, Spain renounced all claims to the region in favor of England. The United States denied British rights to the area. President Jefferson sent Meriwether Lewis and William Clark to explore the area, and they reached the Columbia in 1805.

During the period leading up to and during the war of 1812, the United States lost most of her European trade. Consequently, ships from New England, New York, and Chesapeake Bay ports began to look for trade in the Pacific. John Jacob Astor established a fort and fur post at Astoria in 1811. With Astor began the era of the fur brigades, whose depots soon were scattered throughout the virgin wilderness. The British Hudson's Bay Company men had gradually worked westward across Canada. A bitter rivalry developed between these great fur companies; the actual ownership of the vast territory of the Pacific Northwest was in dispute.

New Englanders began to settle in the Willamette Valley in 1832, and a Methodist mission was established at Salem in 1834. Overland wagon trains for Oregon left from Independence, Missouri. A regular route across the Great Plains, through the Rocky Mountains, and on to the Columbia River was established and became known as the "Oregon Trail."

The first sawmill on Puget Sound was located at Tumwater in 1844. Settlers first came by boat from Oregon; later, by the Oregon Trail up the Cowlitz Valley. Other settlements soon were made. Fortunately, the lumber trade grew as the fur trade declined. Later, land was cleared and agriculture began. Many California gold seekers who were disappointed in their quest continued their journey into the Northwest where they went into farming.

On June 15, 1846, the 49th parallel was defined as the international boundary. The United States portion was organized into the Oregon and the Washington Territories. Oregon was admitted to the Union in 1859, Washington in 1889.

MANUFACTURING

Present industry in the region is based mainly on the natural resources of the area. Forest products and food processing have been the major sources of employment. In Washington and Oregon these groups account for 60 per cent of the total manufacturing employment. Another sizable and growing component of the region's industry is the production of aluminum. This, too, is resource based, for it was attracted to the region and has flourished there because of great hydroelectric resources. Like logging and lumbering, aluminum production is spawning a fabricating industry that already outnumbers basic processing in employment by six to one.

During the last 20 years, the population of the region has increased enormously. In the period from 1942 to 1952 the increase was 35 per cent. Since 1952, a more gradual increase has taken place. The basic industries have been able to supply the major share of the jobs necessary to keep the increasing population employed.

This is not to say that the industrial economy in the Northwest has not changed or has not acquired new elements. As population grows, so do markets. This growth of markets has resulted in a considerable number of new industries that are essentially market oriented —established to serve local or regional markets. A good example is afforded by the new Kaiser gypsum plant in Seattle. The raw materials for this plant are shipped from San Marcos Island off the coast of Mexico, but the market is the industry within the Pacific Northwest. Thus markets rather than resources are now the factor attracting new industry to the region. The region is in a transition stage from its earlier resource based economy to one that is diversified, and therefore more stable and healthier.

Still another part of the industrial picture is presented by the growing number of companies manufacturing products with value so

Figure 19-2. Oregon's greatest industry is lumbering; six to eight billion board feet of timber are produced annually. Logs are usually towed down the rivers, as shown here at the mouth of the Umpqua River at Reedsport. (Oregon State Highway Commission)

high in relation to weight that they can be produced economically almost anywhere. Electronics equipment and various kinds of instruments are examples of such products. Growth of the region's lumber and lumber products industries was a response primarily to wartime needs and the postwar construction boom.

The older, resource based industries are expanding. Many new developments are occurring in utilization of wood wastes. New products now in laboratory and development stages will not only result in the use of a greater percentage of the trees, but will also provide more diversified sources of income to members of the industry. Among these new products are hardboards, wall boards, soil conditioners, cement extenders, and bark products.

In the food processing field, the growth of the freezing industry is notable. Not only berries, fruits, and vegetables, but also more highly processed foods are being frozen.

Expansion of the region's manufacturing since 1939 has been due more to the increased demand for its products by outside purchasers than to growth of regional market, rapid as that has been. The five largest industries, which produce chiefly for outside purchasers—lumber and lumber products, food processing, paper products, primary metals (mainly aluminum), and transportation equipment (chiefly aircraft) groups—account for about 82 per cent of the total rise in value added by manufacturing since 1939. For each of these industrial fields the gain in value added by manufacturing has been relatively greater in the region than in the nation.

One of the deficiencies of manufacturing in the Puget-Willamette Lowland and Coastal Mountains Region is that so much of the output is sold to outside purchasers in the form of semifinished materials, such as rough lumber or aluminum bars and sheets, instead of as furniture or pots and pans. Further local processing and fabricating of these semifinished materials would certainly benefit the region.

Most of the region's factories are small. Both Washington and Oregon have fewer large industrial plants and more small factories than the country as a whole. Factories having 100 or more employees constitute only eight per cent of all manufacturing establishments in Wash-

ington and 7.6 in Oregon, whereas the national average is 10.2 per cent. Nevertheless, the region's large plants, those employing 100 or more workers, provide one-half or more of all manufacturing employment.

GEOGRAPHICAL CONCENTRATION OF INDUSTRY

Although manufacturing has expanded generally throughout the region, the trend has been toward concentration in the Seattle and Portland areas. These two sections offer advantages not available in other parts of the region for the location and growth of many types of industries. Their access to waterborne shipping, large pools of experienced workers, terminal freight rates, and variety of services available to industry have been important factors in their industrial expansion. The awarding of large wartime contracts for airplanes and ships to plants in these two areas also accelerated industrial growth.

The extent to which manufacturing will become further concentrated in the Seattle and Portland industrial areas will be determined largely by the rate at which the lumber industry continues to move southward and by the types of industries that expand in the future. Since 1939, the lumber industry has been moving gradually from cutover areas in the north to forest stands farther south. This southward movement undoubtedly will bring further expansion of the lumber and lumber products industries in southwestern Oregon. Extension of power transmission lines from the Columbia River generators to the Coos Bay and Douglas County areas should further aid the growth of the lumber products industry in southwestern Oregon.

In the light of recent trends, however, and the locational advantages of Seattle and Portland for manufacturing, these two areas probably will continue to receive a substantial part of the region's industrial development during the next decade.

LUMBER AND LUMBER PRODUCTS

Today the Pacific Northwest as a whole produces the finished lumber for over a million homes a year. It provides the bulk of the nation's wood shingles; cooks up nearly a fifth of the wood pulp for paper products and syn-

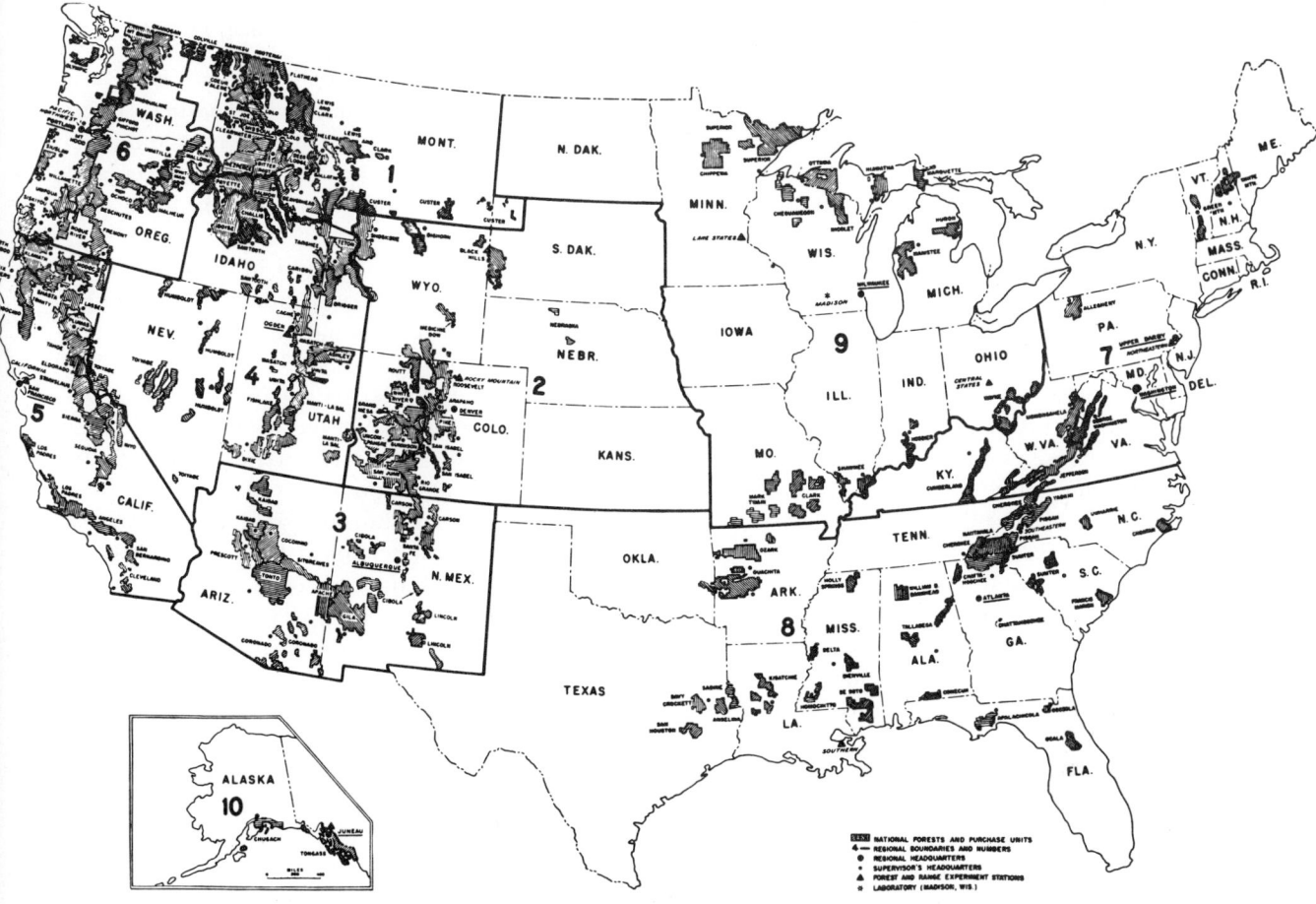

Figure 19-3. National forests and research headquarters in the United States. The Pacific Northwest was the first region in the nation to realize the need for timber management and forest research. Much of its timber land is in national forest preserves. (U.S. Department of Agriculture)

thetic fibers; and turns out about seven-tenths of the plywood and more than two-thirds of the laths. The Pacific Northwest supplies the nation with approximately 35 per cent of its total lumber needs. About half the area's employed people work in the manufacture of wood products, which pays 52 per cent of the industrial payroll. The majority of production occurs in western Washington and Oregon, in the Puget-Willamette Lowland and Coastal Mountains Region.

That part of the timber harvest that was once wasted is used today in a way almost beyond the average man's comprehension. Bark goes into tannin extract for leather tanners, to control the drilling muds for the world's oil wells, or to aid in the concentration of low-grade iron ores. Chips that once were burned are now remanufactured into new lumber products—hardboards, softboards, insulation, and a score of other useful materials.

The region's fabricated timbers play a large role in the nation's construction industry, and its prefabricated homes have a national market. Greater utilization of each log and the safeguarding of the forests from wanton waste are new trends in this industry.

MANUFACTURING IN WESTERN OREGON

Oregon is rapidly coming of age as a manufacturing state with a strong bent toward diversity of industry. The metalworking, textiles, paper, printing, chemicals, and electrical equipment industries have made rapid advances during the past decade. At the same time, increased processing has taken place in the two basic industries—timber and food products.

Manufacturing is concentrated primarily west of the Cascades, and every county has at least 1,000 industrial workers. In most counties lumber is the predominant industry. Roughly one-third of the manufacturing employment is in Multnomah County (Portland).

Although Oregon has attracted many national concerns since World War II, most of the state's new manufactories were organized and developed by local people. A significant factor concerning these new industrial plants is that a large proportion of them are turning out products not formerly made in the state or in the Pacific Northwest—aluminum shingles, irrigation systems, electronic devices, and many other household and industrial products.

Lumber industries. One-fifth of the lumber produced in the United States comes from Oregon, where more than eight billion board feet have been cut annually. Although much of the lumber is shipped out of the region in a rough or semifinished state, the manufacture of highly finished wood products, such as doors, roof trusses, plywood, and furniture, is taking place.

The Portland area is the center of Crown Zellerbach's operations, and 14 tree farms in the area furnish an estimated nine billion board feet of timber to other companies' paper mills at Camas, West Linn, St. Helens, and Lebanon, where nearly 600,000 tons of paper and paper products are turned out annually. The industry employs about 6,000 people and has a yearly payroll of some $26 million.

Food processing. The second leading industry, food processing, employs about one-sixth of the industrial workers. Over 13 million cases of fruits and vegetables have been packed in the area in recent years; and, in addition, some 200 million pounds of products are quick-frozen. Backed by heavy wheat production in Oregon and Washington, flour now is milled in large quantities at Astoria and Portland. Although great quantities of wheat and flour are exported, an expanding consumer market has led to extensive manufacture of crackers, cookies, cereals, and other bakery products. Stemming from the high volume of livestock handled in stockyards throughout the state, Portland and other centers have developed a flourishing meat processing industry.

Metalworking. Including the production of primary metals, metalworking employs about 11 per cent of all industrial workers in the area. It has become the leading employer

of the Portland metropolitan area. The variety of products includes: mechanics' tools, heating apparatus, automotive trucks and trailers, factory lift trucks, foundry products, and specialized machinery for lumber, food, and chemical plants.

Textiles. Fourth highest in employment is the textile and apparel industry. Although originally processing native wool, certain of the textile plants now use nylon, rayon, and other synthetic fibers. Principal textile products include blankets, outdoor sport clothes, sweaters, swim suits, and a variety of other garments, bags, and similar items.

Chemicals. Promising great expansion for the future is the chemical industry, which already lists manufacture of such products as pharmaceuticals, insecticides, paints, cleaning compounds, fertilizers, carbide, alum, ferroalloys, sodium chlorate, caustic soda, chlorine, oxygen, and acetylene. Oregon's natural resources, coupled with abundant supplies of water and low-cost electric power, should lead to production of additional basic chemicals in the region.

Electronics. Most of the electronics plants are centered around the larger industrial areas. Typical of these new plants is that of the Tektronix Company in Beaverton, Oregon—just outside Portland. Over 3,000 workers turn out oscilloscopes and other scientific equipment worth $40 million annually.

MANUFACTURING IN THE PUGET SOUND AREA

Puget Sound's manufacturing base rests heavily upon three industry groups—transportation equipment, lumber, and food.

Transportation equipment is the area's most important industry, employing over 34 per cent of all persons engaged in manufacturing. The transportation equipment industry dwarfs all others. It includes establishments engaged in manufacturing aircraft, motor vehicles, ships, and railroad equipment. The producers of aircraft and ships have been relatively more important than companies engaged in making other transportation equipment products.

Aircraft industry. By any standard of measure the Boeing Airplane Company is one of the few very large industrial firms with both headquarters and major manufacturing facilities located in the Pacific Northwest. Probably the entire past and future of the area's aircraft industry lie in the hands of this one company, which located in Seattle because its founder liked to live there. Growing with the area, the Boeing Airplane Company has developed a tremendous pool of skilled manpower that would be difficult to transplant or replace, especially in the engineering field. With a present employment of about 37,000 employees in its Seattle-Renton plants, the company occupies an important place in the economic life of the whole region, and particularly of Seattle.

Shipbuilding. The Puget Sound area is endowed with all the natural resources favorable to ship construction. With its many deep-water harbors, the area offers alternative location possibilities for the manufacturer. It was first established as a shipbuilding center with the construction of the battleship *Nebraska* (begun in 1902 and commissioned in 1907), and again entered a period of intense activity during World Wars I and II. As in all other shipbuilding centers, local yards operate largely on a "feast or famine" basis. During periods of national emergency, a sudden demand arises for ships and ship repairs, and the industry undergoes a tremendous expansion. After the emergency subsides, activities decline rapidly. As the Puget Sound area's population increases, the demand will grow for all boat types, thereby stimulating the local small boat industry to greater activities.

Motor vehicles and equipment. Some 1,500 persons are employed in producing motor vehicles and equipment. Although the area neither manufactures nor assembles any passenger automobiles, local companies produce truck and bus bodies and truck trailers. Much of this latter equipment is made to custom requirements.

Railroad equipment. Puget Sound manufacturers produce freight and refrigerator cars for carriers in all sections of the United States. At present, rail carriers are replacing many obsolete freight cars and purchasing additional equipment. The producers now receive their steel from nearby Western fabricators. In addition, opportunities exist for the construction of railroad equipment from lighter metals. Therefore, this segment of the industry faces

good growth prospects, at least equal to the area's rate of population expansion.

Lumber manufacturing. One of every five persons engaged in manufacturing activities throughout the area works in this industry; almost half are engaged in sawmill and planing mill operations. Since logs are costly to transport from forests and tree farms to mills, this industry locates its manufacturing plants near the source of its raw materials. With one of the world's best climates for growing timber and with natural waterways to permit economical transportation of bulky logs, the Puget Sound area has always been an important manufacturer of lumber and wood products.

Since the lumber industry's foundation rests upon forest lands, additional attention is being given to increasing yield per acre. Consequently, a greater volume of wood should become available for use as the additional benefits arising from scientific forest management can be enjoyed.

Food products. As the third largest manufacturing industry in the Puget Sound area, the food industry employs about 12 per cent of the manufacturing employees. Puget Sound itself has always supplied its residents, and the rest of the world as well, with salmon, crab, and halibut. The lands cleared by the lumber industry provided the space in which dairying and small fruit and vegetable farms could develop. Generally, the area's food manufacturers have been hindered in seeking wide markets for their products because of high production and distribution costs.

Canned and frozen food items produced around Puget Sound are distributed throughout the nation. In addition, much of the sea food caught in Puget Sound and Alaskan waters is processed in the region before being distributed nationally. Because of the quality of their canned and frozen items, Puget Sound manufacturers should be able to continue the successful selling of their items in national and world markets.

Grain mill products. As the result of a 50 per cent decrease in flour consumption per family throughout the country, the Puget Sound millers have diversified their product lines and expanded their production of prepared mixes, other packaged products, and specialized stock and poultry feeds. Since prepared products are costly to transport great distances, the major markets for packaged items will continue to be found in the Western States. An immediate problem is the short supply of high protein, hard milling wheats normally obtained from Montana. This problem has been aggravated by Federal farm regulations that cut back all wheats alike and caused shortages in the already limited supply of hard wheat. Continual new product development is essential to insure the future of the millers.

Aluminum fabrication. The spectacular rise of aluminum smelting in the Pacific Northwest since 1940 has been particularly significant to the growth and development of this area.

The aluminum industry developed in the Puget Sound area largely in response to military needs for the metal and the availability of unsold or uncommitted power from the newly completed Federal hydroelectric projects in the area. Almost overnight the region became the leading center of aluminum production in the United States. In 1939, no aluminum was produced there; by 1941, the area accounted for 22 per cent of the national output; in 1944, 36 per cent. Production in the area continued to expand until 1950 when a movement took place to the Southwest, where aluminum firms could draw on natural gas and lignite supplies. In 1955, the Puget Sound area produced 35 per cent of the national output as compared with 48 per cent in 1950, and this trend is continuing.

As basic producer, or mother industry, aluminum plants have attracted scores of fabricators of finished products into the area. Irrigation systems, furniture, signs, packaging, building products, cameras, electrical conductors, and sporting equipment are but a few of the products now being made there.

One projection about the future of the aluminum industry in the Puget Sound area can be made with relative certainty. As total aluminum smelting capacity continues to expand, this area will not share proportionately in its increase. Although present low power rates compensate for a good part of the other cost disadvantages of location in the region, additions to capacity can be supplied only by higher-cost power that will increase production costs beyond smelters located nearer raw materials and markets. The area will, however, continue to supply an impressive fraction of the national aluminum output in the foreseeable future.

MANUFACTURING IN GREATER VANCOUVER

Greater Vancouver, including Vancouver itself, the thriving Fraser River port city of New Westminster, Burnaby, the North Shore, and adjacent municipalities, is in the midst of the largest industrial boom in the history of Canada; projects now under way or on the drawing boards total over $1 billion.

Although much of the industrial activity centers on huge capital investments for construction of pulp and paper plants, many other types of industry have commenced operation in recent years. Among these was a $7 million steel pipe and tube mill at Port Moody to manufacture black and galvanized pipe. The potential of this mill is more than 60,000 tons annually, and much of the production will find a ready market in natural gas operations. Construction also began on an $11 million chemical plant in North Vancouver that will produce chlorine and caustic soda to serve the rapidly growing pulp, oil refining, and plywood industries. Preparations are also under way for the construction of a $5 million chemical plant in North Vancouver to make sodium chlorate, and a $1 million plant has been erected at Marpole to manufacture from hemlock bark a chemical that is used as an additive in drilling lubricants. A new $1 million corrugated paper box company at New Westminster has an annual capacity of 150 million square feet.

Many similar enterprises have been established. Among these are a new chain saw plant in Burnaby, a new aluminum fabricating plant in Vancouver capable of cold rolling 150 linear feet per minute, and a new plant in South Westminster to manufacture a volcanic aggregate for use in plaster and concrete mixes.

One of the greatest boons to expansion of new industries and manufacturing is the multimillion dollar natural gas pipeline from the Peace River area to Vancouver. This means that cheap fuel will be available to allow a greater diversification of industry. With the advent of natural gas and oil at tidewater, it appears certain that the area will attract new petrochemical industries; expansion of existing industries can also be expected through this cheap and adaptable fuel.

Figure 19-4. Blossoming fruit trees and grazing cattle in the Willamette Valley near Newberg, a region well known for its diversity of agricultural products. (Oregon State Highway Commission)

AGRICULTURE

Agriculture is of prime importance in the Puget-Willamette Lowland and Coastal Mountains Region. The lowlands are well settled and are occupied by many small farms on which diversified, dairy, or specialized farming is practiced.

WILLAMETTE VALLEY

The Willamette Valley of Oregon stretches along the basin of the Willamette River in a north-south direction for some 140 miles, and east and west from 30 to 60 miles between the Cascades and the Coast Ranges. It is essentially a nonglaciated alluvial plain produced by the partial filling of a broad trough with sediments carried by streams from the nearby mountains.

Agriculture is highly diversified and growing seasons are long. Most crops of the temper-

ate zone thrive there. Green valleys and timbered hills characterize the landscape.

Some specialty crops, truck crops, and pastures are irrigated, but most other field, fruit, and nut crops are grown without irrigation. Supplemental irrigation during June, July, and August provides higher yields for most valley crops.

In general, the valley produces grains, hays, forage, legume seeds, potatoes, tree fruits, and truck crops.

Cherry production centers in the Willamette Valley. Cherries are shipped fresh, canned, and brined. Bings and Lamberts are the favorite black varieties while the Royal Anne is used extensively to brine for the maraschino trade.

Prunes are sold fresh and dried, canned, and frozen. Nearly 30 processors of Northwest Italian prunes have formed the Purple Plum Association for the national promotion of this

Figure 19-5. This strawberry field near Gresham, Oregon, in the Willamette Valley, is typical of those that make Oregon a leading berry producing state. (U.S. Department of Agriculture)

Figure 19-6. A hopyard near Oregon City, Oregon. (Photo-Art Commercial Studios)

fruit. Berry production is significant and the area ranks among the leaders nationally both in acreage and yield. The mild climate combines with much cloudy weather to provide ideal growing conditions. Many varieties are cultivated, but strawberries are the biggest money crop. More than 93 per cent of the strawberry production is sold to local processing plants, mostly to freezers. The rest are marketed fresh, chiefly in Portland.

Specialty crops include peppermint, hops, and nursery products. Oregon is the number one state in mint production, with over 13,000 acres sown to the crop. Hop acreage dropped to 3,900 acres in 1955, and has continued to decline because of oversupply and higher production costs on a yield basis. The nursery industry is another major specialty; it grosses from $12 million to $15 million annually.

Grain and hay are the most important crops in terms of both acreage and value of sales. Over three-fourths of the oats for grain are grown in the Willamette Valley along with other grains. Barley acreage brings in an annual return of around $4 million. Wheat has remained of secondary importance in a diversified farming system.

The bulk of Oregon's walnut and filbert crops are found in this valley. Total harvest generally exceeds 15 million pounds of walnuts and 14 million pounds of filberts, bringing in a return of about $6 million annually. Most of the nuts go to outside markets.

Dairying is the chief source of income on many valley and coast farms. The Willamette Valley normally accounts for most of the cash receipts from farm marketings of dairy products. The greatest number of cows are on diversified farms, and, except for the market milksheds, generally are on a fall freshening program.

With greater use of irrigation on dairy pastures, by ensiling and drying hay crops, and with a shift from forage seed production to hay production, the amount of dairy products in the Willamette Valley could readily be doubled. Increased importation of grain feeds would have to accompany such an expansion.

COASTAL MOUNTAINS AND VALLEYS OF OREGON

West of the Willamette Valley and the Cascade Mountains from California north to the

Columbia River lie the Coast Ranges of Oregon, indented by the valleys of several rivers and bordered in places by coastal terraces. On the bottom lands along these streams and on a few of the coastal terraces a flourishing dairy enterprise has developed, based primarily upon mild weather and the luxuriant pasturage of fertile alluvial soils. These soils are generally well supplied with moisture, and may lack drainage. An annual period of two or three months occurs, however, when the precipitation drops to low levels and a strange situation arises in which plant life suffers from lack of moisture in an area having a normal precipitation rate of from 60 to 100 inches annually.

In this belt, dairy conditions are ideal, for there is little freezing weather; on the rare occasions when snow falls, it seldom remains on the ground more than a few hours. The mean minimum temperature in midwinter is generally between 36° and 40° F., and only a few places in this section have experienced freezing weather. The mean maximum temperature for July ranges between 65° and 70°, and only occasionally does the temperature reach 90°.

These bottom land pastures almost within sight of the sea—many of them below the level of high tide—are responsible for a type of farming somewhat like that of Holland or Denmark. The land is in such demand for pasture that it is seldom plowed.

Most of the milk is used for manufacturing cheese. Tillamook leads all other Oregon counties in this respect. Its famous Cheddar cheese is widely marketed within the Pacific Coast States. Tillamook dairies also supply fluid milk to Portland markets.

The dairy sections of the coastal valleys have relatively limited possibilities for change in agricultural production. Nearly all land suitable for dairy pastures in these areas is now in use. Some increase is possible through more widespread ensiling of surplus hay and grass crops. Limited acreages are available for such specialty crops as bulbs, nursery stock, and small fruits and berries, including cranberries. With increased population and increased tourist travel in the area, some expansion of vegetable production for local consumption may be justified. Ample acreage of suitable land for the production of these specialties is available in most of the area.

The rearing of beef cattle, usually in small herds, has grown rapidly and is a year-round farm enterprise. Sheep flocks are also increasing. Poultry and poultry products, including turkeys and ducks, gross between $30 million and $35 million annually. Minor livestock items are hogs, rabbits, specialty poultry, and mink and other fur-bearing animals.

THE PUGET LOWLAND

The Puget Lowland is an area where the soils have been formed from ground rocks brought in by the ice during the glacial age. The glacial deposits that have not been water worked during deposition have compact understrata about as impenetrable as concrete. Deposits reworked by water from the melting ice consist largely of gravelly and sandy material. Soils on this material have porous sub-strata. Local glaciers from the Cascade Range, remnants of which remain today on the snow-capped mountain peaks, brought down a different kind of glacial deposit than that left by the large Puget Sound ice sheet. Soils on these deposits are generally stony and heavily forested. Annual deposits of alluvium are being laid down in the coastal river valleys where most of the fertile soils are found. The deposits consist of glacial flour derived from the mountain glaciers and variable amounts of wash from glaciated uplands.

The area west of the Cascade Range and south of the glaciated area is the Salkum Plain, apparently of glacial orgin but of ancient age. In the area north and west of Grays Harbor, fine textured soils are developed in old gravel deposits, possibly of glacial origin from the Olympic Mountains. Finally, along the Pacific Coast, extensive areas of old beach deposits interspersed with acid peat bogs form the basis for specialized farming enterprises.

Agriculture in western Washington is a response to proximity to large consuming markets and climatic conditions. The temperate oceanic climate provides an approximate growing season of 200 days in the farming areas. Rainfall varies greatly within short distances, but the greater part of the precipitation occurs between the months of October and May. As a result, pastures and cash crops are usually in need of moisture by the end of July.

Fertile land exists in the valleys, but it is so limited—and expensive—that the farmer is com-

pelled to specialize in dairy and poultry enterprises, supplemented in many instances by
truck crops, berries, fruits, nuts, and small
grains. The average size of a farm in the area
is 65 acres.

Conditions for dairying are generally very
favorable. The marine climate of western
Washington, with mild rainy winters and long
cool summers, favors grazing and high milk
production. Good pastures are found in the
rainy lowlands. Many dairymen raise oats or
other concentrated feed, but the region is not
self-sufficient in grain; farmers import their
grain from eastern Washington or farther away.
Comparatively speaking, the costs for shelter
and winter feeding are low. Where the cost of
land is high, dairying tends to be replaced by
intensive use of the land for small fruits, tree
fruits, and vegetables.

Climatic and economic conditions favor
poultry in western Washington. The mild winters help make possible high egg production
at a time when areas in the Midwest and East
produce at a much lower rate. Less favorable
is the factor of feed, most of which must be
imported. Many poultry farmers work in some
other industry in addition to managing their
farming enterprises. Poultry products find a
ready market in Seattle and other Puget Sound
cities.

This section ranks among the leading areas
of the nation in production of strawberries and
cranberries. Washington berry producers are
usually first nationally in output of red raspberries, second in cultivated blackberries, third
in strawberries and blueberries, and fourth in
cranberries. These berries usually account for
more than 90 per cent of the $10 million real-
ized annually from sales of berry crops.

BRITISH COLUMBIA

Early settlers of British Columbia were of
the gold seeking and timber cutting breed who
for a long time paid little or no attention to
farming. Consequently, it is only in comparatively recent years that agriculture has begun
to grow in importance. Most of the land now
under tillage lies in the river valleys, particularly in the Fraser Valley and on Vancouver
Island. Agricultural statistics show that most
successful farms were those engaged in mixed
farming. In recent years, however, there has
been a considerable increase in the number of

such specialized establishments as dairy farms,
tree fruit farms, poultry ranches, and seed and
bulk farms. Immigrants from Holland and
other areas are rapidly developing many sections of the province. Small holdings—berry
and poultry farms of from three to ten acres—
are popular near the larger centers where intensive cultivation is practiced. Cultivation
under glass is featured strongly in the vicinity
of Victoria and Vancouver, and altogether
there are over five million square feet of greenhouses. Successful dairy farms in the lower
Fraser Valley vary in size from 40 to 100 acres.

FISHING

Fishery resources are the basis for one of the
major industries in the Puget-Willamette Lowland and Coastal Mountains Region. The commercial fisheries, located mainly in the coastal
waters, harbors, and lower portions of the rivers of the region, produce an estimated annual
catch of approximately 230 million pounds,
worth about $30.5 million to the fishermen.

SALMON

Salmon are the most valuable fish of the region. Pacific salmon are anadromous, that is:
they are hatched in fresh water, descend to salt
water, attain most of their growth there, and
then return to the streams to spawn. They have
a well-developed homing instinct; most of them
return to spawn in their streams of origin.

Five species of salmon are native to the region—chinook, sockeye, coho, pink, and chum.
All are so high in food value and so admirably
adapted to the process of canning that an enormous trade has been developed.

Fishing intensity, both sport and commercial, has increased in recent years, accentuating
the need for greater rehabilitation and management effort. Salmon have been especially vulnerable because they depend upon a fresh
water environment to satisfy their spawning
and feeding requirements. Some of the major
causes of salmon depletion can be traced to the
environmental changes that have taken place
since the advent of civilization in the region.
Hundreds of miles of spawning grounds have
been cut off by construction of power dams.
Some have included no provision for the passage of fish and the upstream area now is totally
inaccessible to salmon. Extensive deforestation,

Figure 19-7. A freighter loads British Columbian fir in the port of Vancouver, British Columbia. (National Film Board)

by lowering the capacity of watersheds to retain moisture, has increased the rapidity of spring and fall runoffs and reduced the water supply available in the low flow months. This has automatically impaired the ability of the streams to rear a normal population of fish. Pollution has become a problem with increasing industrialization. Pulp mill wastes, especially, are harmful in estuarial areas at the mouths of rivers where downstream migrants linger while adjusting from fresh to salt water.

The principles of conservation apply to the control and preservation of current fish stocks and the habitat still accessible to them. Ultimate success of the program will rely upon a broad co-ordinated policy of resource development among fishery, forestry, agricultural, hydroelectric, and other interests.

HALIBUT AND OTHER FISH

Halibut supports an extremely important fishery in the northeastern Pacific, a fishery that

has been under the control of the International Pacific Halibut Commission since 1924. The center of abundance appears to be off the coast of British Columbia. Approximately 60 per cent of the catch is taken by fishermen operating from Washington ports.

Herring fishing, although of comparatively recent growth, has become increasingly important. The fish are reduced for conversion into oil and meal; the latter is used to feed stock and poultry. Herring oil finds a ready market with manufacturers of soaps and paints and as a cooking oil.

Occasional catches of albacore tuna are taken by fishermen operating 40 to 60 miles offshore during summer.

FOREST RESOURCES

The West Coast forest belt within the Puget-Willamette Lowland and Coastal Mountains Region stretches from the eastern slopes of the

Cascades westward to the Pacific Ocean and northward from the California-Oregon border into British Columbia. It covers an area roughly 1,000 miles long and 140 miles wide. With abundant rainfall and deep, fertile soils, this is a distinct forest region, different from any other in Anglo-America. Nowhere else in the world does so much accessible high-quality commercial timber grow so rapidly and compactly. From these forests comes a quarter of the softwood lumber used each year in the United States. Four principal species—Douglas fir, West Coast hemlock, Western red cedar, and Sitka spruce—dominate. There are also several species of white firs, Port Orford and Alaska yellow cedars, and a few hardwoods.

The Douglas fir forest often has 50,000 board feet or more per acre. Its productive soils can grow an average of 700 board feet or more on an acre each year. In the Douglas fir region there are 26 million acres of commercial forest land. According to latest complete estimates, the saw timber volume is 426 billion board feet. Douglas fir is the most important softwood species on earth; it comprises the largest production of any species in the world and fills more construction needs than any other wood. Its most important uses are for residential construction and repair, farm structures, and railroads. Timber harvests bring more than $1.6 billion in new wealth to the region each year in forest industry wages and income from sale of lumber, plywood, pulp and paper, shingles, doors, and other products made from wood.

West Coast hemlock is a wood of superior properties and, when properly manufactured, seasoned, and used, is an excellent wood for many purposes. What really brought this species into its own was the sulfate pulp industry that has developed into an industrial giant along the Columbia River and on Puget Sound. Sulfate pulp from West Coast hemlock is converted into rayon, cellophane, nitrocellulose, and photographic film. Sulfate pulp is manufactured into a wide variety of products, including tissue paper and high-grade book and magazine papers. It is blended with ground wood pulp to increase the strength of newsprint.

Western red cedar is one of the more durable species. For over a century it has been manufactured extensively into shingles, lumber, poles, and piling. Because it resists decay and insects it is extremely desirable as lumber for siding and exterior paneling. Western red cedar has been the primary shingle species in the United States for nearly 50 years, during which time the state of Washington has produced about 90 per cent of the nation's wood shingles. The trend toward patented roofing, encouraged by building code restrictions and fire insurance premium rates, has resulted in a declining market for wood shingles. However, the Western red cedar shingle industry is still a lusty giant. Its principal market is the agricultural Middle West, where farmers prefer wood shingles to substitutes that cannot weather violent winds and hailstorms.

Sitka spruce grows principally in the fog belt ten to 15 miles inland from the Pacific Ocean. The principal use of high-grade spruce is for lumber. About nine-tenths of the lumber from this species is further manufactured into a wide variety of planing mill products, Venetian blinds, and boxing and crating. One of Sitka spruce's important uses is as sliced veneer for berry boxes and other small fruit containers.

MINERAL RESOURCES

The mineral deposits in this region are insignificant when measured against those of the Intermountain States or interior British Columbia. Oregon nickel is being mined and smelted at a $28.5 million plant at Riddle, south of Roseburg, by the Hannah interests, who are working with the government under a defense subsidy. This plant supplies five per cent of the nation's requirements. Near Portland, Oregon, there are large deposits of laterite containing alumina, iron, silica, titanium, and other minerals. Some of the deposits are reported under lease to the Aluminum Company of America. There are 25 or 30 limestone mines and a doubling of limestone output is expected because the region produces less than half the amount it now needs for pulp and paper operations, for sugar refining, and for the cement industry. Large bodies of high-grade bituminous coal are located on Vancouver Island at tidewater. Sizable deposits of iron ore have been known for many years, but it was not until very recently that these·were opened to any extent. The major operation is on the east

Figure 19-8. Bright yellow and white daffodils color the Oregon countryside in springtime. In the background is Mt. Hood (11,245 feet), the highest point in Oregon. (Oregon State Highway Commission)

coast of Vancouver Island; this ore is shipped to Japanese furnaces, but some of it is being considered for local use.

RECREATION AND TOURISM

The Puget-Willamette Lowland and Coastal Mountains Region has infinitely varied scenery on a majestic scale. Lush meadowlands lead to snowy mountain tops rising from green foothills, park-like valleys, and deep canyons. The coastal scenery is incomparably fine. The insular system of the Puget Sound extends for its entire length. Almost all of them are heavily wooded; combined, they form a labyrinth of sheltered channels. The hunter, camper, boater, fisherman, or ski enthusiast can find much to enjoy. There are seashores and inland waters. There are mountain peaks to scale and

glaciers to traverse. There are hundreds of miles of trails through Alpine forests and meadows. One can ski on snow fields or on the waters of the lakes; or one can drive to vantage points to view lovely vistas.

POPULATION

Along with rapid growth, the composition and distribution of the region's population are changing. On the whole, the population, compared to that of 1940, is more urban and less rural. It is characterized by more females relative to males, although males still dominate. The population is younger, with only a small increase in the proportion of population 65 years and older. It is assured of continued growth, even without new immigration, because of the great increase in children in the last decade. More specifically, the population

Figure 19-9. An aerial view of Victoria on the southeast coast of Vancouver Island, a city with a population of approximately 55,000. The capital of British Columbia, it is a trading center for lumber, canned salmon, grain, and coal, and has a variety of manufacturing enterprises. (British Columbia Government Photograph)

Figure 19-10. Portland, Oregon, is the leading United States dry cargo port on the Pacific Coast and a major ship repair center. About 100 miles inland, it is visited by approximately 1,700 vessels a year and handles about ten million tons of cargo. (Portland Public Docks)

has become concentrated in certain localities, especially west of the Cascade Range. With a few outstanding exceptions, such as Douglas County, Oregon, the greatest growth has occurred in the urban areas where people already were clustered.

POPULATION CENTERS

Portland. Portland, with a metropolitan population slightly in excess of 400,000, is Oregon's major city. Located on the Willamette River near its confluence with the Columbia, Portland serves the vast Columbia River Basin and is the gateway to its many vacation areas.

The city is a leading distribution center for the Pacific Northwest. From its location at the western gateway of the only water-level route through the Cascade Mountains, the entire area is easily accessible by rail and highway. River transportation is also available well into the hinterland.

Portland is one of the world's largest freshwater ports. It is 110 miles inland from the Pacific Ocean, up a channel with a minimum depth of 35 feet. The port has 27 miles of deepwater frontage and 29 marine terminals. Available are two 85-ton floating cranes, a 125-ton capacity stiff-leg stationary derrick, bulk handling equipment, and adequate cargo handling and storage facilities.

The city's manufacturing is greatly diversified. Lumber and other wood products manufacturing are the chief industries. Metals and machinery manufacturing have been expanding rapidly in the past decade. Food products, pulp, paper, woolen textiles, apparel, printing, furniture, and many other items are produced in Portland. Because low-cost power and other natural resources are available, the output of chemicals and electrometallurgical products has grown sharply. Many concerns with nationwide manufacturing and marketing organizations have branch manufacturing plants in Portland.

Seattle. Seattle is the largest city in Washington. The 1970 projected population for the Seattle metropolitan area is 1,018,000. Of this number 602,000 are expected to dwell within the city's incorporated limits.

Much of Seattle's municipal personality has been shaped by its remote location in the "upper left-hand corner of the nation." From Seat-

tle it is 1,800 miles across three mountain ranges and over the plains to Minneapolis. It is nearly 1,000 miles southward along the rugged seaboard to San Francisco.

From the start Seattle has handled the bulk of the commerce with Alaska. Big freighters and oil tankers load and discharge cargo in the burgeoning Alaskan trade that today amounts to over $150 million a year. Seattle has 193 miles of waterfront.

Seattle began as a lumber town. When the lumber industry slowed down for lack of logs, Columbia River hydroelectric power production brought into existence a new industry—aluminum. Now the 28,000 workers at the Boeing aircraft plant are largely dependent on this light metal in their work. Low-cost power also has encouraged many small iron and steel foundries in the city. Men who once were lumberjacks have learned to be metal workers, welders, and steamfitters.

Figure 19-11. The Lake Washington Floating Bridge is the eastern gateway to Seattle, the commercial center of Washington and a major port. (Seattle Chamber of Commerce)

Figure 19-12. Vancouver, British Columbia, with its excellent natural harbor and its situation as the terminus for transcontinental railroads, enjoys a strategic geographic position. (National Film Board)

Figure 19-13. An aerial view of downtown Tacoma, Washington, and Commencement Bay. The Port-Industrial District (right) has over 300 diversified industries. (Tacoma Chamber of Commerce)

Vancouver (390,325). Canada's third-largest city, and the largest city in British Columbia, Vancouver is the focal point of the Dominion's western expansion. In testimony to its extraordinary growth, Vancouver has risen from an obscure hamlet to become in 70 years the financial, shipping, and industrial hub of British Columbia. Greater Vancouver has a population of 600,000. It occupies a commanding position as a grain port, and its swelling tide of commercial and industrial activity point to an even greater future.

Tacoma, Washington (160,000). Tacoma is a deep-sea port on Commencement Bay, an arm of Puget Sound. Commencement Bay has a depth of water sufficient for vessels of any draft. Docking facilities have been and are being developed to take care of a large volume of domestic and foreign commerce.

Tacoma is an important center for the manufacture of wood products, principally wood pulp, paper and newsprint, furniture, doors, and plywood. It has a considerable flour milling industry, and its other manufactured products include: chemicals, machinery, hardware, food products, and clothing.

Nearby are Fort Lewis, McCord Air Force Base, an ordnance depot, and the Tacoma Naval Station.

Smaller centers. Smaller population centers include Bellingham, Washington, which is noted for shipbuilding, wood products, and cement; Bremerton, Washington, where the Puget Sound Naval Yard maintains repair facilities for large vessels; and Olympia, Washington, the state capital and a large brewing center, as well as the headquarters of a large wood products industry.

In Oregon, important smaller cities include the state capital, Salem, where there is considerable pulp and paper manufacturing. It is the second most important canning and food processing center in the United States. Over seven million cans of processed food leave Salem's ten plants annually. Eugene, the site of the University of Oregon, is a major sawmilling and pulp and plywood city and a transportation focal point. Springfield is the site of huge sawmills. Corvallis is the home of Oregon State University; Adair Air Force Base, one of Oregon's two major defense installations, is located nearby.

Part VII | BERING-ARCTIC BORDERLANDS

The Bering-Arctic Borderlands comprise the remotest section of Anglo-America. They are lands of extreme climates and sparse population. Great distances separate them from the more densely settled regions of Anglo-America. The Air Age has brought them into world prominence because of their strategic position in the North Polar region. Joint United States-Canadian defense operations have established radar networks and bases in the Far North. Other than military activities, however, a subsistence economy largely prevails.

20 | *Central and Northern Alaskan*

Mountains and Valleys

(*Relief map copyright Aero Service Corp.*)

THE Central and Northern Alaskan Mountains and Valleys Region includes central and northern Alaska, the northern part of the Yukon Territory of Canada, and that portion of the District of MacKenzie (Northwest Territories of Canada) west of the Peel River. It is divided into the Central Uplands Subregion and the Arctic Slope Subregion.

CENTRAL UPLANDS SUBREGION

SURFACE FEATURES

North of the crescent formed by the Alaska Range, and between it and the Brooks Range, lies the Central Uplands Subregion, a broad expanse of tablelands and lowlands dotted by mountain groups and drained by several large rivers, including the Yukon, Kuskokwim, Porcupine, Tanana, and Koyukuk. These rivers flow in wide valleys choked with sediments brought down from the higher lands north and south of the Uplands. The Uplands continue east into the Yukon Territory and west to the Bering Sea.

The principal interior valleys are those of the Yukon River and its tributaries. The Endicott Mountains, lying north of the Arctic Circle and sloping northward to the ocean and southward into the Koyukuk Valley, form the northern limits of the subregion, and between these mountains and the Alaska Range lies the drainage basin of the great Yukon River.

The Yukon River, rising within 25 miles of tidewater in southeastern Alaska and emptying into the Bering Sea after a 1,800-mile course, constitutes, with its tributaries, the fifth-largest river system in Anglo-America.[1] Its drainage basin has an area estimated at 330,000 square miles, over half of which is in Canada. Physical features of this basin are the Yukon Flats, on or near the Arctic Circle, and the coastal lowland and delta area, extending inland about 100 miles from the Bering Sea. The Tanana River Valley, with an area of about 24,000 square miles, lies to the north of the Alaska Range, the glaciers of which form the source of most of the southern tributaries of the river. Although the upper half of the valley is rough and broken, there is considerable level and

gently rolling country in the lower half, some of it well adapted to agriculture, particularly in the vicinity of Fairbanks.

CLIMATE AND VEGETATION

The Central Uplands Subregion has cold, dark winters, and summers with continuous daylight. January temperatures vary from 7° F. at Bethel near the coast to —29° at Bettles in the interior; the average is —10°. In the Yukon and Tanana Valleys temperatures range from an average of lower than —20° for January in the coldest parts to about 60° in July. A maximum of 91° and a minimum of —76° have been recorded at Tanana.

Precipitation is relatively light, averaging about 13 inches annually; it occurs principally during the summer. The forests are of black and white spruce, and the timber line is at 2,500 to 3,000 feet. Because of the severe climate and frozen soils, trees are small. Treeless tundra borders the Bering Sea.

ARCTIC SLOPE SUBREGION

SURFACE FEATURES

The land sloping from the northern foothills of the Brooks Range (including a small portion of the Northwest Territories west of the Peel River in Canada) to the Arctic Ocean is called the Arctic Slope. Some of the mountains are separated by wide valleys but in places the range is extremely rugged. A number of mountain groups are in the area—the De Long, the Schwatka, the Endicott, the Baird, and the Davidson. Tundra country, consisting of large areas of rolling uplands and coastal plains, stretches northward from the Brooks Range.

CLIMATE

The climate is cold and arid with only six to eight inches of precipitation annually, occurring in late summer and early fall. Barrow has a January average of —17° F. and a July average of 40.2°. Maximum and minimum recorded temperatures are 78° and —56°, respectively. Winters are long, dark, and bitterly cold; summers, though short and cool, have virtually continuous sunshine from May to August. There is a luxuriant growth of mosses, bright flowers, lichens, and grasses, even though

---

[1] The Missouri, Mississippi, Mackenzie, and St. Lawrence Rivers are longer.

Figure 20-1. Point Barrow, Alaska. For the most part, this is a treeless and barren wasteland. It is characterized by long, cold winters and very short, cool summers; as a result, it is virtually uninhabited. (Official U.S. Navy Photograph)

the soil cover. thaws to only a foot in depth. Timber is thin or nonexistent. Willows, some only a few inches high, are the predominant tree growth in the subregion.

AGRICULTURE

SETTLEMENT

In 1720, Vitus Bering, a Dane in the service of the Czar of Russia, sailed through what is now called Bering Strait to establish that the area now known as Alaska was part of the North American continent. In 1741, Bering made a landing off south-central Alaska. Russia claimed ownership of northwestern North America on the basis of these voyages. Soon after the second expedition, Russian fur traders advanced along the Aleutians. The United States purchased the area from Russia in 1867, but for many years there was no effort made to develop the country.

Although some farming had been practiced in Alaska for more than two-thirds of a century, the first great upsurge in modern farm settlement followed the gold rush at the turn of the century. Many adventurers found their mining claims unprofitable and turned to growing food for a living. A second increase in farm settlement accompanied railroad construction in the early 1920's. World War II and postwar defense expenditures paved the way for agricultural expansion within Alaska's economy. From 1942 through 1959, the farm value of agricultural production increased from a half-million dollars to approximately $3.5 million.

An estimated 41,603 tons of farm produce was harvested from 14,931 acres of cropland in Alaska in 1960. The output included 22,700 tons of silage from 5,100 acres; 7,900 tons of hay from 5,200 acres; 7,621 tons of vegetables, mostly potatoes, from 903 acres; and 3,382 tons of small grains, mostly oats and barley, from 3,728 acres. In 1960 there were 367 farms in Alaska, about half part-time farms.

There are certain factors that make agriculture difficult in the region: (1) No market. Alaska depends upon the other states for roughly 90 per cent of its food. Only a very few local specialty products—certain types of seeds, for example—might conceivably be sold outside Alaska. (2) Poor climate. Many crops cannot mature in a short growing season, even with the great advantage of long hours of summer sunshine. (3) The most important factor is the high cost of production, so great that even the high Alaska prices fail to give the farmer an attractive margin of profit. Land clearing is very difficult, farm machinery is expensive, large quantities of fertilizer generally are needed, and livestock require a great deal of purchased feed.

Although skillful farmers with adequate resources earn good incomes, statistics on average income are often depressed by a preponderance of records from underdeveloped places and from homesteads only a few years old. It must be borne in mind that the good earnings of Alaska's productive farms are sometimes overshadowed by the struggles of the homesteaders. Many farms pay poorly because of their extreme youth. For four out of five years new farms yield no income at all. For ten to 15 years their owners depend chiefly on off-farm income for both living and capital to clear land, buy machinery, and erect buildings.

THE TANANA VALLEY

Commercial agriculture in the Tanana Valley reached a peak in the 1920's, when 107 farmers were reported to have cropped 1,764 acres. At that time, railroad construction and gold mining created large temporary outlets for home-grown food. Fifteen years later not more than ten farmers remained.

World War II and a postwar construction boom brought new agricultural settlement, spearheaded by veterans and their families. About 30 of them reported growing and selling crops in 1949. Six years later well over 50 families grew food commercially. By 1954 Tanana Valley farmers received almost a half-million dollars for their products. Potatoes were the leading cash crop. Two commercial dairy farms and two poultry farms were important in the local farm economy. The Tanana Valley's chief markets are the city of Fairbanks and nearby military installations.

Although farm holdings were fairly large— 160 acres or more—the average commercial farmer had less than a quarter of his land available for growing crops. In no year did the average farm planting exceed 40 acres. On

Figure 20-2. A dairy farm near Fairbanks, Alaska. The rolling hills in the distance are typical of much of the Tanana Valley. (Division of Economic Tourist Development, Alaska)

every farm there were many acres of land suitable for cropping still not cleared. Farmers cleared about five acres per farm per year during the years between 1949 and 1954.

A local reason for idle cleared land is a soil condition known as permafrost (permanently frozen soil) that impedes vertical drainage. Many sites otherwise suitable for cropping are underlain by permafrost. When first cleared, these sites are too wet for cropping. Such fields are commonly allowed to remain unused for about five years—or until the soil dries out and warms up sufficiently to be worked. Because permafrost is rather widespread in the Tanana Valley, this practice is common and accounts for a large share of the fallow cleared land on farms in the area.

One of the most severe problems faced by farmers is the uneven thawing of cleared land, which results in a hummocky surface often too rough to permit economical operation of farm equipment. Before clearing, the natural vegetation acts as insulation to protect large subsurface blocks of nearly clear ice from melting. When the bare surface soil is exposed to the direct rays of the sun, it heats and eventually causes the chunks of ice to melt. If the ice is close to the surface, the soil above gradually sinks into the space formerly occupied by the ice as the ice melts. If the melting takes place a good distance below the surface, there may be a sudden collapse into a large cavity left by the melted ice.

The acreage devoted to potatoes remains fairly constant. Additional cleared acres are planted mostly to oats, barley, and green vegetables. A start toward dairying is seen in the use of some uncleared land for pasture.

Vegetable and potato yields vary considerably from year to year, chiefly because of climatic conditions. The frost-free period usually occurs between June 3 and August 26, a total of 84 days. The unusual length of the summer day compensates somewhat for the shortness of the growing season. Low areas are susceptible to frost in August. Spring droughts are often followed by rains in summer and during harvest. Scab, growth cracks, harvest injury, knobby tubers, and ring rot cut profits on many farms and contribute to risks facing unskilled growers.

Because the figures for average potato yields are weighted downward by low yields of many small farms, they fail to indicate the potential of the area. In 1953, for example, several farmers grew over 15 tons of potatoes per acre. A theoretical ceiling without supplemental irrigation is estimated at 18 tons per acre.

Building costs have posed special problems to Tanana Valley farmers, most of whom began on homesteads equipped only with a cabin. Lack of buildings kept many interested persons from establishing dairy farms. Water is scarce and well drilling is expensive. Domestic wells often freeze in winter and spring.

Most farmers are newcomers to the valley—nearly all are veterans of World War II and over half came to the valley after 1949. Building up family holdings are major goals of most of these farmers.

OTHER AREAS

Many farming areas of the Central and Northern Alaskan Mountains and Valleys Region can be reached only by air or water. Agricultural activity in these isolated places usually consists of home gardens, family cows or milk goats, small flocks of chickens, and crops such as tomatoes, cucumbers, and green vegetables, raised in small greenhouses for family consumption. Although not contributing a great deal to the economy of the region, domestic foodstuff plays an important role in the home life of families living in semi-isolation.

Agriculture is not, nor is it ever likely to be, of much importance in the economy of the region. As industry expands and attracts more people, however, farming will find further opportunity to grow and contribute its share to a rounded economy.

HUNTING AND TRAPPING

Before the white man first ventured into the Central and Northern Alaskan Mountains and Valleys Region, the primitive Eskimos and Indians of the interior relied almost exclusively upon hunting and trapping for their survival. The fur trade was the lure that encouraged the early explorations by white men. The fur trade, in turn, played an important role in the development of mineral resources, for many of the early gold strikes were made by trappers. When prospectors began to venture farther

Figure 20-3. A fish trap on the Yukon River at Marshall, Alaska. After the hole has been cut in the ice, care must be taken to see that it does not freeze over again. (P. D. Adams, U.S. Fish and Wildlife Service)

and farther into the unknown hinterland, it was the abundance of wildlife that permitted them to live off the land for months at a time. Large numbers of people, mostly Indians and Eskimos, still depend directly upon this resource for their physical and economic well-being. Fur-bearing animals are an important source of income. Mink; blue, red, and white fox; muskrat; beaver; marten; and lynx are the most important. In recent years the value of fur taken from the Tanana Valley alone has averaged around $400,000 annually.

Mink, wild or ranch-raised, is the most valuable of the land fur-bearing animals. Wild mink is distributed widely to the south of the Brooks Range. Approximately 40,000 pelts of this semiaquatic animal are exported annually. The decrease in the demand for fox fur has worked a hardship on the Eskimo population of the Arctic Coast.

At the present time, fur-bearing animals are being cropped as closely as appears consistent with the maintenance of a safe breeding stock. Trappers alternate their lines or limit their catches to keep fur species in relative abundance. In contrast to an earlier era of gross exploitation, the trappers of today tacitly accept conservation methods applied by the State Fish and Wildlife Service.

FUR SEALS

The Alaskan fur seal herd is national property, managed by the Fish and Wildlife Service of the U.S. Department of the Interior. It comprises 80 per cent of all the fur seals in the world. Each summer the herd returns from the open waters of the Pacific Ocean to breed on the Pribilof Islands. Since 1910, seal fur, and more recently seal meal and oil, have added over $19 million to the Federal treasury, of which $11.5 million was profit. This is an example of a resource depleted by imprudent hunting and restored through good management.

When the Pribilof Islands were discovered in 1787, the seal herd approached three million animals. The annual catch declined from 165,000 in 1868, to 13,000 in 1910, chiefly as a result of pelagic sealing—killing the seals at sea —which resulted not only in the death of the mother seals but also starvation of the pups. In order to re-establish the fur seal herd, the United States took over its management in 1910, and in 1911 the United States, Great Britain, Russia, and Japan signed an agreement known as the North Pacific Sealing Convention to outlaw pelagic sealing.

THE REINDEER INDUSTRY

Fringing the Arctic Ocean and the Bering

Sea in Alaska is a long strip of lowland country, a flat, monotonous coastal land of mud, sand, gravel, and sand dunes. With the Brooks Range and its northern piedmont, this lowland constitutes the great barrens of the tundra grasslands of the Arctic Slope Subregion.

Like the Yukon, the tundra grasslands are in a high latitude, and winters are correspondingly cold. This section is moderately mantled with snow that occurs only in winter. With the coming of spring, the warm temperatures melt the snow, driving it into the thousand little ponds and lakelets dotting the lowlands. The soil thaws and opens, and hundreds of flowering plants of the most brilliant colors spring into being in the long days. There are several hundred varieties of mosses and lichens. Flowering plants, however, not only outrank them in species but bury them in tonnage. For every ton of mosses and lichens there are ten tons of flowering plants with the advantage of

Figure 20-4. A seal rookery in the Pribilof Islands during the annual harem census. The larger seals are males. Note the groupings of females, each guarded by a bull seal. (V. B. Scheffer, U.S. Fish and Wildlife Service)

rapid recovery. Grasses and sedges grow anew each year, but certain lichens cropped by animals require many years to replace themselves.

Eskimos live in the tundra grasslands by hunting caribou, rabbit, and wild duck and by catching fish, seal, and walrus in the ocean. In winter the Eskimos live in semipermanent structures, using snow houses as base camps for hunting trips. In summer they dwell in portable tents made of skins.

Soon after the coming of the white man, the Eskimos of the tundra became skilled in shooting. It did not take long for the caribou and other native game to be reduced to such numbers that the Eskimos were forced to leave the interior and seek sustenance along the seacoast. Here they lived in "civilized" houses the white man taught them to build, and tried to operate in an alien economy. The Eskimo population dropped drastically, as starvation, cold, and disease took their toll.

The government, fearing the Eskimos might become extinct, brought 16 reindeer to Alaska from Lapland as the base for a future food supply. Later, 1,200 more reindeer were obtained. Today the Alaskan herds number 43,000, of which 15,000 are on Nunivak Island. Herds are increasing by about 3,000 animals a year.

No animal that man has domesticated within historic times is better adapted to his environment than is the reindeer. The reindeer is at home in a snowstorm, contentedly eats the food of his clime, and needs very little care—1,000 to 1,500 head are easily handled in one band. Their introduction has been the salvation of the Eskimos. As the earth's population continues to increase rapidly, reindeer meat from subpolar lands might offer a partial solution to the world's food problem. Scientific grazing, the feeding of hay and tame forage grasses grown in the Yukon Basin, and crossbreeding with the wild caribou are possible ways of improving this industry.

The musk ox, or ovibos, provides excellent meat. This beast, native to the region, is easily domesticated and has three advantages over the reindeer: It is larger, wolf-proof, and has wool that makes a fabric of the softness of cashmere. Like the reindeer, it is a complete factory for the Eskimo, furnishing meat, hide, milk, and power. It not only pulls a load, but

Figure 20-5. A male reindeer in Alaska. (V. B. Scheffer, U.S. Fish and Wildlife Service)

also can carry a pack. It is aptly called "the camel of the frozen desert."

FORESTRY

Forests occupy the greater part of the Central Uplands Subregion, chiefly the bottom lands and lower slopes of the Yukon, Tanana, Kuskokwim, and Copper Rivers. These forests of the interior have frequently been belittled as slow-growing, stunted stands of little value. This opinion has no basis in fact; to a large measure, it has hindered the proper development and protection of this important resource. Although the forests of the interior do not compare in commercial importance with those of the coastal area, they are of great local value as a present and future source of forest products, as a habitat for wildlife, and as an attraction for tourists.

These forests, the westward extension of the sub-Arctic type of northern Canada, are found in extensive stands on the low valley bench lands and in narrow belts along most of the stream courses. They are moderately to heavily interspersed with wet muskeg areas, lakes, and ponds. The timber line generally lies between 1,500 and 2,000 feet, but in some places it rises to 3,000 feet or falls to less than 600 feet.

Although most of the country has never been mapped nor the forests accurately inventoried, the Bureau of Land Management estimates that there are 125 million acres of public domain bearing tree growth, of which possibly 40 million acres bear trees of sufficient size and quality and in sufficient quantity to justify their classification as commercial forests. The 85 million acres of noncommercial forests are found at the limits of tree growth and on the upper bench lands, on poorly-drained soils, and in severely burned areas. In certain areas, the topography is such as to permit extensive stands to occur; typically, however, the stands are narrow belts tracing the courses of rivers.

The forests of the interior are composed of white spruce, white birch, cottonwood, black spruce, aspen, and tamarack. The most typical stand, commercial or noncommercial, is a mixture of white spruce and white birch.

Presently, there are about 80 sawmills operating in the interior, but many run only a few days a year to satisfy local demand. The heaviest concentration of sawmills is in the Fairbanks area, where population and market are greatest. The extensive logging of the past 50 years, combined with the deep inroads made by forest fires during the same period, has seriously depleted the more easily accessible stands of merchantable timber in this area. Loggers must now go farther afield—away from the roads and at greater cost to themselves—in order to obtain satisfactory timber.

It is doubtful if the forests of the interior, even when fully developed, could ever become as important commercially as the forests of southeastern Alaska. They represent, however, a resource that, if properly protected and developed, could eventually become an integral part of the area's economy. These forests, whether commercial or noncommercial, will continue to be of considerable local value as sources of fuel wood, building materials, and miscellaneous forest products for prospectors, trappers, homesteaders, and itinerants.

MINERAL RESOURCES

Throughout Alaska's history high costs have limited the types of mining and volume of mineral output. Since World War II, production costs have risen continuously. Labor is exceedingly scarce, wage scales are greatly inflated, supplies and equipment are costly and difficult to obtain, and taxes are high. Furthermore, in the case of gold, the chief mineral produced in the Central and Northern Alaskan Mountains and Valleys Region, the price has not been increased since 1932 when the government fixed it at $35 an ounce. The inevitable result of these conditions has been a severe restriction on gold mining and a corresponding avoidance of other marginal mining activities.

There are some bright spots, however. The demand for various strategic minerals has created new interest in the exploration and development of many mining operations heretofore considered uneconomic. The growing population of the region has increased the demand for local coal. Intensive construction activity has produced new markets for local sand, gravel, limestone, gypsum, and many other ingredients for building materials. An improved transportation network has opened to the prospector and miner new and once inaccessible areas. Research, field studies, mapping, mineral investigations, and financial assistance have been stepped up by government agencies. Interest is being shown in providing tax incentives for new mining ventures and a prospectors' aid program has been proposed for Alaska. It is not unlikely that in future years the mining industry may far surpass all previous mineral development in type, volume, and diversity of production.

GOLD

Gold continues to be the mineral with the greatest value by output in Alaska, despite a production decline of more than 300 per cent since 1940. In that year there were 672 active gold mines employing 6,162 men. Today, less than 200 mines are in operation, yielding approximately $7 million annually.

The two major types of gold mining in the region are lode, or quartz, which is the mining of mineralized veins, and placer mining, which is the recovery of gold deposited along the courses of streams. Although some gold lodes have been under production, only the gold placers have been worked extensively. In fact, over half of the gold mined in Alaska has come from the placer seams of the Central Uplands Subregion, principally in the Yukon-Tanana area near Fairbanks.

The largest and most productive gold mining operation in Alaska today is conducted by the United States Smelting and Refining Company near Fairbanks. The company has six

Figure 20-6. Gold dredging near Fairbanks, Alaska. Giant dredges work their way upstream scooping up gravel, extracting the gold, and depositing the tailings on the banks. (Division of Economic and Tourist Development, Alaska)

dredges working the placers within a 30-mile radius of the city, employing about 500 men at the peak of the season. The company also operates three dredges in the vicinity of Nome, which ranks second to the Fairbanks area as a gold producer.

Large companies produce most of the gold of the region, but many individuals and groups still derive their livelihood from gold mining. Numerous small placer operations are found in almost every mining district.

COAL

Coal mining is rapidly becoming one of the important elements of the mining industry in Alaska. In the last decade, military and civilian requirements for coal as a fuel for heating and for the generation of electricity have greatly expanded the market for locally produced coal. About one million tons are mined annually.

Although coal beds are present in many parts of the region, mines of more than local importance are to be found only in the Nenana coal field, about 75 miles southwest of Fairbanks.

The Nenana coal field is located in a tract about 20 miles wide and about 30 miles in length extending from the Toklat River eastward to the Delta River. It contains high-grade lignite and subbituminous coal beds that range in thickness from six feet to more than 50 feet. The Geological Survey estimates known reserves at 850 million tons and "inferred" reserves at an additional 215 million tons.

OIL AND GAS

Alaska's population annually consumes some ten million barrels of oil and, since there are no refineries in the state, all petroleum products must be shipped from West Coast refineries at considerable cost. No natural gas is in commercial use.

Petroleum and natural gas deposits have been known to exist in Alaska for over a century. Their remote location from the rest of the United States, however, has prevented any large-scale exploitation to date. Within the past few years, however, there has been a great revival of interest in Alaskan petroleum and gas development. Several large companies and many smaller local companies have made explorations in what are believed to be likely areas.

Available data on several potential areas indicate prospects for discovery of petroleum and natural gas in commercial quantities and

Figure 20-7. A typical section of the Alaskan Highway; a railroad runs on the opposite side of the river. (Division of Economic and Tourist Development, Alaska)

Figure 20-8. The University of Alaska, Anglo-America's most northerly seat of learning, is in a spruce and birch forest at College, Alaska, near Fairbanks. (University of Alaska)

have provided the incentive for the recent extensive investigations. The Arctic Slope Subregion is the area of greatest potential.

The petroleum industry now has an investment of $63 million in physical assets in Alaska; daily oil production in 1961 amounted to 6,700 barrels.

TIN

Tin is found in placer deposits in many locations throughout the region. The area of most importance, however, is the Seward Peninsula in western Alaska. Lode tin deposits also are common. However, because of economic conditions, all placer tin mining has been at a standstill since 1953. The only significant lode operation that ever existed under United States jurisdiction was forced to close late in 1955. This was the United States Tin Corporation mine at Lost River, 90 miles northwest of Nome. The mine came into being with government help in 1952 and produced steadily through 1954 and most of 1955. It produced 321 tons of tin concentrates in 1954, and 173 in 1955. Something of a test case, if the mine could have been operated until its problems were ironed out, sufficient knowledge might have been acquired on lode tin mining in this difficult area to make possible the mining of some of the other tin lodes in the district.

OTHER MINERALS

Many other minerals of value have been found within a 200-mile radius of Fairbanks. Although none is being mined successfully at present, some may well prove to be commercially exploitable at a later date when marketing conditions are more favorable, when greater accessibility is possible, and when more prospecting and exploration are completed. Among the minerals reported are chromium, platinum, mercury, nickel, molybdenum, asbestos, mica, jade, and various construction materials, such as clay, limestone, gypsum, sand, and gravel, which are being utilized extensively in new construction projects. Uranium also has been found in several localities, but no deposits of commercial grade have been located.

POPULATION

Most of Alaska's 224,386 people live in or near her four major cities—Anchorage, Fairbanks, Ketchikan, and Juneau. Only Fairbanks lies within the Central and Northern Alaskan Mountains and Valleys Region. It has a population of 12,000 within its city limits, a suburban population of 18,000, and an Air Force population of 7,720—an area total of 37,720. Projected city population for the year 1968 is 20,400.

21 | *Canadian Arctic Lowlands and Plains*

(Relief map copyright Aero Service Corp.)

THE Canadian Arctic Lowlands and Plains Region occupies approximately 40 per cent of the surface of Canada. It includes all of the Northwest Territories east of and including the Mackenzie-Liard Lowlands, the northeastern tip of Alberta, the northern thirds of Saskatchewan and Manitoba, and the western shield of Quebec. By far the largest portion of the region is the Northwest Territories. This section will be discussed in detail.

THE NORTHWEST TERRITORIES

The Northwest Territories is made up of portions of four of the six physiographic provinces into which Canada falls on the basis of topography. The islands to the north form the Arctic Archipelago. On the west the Mackenzie Mountains form the northeastern portion of the Great Cordilleran area that makes up most of the Yukon. The belt bordering the Mackenzie River is the northern prolongation of the interior plains of central Canada. East of the belt and extending over to Hudson Bay is a broad zone that forms part of the Canadian Shield. The rocks of which it is comprised are Pre-Cambrian. In places, particularly along the Arctic Coast on the border of the shield, considerable areas of the Pre-Cambrian rock are concealed by a capping of younger sediments.

SURFACE FEATURES

Canadian Shield. The Canadian Shield portion of the Northwest Territories is an area of comparatively low relief, rising gradually from the Arctic Ocean on the north and from Hudson Bay on the east to elevations of about 1,500 feet in its central part east of Great Bear and Great Slave Lakes. In detail, the topography is hummocky, consisting of ridges and hills separated by depressions commonly occupied by lakes or muskegs. The hundreds of lakes are of many sizes and shapes with very irregular shorelines and numerous islands. Over wide areas the land only here and there rises as much as 100 feet above the level of the immediately adjacent lakes. In other places differences in local relief amount to more than 1,000 feet. The lakes owe their origin to the work of the continental ice sheet that spread over the region during the Pleistocene period.

The low relief was produced by continuous erosion in late Pre-Cambrian time, action that eventually leveled the mountain belts that had been produced earlier by folding.

The last great event in the geological history of the area was the spread of a continental ice mass in Pleistocene times. This had its focal point west of Hudson Bay, from which center it advanced in all directions. Erratics and morainal material left by the ice are scattered over the entire area.

The Interior Plains. The Mackenzie Lowland includes the belt between the Cordilleran area on the west and the Canadian Shield on the east. It begins on the Slave River, embraces the basin at the west end of Great Slave Lake, and continues down to the Arctic Coast. On the Slave River its elevation is about 700 feet, and from there northward the surface slopes gradually to the Arctic. North of the Nahanni River, the Mackenzie Lowland is divided into two parts by the long, narrow ridge of the Franklin Mountains—a western portion varying in width from 20 to 80 miles through which the Mackenzie flows, and an eastern portion occupying all but the eastern part of the drainage basin of Great Bear Lake. The highest summit is Mt. Clark in the Franklin Range, with an elevation of between 3,000 and 4,000 feet.

Arctic Archipelago. Comparatively little is known of the landforms and geology of the Arctic Archipelago. Available information suggests that, like the mainland part of the Northwest Territories, a threefold division into Shield, Plains, and Mountains is warranted. Thus, the southeastern islands are composed chiefly of hard crystalline rocks of Pre-Cambrian age. Proceeding northwesterly, these become overlain by nearly flat Paleozoic sandstones and limestones, with successively younger strata, including carboniferous coal seams, appearing at the surface, generally similar in age and structure to the rocks of the Interior Plains. In the extreme northwestern part of the Archipelago, observations in a few widely separated districts suggest the existence of a mountain range consisting largely of even younger, folded Mesozoic rocks extending southwesterly for nearly 1,000 miles from northern Ellesmere Island through the Sverdrup group.

Figure 21-1. The Canadian Shield area in the vicinity of Indian House Lake, Quebec. Scattered lakes, clumps of trees, muskegs, erratics, and morainal material are characteristic features. (Geographical Branch, Canadian Department of Mines and Technical Surveys)

Figure 21-2. An aerial view of the Peace River country. Note the flatness of the landscape and the abundance of coniferous trees. (National Film Board)

CLIMATE

The climate of the Northwest Territories is what might be expected in Arctic and sub-Arctic regions, with the exception that temperatures in the MacKenzie District are more moderate than its latitude would suggest. Charts of summer temperatures show the 55° isotherm, which passes just a few miles north of Port Arthur, Ontario, as swinging northward to include the Mackenzie Valley as far as Fort Good Hope and the Arctic Circle. The low-lying parts of the area forming the Mackenzie Valley proper are favored with an exceptionally agreeable climate, doubtless influenced by the presence of large bodies of water, the forest covering the land areas, and the general low altitude. A three-month period of daylight is experienced in all parts of the MacKenzie District—the twilight continuing throughout the short time the sun is below the horizon—and north of the Arctic Circle the midnight sun is a feature of note. At Fort Simpson, the average possible number of hours of sunshine daily during the summer season is nearly 18. Because of these favorable conditions, many gardens are cultivated in the district at missions, Indian agencies, and trading posts.

Precipitation in most parts of the Northwest Territories is normally under ten inches a year, except in the Mackenzie Valley west of Great Slave and Great Bear Lakes, where it varies from ten to 20 inches. Moisture is retained longer than in southerly regions, for low temperatures reduce the amount of evaporation and the permanently frozen subsoil prevents underground drainage.

There is a marked distinction between the climates of the eastern and western Arctic regions of Canada, a distinction most clearly manifested in July. Along the Arctic Circle the average temperature in July ranges from about 42° F. in southern Baffin Island to about 60° in the northern Mackenzie Valley. On the lower portion of Ellesmere Island and throughout the Parry Islands the average temperature is less than 40°. If the isotherm of 50° in July is taken as the criterion of a northern summer, then there is no summer north and east of a line that begins on the Labrador Coast, touches the southern end of Ungava Bay, and passes across Hudson Bay from the Belcher Islands to Eskimo Point, then northwestward to the mouth of the Coppermine River and along the Arctic Coast to the mouth of the Mackenzie River.

In midwinter all the Arctic territory is subject to periods of great cold, and these periods are associated with the slow outflow of probably shallow but extremely dry and cold domes of surface air from the area west of the Parry Islands and Victoria Island. These masses move up the Mackenzie Valley to spread out over the Canadian prairies before showing much tendency to drift eastward. As the year advances, the eastward component of motion becomes much more important than the southward component, so that in midsummer the eastern Arctic continues to be dominated by wintry conditions, while the western Arctic is increasingly influenced by air masses modified over Alaska and the North Pacific. In fact, air masses that have been recently modified in more southerly latitudes of the continent frequently affect the weather of the western Arctic. As a consequence, the highest temperature in Baffin Island averages about 65°, while on the Arctic Circle in the Mackenzie Valley it is 85° or higher.

THE NATIVE POPULATION

Indians. Most of the 4,000 Indians in the Northwest Territories live in the valley of the Mackenzie River. The principal tribes are the Chipewyan, Beaver, Sekani, Slave, Yellow-knife, Dogrib, Hare, Nahani, and Kutchin or Loucheux.

Intertribal raids among the Indians came to an end about a century ago, and they began to congregate about the posts and settlements of the fur traders who tried, not very successfully, to elevate as chiefs the most influential and reliable hunters and to give them a limited authority over their own countrymen. Missionaries have been very active and, in consequence, the Indians in the Territories now adhere to Christianity, though they may still harbor many of their old beliefs. In recent years, exploration, settlement, and mining activities have led to a demand for Indian guides, canoe men, and packers, and have resulted in increasing the Indians' dependence on flour, beans, bacon, and other imported food supplies. From the earliest times, too, many white traders and trappers have taken Indian women as wives, and more or less consciously have modified the whole outlook and manners of the tribes among whom they have resided. So extensive, indeed, has been this intermarriage that today in the whole area there are probably few Indians of pure stock.

Through most of the 19th century, social and economic changes threatened to bring about the extinction of the Indians. Alcoholic excesses and diseases previously unknown, particularly smallpox, tuberculosis, and influenza, reduced their number from what was estimated

Figure 21-3. Wrigley, a settlement on the Mackenzie River in the Northwest Territories of Canada, is located in a typical plains area, with forest vegetation. (National Film Board)

Figure 21-4. The settlement at Grise Fiord on the south coast of Ellesmere Island, a predominantly mountainous island. (Northern Affairs Photograph)

by some authorities to be 13,000 to one-third of that total. Nevertheless, the outlook for the future is promising. It is confidently felt that increasing settlement and a great development of the resources of the Territories will open up new avenues of employment for the Indians, lower their heavy infant mortality rate, and, through a general improvement in living conditions, arouse in them new vigor and new ambitions.

Eskimos. Eskimos inhabit the entire Arctic Coast of Canada from the Yukon-Alaska boundary to the eastern limits of Canadian territory, the more southerly islands of the Arctic Archipelago, and some of the islands of Hudson Bay and James Bay. About 5,400 Eskimos are in the Northwest Territories, and most of these live in the Franklin and Keewatin Districts. There are also about 1,800 Eskimos in northern Quebec, formerly the Ungava District of the Northwest Territories.

There are no Eskimo tribes; the term "tribe" is associated with North American Indians. The Eskimos of the eastern Arctic live and travel in bands or groups of two or more families, and each band or group usually contains some outstanding individual who acts as leader.

Contact between the bands is limited mainly to communication with those hunting or trapping in adjoining areas. Each band secures its livelihood in its own district, which has no definite boundaries. Bands move about to match the movement of game and the changing seasons. In bad seasons it may become necessary to look for new hunting grounds, but Eskimos are very likely to return to the old district when they think conditions have improved. The hunting and trapping grounds of eastern Arctic Eskimos are along the coast, the sea furnishing the greater part of their requirements for food, fuel, and clothing.

The Eskimo of the eastern Arctic lives in a snowhouse, or igloo, in winter and a tent in summer. Sealskin, canvas, sacking, pieces of board, stone, and even glazed glass may be used to make up the tents or houses.

Travel in summer is by boat; in winter, by dog sled. The usual type of cruising boat is the open whaleboat to which a sail is attached. Other types are also brought in on order by the trading companies and are equipped, when the owners can afford it, with gasoline engines. Eskimos are mechanically inclined and with a little coaching quickly learn to operate and keep in repair complicated marine engines. They know thoroughly the districts in which they hunt and trap, and the actions of the tides, currents, and ice; they frequently go out to sea under conditions that would keep other men ashore. The smaller, one-man kayak is still used extensively by the Eskimos and is probably the outstanding article of equipment made by these remarkable people.

Coastal Eskimos of the western Arctic move out on the ice to sealing grounds, where many of them live in igloos. These sealing camps may be from five to 20 miles out on the ice and are frequently used as bases for trapping operations. In summer those who own whaleboats go to the whaling grounds where they fish for white whale. A successful whaling season means prosperity for all. The flesh of the white whale is used for both human consumption and for dog food. Oil extracted from the blubber is stored in barrels or sealskin bags for use as part of every meal in the winter. Those who have no whaleboats live in tents in summer and do their fishing and whaling from the shore.

For generations Eskimos of the Canadian Northland have wrested a living, mated, and reared families in a country where only a hardy and intelligent race could survive. They are slowly assimilating a certain amount of civilization while still retaining their independence, pride, and ability to care for themselves.

Figure 21-5. A dog team and sled in northern Manitoba. This is still the only dependable form of surface transportation in the Canadian Arctic during the winter season. (R. Harrington, Hudson's Bay Co.)

Figure 21-6. *Indian trappers from the MacKenzie District return home on snowshoes with the animals that were caught in their traps. (National Film Board)*

THE FUR TRADE

The fur trade in the Northwest Territories had its beginning in the latter part of the 17th century when the Hudson's Bay Company received its charter. From then until 1939, when the value of fur production was exceeded by that of minerals, fur trading was the most important industry in the Northwest Territories. The trapping of fine furs is still, and is likely to remain, the chief occupation of most of the native population. Trading posts are scattered throughout the region, whose history is intimately associated with that of the fur trade.

From the viewpoint of value, white fox pelts are far in the lead in the Northwest Territories. Chief among the other furs of economic importance are the red fox, in its three color phases—red, cross, and silver—and beaver, lynx, mink, marten, and muskrat. Smaller numbers of ermine, otter, wolf, wolverine, bear, and others are obtained also. Their combined value exceeds $2 million annually.

REINDEER

The delivery in 1935 of a herd of semidomesticated reindeer from northwestern Alaska to the Northwest Territories introduced an industry designed to broaden the basis of subsistence of the native population by augmenting the wildlife resources on which it depends. Since the inception of the industry there has been a steady growth in the number of animals. About 5,600 form the main herd on the reserve along the Arctic Coast east of the Mackenzie Delta; the remainder are in two herds under native management, near the Anderson and Horton Rivers, east of the reserve.

In the spring, reindeer migrate from the inland winter ranges to summer feeding grounds in the coast area; they return to the inland ranges in early winter. The winter feed is principally reindeer moss, but in summer the diet includes a variety of vegetation—grasses, shrubs, sedges, and the like. One of the reasons that the reindeer seek the coast in the summer is to escape from inland insect pests, which are restricted to some extent on the coast by the winds from the Arctic Ocean.

Reindeer are a convenient and dependable source of food and clothing and form a valuable reserve against periods of shortage in other necessaries. As natives learn to depend more and more on reindeer herds for subsistence they will become independent of fluctuations in the game supply and fur prices, and eventually achieve a more stable economic life than is possible under the ordinary conditions of nomadic life.

MINING

The occurrence of potentially valuable minerals in the Northwest Territories was first reported more than 350 years ago, but most of the present knowledge of the mineral possibilities of the region has been acquired since 1920. In that year, oil was obtained from two wells drilled about 48 miles north of Fort Norman, but because there was no market for the oil, the wells remained capped for several years. Norman Wells did not become an important petroleum producer until World War II, when a pipeline was completed to carry crude oil to Whitehorse. The Canadian Northland currently uses more than one million barrels of oil a year. Norman Wells supplies 420,000 barrels of this in the northwest and could supply more. The refinery capacity is 1,350 barrels a day.

Interest in the mineral possibilities of the Northwest Territories can be attributed mainly to the discovery of radium-bearing ores and silver ores at Echo Bay on the east side of Great Bear Lake in 1930. The spectacular nature of the discovery; the idea that a Canadian source of supply of radium—one of the rarest of all elements—had been found; and the likelihood that a marked reduction in the price of radium eventually would follow, inspired wide interest in the discovery.

This interest has continued, intensified by the discovery of gold at Yellowknife in 1935, with the result that more knowledge of mineral possibilities has been gained within the past 25 years than in the previous century. To date, this knowledge is confined largely to a relatively narrow strip of country forming part of the western fringe of the Canadian Shield between Great Slave and Great Bear Lakes. Comparatively little is yet known, except in a general way, of the mineral possibilities of the country lying west, north, and east of this belt.

Copper, nickel, lead, and zinc have already been spotted in several areas. Uranium, platinum, cobalt, and tungsten also exist, along with deposits of tantalum, columbium, and beryllium. Claims have been staked for lithium—a possible source of fuel for jet aircraft, guided missiles, and rockets. Iron has been discovered, too, though not in the quantities found in Labrador.

Figure 21-7. The Consolidated Mining and Smelting Company's gold mine at Yellowknife, Northwest Territories. In operation since 1938, the mine presently employs 250 people. (Consolidated Mining and Smelting Co.)

Figure 21-8. Spring thaw on Great Slave Lake. Navigation is possible for about four months of the year, during which time many supplies are brought to the Yellowknife area by barge. (National Film Board)

There is silver and cobalt near Great Bear Lake, copper and nickel along the Coppermine River (and a producing nickel mine far above the tree line at Rankin Inlet), coal on the Mackenzie, and gypsum in huge quantities in the Arctic Archipelago. Geologists believe there is oil in the Arctic Islands and the Mackenzie River Delta.

A lead and zinc deposit at Pine Point, on the south shore of Great Slave Lake, is rated among the largest in North America; a conservative estimate places its recoverable reserves at 60 million tons of ore. But Pine Point, like many other big mineral deposits in the Northwest Territories, suffers from lack of good transportation to haul its ores to market.

Canada is being urged to build a line to link Pine Point with the present railhead at Grimshaw, Alberta, 400 miles away. Cost of the project is put at $50 million.

Manpower and capital are moving into this area. Bush planes—light aircraft equipped with pontoons in summer and skis in winter—take off from Yellowknife at all hours of the day, carrying prospectors, geologists, and mining company officials to mineral fields.

All this activity is aimed at getting in on the ground floor of a mineral boom. The search is reaching even above the Arctic Circle. One company has agreed to spend $900,000 in the next four years in return for exclusive prospecting rights to a copper deposit near the Arctic Ocean. Canada has recently carried out its first geological survey of the Arctic Islands.

Prospecting is carried on mostly by large companies, for only they can afford to spend large sums to locate ore deposits that cannot be put into production immediately. Gold and uranium are the chief metals mined at this time in the Northwest Territories. In the Yellowknife area, three lode gold mines are in operation. In the case of uranium, the demand has been sufficient to offset the high cost of shipping ore concentrates out by plane and by river barge. One mine is in production at Port Radium, on the east shore of Great Bear Lake, only 21 miles south of the Arctic Circle; another is at Yellowknife. A mine at Rankin Inlet on Hudson Bay, just above the 62nd parallel, contains nickel, copper, and platinoids; it began operations in the spring of 1957 and ships its concentrates by sea through Hudson Strait to the North Atlantic.

The rest of the landlocked riches of the Northwest Territories must await the arrival of railways and roads. With the rising demand for metals in Canada, the United States, and the rest of the world, these riches will not stand idle for long.

MINING OUTSIDE THE NORTHWEST TERRITORIES

The northern portions of Alberta, Manitoba, Saskatchewan, and Ontario and western Quebec lie within the southern portion of the Canadian Arctic Lowlands and Plains Region.

Northern Alberta. This area contains a vast expanse of sand saturated with oil. Rough estimates are that this deposit, called the Athabasca oil sands, holds 100 to 300 billion barrels of oil. The sands run 13 to 16 per cent oil by weight. They are found on or near the surface along the Athabasca River, from the town of Fort McMurray, which is close to railhead, to a point about 70 miles north. They also occur on tributary streams. Geologists estimate that the sands are 2,000 to 10,000 square miles in extent.

There has been no commercial production at the Athabasca sands to date, but the situation is changing. Oil experts claim that oil could be extracted from the sands and piped to Lake Superior at a cost of $3.10 a barrel— 40 cents per barrel under the present market price.

Northern Manitoba. This section is an important mining frontier that is developing rapidly because it has a modern transportation network. There is a railroad to the mining town of Flin Flon; a branch 155 miles long was pushed to Lynn Lake in 1953 at a cost of $15 million. Roads, too, have been built. In Flin Flon itself, a large mine operated by the Hudson Bay Mining and Smelting Company produces copper, zinc, and cadmium.

Farther north, at Lynn Lake, Sherritt Gordon Mines, Ltd., is producing nickel, copper, and cobalt. East of Flin Flon, at Mystery and Moak Lakes, the International Nickel Company is developing a nickel deposit that may

Figure 21-9. Tar sands in the Athabasca River. The province of Alberta has established an experimental refinery at Bitumount on the Athabasca River to determine the feasibility of extracting oil from the tar sands of the area. (National Film Board)

Figure 21-10. Flin Flon, Manitoba. The Canadian National Railroad built a line 87 miles long from The Pas to Flin Flon in 1928 to open the area to mining operations. A hydroelectric plant at Island Falls, Saskatchewan, on the Churchill River, supplies power for the zinc recovery plant and the copper smelter in Flin Flon. (Hudson Bay Mining and Smelting Co., Ltd.)

prove to be second only to the Sudbury district of Ontario.

Northern Saskatchewan. Uranium development has transformed Saskatchewan's north, for there the uranium industry straddles one million acres of ancient rock formations in the Beaverlodge Lake area, 500 miles by air from Prince Albert. Little more than a decade ago, this was a forgotton frontier, populated by a handful of trappers and casually explored by a few prospectors. Indians fished its waters and hunted its caribou. It was the place of lonely outposts and the site of an abandoned gold mine; communications were sparse and transportation uncertain.

Today more than 75 mining companies have uranium properties at Beaverlodge. Six companies are producing uranium and others are rapidly approaching the production stage. Capital expenditure today is nearing $100 million. Production value of the radioactive mineral averages about $15 million annually. With a greatly expanded milling capacity in prospect, this value may be doubled or even tripled within the next few years.

Northern Ontario and western Quebec. These areas are extensively developed for their minerals and were the first of the shield areas so developed. Much of the capital that went into the mining enterprises of the Northwest Territories came from these older areas. Ontario has been the main gold producer in Canada for years. The largest share of gold has been mined from the Kirkland Lake field, which extends across the boundary through Noranda and Val d'Or in Quebec. Copper, silver, cobalt, iron, nickel, and platinum also are mined on a large scale.

Ontario produces all of Canada's magnesium, calcium, platinum, and tellurium, most of the cobalt, over 90 per cent of the nickel, 55 per cent of the gold, and 45 per cent of the copper.

FORESTS

There is no forest industry in the usual sense of the term in the Northwest Territories, nor is there any prospect of such an industry developing on a considerable scale. The principal tree species are aspen and balsam,poplar, white and black spruce, white birch, tamarack, and jack pine. The eastern part of the Northwest Territories is almost devoid of forests, but in the MacKenzie District there are several areas of forested land, varying in nature from scattered clumps of stunted conifers and birches near the northern limits of tree growth, to fairly heavy stands of poplar and spruce in the vicinity of the larger rivers. These forests are of value chiefly as a source of building materials and fuel for the local population and as a favorable environment for fur-bearing and game animals.

Because of the high cost of transportation, most of the lumber used is of local manufacture. Small sawmills, usually equipped with planing machines, are operated at various points on the Slave River, Great Slave Lake, and the Mackenzie River. Most of the lumber sawed is white spruce; the wood of this species is used for all parts of buildings. It is also in demand for boat building and for almost every other lumber use.

The natives use white birch for snowshoe frames and for framing canoes; its bark has been largely superseded by canvas for canoe covering. Black spruce is occasionally sawed in small quantities, and it and jack pine are used in the construction of log cabins. Poplars are cut mainly for fuel.

The notable development of the mining industry during recent years has created new demands for building material and firewood in the vicinity of the mines. Unfortunately, the increase in prospecting has greatly increased the danger of forest fires.

All forested lands within the Northwest Ter-

ritories are included in four subdivisions of the Boreal forest region. Two of these, the mixed wood and northern coniferous sections, are represented by relatively small areas adjacent to the boundaries of Alberta and western Saskatchewan, the other two sections are the Mackenzie Lowlands and northern transition sections.

The mixed wood section, a small area along the Alberta boundary south of the west end of Great Slave Lake and the Mackenzie River, is believed to afford the best growing conditions for forest trees in the Northwest Territories. Soils are of glacial origin, of considerable depth, and usually well drained. Aspen and spruce are the typical trees, and these are accompanied by all the other species found in the region.

The northern coniferous section occupies a small triangle with its base on the northern Alberta boundary and lying immediately east of Fort Smith. Here soils are shallow and drainage is poor. Black spruce predominates. It is sometimes found in mixture with jack pine, and with tamarack in the lower and wetter areas.

The Mackenzie Lowlands section is the most important forest area of the Northwest Territories. The soil is of glacial, alluvial, and lacustrine origin and is generally of good depth.

Figure 21-11. A base for chartered seaplanes at Martin Lake, near Uranium City, Saskatchewan. Small aircraft provide the only link with the outside world in much of this area. (National Film Board)

Although the subsoil is never free from frost, trees grow to a fairly good size. White spruce, poplars, and birch are all well represented; black spruce and tamarack occupy the swamps; jack pine is found in the sandy areas.

The northern transition section lies north and east of a line passing through the mouth of the Mackenzie River to Great Bear and Great Slave Lakes. Unfavorable climatic conditions, together with thin soils and poor drainage, restrict the stunted tree growth to the most favorable areas in the valleys and along streams.

FISHING

Fish of several varieties are abundant in many parts of the Northwest Territories. For the most part, however, it has not been considered commercially feasible to export them because of the great distances from large markets. As a result of peculiar water conditions and of a deficiency of fish food, the main portion of Hudson Bay is not very favorable to fish, and it is questionable whether over a period of several years the coastal rivers and shore fisheries can do much more than support the needs of the local population.

In 1931, the Canadian Department of Fisheries made a study of the deep-sea fisheries of the bay, using steam trawlers and drag nets; but after three weeks of effort, during which more than 200 miles of sea bottom were covered, no commercial fish were taken. During the same season, the Department of Fisheries investigated the coastal fisheries north of Churchill. Competent fishermen, using nets, covered the area, but obtained only about 6,000 pounds of fish during the summer and autumn seasons. The chief varieties taken were char and ciscoes.

Arctic char, also called sea trout or salmon, are perhaps the most important food fish of the Arctic Region. Occurring in great numbers in certain seasons of the year, they are found in both fresh and salt water, chiefly near the mouths of the rivers in the latter case. They are plentiful in portions of the eastern Arctic and Baffin Island, in the rivers of Melville Peninsula, and in the Frobisher Bay area. They also frequent the northern parts of Hudson Bay and the coastal waters of the northwestern mainland of the Northwest Territories.

Cisco, or lake, herring are found in the brackish portions of Hudson and James Bays and also along the Arctic Coast and in the Arctic Red River, where they are abundant in the spawning season in September.

Whitefish of one or more species are found in almost every lake or stream of the mainland. Many of the early explorers depended on whitefish for food to a large extent, and they still play an important part in the food economy of sparsely settled sections.

AGRICULTURE

Farming is of little importance at present in the Northwest Territories, except for local requirements. In the other parts of Canada, however, notably in the southern part of the Canadian Arctic Lowlands and Plains Region in northern Ontario, mining has provided a steadily increasing outlet for farm products; and mining activities are becoming more significant in sections of the Northwest Territories. Whether or not these activities will eventually pave the way for farming on a much larger scale than at present is difficult to say, but in any event development tending to promote settlement will in turn encourage an interest in the agricultural possibilities. So far, however, farming has been confined to the efforts of scattered missions and a few individuals, chiefly in the Mackenzie River Valley. Some of these efforts have been highly successful, even though they are of a small-scale nature. They provide, in many instances, valuable information on future possibilities.

Part VIII | HAWAIIAN ARCHIPELAGO

The Hawaiian Archipelago is a chain of volcanic islands near the center of the North Pacific. The larger islands form a group about 375 miles long at the eastern end of the chain and lie entirely within the tropics. Their isolation and their great diversity of soil, relief, drainage, and climate have led to the development of a unique and extremely varied flora. Many of the native species are found nowhere else.

22 | *Hawaiian Islands*

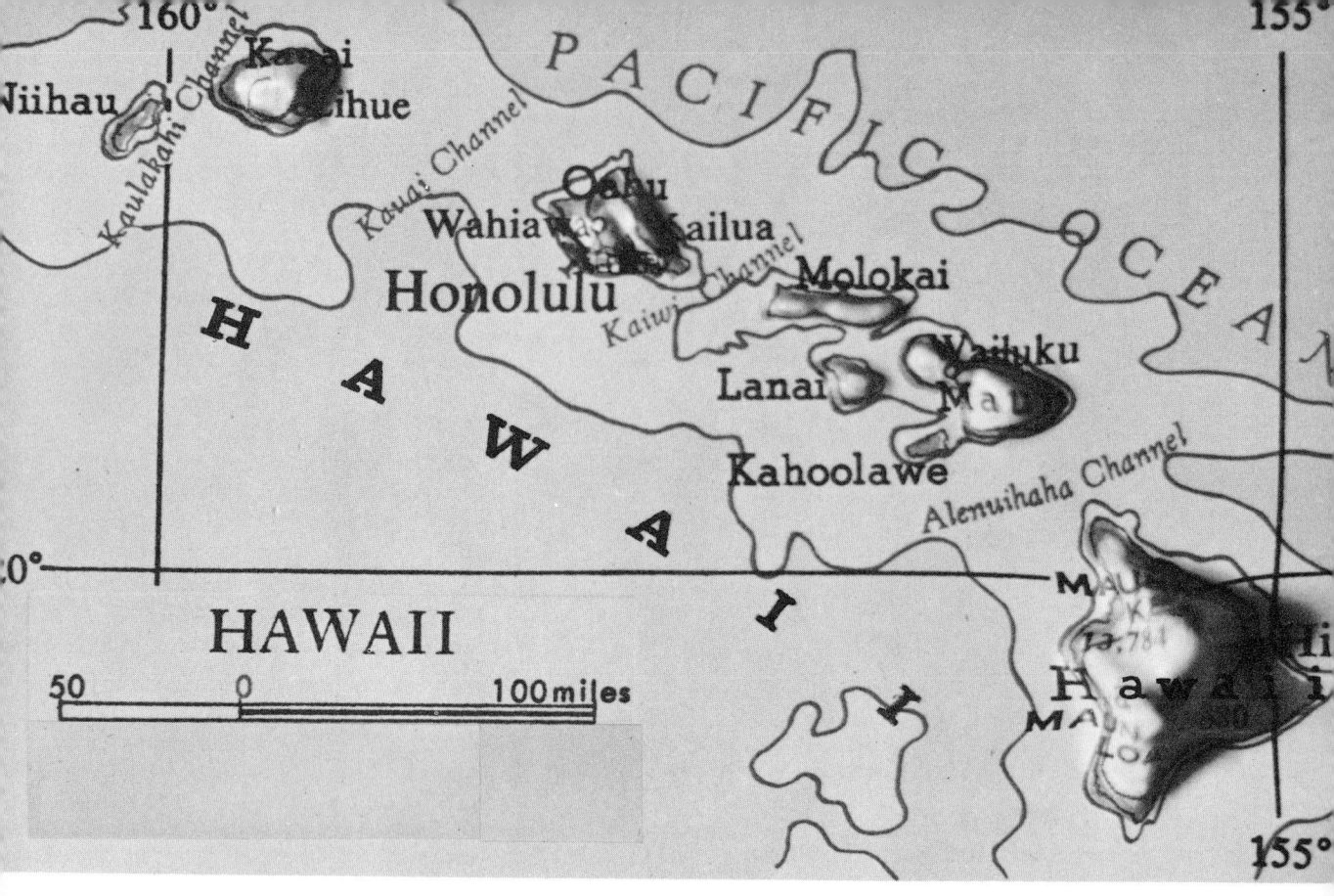

PACIFIC OCEAN

160°   155°

Niihau   Kauai   Lihue

Kaulakahi Channel   Kauai Channel

Oahu

Wahiawa   Kailua

Honolulu   Molokai

HAWAII   Kaiwi Channel   Lanai   Wailuku

Kahoolawe   Maui

Alenuihaha Channel

20°

HAWAII   Mauna Kea   Hilo
13,784

50   0   100 miles   Mauna Loa

155°

(Relief map copyright Aero Service Corp.)

THE main group of the Hawaiian Islands, eight relatively large islands lying between 18°55′ and 22°16′ N., and between 154°49′ and 160°15′ W., is near the northern limit of the tropics, due south of the Alaska Peninsula, and directly west of Yucatan. From Honolulu, the capital, it is 2,089 miles to San Francisco and 4,420 to Sydney, Australia. The total area of the main group is 6,435 square miles, slightly more than that of Connecticut and Rhode Island combined. A series of about 15 small, uninhabited, and seldom visited islands, lying to the northwest of the main group, terminates not far from Midway Island.

SURFACE FEATURES

The islands are the summits of a submarine range of volcanic mountains 2,000 miles long. Elevations have built up from the ocean floor, some 18,000 feet below sea level, to a maximum height of nearly 14,000 feet above sea level—a total of 32,000 feet. Formation of the islands occurred at various periods; the western end of the chain is the oldest and the eastern end the youngest. Decided contrasts in the effects of weathering and erosion, found within short distances, are caused by the marked local variations in rainfall and the resultant vegetation. Kauai, the oldest and most northwesterly of the larger islands, is badly cut up by gorges and ravines, while Hawaii, the youngest and most southeasterly, shows much less evidence of erosion. Since its volcanoes are not yet extinct, Hawaii is still in a formative stage.

Nearly half the area encompassed by the state of Hawaii, including the greater part of all the islands except Hawaii, lies within five miles of the ocean. Approximately one-fourth the land is at an elevation of less than 650 feet, one-half below 1,950 feet, and one-fourth above 4,500 feet. All but a small percentage of the population lives in the areas with elevations of less than 650 feet. On each of the islands there is a considerable percentage of land that cannot be utilized for cultivation for various reasons, such as excessive rainfall, deficient rainfall and impracticability of irrigation, shallow soil or a complete lack of soil, or topographical unsuitability.

Hawaii, the largest island, from which the group takes its name, has an area of 4,090 square miles. The other seven principal islands, in order, are Maui, 728 square miles; Oahu, 604 square miles; Kauai, 555 square miles; Molokai, 260 square miles; Lanai, 141 square miles; Niihau, 72 square miles; and Kahoolawe, 45 square miles.

CLIMATE

The outstanding features of the climate of the Hawaiian Islands are the remarkable differences in rainfall over adjacent areas, the persistently equable temperature—the cycle of the seasons is devoid of marked or sudden changes and has only a very moderate difference between the averages of winter and summer months—and the prevalence of the northeast trade winds over the general locality. The trade winds dominate throughout all seasons and pass over the greater part of all the islands. A number of local influences, such as the size and trend of mountains and valleys, the nearness to or relative remoteness from the sea, and the direction from the sea in relation to the prevailing winds, are very important in the climatic picture. For instance, heavy rainfall is normal on many windward mountain slopes while the lee slopes and valleys may be quite arid.

In general, it may be said that the climate of the Hawaiian Islands is unusually pleasant for the latitude and insularity. The marked marine influence, combined with the persistent trade winds, makes for relatively little uncomfortable heat for the latitude, although at times the trade winds temporarily give way to light changeable or southerly winds, with resultant comparatively high humidity. In summer, the trade winds blow with a high degree of persistency, and the few uncomfortable periods are consequently most noticeable in the fall. The least comfortable time of the year, therefore, may be experienced some weeks, or possibly a month or two, later than the time when the highest temperatures are recorded. In some areas, the large amount of rain that falls may be a somewhat disagreeable feature, but this is ameliorated by the occurrence of a large percentage of the rainfall at night.

There is almost uninterrupted summer all year in the lowlands, whereas at the highest elevations, particularly on the island of Ha-

Figure 22-1. Kaanapoli Beach on the island of Maui is typical of the island's beaches. The mountains are typical of the whole island chain. (Hawaii Visitors Bureau)

waii, conditions approach the continental type of climate, though the winters are mild. Mountain peaks are usually hidden by clouds, but over leeward lowlands nearby, the sun shines at least several hours nearly every day—and on many days uninterruptedly.

August and September are the warmest months; January and February are the coolest. Elevation is the major controlling influence in determining the average temperature, but location—to leeward or windward—is also a factor.

The highest official recorded temperature is 100° F. at Pahala on the island of Hawaii, elevation 850 feet; the lowest is 25° at Humuula, elevation 6,685 feet, on the southern edge of Mauna Kea on the same island.

In the Hawaiian Islands as a whole considerably more rain falls from November to April than from May to October. The Maui Isthmus and the leeward west Maui Lowlands show this

seasonal difference most decidedly, though it is also strongly in evidence in areas in the islands of Oahu and Kauai. It is not unusual for an entire month to go by in the summer without measurable rain falling at some points on the Maui Isthmus, and sometimes considerably longer dry periods may occur in that locality.

From windward to leeward slopes, instances of pronounced and sudden decline in rainfall may be found. This is well-illustrated in central Kauai, where at the summit of Mt. Waialeale (5,075 feet), the average amount of rain is over 450 inches, while about 15 miles southwest, on the leeward side, it is less than 20 inches.

Not only does rainfall vary greatly within short distances, but monthly amounts received at a station over a period of years may also show a phenomenal range. Most stations, even many where the annual normal precipitation is 100 inches or more, occasionally have a dry period when the monthly total is less than one inch. Conversely, some of the driest points, where the annual average rainfall is 20 to 30 inches, may occasionally have an amount approaching or surpassing the annual normals during a single wet month, or sometimes even within a period of a few days.

HISTORY

The world first heard of Hawaii in 1778, when the British explorer, Captain James Cook, visited the islands during one of his voyages. Captain Cook gave the name Sandwich Islands to the group. At that time, four kingdoms existed in the islands. By 1810, one ruler had conquered the others and a single kingdom was established. In 1893, a group of Americans on the islands managed to promote the overthrow of the monarchy, hoping that the United States would annex the islands. The United States refused, and therefore a republic was created. Later, in 1898, Congress voted to annex Hawaii and, in 1900, established the Territory of Hawaii. In 1959, Hawaii was admitted to the Union as the 50th state.

AGRICULTURE

Agriculture always has been of prime importance in the economy of the Hawaiian Islands. This is still true despite a growing diversification that is giving Hawaii a broader economic base. In terms of agricultural production, two crops are outstanding—sugar cane and pineapples.

SUGAR CANE

For almost a century sugar has been the most important trade commodity of the Hawaiian Islands. Although its position has slipped considerably during recent years, it still accounts for one-half of the state's income from products marketed on the mainland—approximately

Figure 22-2. One of Hawaii's 27 sugar mills; sugar cane grows in the foreground. The state produces more than a million tons of raw sugar annually, which adds about $150 million to the economy. (Hawaii Visitors Bureau)

$150 million annually. Hawaii ranks first as a producer of sugar among the fifty states; it is responsible for almost 30 per cent of all the sugar produced in the nation. Production is about 1.1 million tons per year, one-fiftieth of world production.

About 50,000 people work in the sugar industry, either in the growing of sugar cane on the 225,000 acres of land devoted to its cultivation, or in the 27 mills that grind the cane. About ten per cent of the Hawaiian Islands consists of improved farm land; of this total 28 per cent is in sugar cane. Almost all the cane comes from four islands—Oahu, Hawaii, Maui, and Kauai, with the economy of the last three heavily dependent upon sugar cane. The cane is grown either on the rainy (trade winds) side of the islands or on the leeward side under irrigation.

Most of the sugar cane is raised on large plantations where the addition of Chilean nitrate to the already rich volcanic soils gives ex-

ceedingly high yields—up to 9,000 pounds of sugar per acre.

The sugar industry is organized under the Hawaiian Sugar Planters Association, which is credited with the establishment of a successful manufacturing and merchandising organization. The association ships the raw sugar in bulk form to Crockett, California, where it undergoes final refinement prior to marketing.

PINEAPPLES

Pineapples constitute the state's second most important agricultural crop. At the peak of the harvest, 23,000 people are employed in harvesting and canning pineapples. Nine companies are engaged in the business.

Recent developments indicate that the pineapple industry may face increasing competition from Formosa, which has lower labor costs.

OTHER CROPS AND LIVESTOCK

Other agricultural crops include fruits and

Figure 22-3. Pineapple fields in Hawaii. Pineapples occupy about 77,000 acres on the islands of Oahu, Molokai, Lanai, Kauai, and Maui. Hawaiian pineapple output is valued at about $125 million annually. It accounts for 65 per cent of the world's total output. (Hawaii Visitors Bureau)

vegetables, nuts, flowers, and coffee. Although fruits and nuts account for only one per cent of the islands' agricultural products, their importance is increasing yearly. Products include bananas, papayas, macadamia nuts, cantaloupes, oranges, tangerines, avocados, and watermelons. Approximately nine million pounds of green coffee is produced on about 6,000 acres on the island of Hawaii's Kona (western) Coast. The annual coffee crop is valued at $6 million.

The raising of beef cattle is also of economic significance, with more than 400 ranches occupying 77 per cent of the total agricultural land. The island of Hawaii is the main area for ranching. Slaughtering activities, however, are concentrated in the city of Honolulu on Oahu.

Figure 22-4. The Parker Ranch on the island of Hawaii is one of the world's largest ranches. Note the typical vegetation in the background. (Hawaii Visitors Bureau)

DEFENSE ESTABLISHMENTS

Extremely important in terms of the Hawaiian Islands' economy is the spending by the armed forces of about $335 million annually, chiefly on the island of Oahu, where 16 military installations are concentrated. The armed forces maintain some 53,000 men in Hawaii. Counting service personnel, one in every four persons in the state is directly dependent upon the defense establishments for a livelihood. Most significant of latest developments is the modernization work done by the Pearl Harbor Naval Shipyard.

TOURISM

Tourism in Hawaii is a brisk, booming industry. The state has one of the best-organized visitor promotion services in the world. In 1959, 240,000 tourists spent $101 million. The forecast is for 1.2 million visitors annually by 1970, spending about $550 million a year. The main tourist area continues to be the Waikiki Beach section of Honolulu, although new developments are scheduled on all the main islands. Excellent hotel facilities, lush tropical scenery, a perfect climate, fine restaurants, and wonderful beaches are attractions that few other areas can match. A significant factor in the increasing tourist activity is the convenience of jet travel from major West Coast cities at reasonable prices.

Figure 22-5. The United States Navy shipyard at Pearl Harbor, Oahu. The shipyard is a major contributor to the economy of Hawaii. (Official U.S. Navy Photograph)

Figure 22-6. The famous beach at Waikiki on the Island of Oahu. Diamond Head is in the background. (Hawaii Visitors Bureau)

The growing popularity of Hawaii as a site for conventions is adding to the tourist boom. In 1960, tourist ranks were swelled by 36,000 convention visitors.

COMMERCE AND MANUFACTURING

The basic commerce of Hawaii involves the shipment of raw sugar and pineapples to the mainland of the United States and receiving in return food, lumber, building materials, and manufactured goods.

Local manufacturing is concentrated on the island of Oahu and includes food processing, ship repair and maintenance, clothing manufacturing, furniture making, some farm machinery production, raw materials processing, and the making of tourist goods. Clothing manufacturing is becoming increasingly important as mainland interest in Hawaiian print shirts and other sportswear increases. Today,

the clothing industry does an $18 million gross business and employs 2,400 people. It is leading all export industries in annual percentage increase. Economists foresee a $70 million to $100 million annual production figure by 1970 if the industry maintains its rate of increase.

CONSTRUCTION

One of the key industries in Hawaii is construction. Buoyed by extensive military and state construction projects, the expanding tourist trade, and mounting population, the industry achieved over $200 million gross business in 1960. Ninety per cent of this activity was concentrated on the island of Oahu. Employment in 1960 was approximately 13,000, some 5,000 more workers than in 1955. By 1970, construction employment is forecast at 16,000, with estimated expenditures of $230 million. An example of projected construction activity, now in its initial stages, is Henry J. Kaiser's planned

$350 million residential resort community near Honolulu. This project will provide 12,000 new homes and all other community facilities.

METALS, CEMENT, AND OIL REFINING

Hawaiian Western Steel, Ltd., installed in its plant at Barbers Point on Oahu an arc furnace producing 2,000 tons of steel ingots a month, with a future capacity of 4,000 tons.

Permanente Cement constructed, in 1960, a $13.5 million plant at Waianae, Oahu, with an annual production capacity of 1.7 million barrels of cement. In the same year, at nearby Barbers Point, the Hawaiian Cement Corporation built a $12 million cement plant with an initial capacity of one million barrels annually and an ultimate capacity of three million barrels.

The Standard Oil Company of California recently built a $65 million oil refinery at Barbers Point for the storage and processing of crude oil.

TRANSPORTATION

Vital to the island state of Hawaii is a network of transportation facilities that link it with the mainland and markets in Europe and Asia. In 1960 nearly 1,300 ships arrived in the port of Honolulu, the principal harbor. Pressure is very intense on the dock space and berthing facilities for ships. Millions of dollars are being invested by large firms such as Matson to enlarge terminal facilities. The Honolulu Harbor Board spent $6.5 million to finance an adequate cargo and passenger terminal. Honolulu's International Airport, the tenth busiest in the nation, opened a $25 million jet airport in 1961 to handle the 570 commercial flights scheduled every week by 15 major airlines. Some 3,120,000 passengers are expected by 1970.

POPULATION

When first discovered by Captain Cook, the Hawaiian Islands contained around 300,000

Figure 22-7. Honolulu, a modern metropolis, has the distinction of being the farthest west of any United States state capital. (Hawaii Visitors Bureau)

Figure 22-8. Hilo is the only large urban center on the island of Hawaii. The city boasts an excellent harbor and is the starting point for visits to such nearby volcanoes as Mauna Loa. (Tribune-Herald)

primitive people of Polynesian stock. Since then a vast admixture of other races has taken place. In succession, plantation workers were brought from China, Japan, Korea, Portugal, and the Philippines. As a result, the typical Hawaiian is a second-to-fifth-generation resident of various races and nationalities. About 90 per cent of Hawaii's people are either island born or have migrated from the mainland United States.

The population of the Hawaiian Islands in 1960 was 632,772, of which 52,881 were military personnel and an additional 60,000 were military dependents. The bulk of the population is concentrated on the island of Oahu, which has 500,409 people, 300,000 of whom are within the city of Honolulu. The island of Hawaii has a population of 61,332, with the major city, Hilo, containing roughly 26,000.

Significant islands with smaller populations are: Maui, 35,717; Molokai, 5,023; Lanai, 2,115; Kauai, 27,922; and Niihau, 254.

THE FUTURE

With about 45 per cent of the population under 20 years of age and soon to enter the labor market, and with limited natural resources, Hawaii is approaching a surplus labor situation. The need, therefore, is for industrialization. An intensive effort is being made by the state government and private groups to attract light industry, such as electronics, whose value added by manufacture is high. Hawaii's future would seem to lie with such a proposal, but also with vigorous promotion of tourist facilities and establishment of the islands as a center for retirement and relaxation.

Bibliography

INTRODUCTION

Atwood, Wallace W., *The Physiographic Provinces of North America*, Boston: Ginn & Co., 1940.

Bogue, Donald J., "The Geography of Recent Population Trends in the United States," *Annals of the Association of American Geographers*, Vol. 44, June, 1954, pp. 124-134.

Brown, R. E., *Historical Geography of the United States*, New York: Harcourt, Brace & World, Inc., 1948.

Deasy, G. F., and others, *The World's Nations*, Philadelphia: J. B. Lippincott Co., 1958, pp. 18-193.

Dewhurst, J. Frederic, and others, *America's Needs and Resources: A New Survey*, New York: The Twentieth Century Fund, 1955.

Fenneman, Nevin M., *Physiography of Eastern United States*, New York: McGraw-Hill Book Co., Inc., 1938.

————, *Physiography of Western United States*, New York: McGraw-Hill Book Co., Inc., 1931.

Harris, Chauncy D., "The Market as a Factor in the Localization of Industry in the United States," *Annals of the Association of American Geographers*, Vol. 44, December, 1954, pp. 315-348.

Haystead, Ladd, and Fite, Gilbert C., *The Agricultural Regions of the United States*, Norman, Okla.: University of Oklahoma Press, 1955.

Higbee, Edward, *American Agriculture*, New York: John Wiley & Sons, Inc., 1958.

James, Preston E., "Toward a Further Understanding of the Regional Concept," *Annals of the Association of American Geographers*, Vol. 42, September, 1952, pp. 195-222.

Kiang, Ying-Cheng, "Water for American Cities," *The Journal of Geography*, Vol. 60, September, 1961, pp. 277-282.

Kimble, George H. T., *Our American Weather*, New York: McGraw-Hill Book Co., Inc., 1956.

Klove, Robert C., "The Growing Population of the United States," *The Journal of Geography*, Vol. 60, May, 1961, pp. 203-213.

Kohn, Clyde F., ed., *The United States and the World Today*, Chicago: Rand McNally & Co., 1957.

Lobeck, A. K., *Physiographic Diagram of North America*, New York: C. S. Hammond & Co., Inc., 1950.

Loomis, F. B., *Physiography of the United States*, Garden City, N. Y.: Doubleday & Co., Inc., 1937.

Meigs, Peveril, "Water Problems of the United States," *Geographical Review*, July, 1952, pp. 346-366.

Miller, E. Willard, "Changing Patterns in the Mineral Economy of the United States, 1939-1954," *The Professional Geographer*, Vol. 13, May, 1961, pp. 1-6.

Miller, J.; Parkins, A. E.; and Hudgins, B.; *Geography of North America*, New York: John Wiley & Sons, Inc., 1954.

Mineral Facts and Problems (U. S. Bureau of Mines), Washington: U. S. Government Printing Office, 1960.

Olmstead, Clarence W., "American Orchard and Vineyard Regions," *Economic Geography*, Vol. 32, July, 1956, pp. 190-236.

Patton, Donald, "The Traffic Pattern on American Inland Waterways," *Economic Geography*, Vol. 32, January, 1956, pp. 29-37.

Putnam, D. F., ed., *Canadian Regions: A Geography of Canada*, New York: Thomas Y. Crowell Co., 1952.

Putnam, Donald F., and Kerr, Donald P., *A Regional Geography of Canada*, Don Mills, Ont.: J. M. Dent & Sons, Ltd., 1956.

Raup, H. F., "The United States in Professional Geographical Literature," *Annals of the Association of American Geographers*, Vol. 46, March, 1956, pp. 140-149.

Renner, G. T., and Renner, M. P., "Regionalism in American Life," *Teachers College Record*, Vol. 43, February, 1942, pp. 337-357.

Robinson, J. Lewis, and Robinson, M. Josephine, *The Geography of Canada*, New York: Longmans, Green & Co., Inc., 1950.

Shaw, Earl B., *Anglo-America: A Regional Geography*, New York: John Wiley & Sons, Inc., 1959.

Smith, J. R., and Phillips, M. O., *North America*, New York: Harcourt, Brace & World, Inc., 1942.

"Timber Supply and Demand in the United States," *Geographical Review*, July, 1956, pp. 409-411.

Watson, J. Wreford, "North America in a Changing World," *The Journal of Geography*, Vol. 57, November, 1958, pp. 381-389.

White, C. Langdon, and Foscue, E. J., *Regional Geography of Anglo-America*, Englewood Cliffs, N. J.: Prentice-Hall, Inc., 1954.

Wright, Alfred J., *United States and Canada, an Economic Geography*, New York: Appleton-Century-Crofts, Inc., 1956.

Yearbook of Agriculture, 1938, 1941, 1943-1947, 1948, 1949, 1951, 1952, 1955, 1957, 1958 (U. S. Department of Agriculture), Washington: U. S. Government Printing Office.

CHAPTER 1

Alexander, Lewis M., "The Impact of Tourism on the Economy of Cape Cod, Massachusetts," *Economic Geography*, Vol. 29, October, 1953, pp. 320-326.

Bird, J. Brian, "Settlement Patterns in Maritime Canada," *Geographical Review*, July, 1955, pp. 385-404.

Black, John D., *The Rural Economy of New England*, Cambridge, Mass.: Harvard University Press, 1950.

Bright, A. A., Jr., *Economic State of New England*, New Haven, Conn.: Yale University Press, 1954.

Franklin, Henry J., "Cranberry Growing in Massachusetts," *Massachusetts Agricultural Experiment Station Bulletin No. 447*, April, 1948.

Gentilcore, R. Louis, "The Agricultural Background of Settlement in Eastern Nova Scotia," *Annals of the Association of American Geographers*, Vol. 46, December, 1956, pp. 378-404.

Gibson, J. Sullivan, "Prince Edward Island—Gem of the Maritimes," *The Journal of Geography*, Vol. 59, October, 1960, pp. 301-307.

Gottmann, Jean, "Megalopolis or the Urbanization of the Northeastern Seaboard," *Economic Geography*, Vol. 33, July, 1957, pp. 189-202.

Harris, Seymour E., *The Economics of New England*, Cambridge, Mass.: Harvard University Press, 1952.

Hart, J. F., and Mather, E. C., "The Character of Tobacco Barns and Their Role in the Tobacco Economy of the United States," *Annals of the Association of American Geographers,* Vol. 51, September, 1961, pp. 274-293.

HIGBEE, E. C., "The Three Earths of New England," *Geographical Review,* July, 1952, pp. 425-438.

ISARD, WALTER, and CUMBERLAND, JOHN H., "New England as a Possible Location for an Integrated Iron and Steel Works," *Economic Geography,* October, 1950, pp. 245-259.

KLIMM, LESTER E., "The Empty Areas of the Northeastern United States," *Geographical Review,* July, 1954, pp. 325-345.

LAING, JEAN, "The Pattern of Population Trends in Massachusetts," *Economic Geography,* July, 1955, pp. 265-271.

MANCHESTER, LORNE, "Science in Fisheries," *Canadian Geographical Journal,* Vol. 41, 1950, pp. 189-209.

PHILLIPS, FRED H., "New Brunswick: Varied Vacationland of the Maritimes," *Canadian Geographical Journal,* Vol. 40, 1950, pp. 12-43.

"The Bay of Fundy Salt Marshes," *Geographical Review,* April, 1956, pp. 263-264.

WALLACE, WILLIAM H., "Merrimack Valley Manufacturing: Past and Present," *Economic Geography,* Vol. 37, October, 1961, pp. 283-309.

CHAPTER 2

ANGELL, ORSON, "The Eastern Shore," *The Lamp,* Spring-Summer, 1958, pp. 10-15.

BROWN, RALPH H., *Historical Geography of the United States,* New York: Harcourt, Brace & World, Inc., 1948, pp. 173-191.

BRUSH, JOHN E., *The Population of New Jersey,* New Brunswick, N. J.: Rutgers University Press, 1956.

CLINE, MARLIN G., "Soils and Soil Associations of New York," *Cornell Extension Bulletin 930,* January, 1957.

FENNEMAN, NEVIN M., *Physiography of Eastern United States,* New York: McGraw-Hill Book Co., Inc., 1938, pp. 22-38.

GOTTMANN, JEAN, "Megalopolis or the Urbanization of the Northeastern Seaboard," *Economic Geography,* Vol. 33, July, 1957, pp. 189-200.

————, *Virginia at Mid-Century,* New York: Holt, Rinehart & Winston, Inc., 1955.

HANCE, WILLIAM A., and VAN DONGEN, IRENE S., "General Cargo Hinterlands of New York, Philadelphia, Baltimore, and New Orleans," *Annals of the Association of American Geographers,* Vol. 48, December, 1958, pp. 436-455.

HAYSTEAD, LADD, and FITE, GILBERT C., *The Agricultural Regions of the United States,* Norman, Okla.: University of Oklahoma Press, 1955, pp. 47-81.

HIGBEE, EDWARD, *American Agriculture,* New York: John Wiley & Sons, Inc., 1958.

HOYT, HOMER, *An Economic Survey of New Jersey,* Trenton, N. J.: State of New Jersey, 1950.

ISAAC, ERICH, "Jamestown and the Mid-Atlantic Coast: A Geographic Reconsideration," *The Journal of Geography,* Vol. 57, January, 1958, pp. 17-29.

LOBECK, A. K., *The Physiography of the New York Region,* New York: The Geographical Press, 1930.

"New York City in Trouble," *U. S. News and World Report,* March 11, 1955, pp. 48-62.

WOLMAN, ABEL, "Utilization of Surface, Underground, and Sea Water," *United Nations Scientific Conference on the Conservation and Utilization of Resources,* Vol. 4, 1951, pp. 98-102.

CHAPTER 3

CARSON, ROBE B., "The Florida Tropics," *Economic Geography,* October, 1951, pp. 321-339.

CHAPMAN, H. H., and others, *The Iron and Steel Industries of the South,* Montgomery, Ala.: University of Alabama Press, 1953.

DYER, DONALD R., "The Place of Origin of Florida's Population," *Annals of the Association of American Geographers,* Vol. 42, December, 1952, pp. 283-294.

————, "Urban Growth in Florida; Exemplified by Lakeland," *The Journal of Geography,* Vol. 55, September, 1956, pp. 278-285.

FORD, ROBERT N., *The Everglades Agricultural Area,* University of Chicago Research Paper No. 42, 1956.

HART, JOHN F., "Functions and Occupational Structures of Cities of the American South," *Annals of the Association of American Geographers,* Vol. 45, September, 1955, pp. 269-286.

HOOVER, CALVIN B., and RATCHFORD, B. V., *Economic Resources and Policies of the South,* New York: The Macmillan Co., 1951.

LATHROP, H. O., "Distribution and Development of the Beef Cattle Industry of Florida," *The Journal of Geography,* April, 1951, pp. 133-144.

LAUBENFELS, D. J. de, "Where Sherman Passed By," *Geographical Review,* July, 1957, pp. 381-395.

PARKINS, A. E., *The South: Its Economic-Geographic Development,* New York: John Wiley & Sons, Inc., 1938.

PHILLIPS, COY T., "North Carolina's Rich Crescent," *The Journal of Geography,* Vol. 54, April, 1955, pp. 182-186.

————, "Population Distribution and Trends in North Carolina," *The Journal of Geography,* Vol. 55, April, 1956, pp. 182-193.

PRUNTY, MERLE J., JR., "Land Occupance in the Southeast," *Geographical Review,* Vol. 42, July, 1952, pp. 439-461.

————, "Recent Expansions in the Southern Pulp-Paper Industries," *Economic Geography,* Vol. 32, January, 1956, pp. 51-57.

————, "The Renaissance of the Southern Plantation," *Geographical Review,* October, 1955, pp. 459-491.

STOKES, GEORGE A., "Lumbering and Western Louisiana Cultural Landscapes," *Annals of the Association of American Geographers,* Vol. 47, September, 1957, pp. 250-266.

VANCE, RUPERT B., and DEMERATH, NICHOLAS J., eds., *The Urban South,* Chapel Hill, N. C.: University of North Carolina Press, 1954.

WOODRUFF, JAMES F., and PARIZEK, ELDON J., "Influence of Underlying Rock Structures on Stream Courses and Valley Profiles in the Georgia Piedmont," *Annals of the Association of American Geographers,* Vol. 46, March, 1956, pp. 129-139.

ZELINSKY, WILBUR, "The Changing South," *Focus*, October, 1951.

————, "The Log House in Georgia," *Geographical Review*, April, 1953, pp. 173-193.

CHAPTER 4

"A Decade of Growth in the Southwest," *Monthly Business Review* (Federal Reserve Bank of Dallas), February, 1950.

"A Shortcut to the Gulf," *The Orange Disc*, Vol. 14, No. 12, May-June, 1961, pp. 12-15.

CARTER, HODDING, "The South Is on Its Way," *The Lamp*, November, 1951, pp. 20-25.

COLBY, D. S., and OPPEGARD, B. E., "Natural Gas," *Minerals Yearbook* (U. S. Department of the Interior), Washington: U. S. Government Printing Office, 1951, pp. 865-892.

FOSCUE, EDWIN J., "The Ports of Texas and Their Hinterlands," *Journal of Economic and Social Geography*, January, 1957, pp. 1-13.

GRAY, RALPH, "Manufacturing Growth Trends," *The Arkansas Economist*, Vol. 3, No. 1, Fall, 1960, pp. 19-24.

HAYSTEAD, LADD, and FITE, GILBERT C., *The Agricultural Regions of the United States*, Norman, Okla.: University of Oklahoma Press, 1955, pp. 204-217.

McKNIGHT, TOM L., "The Distribution of Manufacturing in Texas," *Annals of the Association of American Geographers*, Vol. 47, December, 1957, pp. 370-378.

OWENS, W. A., "Tankers to Texas," *Dupont Magazine*, August-September, 1959, pp. 17-19.

PARKS, M. H., "Petroleum Production from Continental Shelves," *Proceedings of the United Nations Scientific Conference on the Conservation and Utilization of Resources*, Vol. 3, 1951, pp. 21-23.

PARSONS, JAMES J., "Recent Industrial Development in the Gulf South," *Geographical Review*, January, 1950, pp. 67-83.

PUTNAM, HOWARD, "South Texas: Intercultural Gateway," *The Journal of Geography*, Vol. 56, February, 1957, pp. 74-77.

RESEN, F. LAWRENCE, "The Gulf Coast Today: Its Billion Dollar Petro-Chemical Industry," *The Oil and Gas Journal*, Vol. 51, No. 6, 1952, pp. 190-192.

SCHLESSELMAN, G. W., "The Gulf Coast Oyster Industry of the United States," *Geographical Review*, October, 1955, pp. 531-541.

SITTERSON, J. CARLYLE, *The Cane Sugar Industry in the South, 1753-1950*, Lexington, Ky.: University of Kentucky Press, 1953.

"Soil and Water Conservation in Arkansas," Little Rock, Ark.: U. S. Department of Agriculture Soil Conservation Service, 1960.

STOCKTON, J. R.; HENSHAW, R. C., JR.; and GRAVES, R. W.; *Economics of Natural Gas in Texas*, Austin, Texas: The University of Texas Press, 1952.

WILLIAMS, NORMAN F., "Mineral Resources of Arkansas," *Arkansas Geological and Conservation Commission Bulletin 6*, 1959.

CHAPTER 5

BLACK, JOHN D., *The Rural Economy of New England*, Cambridge, Mass.: Harvard University Press, 1950.

BRIGHT, ARTHUR A., and ELLIS, GEORGE H., *Agriculture in New England*, Boston: The New England Council, 1954.

DUTHIE, GEORGE A., "The Community Forest," *American Forests*, Vol. 59, No. 5, May, 1953, pp. 1-14.

"Forest Land as an Investment in New England," *New England Business Review* (Federal Reserve Bank of Boston), October, 1956.

HARE, KENNETH F., "Climate and Zonal Divisions of the Boreal Forest Formation of Eastern Canada," *Geographical Review*, October, 1950, pp. 615-635.

————, "The Labrador Frontier," *Geographical Review*, July, 1952, pp. 405-424.

HARRIS, SEYMOUR E., *The Economics of New England*, Cambridge, Mass.: Harvard University Press, 1952.

HAYSTEAD, LADD, and FITE, GILBERT C., *The Agricultural Regions of the United States*, Norman, Okla.: University of Oklahoma Press, 1955, pp. 29-46.

HIGBEE, E. C., "The Three Earths of New England," *Geographical Review*, July, 1952, pp. 425-438.

"Inside New Brunswick," Fredericton, N. B.: Department of Industry and Development, 1960.

KLIMM, LESTER E., "The Empty Areas of the Northeastern United States," *Geographical Review*, July, 1954, pp. 325-345.

NICHOLLS, ROY, "Newfoundland—New Look at an Old Land," *Imperial Oil Review*, Vol. 45, No. 1, February, 1961, pp. 14-19.

PEATTIE, RODERICK, *The Friendly Mountains*, New York: Vanguard Press, 1942.

PHILLIPS, FRED H., "New Brunswick: Varied Vacationland of the Maritimes," *Canadian Geographical Journal*, Vol. 40, 1950, pp. 12-43.

"The Changing Fertility of New England Soils," *Agriculture Information Bulletin 133* (U. S. Department of Agriculture), December, 1954.

"The Maine Broiler," *New England Business Review* (Federal Reserve Bank of Boston), June, 1961.

CHAPTER 6

BROWN, J. D., "Twenty-five Years of TVA," *The Americas*, May, 1958.

DEASY, GEORGE F., and GRIESS, PHYLLIS R., "Coal Strip Pits in the Northern Appalachian Landscape," *The Journal of Geography*, Vol. 58, February, 1959, pp. 72-80.

————, "New Maps of Underground Bituminous Coal Mining," *Annals of the Association of American Geographers*, Vol. 47, December, 1957, pp. 336-349.

DURAND, LOYAL, JR., "Mountain Moonshining in East Tennessee," *Geographical Review*, April, 1956, pp. 168-181.

DURAND, LOYAL, JR., and BIRD, ELSIE T., "The Burley Tobacco Region of the Mountain South," *Economic Geography*, July, 1950, pp. 247-300.

FOSCUE, EDWIN J., "Gatlinburg: A Mountain Community," *Economic Geography*, 1945, pp. 192-205.

GOTTMANN, JEAN, *Virginia at Mid-Century*, New York: Holt, Rinehart & Winston, Inc., 1955.

GUERNSEY, LEE, "Strip Coal Mining: A Problem in Conservation," *The Journal of Geography*, Vol. 54, April, 1955, pp. 174-181.

————, "The Reclamation of Strip Mined Lands in Western Kentucky," *The Journal of Geography*, Vol. 59, January, 1960, pp. 5-11.

HAYSTEAD, LADD, and FITE, GILBERT C., *The Agricultural Regions of the United States*, Norman, Okla.: University of Oklahoma Press, 1955, pp. 82-101.

MAGIN, IRVIN D., "The Wilderness Road," *The Journal of Geography*, Vol. 57, April, 1958, pp. 191-195.

MILLER, E. WILLARD, "Some Aspects of Population Trends in Pennsylvania," *The Journal of Geography*, Vol. 54, February, 1955, pp. 64-73.

————, "The Southern Anthracite Region: A Problem Area," *Economic Geography*, Vol. 31, October, 1955, pp. 331-350.

RIGGS, FLETCHER E., "Income Levels in the Upper Tennessee Valley: A Comparative Analysis," Knoxville, Tenn.: Division of Agricultural Relations, Tennessee Valley Authority, 1957.

RUDD, R. W., and SHUFFETT, D. M., "Trends in Kentucky Agriculture," *Kentucky Agricultural Experiment Station Bulletin 653*, November, 1957.

CHAPTER 7

"A New Profile for the Ohio River," *Monthly Business Review* (Federal Reserve Bank of Cleveland), February, 1960.

BARTON, THOMAS F., "The Sewer or Waste Disposal Use of the Ohio River," *The Journal of Geography*, Vol. 59, October, 1960, pp. 326-335.

BEST, T. D., and others, *Summary Report on the Economic Potentialities of the Upper Ohio Valley*, Columbus, Ohio: Batelle Memorial Institute, 1960.

CARLSON, FRED A., "Traffic on the Ohio River System," *The Journal of Geography*, Vol. 59, November, 1960, pp. 357-359.

CARR, CHARLES C., *Alcoa, an American Enterprise*, New York: Holt, Rinehart & Winston, Inc., 1952.

"Expansion in Steel Finishing Capacity, Fourth District," *Monthly Business Review* (Federal Reserve Bank of Cleveland), December, 1957.

HARPER, ROBERT A., "River Junction Communities of the Lower Ohio Valley—a Study of Functional Change," *The Journal of Geography*, Vol. 59, November, 1960, pp. 364-370.

LOUNSBURY, JOHN F., "Industrial Development in the Ohio Valley," *The Journal of Geography*, Vol. 60, September, 1961, pp. 253-262.

MILLER, E. WILLARD, "Strip Mining and Land Utilization in Western Pennsylvania," *The Scientific Monthly*, Vol. 69, 1949, pp. 94-103.

"Pittsburgh, Youngstown, and the Upper Ohio Valley," *Monthly Business Review* (Federal Reserve Bank of Cleveland), May, 1957.

RODGERS, ALLAN, "The Iron and Steel Industry of the Mahoning and Shenango Valleys," *Economic Geography*, October, 1952, pp. 331-342.

SMITH, R. A., "The Boiling Ohio," *Fortune*, June, 1956, pp. 109-114, 250-258.

THOMPSON, J. L., and HUMPHREY, J. W., *Ohio Population-Growth and Distribution*, Columbus, Ohio: The F. J. Heer Printing Co., 1960.

"Urban Renewal in Three Large Cities—Pittsburgh, Cleveland, and Cincinnati," *Monthly Business Review* (Federal Reserve Bank of Cleveland), August, 1959.

WHITE, C. LANGDON, "Water—a Neglected Factor in the Geographical Literature of Iron and Steel," *Geographical Review*, October, 1957, pp. 463-489.

CHAPTER 8

COLLIER, JAMES E., "Agricultural Atlas of Missouri," *University of Missouri Agricultural Experiment Station Bulletin 645*, February, 1955.

————, "Geographic Regions of Missouri," *Annals of the Association of American Geographers*, Vol. 46, December, 1955, pp. 368-392.

————, *Geography of the Northern Ozark Border Region*, University of Missouri Studies, Vol. 26, No. 1, Columbia, Mo.: University of Missouri Press, 1953.

CRISSLER, ROBERT M., "Recreation Regions of Missouri," *The Journal of Geography*, Vol. 51, 1952, pp. 30-39.

HEWES, LESLIE, "Tontitown: Ozark Vineyard Center," *Economic Geography*, April, 1953, pp. 125-143.

KERSTEN, EARL W., JR., "Changing Economy and Landscape in a Missouri Ozarks Area," *Annals of the Association of American Geographers*, Vol. 48, December, 1958, pp. 398-418.

MOKE, IRENE A., "Distribution of Major Manufacturing Industries in Arkansas," *The Journal of Geography*, Vol. 54, May, 1955, pp. 239-245.

OHLE, E. L., and BROWN, J. S., "Geologic Problems in Southeast Missouri Lead District," *Bulletin of the Geological Society of America*, March, 1954.

STERNITZKE, H. S., "Arkansas Forests," New Orleans, La.: U. S. Department of Agriculture Forest Service, 1960.

WILLIAMS, NORMAN F., "Mineral Resources of Arkansas," *Arkansas Geological and Conservation Commission Bulletin 6*, 1959.

CHAPTER 9

ALEXANDERSSON, GUNNAR, "Changes in the Location Pattern of the Anglo-American Steel Industry: 1948-1959," *Economic Geography*, Vol. 37, April, 1961, pp. 95-114.

BALLERT, ALBERT G., "Commerce of the Sault Canals," *Economic Geography*, April, 1957, pp. 135-148.

————, "The Great Lakes Coal Trade: Present and Future," *Economic Geography*, Vol. 29, January, 1953, pp. 48-59.

BROWN, ANDREW H., "New St. Lawrence Seaway Opens the Great Lakes to the World," *The National Geographic Magazine*, Vol. 115, No. 3. March, 1959, pp. 299-339.

BROWNELL, JOSEPH W., "The Cultural Midwest," *The Journal of Geography*, Vol. 59, February, 1960, pp. 81-85.

BURGHARDT, ANDREW F., "The Location of River Towns in the Central Lowland of the United States," *Annals of the Association of American Geographers*, Vol. 49, September, 1959, pp. 305-323.

COLLIER, JAMES E., "Geographic Regions of Missouri," *Annals of the Association of American Geographers*, Vol. 45, December, 1955, pp. 368-392.

DURAND, LOYAL, JR., "The American Centralizer Belt," *Economic Geography*, Vol. 31, October, 1955, pp. 301-320.

————, "The Migration of Cheese Manufacture in the United States," *Annals of the Association of American Geographers*, Vol. 42, December, 1952, pp. 263-282.

GARLAND, JOHN H., *The North American Midwest—a Regional Geography*, New York: John Wiley & Sons, Inc., 1954.

HEIMONEN, HENRY S., "Low Grade Iron Ores in the Lake Superior Region," *The Journal of Geography*, Vol. 57, March, 1958, pp. 130-135.

HEWES, LESLIE, "The Northern Wet Prairie of the United States: Nature, Sources of Information, and Extent," *Annals of the Association of American Geographers*, Vol. 41, 1951, pp. 307-323.

HEWES, LESLIE, and FRANDSON, PHILLIP E., "Occupying the Wet Prairie: The Role of Artificial Drainage in Story County, Iowa," *Annals of the Association of American Geographers*, Vol. 42, March, 1952, pp. 24-50.

HILLS, THEO. L., "The St. Lawrence Seaway," *Focus*, Vol. 11, No. 4, December, 1960.

JOHNSON, H. B., "King Wheat in Southeastern Minnesota: A Case Study of Pioneer Agriculture," *Annals of the Association of American Geographers*, Vol. 47, December, 1957, pp. 350-362.

KERR, DONALD, "The Geography of the Canadian Iron and Steel Industry," *Economic Geography*, Vol. 35, April, 1959, pp. 151-163.

LAIDLY, W. T., "Submarine Valleys in Lake Superior," *The Geographical Review*, Vol. 51, April, 1961, pp. 277-283.

LANGDON, GEORGE, "The Mesabi Range—a Fabulous Iron Ore Producer Shows Evidence of Decline," *The Journal of Geography*, Vol. 57, March, 1958, pp. 119-129.

MCDERMOTT, GEORGE L., "Frontiers of Settlement in the Great Clay Belt, Ontario, and Quebec," *Annals of the Association of American Geographers*, Vol. 51, September, 1961, pp. 261-273.

MAYER, HAROLD M., "Great Lakes—Overseas: An Expanding Trade Route," *Economic Geography*, Vol. 30, April, 1954, pp. 117-143.

————, "Prospects and Problems of the Port of Chicago," *Economic Geography*, Vol. 31, April, 1955, pp. 95-125.

MERRIAM, WILLIS B., "Reclamation Economy in the Holland Marsh Area of Ontario," *The Journal of Geography*, Vol. 60, March, 1961, pp. 135-140.

MORRIS, KENTON W., "The St. Lawrence Seaway—Its Development and Economic Significance," *The Journal of Geography*, Vol. 55, December, 1956, pp. 447-453.

OLMSTEAD, CLARENCE W., "The Application of a Concept to the Understanding of a Region: People, Time, Space, and Ideas in the Economic Core Region of Anglo-America," *The Journal of Geography*, Vol. 59, pp. 53-61.

PRICE, WILLARD, "The Upper Mississippi," *The National Geographic Magazine*, Vol. 114, No. 5, November, 1958, pp. 650-699.

REEDS, LLOYD G., "Agricultural Regions of Southern Ontario, 1880 and 1951," *Economic Geography*, Vol. 35, July, 1959, pp. 219-227.

RUDD, R. D., "The Red Ember Coal Mine: An Illinois Stripping Operation," *The Journal of Geography*, Vol. 59, January, 1960, pp. 11-15.

SAS, ANTHONY, "Dutch Concentrations in Rural Southwestern Ontario During the Postwar Decade," *Annals of the Association of American Geographers*, Vol. 48, September, 1958, pp. 185-194.

VANDERHILL, BURKE G., "The Direction of Settlement in the Prairie Provinces of Canada," *The Journal of Geography*, Vol. 58, October, 1959, pp. 325-333.

WEAVER, JOHN C., "Changing Patterns of Cropland Use in the Middle West," *Economic Geography*, Vol. 30, January, 1954, pp. 1-47.

YATES, THOM, "Toronto—City of Superlatives," *Ethyl News*, November-December, 1960, pp. 4-7.

CHAPTER 10

ACKERMAN, EDWARD A., "Water, Drought, and the Land," *Think*, Vol. 23, April, 1957, pp. 2-5.

CALEF, WESLEY, "The Winter of 1948-49 on the Great Plains," *Annals of the Association of American Geographers*, December, 1950, pp. 267-292.

CASE, LELAND D., "Back to the Historic Black Hills," *The National Geographic Magazine*, Vol. 110, No. 4, October, 1956, pp. 479-509.

CURTIS, JOHN T., "The Modification of Mid-Latitude Grasslands and Forests by Man," in *Man's Role in Changing the Face of the Earth*, Chicago: University of Chicago Press, 1956, pp. 721-736.

DOERR, ARTHUR H., and MORRIS, JOHN W., "The Oklahoma Panhandle—a Cross Section of the Southern High Plains," *Economic Geography*, Vol. 36, January, 1960, pp. 70-88.

HAYSTEAD, LADD, and FITE, GILBERT C., *The Agricultural Regions of the United States*, Norman, Okla.: University of Oklahoma Press, 1955, pp. 179-203.

HENDERSON, DAVID A., "'Corn Belt' Cattle Feeding in Eastern Colorado's Irrigated Valleys," *Economic Geography*, Vol. 30, October, 1954, pp. 364-372.

HEWES, LESLIE, "Wheat Failure in Western Nebraska," *Annals of the Association of American Geographers*, Vol. 48, December, 1958, pp. 375-397.

HEWES, LESLIE, and SCHMIEDING, ARTHUR C., "Risk in the Central Great Plains," *Geographical Review*, Vol. 46, July, 1956, pp. 375-387.

KOLLMORGEN, WALTER M., and JENKS, GEORGE F., "Suitcase Farming in Sully County, South Dakota," *Annals of the Association of American Geographers*, Vol. 48, March, 1958, pp. 27-40.

KRAENZEL, CARL F., *The Great Plains in Transition*, Norman, Okla.: University of Oklahoma Press, 1955.

MEIGS, PEVERIL, "Outlook for the Arid Realm of the United States," *Focus*, Vol. 4, December, 1953.

MORRIS, JOHN W., and DOERR, ARTHUR H., "Irrigation in Oklahoma," *The Journal of Geography*, Vol. 58, December, 1959, pp. 421-429.

SIMONETT, DAVID S., "Development and Grading of Dunes in Western Kansas," *Annals of the Association of American Geographers*, Vol. 50, September, 1960, pp. 216-241.

STEVENS, W. R., "Some Causes of Drouths in the Great Plains," *Journal of Geography*, Vol. 54, September, 1955, pp. 304-307.

STOCKTON, JOHN R., and ARBINGAST, STANLEY A., *Water Requirements Survey: Texas High Plains*, Austin, Texas: University of Texas Press, 1953.

VANDERHILL, BURKE G., "Post-war Agricultural Settlement in Manitoba," *Economic Geography*, Vol. 35, July, 1959, pp. 259-268.

VILLMOW, JACK R., "The Nature and Origin of the Canadian Dry Belt," *Annals of the Association of American Geographers*, Vol. 46, June, 1956, pp. 211-232.

WEAVER, J. E., and ALBERTSON, F. W., *Grasslands of the Great Plains: Their Nature and Use*, Lincoln, Nebr.: Johnson Publishing Co., 1956.

WEBB, WALTER P., "The American West: Perpetual Mirage," *Harper's Magazine*, Vol. 214, May, 1957, pp. 25-31.

————, *The Great Plains*, Boston: Ginn & Co., 1931.

CHAPTER 11

BIRCH, ROBERT W., *Wyoming's Mineral Resources*, Laramie, Wyo.: University of Wyoming Press, 1955.

BUTTS, ALLISON, *Copper, the Metal, Its Alloys and Compounds*, New York: Reinhold Publishing Corp., 1954.

CALEF, WESLEY, "Problems of Grazing Administration in the Basins of Southern Wyoming," *Economic Geography*, April, 1952, pp. 122-127.

GARWOOD, JOHN D., "An Analysis of Postwar Industrial Migration to Utah and Colorado," *Economic Geography*, January, 1953, pp. 79-88.

HARMISTON, FLOYD, "A Study of the Resources, People, and Economy of the Powder River Basin," *Wyoming Industrial Research Council Monograph*, Laramie, Wyo.: University of Wyoming Press, 1957.

HARTLEY, F. L., and BRINEGAR, C. S., "Oil Shale and Bituminous Sand," *The Scientific Monthly*, June, 1957, pp. 275-289.

HAYSTEAD, LADD, and FITE, GILBERT C., *The Agricultural Regions of the United States*, Norman, Okla.: University of Oklahoma Press, 1955, pp. 218-232.

HELBURN, NICHOLAS, "Human Ecology of Western Montana Valleys," *The Journal of Geography*, Vol. 55, January, 1956, pp. 5-13.

HOFFMEISTER, HAROLD A., "Middle Park and the Colorado-Big Thompson Diversion Project," *Economic Geography*, July, 1947, pp. 220-231.

IVES, RONALD L., "Frequency and Physical Effects of Chinook Winds in the Colorado High Plains Region," *Annals of the Association of American Geographers*, December, 1950, pp. 293-327.

LACKEY, EARL B., "Mountain Passes in the Colorado Rockies," *Economic Geography*, July, 1949, pp. 211-215.

McINNIS, WILMER, "Molybdenum—a Materials Survey," *Bureau of Mines Information Circular 7784*, April, 1957.

McKNIGHT, TOM L., "Recreational Use of the National Forests of Colorado," *The Southwestern Social Science Quarterly*, Vol. 32, 1951, pp. 264-270.

"Ranching in the Rockies," *Monthly Review* (Federal Reserve Bank of Minneapolis), October, 1961.

SOLOW, HERBERT, "Anaconda: One Face to the Future," *Fortune*, January, 1955, pp. 89-95, 148-150.

"This Is Colorado," *The Denver Post*, June 21, 1959.

WOLLE, M. S., *Stampede to Timberline: The Ghost Towns and Mining Camps of Colorado*, Boulder, Colo.: University of Colorado Press, 1949.

ZIERER, CLIFFORD M., "Tourism and Recreation in the West," *Geographical Review*, July, 1952, pp. 462-481.

CHAPTER 12

ALLEN, EDWARD W., "Fishery Geography of the North Pacific Ocean," *Geographical Review*, October, 1953, pp. 558-563.

CADZ, W. M., "The Central Kuskokwim Region, Alaska," *U. S. Geological Survey Professional Paper 268*, 1955.

CHAPMAN, W. McLEOD, "The Bering Sea Fisheries," *Far Eastern Survey*, Vol. 22, No. 4, March 25, 1953, pp. 33-36.

CRITCHFIELD, HOWARD J., "Seward Peninsula," *Economic Geography*, Vol. 25, No. 4, October, 1949, pp. 275-284.

EITEMAN, WILFORD J., and SMUTS, ALICE B., "Alaska, Land of Opportunity, Limited," *Economic Geography*, January, 1951, pp. 33-42.

GRUENING, ERNEST, "The Political Ecology of Alaska," *The Scientific Monthly*, December, 1951, pp. 376-386.

HEWES, GORDON W., "The Fisheries of Northwestern North America," *Economic Geography*, Vol. 28, 1952, pp. 66-73.

KELLOG, CHARLES E.; and NYGARD, I. J., "Report on Exploratory Investigations of Agricultural Problems of Alaska, *U. S. Department of Agriculture Miscellaneous Publication No. 700*, 1950.

MATHIESON, RAYMOND S., "The Alaskan Salmon Industry —Prologue and Prospect," *Yearbook of the Association of Pacific Coast Geographers*, Vol. 16, 1954, pp. 35-45.

MILLER, E. WILLARD, "Agricultural Development in Interior Alaska," *Scientific Monthly*, Vol. 73, October, 1951, pp. 245-254.

ROBINSON, J. LEWIS, and ROBINSON, M. J., *The Geography of Canada*, Toronto, Ont.: Longmans, Green & Co., 1950.

SMITH, RICHARD A., "Alaska: The Last Frontier," *Fortune*, September, 1955.

STANTON, WILLIAM J., "The Purpose and Source of Seasonal Migration to Alaska," *Economic Geography*, Vol. 31, April, 1955, pp. 138-148.

STEAD, ROBERT J. C., "The Yellowhead Pass—Canadian Rockies," *Canadian Geographical Journal*, Vol. 36, 1948, pp. 51-65.

STONE, KIRK H., "Alaskan Problems and Potentials," *The Journal of Geography*, May, 1951, pp. 177-188.

———, "Populating Alaska: The United States Phase," *Geographical Review*, July, 1952, pp. 384-404.

VAN CLEEF, EUGENE, "Prince Rupert—an Error in Location," *The Journal of Geography*, Vol. 58, March, 1959, pp. 127-132.

WALKER, J. F., "Mining Developments in British Columbia," *Canadian Geographical Journal*, Vol. 45, 1952.

WEIR, THOMAS R., "The Winter Feeding Period in the Southern Interior Plateau of British Columbia," *Annals of the Association of American Geographers*, Vol. 44, June, 1954, pp. 194-204.

CHAPTER 13

BEATY, CHESTER B., "Topographic Effects of Faulting: Death Valley, California," *Annals of the Association of American Geographers*, Vol. 51, June, 1961, pp. 234-240.

CALEF, WESLEY, "The Salines of Southeastern California," *Economic Geography*, January, 1951, pp. 43-64.

DUISBERG, PETER C., ed., "Problems of the Upper Rio Grande, an Arid Zone River," *U. S. Commission for Arid Resources Improvement and Development Publication No. 1*, Albuquerque, N. M.: University of New Mexico Press, 1957.

GARRISON, JEANNE, "Barstow, California: A Transportation Focus in a Desert Environment," *Economic Geography*, Vol. 29, April, 1953, pp. 159-167.

GREGOR, HOWARD F., "An Evaluation of Oasis Agriculture," *Yearbook of the Association of Pacific Coast Geographers*, Vol. 21, 1959, pp. 39-50.

GRIFFIN, PAUL F., and YOUNG, ROBERT N., *California, the New Empire State: A Regional Geography*, San Francisco: Fearon Publishers, Inc., 1957, pp. 165-199.

HAYSTEAD, LADD, and FITE, GILBERT C., *The Agricultural Regions of the United States*, Norman, Okla.: University of Oklahoma Press, 1955, pp. 233-271.

HOFFMEISTER, HAROLD A., "Alkali Problem of Western United States," *Economic Geography*, Vol. 23, 1947, pp. 1-9.

KELLEY, WILFRID D., "Settlement of the Middle Rio Grande Valley," *The Journal of Geography*, Vol. 54, November, 1955, pp. 387-398.

KENNELLY, ROBERT A., "Cattle Feeding in the Imperial Valley," *Yearbook of the Association of Pacific Coast Geographers*, Vol. 22, 1960, pp. 50-56.

LEOPOLD, LUNA B., "Vegetation of Southwestern Watersheds in the Nineteenth Century," *Geographical Review*, April, 1951, pp. 295-316.

LOGAN, RICHARD F., "Winter Temperatures of a Mid-Latitude Desert Mountain Range," *The Geographical Review*, Vol. 51, April, 1961, pp. 236-252.

McFARLANE, N. L.; AYERS, R. S.; and WINRIGHT, R. S.; "California Desert Agriculture," *California Agricultural Experiment Station Circular 464*, 1957.

MANNING, R. I. C., "Mining in Arizona," Phoenix, Ariz.: Department of Mineral Resources, 1953.

MOORE, W. ROBERT. "Escalante: Utah's River of Arches," *The National Geographic Magazine*, Vol. 108, September, 1955, pp. 399-426.

"The Dam Builders," *Bulletin* (Standard Oil Company of California, Vol. 40, No. 3, July, 1961, pp. 18-23.

THOMAS, HAROLD E., "First Fourteen Years of Lake Mead," *Geological Survey Circular 346* (U. S. Department of the Interior), 1954.

WHITE, GILBERT F., ed., *The Future of the Arid Lands*, New York: American Geographical Society, 1957.

WILSOW, ANDREW W., "Urbanization of the Arid Lands," *The Professional Geographer*, Vol. 12, November, 1960, pp. 4-7.

ZIERER, CLIFFORD M., ed., *California and the Southwest*, New York: John Wiley & Sons, Inc., 1956.

CHAPTER 14

"A Statistical Review of Utah's Economy," *Studies in Business and Economics*, Vol. 20, No. 2, August, 1960, Salt Lake City, Utah: University of Utah Press.

CALEF, WESLEY, "The Salines of Southeastern California," *Economic Geography*, January, 1951, pp. 43-64.

CARTER, GEORGE F., "Man, Time, and Change in the Far Southwest," *Annals of the Association of American Geographers*, Vol. 49, September, 1959, pp. 8-30.

DONNAN, W. W., and BRADSHAW, G. B., "Drainage Investigation Methods for Irrigated Areas in Western United States, *U. S. Department of Agriculture Technical Bulletin 1065*, 1952.

"Four Corners Country," *Arizona Highways*, Vol. 37, No. 9, September, 1961.

FREEMAN, OTIS W., and MARTIN, HOWARD H., eds., *The Pacific Northwest, an Over-all Appreciation*, New York: John Wiley & Sons, Inc., 1954.

GARWOOD, JOHN D., "An Analysis of Postwar Industrial Migration to Utah and Colorado," *Economic Geography*, Vol. 29, January, 1953, pp. 79-88.

GRIFFIN, PAUL F., and CHATHAM, RONALD L., "How Nevada Towns Were Named," *Nevada Highways and Parks*, Vol. 17, No. 2, 1957, pp. 26-31.

GRIFFIN, PAUL F., and YOUNG, ROBERT N., *California, the New Empire State: A Regional Geography*, San Francisco: Fearon Publishers, Inc., 1957, pp. 139-163.

HOLMES, CHARLES H., "Factors Affecting Development of the Steel Industry in Intermountain America," *The Journal of Geography*, Vol. 53, January, 1959, pp. 20-31.

MILLER, ELBERT E., "Ram Pasture and Wall Paper: A Story of the Uranium Boom in the Colorado Plateau," *Yearbook of the Association of Pacific Coast Geographers*, Vol. 17, 1955, pp. 27-33.

"Outlook for the Arid Realm of the United States," *Focus*, Vol. 4, No. 4, December, 1953.

SPIEKER, E. M., "The Transition Between the Colorado Plateaus and the Great Basin in Central Utah," *Guidebook to the Geology of Utah*, No. 4, Salt Lake City, Utah: Geological Society, 1949.

Sunset Discovery Trips in California, Menlo Park, Calif.: Lane Book Co., 1955, pp. 76-101.

"The State of Nevada," *Motorland*, Vol. 77, No. 1, January-February, 1956.

THOMAS, BENJAMIN F., "The California-Nevada Boundary," *Annals of the Association of American Geographers*, Vol. 42, March, 1952, pp. 51-68.

THOMPSON, LAURA, *Culture in Crisis: A Study of the Hopi Indians*, New York: Harper & Brothers, 1950.

"Water in the United States," *Focus*, Vol. 1, No. 4, January 15, 1951.

WHITE, GILBERT F., ed., *The Future of the Arid Lands*, New York: American Geographical Society, 1957.

"Why the Big Boom in the Desert States—Arizona, Nevada, New Mexico," *U. S. News and World Report*, October 11, 1957.

"World of Kennecott," *Fortune*, Vol. 44, November, 1951, pp. 84-97.

ZIERER, CLIFFORD M., ed., *California and the Southwest*, New York: John Wiley & Sons, Inc., 1956, pp. 25-48.

CHAPTER 15

BRIER, HOWARD M., *Sawdust Empire—the Pacific Northwest*, New York: Alfred A. Knopf, Inc., 1958.

FREEMAN, O. W., and MARTIN, H. H., eds., *The Pacific Northwest*, New York: John Wiley & Sons, Inc., 1954.

FULLER, GEORGE W., *A History of the Pacific Northwest*, New York: Alfred A. Knopf, Inc., 1952.

HIGHSMITH, RICHARD M., JR., ed., *Atlas of the Pacific Northwest*, Corvallis, Ore.: Oregon State University, 1962.

————, *Case Studies in World Geography, Occupance and Economy Types*, Englewood Cliffs, N. J.: Prentice-Hall, Inc., 1961, pp. 70-77.

HOLBROOK, STEWART H., *The Columbia*, New York: Holt, Rinehart & Winston, Inc., 1956.

JOHANSEN, D. O., and GATES, C. M., *Empire of the Columbia: A History of the Pacific Northwest*, New York: Harper & Brothers, 1957.

LAVENDER, DAVID, *Land of Giants—the Drive to the Pacific Northwest, 1750-1950*, Garden City, N. Y.: Doubleday & Co., Inc., 1958.

LEWIS, PIERCE F., "Linear Topography in the Southwestern Palouse, Washington-Oregon," *Annals of the Association of American Geographers*, Vol. 50, June, 1960, pp. 98-111.

MARTS, M. E. and SEWELL, W. R. D., "The Conflict Between Fish and Power Resources in the Pacific," *Annals of the Association of American Geographers*, Vol. 50, March, 1960, pp. 42-50.

MEINING, DONALD W., "The Evolution of Understanding an Environment: Climates and Wheat Culture in the Columbia Plateau," *Yearbook of the Association of Pacific Coast Geographers*, Vol. 16, 1954, pp. 25-34.

————, "The Growth of Agricultural Regions in the Far West: 1850-1910," *The Journal of Geography*, Vol. 54, May, 1955, pp. 221-232.

MILLER, E. E., and HIGHSMITH, R. M., "Geography of the Fruit Industry of Yakima Valley, Washington," *Economic Geography*, Vol. 25, 1949, pp. 285-295.

ROCKIE, W. A., "Snowdrift Erosion in the Palouse," *Geographical Review*, July, 1951, pp. 457-463.

————, "The Palouse," *Yearbook of the Association of Pacific Coast Geographers*, Vol. 15, 1953, pp. 3-10.

RUDD, R. D., "An Alternate Application of the Koppen Classification to Eastern Oregon," *Yearbook of the Association of Pacific Coast Geographers*, Vol 21, 1959, pp. 31-38.

"Wheat Supply and Distribution in the Pacific Northwest," *United States Department of Agriculture Bulletin Number 1*, December, 1956.

WINTHER, OSCAR O., *The Great Northwest*, New York: The Macmillan Co., 1949.

CHAPTER 16

"Along the Sierra," *Motorland*, Vol. 76, No. 4, July-August, 1955.

"California's Four Great National Parks," *Motorland*, Vol. 78, No. 1, January-February, 1957.

"California's Shasta-Cascade Wonderland," *Motorland*, Vol. 77, No. 4, July-August, 1956.

DICKEN, SAMUEL N., "The Rogue River Country of Oregon: A Study in Regional Geography," *Yearbook of the Association of Pacific Coast Geographers*, Vol. 14, 1952, pp. 3-18.

FREEMAN, OTIS W., *Resources of Washington*, Seattle, Wash.: Washington State Resources Committee, 1954, pp. 11-14, 18-22, 101-108.

GRIFFIN, PAUL F., and YOUNG, ROBERT N., *California, the New Empire State: A Regional Geography*, San Francisco: Fearon Publishers, Inc., 1957, pp. 201-223.

HIGHSMITH, RICHARD M., JR., ed., *Case Studies in World Geography, Occupance and Economy Types*, Englewood Cliffs, N. J.: Prentice-Hall, Inc., 1961, pp. 78-86, 162-169.

HIGHSMITH, R. M., and BARON, A. M., "Oregon's Hood River Valley," *The Journal of Geography*, Vol. 57, March, 1958, pp. 353-360.

JENKINS, OLAF, "The Mother Lode Country," *Geologic Guidebook Along Highway 49*, California State Division of Mines Bulletin 141, 1948.

"Mother Lode: Historic Region of Gold," *Motorland*, Vol. 77, No. 6, November-December, 1956.

PARK, EDWARDS, and REVIS, KATHLEEN, "Washington Wilderness, the North Cascades," *The National Geographic Magazine*, Vol. 119, March, 1961, pp. 335-367.

STEGNER, WALLACE, "The Sierra Nevada, America's Mightiest Playground," *Holiday*, Vol. 20, No. 1, July, 1956, pp. 34-43.

Sunset Discovery Trips in California, Menlo Park, Calif.: Lane Book Co., 1955, pp. 102-128.

Sunset Discovery Trips in Oregon, Menlo Park, Calif.: Lane Book Co., 1956, pp. 31-68.

"The Feather River Region," *Motorland*, May-June, 1957.

"The Tahoe-Sierra Region," *Motorland*, July-August, 1957.

ZIERER, CLIFFORD M., ed., *California and the Southwest*, New York: John Wiley & Sons, Inc., 1956, pp. 12-14, 192-195.

CHAPTER 17

"California Maps Vast Water Plan," *The New York Times*, March 18, 1956, p. 42.

"Central Valley Project, California," Bureau of Reclamation, U. S. Department of the Interior, Washington: U. S. Government Printing Office, 1950.

COLE, CHESTER F., "California's Agriculture—Some Realities," *The Journal of Geography*, Vol. 67, October, 1958, pp. 341-346.

————, "California's Water Requirements," *The Journal of Geography*, Vol. 59, September, 1960, pp. 268-270.

GREGOR, HOWARD F., "A Sample Study of a California Ranch," *Annals of the Association of American Geographers*, Vol. 41, December, 1951, pp. 285-306.

————, "The Local Supply Agriculture of California," *Annals of the Association of American Geographers*, Vol. 47, September, 1957, pp. 267-275.

GRIFFIN, PAUL F., "The Olive Industry of California," *The Journal of Geography*, Vol. 54, December, 1955, pp. 429-440.

GRIFFIN, PAUL F., and YOUNG, ROBERT N., *California, the New Empire State: A Regional Geography*, San Francisco: Fearon Publishers, Inc., 1957, pp. 225-305.

LANTIS, DAVID W., "California," *Focus*, October, 1957.

LARGE, DAVID C., "Cotton in the San Joaquin Valley," *Geographical Review*, July, 1957, pp. 365-380.

LEIGHLY, JOHN, "Settlement and Cultivation in the Summer Dry Lands," Yearbook of Agriculture, 1941, pp. 197-202.

"San Joaquin Valley—Fertile Empire," *Motorland*, Vol. 77, No. 5, September-October, 1956.

SHULTIS, ARTHUR, *California Agriculture Circular 474*, California Agricultural Experiment Station Extension Service, May, 1959.

STEINER, RODNEY, "Two Water Flow Maps of California," *The California Geographer*, Vol. 1, 1960, pp. 41-44.

"The Sacramento Region," *Motorland*, Vol. 76, No. 2, March-April, 1955.

THOMPSON, KENNETH, "Location and Relocation of a Tree Crop—English Walnuts in California," *Economic Geography*, Vol. 37, April, 1961, pp. 133-149.

————, "Riparian Forests of the Sacramento Valley," *Annals of the Association of American Geographers*, Vol. 51, September, 1961, pp. 294-315.

"Water Utilization and Requirements of California," *State Water Resources Board Bulletin No. 2*, Vols. 1 and 2, June, 1955.

WOHLETZ, LEONARD R., and DOLDER, EDWARD F., *Know California's Land*, Sacramento, Calif.: California Department of Natural Resources and Soil Conservation Service and U. S. Department of Agriculture, 1952.

ZIERER, CLIFFORD M., ed., *California and the Southwest*, New York: John Wiley & Sons, Inc., 1956, pp. 135-182, 213-216, 256-260.

CHAPTER 18

ASCHMANN, HOMER, "The Evolution of a Wild Landscape and Its Persistence in Southern California," *Annals of the Association of American Geographers*, Vol. 49, September, 1959, pp. 34-56.

BAUGH, RUTH E., "Geographic Factors in the Evolution of California," *The Journal of Geography*, Vol. 54, March, 1955, pp. 133-139.

CUNNINGHAM, GLENN, "The Tin Can Industry in California," *Yearbook of the Association of Pacific Coast Geographers*, Vol. 15, 1953, pp. 11-17.

"Fontana Steel Plant," *Forbes*, June 15, 1956.

GENTILCORE, R. LOUIS, "Missions and Mission Lands of Alta California," *Annals of the Association of American Geographers*, Vol. 51, March, 1961, pp. 46-72.

GREGOR, HOWARD F., "Agricultural Shifts in the Ventura Lowland of California," *Economic Geography*, Vol. 29, October, 1953, pp. 340-361.

————, "The Geographic Dynamism of California Market Gardening," *Yearbook of the Association of Pacific Coast Geographers*, Vol. 18, 1956, pp. 28-35.

GRIFFIN, PAUL F., "Some Geographic Aspects of the California and Hawaiian Sugar Industry," *The Journal of Geography*, Vol. 53, November, 1954, pp. 325-335.

GRIFFIN, PAUL F., and CHATHAM, RONALD L., "Population: A Challenge to California's Changing Citrus Industry," *Economic Geography*, Vol. 34, July, 1958, pp. 272-276.

————, "Urban Impact on Agriculture in Santa Clara County, California," *Annals of the Association of American Geographers*, Vol. 48, September, 1958, pp. 195-208.

GRIFFIN, PAUL F., and WHITE, C. LANGDON, "Lettuce Industry of the Salinas Valley," *Scientific Monthly*, Vol. 81, August, 1955, pp. 77-84.

GRIFFIN, PAUL F., and YOUNG, ROBERT N., *California, the New Empire State: A Regional Geography*, San Francisco: Fearon Publishers, Inc., 1957, pp. 1-147.

HOOS, SIDNEY, "Lemon Industry in California," *California Agriculture*, Vol. 10, August, 1956, pp. 2-15.

HOOS, SIDNEY, and BAIN, BEATRICE M., "Fruit and Vegetable Canning Industry," *California Agriculture*, Vol. 14, March, 1960, pp. 2-15.

NELSON, HOWARD J., "The Spread of an Artificial Landscape Over Southern California," *Annals of the Association of American Geographers*, Vol. 49, September, 1959, pp. 80-99.

————, "The Vernon Area, California—a Study of the Political Factor in Urban Geography," *Annals of the Association of American Geographers*, Vol. 42, June, 1952, pp. 177-191.

PRICE, EDWARD T., "The Future of California's Southland," *Annals of the Association of American Geographers*, Vol. 49, September, 1959, pp. 101-116.

RAUP, H. F., "Transformation of Southern California to a Cultivated Land," *Annals of the Association of American Geographers*, Vol. 49, September, 1959, pp. 58-78.

REITH, JOHN W., "Los Angeles Smog," *Yearbook of the Association of Pacific Coast Geographers*, Vol. 13, 1951, pp. 24-32.

ROSTLUND, ERHARD, "Geographic Setting of San Francisco," *The Journal of Geography*, Vol. 54, December, 1955, pp. 441-448.

TAYLOR, ALICE, "San Francisco," *Focus*, Vol. 9, March, 1959.

WHITE, C. LANGDON, and FORDE, HAROLD M., "The Unorthodox San Francisco Bay Area Electronics Industry," *The Journal of Geography*, Vol. 59, September, 1960, pp. 251-257.

YOUNG, ROBERT N., and GRIFFIN, PAUL F., "Recent Land-Use Changes in the San Francisco Bay Area," *Geographical Review*, Vol. 67, No. 3, July, 1957, pp. 396-405.

CHAPTER 19

ALLEN, EDWARD W., "Fishery Geography of the North Pacific Ocean," *Geographical Review*, October, 1953, pp. 558-563.

BOYER, DAVID S., "British Columbia: Life Begins at 100," *The National Geographic Magazine*, Vol. 114, August, 1958, pp. 147-189.

BRIER, HOWARD M., *Sawdust Empire*, New York: Alfred A. Knopf, Inc., 1958, pp. 41-78, 110-178, 189-265.

BROWNE, RALPH, *The Cordova District Opportunities*, Juneau, Alas.: Alaska Development Board, 1951.

CHAPMAN, J. D., "A Preliminary Study of the Seasonal Distribution of Precipitation in British Columbia," *Yearbook of the Association of Pacific Coast Geographers,*" Vol. 14, 1952, pp. 24-33.

CLEVINGER, WOODROW R., "Locational Change in the Douglas Fir Lumber Industry," *Yearbook of the Association of Pacific Coast Geographers*, Vol. 15, 1953, pp. 23-31.

DART, JOHN O., "The Changing Hydrologic Pattern of the Renton Summer Lowland, Washington," *Yearbook of the Association of Pacific Coast Geographers*, Vol. 14, 1952, pp. 19-23.

FREEMAN, OTIS W., and MARTIN, HOWARD H., eds., *The Pacific Northwest*, New York: John Wiley & Sons, Inc., 1954, pp. 121-284, 389-438.

HEINTZELMAN, OLIVER H., "Longview, Washington—a Planned City," *The Journal of Geography*, Vol. 57, April, 1958, pp. 183-191.

HIGHSMITH, RICHARD M., JR., ed., *Case Studies in World Geography, Occupance and Economy Types*, Englewood Cliffs, N. J.: Prentice-Hall, Inc., 1961, pp. 181-187, 203-213.

HIGHSMITH, RICHARD M., JR., "Irrigation in the Willamette Valley," *Geographical Review*, January, 1956, pp. 98-110.

HIGHSMITH, RICHARD M., JR., and BEH, JOHN L., "Tillamook Burn: The Regeneration of a Forest," *The Scientific Monthly*, Vol. 75, 1952, pp. 139-148.

JENSEN, J. GRANVILLE, "The Pacific Northwest Aluminum Smelting Industry—a Re-evaluation," *Yearbook of the Association of Pacific Coast Geographers*, Vol. 14, 1952, pp. 13-14.

————, "Tree Farming in the Douglas Fir Region: An Evaluation," *Yearbook of the Association of Pacific Coast Geographers*, Vol. 17, 1955, pp. 21-26.

LAVENDER, DAVID, *Land of the Giants—the Drive to the Pacific Northwest, 1750-1950*, Garden City, N. Y.: Doubleday & Co., Inc., 1958.

"Life of the Chinook," *Life*, September 4, 1950, pp. 48-58.

MCGOVERN, P. D., "Industrial Development in the Vancouver Area," *Economic Geography*, Vol. 37, July, 1961, pp. 189-206.

MERRIAM, WILLIS B., "Conservation of the Fraser River Sockeye Salmon," *Yearbook of the Association of Pacific Coast Geographers*, Vol. 16, 1954, pp. 46-54.

ROUCEK, JOSEPH S., "The Geopolitics of the Aleutians," *The Journal of Geography*, Vol. 50, No. 1, January, 1951, pp. 24-29.

SIDDALL, WILLIAM R., "Seattle: Regional Capital of Alaska," *Annals of the Association of American Geographers,* Vol. 47, September, 1957, pp. 277-284.

SMITH, RICHARD A., "Alaska: The Last Frontier," *Fortune*, September, 1955.

Sunset Discovery Trips in Oregon, Menlo Park, Calif.: Lane Book Co., 1956, pp. 19-46.

CHAPTER 20

BANK, THEODORE, *Birthplace of the Winds*, New York: Thomas Y. Crowell Co., 1956.

BERTRAM, G. C. L., "Pribilof Fur Seals," *Arctic*, Vol. 3, No. 2, August, 1950, pp. 75-85.

BLACK, ROBERT F., "Aeolian Deposits of Alaska," *Arctic*, Vol. 4, No. 2, September, 1951, pp. 89-111.

CADZ, W. M., "The Central Kuskokwim Region, Alaska," *U. S. Geological Survey Professional Paper 268*, 1955.

CARNES, WILLIAM G., "Novice North of Nowhere: An Adventure in the Landscape of America's Arctic," *Landscape Architecture*, Vol. 46, No. 1, October, 1955, pp. 19-25.

CHAPMAN, WILBERT M., "The Bering Sea Fisheries," *Far Eastern Survey*, Vol. 22, No. 4, March 25, 1953, pp. 33-36.

GRUENING, ERNEST, *The State of Alaska*, New York: Random House, 1954.

HULLEY, CLARENCE C., *Alaska, 1741-1953*, Portland, Ore.: Binfords & Mort, 1953.

KIMBLE, GEORGE H. T., and GOOD, DOROTHY, eds., *Geography of the Northlands*, New York: American Geographical Society, 1955.

LANTIS, MARGARET, "The Reindeer Industry in Alaska," *Arctic*, April, 1950.

MILLER, E. WILLARD, "Agricultural Development in Interior Alaska," *The Scientific Monthly*, Vol. 73, 1951, pp. 245-254.

MONAHAN, ROBERT L., "The Role of Transportation in the Fairbanks Area," *Yearbook of the Association of Pacific Coast Geographers*, Vol. 21, 1959, pp. 7-21.

MOORE, W. ROBERT, "Alaska, the Big Land," *The National Geographic Magazine*, Vol. 109, No. 6, June, 1956, pp. 776-805.

NOYES, JOHN R., "The Alaska Highway Today," *The Military Engineer*, Vol. 47, No. 319, September-October, 1955, pp. 376-379.

"Oil in Northern Alaska," *Polar Record*, Vol. 6, July, 1953, pp. 815-816.

OLIVER, V. J., and OLIVER, M. B., "Ice Fogs in the Interior of Alaska," *Bulletin of the American Meteorological Society*, Vol. 30, No. 1, January, 1949, pp. 23-26.

"Resources of the Arctic," *Focus*, Vol. 2, February, 1952.

ROWLEY, DIANA, ed., "Arctic Research: The Current Status of Research and Some Immediate Problems in the North American Arctic and Sub-Arctic," *Special Publication No. 2* (Arctic Institute of America), 1955.

SCHEFFER, VICTOR B., and KENYON, KARL W., "The Fur Seal Herd Comes of Age," *The National Geographic Magazine*, Vol. 101, No. 4, April, 1952, pp. 491-512.

SHIMKIN, D. B., "The Economy of a Trapping Center: The Case of Fort Yukon, Alaska," *Economic Development and Cultural Change*, Vol. 3, No. 3, April, 1955, pp. 219-240.

SONNENFELD, J., "Changes in an Eskimo Hunting Technology, an Introduction to Implement Geography," *Annals of the Association of American Geographers,* Vol. 50, June, 1960, pp. 172-186.

STANTON, WILLIAM J., "The Purpose and Source of Seasonal Migration to Alaska," *Economic Geography,* Vol. 31, No. 2, April, 1955, pp. 138-148.

STERN, PETER M., "Alaska," *Focus,* Vol. 4, No. 1, September, 1953.

STONE, KIRK H., *Alaska Group Settlement: The Matanuska Valley Colony,* Washington: U. S. Government Printing Office, 1950.

THOMPSON, SETON H., "Alaska Fishery and Fur Seal Industries: 1952," *U. S. Fish and Wildlife Service Statistical Digest No. 33,* 1954.

CHAPTER 21

"An Introduction to the Geography of the Canadian Arctic," *Canadian Geography Information Series No. 2,* Ottawa, 1951.

BROWN, R. J. E., and others, "The Mackenzie River Delta," *The Canadian Geographer,* No. 7, 1956.

"Canada Counts Its Caribou," *The National Geographic Magazine,* Vol. 102, August, 1952, pp. 261-268.

CRAIG, ROLAND D., "The Forests of Canada," *Economic Geography,* Vol. 2, 1926, pp. 394-413.

HARE, KENNETH F., "Climate and Zonal Divisions of the Boreal Forest Formation of Eastern Canada," *Geographical Review,* October, 1950, pp. 615-635.

JACOT, MICHAEL, "Alaska—Where Muskrat Is King," *Imperial Oil Review,* Vol. 38, No. 4, December, 1954, pp. 16-21.

JAMES, PRESTON E., *A Geography of Man,* Boston: Ginn & Co., 1959, pp. 391-410.

JENNESS, JOHN L., "Erosive Forces in the Physiography of Western Arctic Canada," *Geographical Review,* April, 1952, pp. 238-252.

KIMBLE, GEORGE H. T., and GOOD, DOROTHY, eds., *Geography of the Northlands,* New York: American Geographical Society, 1955.

LA FAY, HOWARD, "Dew Line, Sentry of the Far North," *The National Geographic Magazine,* Vol. 114, No. 1, July, 1958, pp. 128-146.

LONG, TANIA, "The Eskimos Meet the Twentieth Century," *The New York Times Magazine,* June 17, 1956, pp. 12-13.

MILLER, E. WILLARD, "The Hudson Bay Railway Route," *The Journal of Geography,* Vol. 57, April, 1958, pp. 163-172.

PORSILD, A. E., "Plant Life in the Arctic," *Canadian Geographical Journal,* Vol. 42, 1951, pp. 121-145.

"Resources of the Arctic," *Focus,* February, 1952.

RUMNEY, G. R., "Settlements on the Canadian Shield," *Canadian Geographical Journal,* Vol. 43, 1951, pp. 116-127.

VANDERHILL, BURKE G., "Observations in the Pioneer Fringe of Western Canada," *The Journal of Geography,* Vol. 57, December, 1958, pp. 431-440.

WEIGERT, H. W.; STEFANSSON, V.; and HARRISON, R. E.; eds.; *New Compass of the World,* New York: The Macmillan Co., 1953, pp. 25-60.

WILKINSON, DOUG, *Land of the Long Day,* New York: Holt, Rinehart & Winston, Inc., 1956.

CHAPTER 22

BRYAN, EDWIN H., *The Hawaiian Chain,* Honolulu, Hawaii: Bishop Museum Press, 1954.

DAY, ARTHUR G., *Hawaii and Its People,* New York: Duell, Sloan, and Pearce, Inc., 1960.

DURAND, LOYAL, JR., "Hawaii," *Focus,* Vol. 9, May, 1959.

———, "The Dairy Industry of the Hawaiian Islands," *Economic Geography,* July, 1959.

EISELEN, ELIZABETH, "Geographic Problems of Our Fiftieth State," *The Journal of Geography,* Vol. 59, March, 1960, pp. 132-135.

GRIFFIN, PAUL F., "Some Geographic Aspects of the California and Hawaiian Sugar Industry," *The Journal of Geography,* Vol. 53, November, 1954, pp. 325-336.

Hawaii: Patterns of Island Growth, Honolulu, Hawaii: Bank of Hawaii, Department of Business Research, 1958.

JONES, STEPHEN B., "The Weather Element in the Hawaiian Climate," *Annals of the Association of American Geographers,* Vol. 29, March, 1939, pp. 29-57.

LIND, ANDREW W., *Hawaii's People,* Honolulu, Hawaii: University of Hawaii Press, 1955.

MELLEN, KATHLEEN, *An Island Kingdom Passes; Hawaii Becomes American,* New York: Hastings House, 1958.

MICHENER, JAMES A., *Hawaii,* New York: Random House, 1959.

NORBECK, EDWARD, *Pineapple Town: Hawaii,* Berkeley, Calif.: University of California Press, 1959.

"On Oahu," *Bulletin,* Standard Oil Company of California, Vol. 39, October, 1960, pp. 18-23.

PEARCY, G. ETZEL, "Hawaii's Territorial Sea," *The Professional Geographer,* Vol. 11, November, 1959, pp. 2-6.

WILSON, JAMES N., "Pineapple Industry of Hawaii," *Economic Geography,* October, 1948, pp. 251-262.

Index